Chingju Liu

METAMORPHIC PETROLOGY

METAMORPHIC PETROLOGY

Mineralogical, Field, and Tectonic Aspects

SECOND EDITION

FRANCIS J. TURNER
UNIVERSITY OF CALIFORNIA, BERKELEY

HEMISPHERE PUBLISHING CORPORATION   *Washington   New York   London*

McGRAW-HILL BOOK COMPANY   *New York   St. Louis   San Francisco*
Auckland   Bogotá   Hamburg   Johannesburg   London   Madrid   Mexico   Montreal   New Delhi
Panama   Paris   São Paulo   Singapore   Sydney   Tokyo   Toronto

METAMORPHIC PETROLOGY:
Mineralogical, Field, and Tectonic Aspects
Second Edition

2 3 4 5 6 7 8 9 0 BRBR 8 9 8 7 6 5 4 3 2

This book was set in Press Roman
by Hemisphere Publishing Corporation.
The editors were Diane Heiberg and Christine Flint;
the designer was Sharon Martin DePass;
the production supervisor was Rebekah M. McKinney;
and the typesetter was Peggy M. Rote.
Braun-Brumfield, Inc. was printer and binder.

Library of Congress Cataloging in Publication Data

Turner, Francis J
  Metamorphic petrology.

(McGraw-Hill international series in the earth
and planetary sciences)
  Includes bibliographies and indexes.
  1. Rocks, Metamorphic. I. Title.
QE475.T89   1980   552´.4   79-27497
ISBN 0-07-065501-4

Contents

v

Preface

The subtitle of this book—were it not for the demands of brevity—would properly be *The nature, field occurrence, tectonic environment, chemistry, and possible physical significance of mineral facies of metamorphic rocks.* Other and perhaps equally important topics that fall within the realm of metamorphic petrology—e.g., structural evolution of metamorphic rocks and the nature of metasomatic (including ore-generating) processes—are scarcely touched on in the present work.

The purpose, scope, and underlying conceptions of this book remain much the same as in the previous edition and its predecessors. The general approach is still by way of Eskola's facies concept, and owes much to Eskola's final synthesis in *Die Entstehung der Gesteine* (Barth, Correns, and Eskola, 1939). Admittedly, there are inherent ambiguities and a lack of precision with regard to nomenclature and individual definition of metamorphic facies. Yet it is through the concept of facies and recognition of facies series that the mineralogical and field material of metamorphic petrology are most readily perceived, marshalled, and analyzed. It is more through case histories than by broad generalization that parts of the total picture can be assembled. Descriptive sections, therefore, focus on specific examples selected for diversity in pattern, quality of documentation, ready access in the literature, and as far as possible some personal acquaintance with the rocks in their field settings. No apology is made for unavoidable inadequacy of coverage. No one person can master the mushrooming literature in ever-multiplying geologic journals. Most readers, like this writer, read freely in not more than two or three languages; and with this limitation in view, references have been drawn where possible from works written in English, with supplementary reference to the more important contributions in German. The great classics in both languages must not be neglected; but the accent in the present bibliography is on newer work, on the assumptions that inquiring readers will follow up for themselves some of the earlier contributions cited in major modern works covering more specialized fields.

With a mind to current trends in geologic thinking, more emphasis than formerly is now placed on regional structural history as revealed by conventional mapping, supplemented all too rarely by geophysical measurements. The body of metamorphic data that has emerged from regional studies has been presented in such a manner that it may be used in building and testing global tectonic and geophysical models—a speculative topic beyond the scope of this book. In keeping with this approach, much more attention has been paid to regional than to contact metamorphism; and the two phenomena have been treated separately even at the cost of distinguishing somewhat arbitrarily between mutually gradational processes and departing to some degree from original strictures of the facies concept.

Underlying the book is this general proposition: within any major metamorphic domain, the diverse metamorphic facies there displayed preserve a partial record of a crustal pressure-temperature regime that prevailed during a corresponding limited episode of its tectonic history and in some cases covered evolution and localization of granitic plutons. Our ultimate goal is to quantify this regime: to translate mineralogical data into numerical expressions of pressure, temperature, and heat flow. This is an ambitious goal, and in the state of present knowledge difficult to attain. The path to be followed is clear enough. Key mineral assemblages must be calibrated against the numerical data of computed and experimentally established phase equilibria; and the numbers that emerge, transferred to the map, then yield information on local pressure-temperature gradients within the broad metamorphic regime. But progress is hindered on all sides by formidable obstacles: lack of adequate geological-mineralogical data, and divergence of opinion among geochemists on numerical evaluation of equilibrium curves and scales of geothermometry and geobarometry.

In this situation all students of metamorphism face a compelling and exacting task: to assess critically and objectively the quantitative constraints that mineral chemistry imposes on pressure-temperature regimes and thermal histories of specific metamorphic domains. It is only after such assessment that the numerical data can be incorporated into some tectonic or geothermal model (the fatal alternative would be to select values suitable to the preferred model—which thereby would become weakened rather than strengthened). Critical appraisal demands some familiarity with the potential and defects of experimental techniques, and above all a feeling for the pervasive power of thermodynamic argument. To facilitate such understanding, the chapters dealing with experimentally reversed equilibria and underlying thermodynamic constraints have been expanded and illustrated with numerical examples that may easily be verified with the help of standard thermodynamic tables. There is no way that the geologist who wishes to use the quantitative data of metamorphic petrology can bypass this aspect of the science.

Nor can geologists afford to neglect the classic work of the founders—H. Rosenbusch, G. Barrow, U. Grubenmann, J. H. van't Hoff, F. Becke, J. J. Sederholm, P. Eskola, V. M. Goldschmidt, P. Niggli, and others. With this in mind, I have introduced the more important aspects of metamorphism semihistorically, in the hope that some of my readers will be prompted to go back into the literature of pre-World War I years.

If individual problems demand critical appraisal by the reader, even more so does the total material of this book. Apart from inevitable errors, all the findings put forward here are tentative. They reflect present attitudes and prejudices of one person—the author. But mindful of such deficiencies and of the adjuration of Karl Popper, I have presented them (with supporting data) as fallible propositions whose predictions can be tested by future observation and experiment. Most will ultimately be modified, some rejected outright, a few perhaps strengthened, none ever certainly proven.

In conclusion, I reiterate my indebtedness to a host of colleagues, students, and critics, and especially acknowledge the benefit of discussion over the past decade with my Berkeley colleagues, J. Verhoogen and H. C. Helgeson.

Francis J. Turner

List of Symbols

Physical Units

cm	centimeter
m	meter
km	kilometer
g	gram
kg	kilogram
kb	kilobar
s	second
min	minute
cal	calorie ($= 4.184$ joules $= 41.84$ cm^3 bar)
kcal	kilocalorie
mole^{-1}	per mole
degr^{-1}	per degree
ppm	parts per million (by weight)

Thermodynamic Quantities and Properties

a	activity
C_p	heat capacity at constant pressure (cal mole^{-1} degr^{-1})
E	internal energy (cal mole^{-1})

f	fugacity
G	Gibbs free energy (cal mole^{-1})
H	enthalpy (cal mole^{-1})
K	equilibrium constant
P	pressure (bar)
p	partial pressure of a gas component (bar)
q	quantity of heat added (cal)
S	entropy (cal mole^{-1} degr^{-1})
T	absolute temperature (Kelvin): $0°C = 273.15$ K
V	volume (cm^3; or cal bar^{-1})
X, Y	molar fractions
γ	activity coefficient or fugacity coefficient
δ	isotope fractionation factor (for example, $\delta^{18}O/^{16}O$)
Δ	finite change in any quantity; for example, ΔV is the change in volume that occurs in a reaction or transformation
μ	chemical potential (cal mole^{-1})
R	gas constant 1.9872 cal ($= 8.3147$ joules $= 83.147$ bar cm^3 degr^{-1})

Subscripts and Superscripts

α	as a superscript, designates a phase; X_i^α is molar fraction of i in phase α
i	as a subscript, designates a component; thus μ_i^α is the chemical potential of component i in phase α; $p_i =$ partial pressure of i in gas
P, T	as subscripts, indicate fixed, constant pressure or temperature; thus $V_{P,T}$ is the volume at pressure P and temperature T; $(\partial V/\partial P)_T$ is the partial derivative of volume with respect to pressure at constant temperature. The notation $V_{1.013, 298.15}$ means volume at 1.013 bars and 298.15 K
E	as a subscript, indicates equilibrium; thus T_E is the equilibrium temperature for a reaction
m	as a subscript, indicates melting; ΔS_m is the entropy of fusion; ΔV_m is the change in volume on melting
r	as a subscript, indicates reaction; $\Delta S_r =$ reaction entropy
$°$	as a superscript, indicates a designated standard state; thus $\Delta G_r^°$ is the free-energy change of a reaction when all reactants and products are in their standard states
$^{-}$	overbar indicates a partial molar quantity; thus $\bar{S}_i^\alpha$ is the partial molar entropy of component i in phase α
liq, sol, soln, ss	as superscripts mean, respectively, in a liquid phase, in a solid phase, in solution, and in solid solution. Phase names as superscripts relate the quantity in question to that phase; for example, $a_{S_2}^{\text{pyrite}}$ is activity of sulfur in pyrite
$\Delta J^°$	change in the quantity J (for example, H, S, G) for 1 mole in the standard states
$\Delta J_f^°$	change in J accompanying formations of 1 mole from elements, all in their standard states

Logarithms

log   common logarithm (base 10)
ln   natural logarithm (base 2.71828); $\ln x = 2.303 \log x$
e exponential (2.71828)

METAMORPHIC PETROLOGY

1

Metamorphism
and Metamorphic Rocks

DEFINITION AND SCOPE OF METAMORPHISM

Since the days of Charles Lyell (e.g., 1860, pp. 591–593), it has been recognized that in some deeply eroded regions there is a gradual transition from sedimentary rocks to rocks whose mineralogical composition and structure have been imprinted by processes other than those of sedimentation. Such is the transition from shale or mudstone, through slate, to mica schist. Newly crystallized muscovite and chlorite appear at the expense of sedimentary clay minerals; detrital quartz and feldspar recrystallize to a coarse aggregate of quartz, albite, and epidote; and the rock becomes increasingly fissile with the development of a newly imposed planar structure, foliation. Yet even in the fully reconstituted rock, evidence of its sedimentary origin persists in the overall chemical composition, in partially obliterated relics of early structures, notably bedding (e.g., Tobisch, 1965), and even in recognizable fossils (e.g., Bucher, 1953; Boucot and Thompson, 1963). It is usually possible to map lithologically distinct formations of rocks such as quartzite and marble whose sedimentary origin is beyond doubt. Transitions of like nature have also been demonstrated between igneous rocks, especially lavas, and other reconstituted rocks that still retain inherited igneous structures such as amygdales and flow banding.

   The term *metamorphism* has been used for well over a century to cover transformations of this kind; and the products of transformation are the *metamorphic rocks.* With increasing geological knowledge, it has become possible on the basis of mineralogical and structural criteria alone to recognize rocks as metamorphic, without demonstrating in every case a field transition from nonmetamorphic sedimentary or igneous parent rocks. The inference has never been seriously challenged that metamorphism is the mineralogical and structural response of a rock to imposed conditions of temperature and pressure markedly different from those of its origin.

For convenience of discussion, arbitrary limits have been set to the range of rock transformations that are to be included within the scope of metamorphism. Purely surface changes such as weathering, leaching and cementation by meteoric waters, and the processes of diagenesis operating close to the earth's surface are excluded. But the boundary is artificially drawn; the student of diagenesis and the petrologist interested in the incipient stages of metamorphism may find themselves studying the same or closely related phenomena. At the opposite end of the scale, another arbitrary limit is customarily drawn between metamorphism, which involves reactions and structural adjustments in solid bodies, and magmatic processes, which involve participation of a silicate-melt phase. Spanning the corresponding interval are the migmatites. In these are intimately associated a truly metamorphic rock component such as amphibolite and a component of granitic composition that is generally thought once to have been liquid. Just where the line between metamorphic and igneous rocks is to be drawn depends on the prejudices of the individual geologist; for petrographic criteria of magmatic origin tend to be ambiguous in coarsely crystalline rocks. Many of the streaked biotite- and hornblende-bearing quartzofeldspathic rocks that figure prominently in older Precambrian cratons fall in this category. Are these products of primary magmatic crystallization whose texture reflects deformation synchronous with intrusion—granodiorite gneisses, in fact? Or are they truly metamorphic, bearing the mineralogical and textural imprint of regional metamorphism long postdating igneous intrusion? Can they be derivatives of sediments—graywackes metamorphosed at near-magmatic temperatures? Convincing cases have been made for specific instances of all these alternatives (see relevant parts of Chap. 10). A similar problem is raised by hornblende-plagioclase rocks in the same kind of situation. In this case, textural criteria and bulk chemistry help to distinguish metamorphic rocks (amphibolites) from somewhat gneissic diorites of primary magmatic origin. Eclogites—garnet-pyroxene rocks of basaltic composition—raise other questions of the same broad genre. Always there is evidence that they are blocks transported from great depths, some certainly from the mantle itself. They are customarily considered as metamorphic rocks, derivatives of gabbro or basalt; but there is an equal possibility that eclogites may form directly by crystallization of basaltic magma at pressures high enough to render stable the garnet-pyroxene pair.

With such reservations in mind, we have defined metamorphism as the mineralogical and structural adjustment of solid rocks to physical and chemical conditions that have been imposed at depths below the surface zone of weathering and that differ from the conditions under which the rock in question originated (Turner, 1948, p. 3; Coombs, 1961, p. 213). Since all rocks contain water, and the range of metamorphic temperatures must extend to those at which melting begins (perhaps 700–800°C), one of the phases participating in metamorphism will be a pore fluid, usually rich in water in the supercritical state; or, especially in calcareous rocks, carbon dioxide or methane may be significant components. In any case, the quantity of this pore fluid at a given moment is likely to be small. Apart from that, the reacting phases involved in metamorphism are solid.

Chemical analyses of many metamorphic rocks fall within the compositional limits of common igneous or sedimentary rocks, except for components such as H_2O and CO_2, which enter into the fluid phase and so are relatively mobile and may be expelled or added during metamorphism. It is convenient therefore as a first approximation to treat metamorphic reactions as if the system were closed with respect to all the "nonvolatile" components. This approach, however, is merely for convenience in discussion. Compositional changes, at least within small domains, are the rule rather than the exception. And in some instances the composition of a rock is drastically changed during metamorphism. Such is the case where limestone is converted to garnet-pyroxene rock at granite contacts, or where peridotite is metamorphosed to talc-magnesite schist. Metamorphic transformations of this kind are termed *metasomatic.*

DESCRIPTIVE CATEGORIES OF METAMORPHISM

Classic comprehensive surveys and textbook presentations of metamorphic phenomena have placed considerable emphasis on possible relations between different kinds of metamorphism and real or imaginary geologic situations and sets of physical controls. The number and validity of such categories will depend on the interests and purposes of individual writers and their potential readers. More than one approach is possible, and some may have equal validity.

In this book, we emphasize the types of metamorphism that can be defined objectively in terms of mineralogical, textural, and field criteria rather than with reference of postulated controls (Turner, 1948, p. 89).

Two Comprehensive Categories: Contact and Regional Metamorphism

Two broad categories generally accepted through time-honored usage together cover most metamorphic phenomena as seen in the field and in the laboratory. These are *contact metamorphism*, which is demonstrably controlled by proximity to plutonic contacts, and *regional metamorphism* of considerable, sometimes very great, extent, which is not directly related to plutonic intrusion of magma. Each definition will be elaborated in the appropriate section later in this chapter.

Subcategories

To discuss specific metamorphic problems relating to geologic (especially tectonic) environment, plutonism, ore geology, and so on, it may be convenient to recognize subcategories within this broad twofold framework. Again, the definitive criteria must relate to direct observation on any desired scale from the microscopic upward. Here are some widely used divisions that fulfill these requirements.

Burial Metamorphism

Coombs (1961, p. 214) introduced the term *burial metamorphism* to cover progressive mineralogical changes that can be directly correlated with depth of stratigraphic burial in thick sedimentary or volcanic piles. Such changes commonly are incomplete, so that the newly generated (metamorphic) mineral assemblage is intimately associated with relict mineral grains inherited from the original rock. Burial metamorphism in fact merges into and cannot be sharply distinguished from deep-seated diagenesis. Well-known examples include those described from southern New Zealand (Coombs, 1954), eastern Australia (Packham and Crook, 1960; R. E. Smith, 1969), Chile (Levi, 1969; Aguirre et al., 1978), and Puerto Rico (Jolly, 1970). Because all these are truly regional in extent and certainly are unrelated to plutonic intrusion, they clearly fall within the general category of regional metamorphism.

Lack of foliation (schistosity) is an essential and obvious mesoscopic characteristic of silicate rocks that bear the imprint of burial metamorphism. For this reason, Coombs (1961, p. 214) separated burial from regional metamorphism, redefining the latter category to include foliation (schistosity) as one of the diagnostic characteristics of its products. This proposal, although since adopted by many workers in the field (e.g., Zen, 1974a, p. 445), is here rejected for two reasons. First, because the word "regional" is widely used in geology in the unambiguous sense implied by its derivation; its meaning should not now be distorted by introducing textural or other extraneous connotations. Second, treating all regionally extensive, nonfoliated silicate rocks as products of burial metamorphism implies that the changes in intensity and mineralogical pattern observed in the field express a depth gradient. This is not necessarily so: regional gradients in heat-flow intensity could have the same effect.

Burial metamorphism, then, is a type of regional metamorphism whose degree and mineralogical imprint can be correlated on field evidence with stratigraphically (or tectonically) controlled depth gradients.

Anchimetamorphism

This term is rather widely applied in Europe (e.g., Kubler, 1967; Frey, 1970) to cover the regional field transition from diagenesis to clear-cut metamorphism. It includes changes unambiguously traceable to a depth gradient as well as identical changes occurring on a regional scale without any demonstrable relation to depth.

Ocean-Floor Metamorphism

Miyashiro et al. (1971, p. 602) introduced this term to cover metamorphic effects, probably of wide extent, that have been observed in rock fragments dredged from the ocean floor mainly in the vicinity of mid-ocean ridges (e.g., Melson and Van Andel, 1966; Cann, 1969). Because most of these specimens are nonschistose, ocean-floor metamorphism was seen as a kind of burial metamorphism. It was justifiably placed in a special category because of the great extent of the oceans and the apparent unity and uniqueness in pattern of ocean-floor tectonics. But this too is simply a special category of regional metamorphism, and, for reasons just given, we must emphatically reject the proposal of Miyashiro and coauthors to restrict the latter term to continental phenomena.

Genetically Defined Subcategories

Where field, petrographic, or chemical characteristics of metamorphic rocks un-equivocally warrant it, it may be convenient to emphasize some specific physical or chemical control by setting up a corresponding genetically defined subcategory of metamorphism (regional, contact, or both).

Thus, *hydrothermal metamorphism* covers changes that can be attributed, by analogy with currently active systems, to passage of hot aqueous fluids. This process is particularly relevant to problems of ore genesis, rock altera-tion, and geothermal energy. A mineralogically interesting but very limited kind of metamorphism, responsible for changes resulting from close contact with hot magma under volcanic or quasi-volcanic conditions, has been called *pyrometamorphism*.

Metamorphism in some instances is an essentially mechanical, irreversible process involving brittle rupture and relative displacement of mineral grains on a microscopic scale. The process has been termed *cataclastic metamorphism*. Experi-ment shows that it is favored by high rates of strain under high shear stress at relatively low temperatures; and that under high confining pressures the strained mass can remain coherent.

Dislocation metamorphism is cataclastic metamorphism localized in zones of dislocation such as major faults. It is of special interest to seismologists and field workers in tectonics, but it fits into neither the contact nor the regional division.

Concluding Statement

For purposes of comprehensive discussion, virtually all metamorphic phenomena can be treated—with a little stretching here and there—within the convenient context of contact and regional metamorphism. This plan is adopted in this book. It has the virtue—with respect to tectonic emphasis in the current fashion of geo-logic thought—of segregating into a single division (regional metamorphism) all patterns of metamorphism that can be directly related to different recognized tectonic situations. Subordinate categories—ocean-floor, burial, geothermal (local-ized or regional), cataclastic, and others—will crop up as occasion demands within the broad twofold framework.

THE METAMORPHIC ROCKS

In a hand specimen or an outcrop, the most striking characteristic that stamps the rock as metamorphic is usually its structure—foliated (schistose or gneissose), lineated, or, in rocks adjacent to igneous contacts, spotted or hornfelsic. Many common metamorphic rocks are defined therefore in terms of structural criteria. Such are the following (Williams, Turner, and Gilbert, 1954, p. 174):

Hornfels. A nonfoliated rock composed of a mosaic of equidimensional grains without preferred orientation (granoblastic or hornfelsic texture). In spotted hornfelses there are porphyroblasts of one or more minerals such as biotite or andalusite.

Slate. A fine-grained rock with perfect planar foliation (slaty cleavage), independent of bedding, resulting from parallel orientation of tabular crystals of mica and chlorite.

Phyllite. A rock resembling slate but somewhat coarser in grain. The cleavage surfaces show a lustrous sheen due to coarsening of mica and chlorite. There may be incipient lamination as recrystallizing quartz and feldspar tends to segregate into thin layers parallel to the cleavage.

Schist. A strongly foliated and commonly lineated rock, coarser than slate and phyllite. Foliation is accentuated by mineral lamination due to segregation of thin layers alternately rich in micaceous minerals, quartz, and feldspar. Very commonly this lamination, though widely mistaken for bedding, is a metamorphic structure due to metamorphic differentiation within what may initially have been homogeneous rock (Turner, 1941; Turner and Verhoogen, 1960, pp. 581–586).

Gneiss. A coarse, discontinuously banded quartzofeldspathic rock with ill-defined or discontinuous foliation.

Granulite (also termed *leptite* or *leptynite*). A plane-foliated nonmicaceous rock that may be laminated parallel to the foliation. The term is usually reserved for rocks containing garnet or pyroxene and believed to have crystallized at high metamorphic temperatures.

Mylonite. A fine-grained, flinty-looking, strongly coherent, banded or streaky rock formed by extreme granulation of coarse-grained rocks without notable chemical reconstruction. Eyes or lenses of undestroyed parent rock persist enclosed in the granulated groundmass. Some mylonites are streaked with veinlets of dark, glassy-looking, microscopically amorphous material known as *pseudotachylite*. A *phyllonite* is a mylonitic rock in which mica and chlorite recrystallizing from the granulated matrix impart a silky sheen (as in phyllite) to the foliation surfaces.

Rocks defined on these structural criteria may be classified further on a chemical or mineralogical basis as follows:

1. Pelitic: derivatives of pelitic (aluminous) sediments. Abundance of micas is characteristic.
2. Quartzofeldspathic: the principal minerals are quartz and feldspar. Here belong metamorphosed sandstones, siliceous tuffs, and granites.
3. Calcareous: derivatives of limestones and dolomites. Typically, calcite or dolomite is abundant; also characteristic are calcium and magnesium silicates such as diopside, tremolite, and grossularite.
4. Basic: derivatives of basic igneous rocks. Characteristic minerals are plagioclase, hornblende, chlorite, and epidote.
5. Magnesian: mainly derivatives of peridotites. Absence of feldspar and abundance of magnesian minerals (antigorite, talc, anthophyllite, magnesite, brucite) are characteristic.
6. Ferruginous and manganiferous: derivatives of cherts and other sediments

containing abundant iron and/or manganese. Quartz is a principal constituent, but feldspar is absent in typical metacherts. Magnetite, hematite, a spessartite-almandine garnet, grünerite, ferrohypersthene, stilpnomelane, and manganiferous epidotes or pyroxenoids are found in various combinations.

Other metamorphic rocks are nonfoliated or weakly foliated and are composed of only one or two essential minerals after which they are named accordingly:

Quartzite. Composed essentially of recrystallized quartz. Sandstone and chert are common parent rocks.

Marble. Composed of calcite or, less commonly, dolomite. Most marbles are metamorphosed limestones.

Amphibolite. A dark rock composed of hornblende and plagioclase. Most amphibolites are derivatives of basic igneous rocks; some have formed by metasomatism of calcareous sediments.

Serpentinites and soapstones. Magnesian rocks composed, respectively, of serpentine and talc, with carbonates, chlorite, and tremolite as possible minor constituents. The parent rocks are peridotites or, more rarely, dolomitic limestones.

CONTACT METAMORPHISM

General Character

Rocks generally show strong local effects of metamorphism in the vicinity of contacts with intrusive igneous bodies. This is contact metamorphism as distinguished from regional metamorphism, which occurs over much broader areas not obviously related to bodies of igneous rock. The characteristic products of contact metamorphism are hornfelses; but foliated rocks such as spotted slates and schists are widely developed in some instances. The zone of contact metamorphism is termed a *contact aureole*. The effects of contact metamorphism are most obvious where sedimentary rocks, especially shales and limestones, are in contact with large bodies of rock of the granite-granodiorite-tonalite family. It has generally been assumed that the sequence of mineralogical changes observed in a radial traverse across an aureole to the contact represents the response of the parent rock to a thermal gradient imposed by intrusion of hot magma into relatively cold rocks and subsequent outward conductance of heat from the magmatic source. That such a gradient has played an essential part in contact metamorphism is indeed likely. But the simple picture of a "thermal" aureole does not express in full what is perhaps a complex sequence of events both in space and in time.

Many of the classic accounts of contact metamorphism (e.g., Harker and Marr, 1891; Harker, 1904, pp. 144–151; Goldschmidt, 1911a; Tilley, 1924a) are detailed statements of the mineral assemblages developed in limited exposures or sections of an aureole. Maps showing the complete zonal distinction of such assemblages in any aureole are somewhat rare.[*] This is partly because of variation in lithology of the parent rocks and imperfect exposures. But the difficulty in mapping an aureole also stems partly from the capricious nature of the metamorphism itself. Within even one formation the width of an aureole may vary notably; and it is usually uncertain to what extent this represents variation in the attitude of the hidden and perhaps subjacent igneous contact, rather than local fluctuation in the thermal gradient. Finally, it must be remembered that many of the most detailed studies of the mineralogy of contact metamorphism are based on material collected, not from complete aureoles, but from isolated masses of metamorphic rocks completely enclosed within igneous plutons.

Since generalization is likely to oversimplify the complex picture of contact metamorphism, we shall refer first to particular well-documented examples.

Illustrative Examples

Comrie Aureole, Scotland

North of Comrie (Perthshire) in the southern Highlands of Scotland, a diorite stock measuring 8 X 1 km in the outcrop cuts a series of slates and fissile grits containing muscovite, chlorite, quartz, albite, and epidote. These rocks represent the earliest stage of regional metamorphism. Around the contact is a contact aureole, averaging 500–600 m in width, the mineralogy of which has been discussed in great detail by Tilley (1924a). The boundaries of the aureole are not shown on Tilley's map. But three stages of progressive metamorphism can be recognized as the contact is approached in each of several well-exposed sections.

The first stage is shown only in the slates. At about 450 m from the contact, spots about 1 mm in diameter appear, in which newly crystallized mica and chlorite are concentrated.

The second stage is marked by crystallization of biotite. In the slates, this occurs at 270 m from the contact in one section, and at about 420 m in another. The first appearance of biotite in the grits on the other hand is 500 or 600 m from the contact.

Within 150 m of the contact, the slates have been completely reconstituted to cordierite-bearing hornfelses. Typical assemblages, each of which contains quartz, plagioclase, and orthoclase, are andalusite-cordierite-biotite and cordierite-hypersthene-biotite. Silica-free aluminous hornfelses with corundum or spinel also occur. In the grits, the zone of cordierite hornfelses extends to about 260 m from the contact.

Marysville Aureole, Montana

One of the earliest documented U.S. accounts of a contact aureole is to be found in Barrell's (1907) description and map of the Marysville granodiorite stock in Montana (see also A. Knopf, 1950). The outcrop of the stock covers 8 km². It is

---

[*]The earliest attempt to map zones of progressive metamorphism is that of Rosenbusch (1877; cf. Harker, 1932, pp. 23, 24). In the aureole of the Barr-Andlau granitic pluton in the Vosges, he traced an inward transition from spotted slates with segregations of graphite, through spotted schists with recrystallized chlorite and muscovite in the groundmass, to completely reconstituted andalusite-cordierite hornfels.

late Cretaceous or Paleocene in age and has developed a continuous aureole, 1–3 km wide, in the surrounding Precambrian (Beltian) dolomites and shales (Fig. 1-1). In certain places the granodiorite contact dips gently; but locally, as revealed by mining operations, the contact maintains a nearly vertical attitude for several hundred meters. The original cover is estimated to have been thin—perhaps 1–2 km.

Within the aureole, shales have been converted to cordierite-biotite-muscovite-hornfels, and dolomitic limestones to marble containing tremolite and diopside. Along the southeast margin of the stock, the limestones have been converted to calc-silicate hornfelses with little or no calcite. Common types consist almost entirely of tremolite or of diopside; other assemblages are diopside-scapolite and diopside-vesuvianite. Clearly, large-scale introduction of SiO_2 and perhaps Al_2O_3, MgO, and FeO, and complete expulsion of CO_2, were involved in this phase of contact metamorphism, which according to Barrell extends only 200–300 m from the contact. Beyond this limit, the diopside and tremolite marbles seem to have formed by reaction between carbonates and siliceous impurities present in the parent dolomites.

Aureoles of Donegal Granite Plutons, Ireland

The Donegal "granites" of northwestern Ireland (Fig. 1-2) comprise a complex of several granodioritic and quartz-monzonitic plutons, covering some 600 km², invading metasediments of the Dalradian formation (late Precambrian and early Cambrian). Intrusion of the granites and preceding regional metamorphism of the Dalradian envelope were successive episodes in the protracted series of pre-Devonian events termed the *Grampian orogeny* (cf. p. 25). The granitic plutons and their contact aureoles have been mapped and described in detail by W. S. Pitcher, H. H. Read, and associates (Pitcher and Read, 1960, 1963); the evolution of the metamorphic or mineral assemblages is the topic of a more recent paper by Naggar and Atherton (1970). Here we shall consider two specific aureoles, both imprinted during and following forceful emplacement of granitic magmas.

The youngest and largest pluton, Main Donegal Granite, is an elongated body of granodiorite 400 km² in outcrop area. The rock itself is strongly foliated parallel to the long axis of the pluton and to the strike of the enveloping metasediments; and it encloses numerous steeply dipping rafts and inclusions of country rock aligned parallel to the trend of foliation. The total structural picture reflects intrusion by magmatic wedging and near-horizontal NE-SW flow. The schist envelope was strongly affected by deformation synchronous with intrusion, which indeed may even have been responsible for its present mesoscopic and macroscopic structure.

The aureole of the Main Granite (Fig. 1-3) is 2–3 km wide, with incipient effects locally visible 4 km from the contact. Consistently steep attitudes in foliation of both the granite and the country rock strongly suggest that the contact is also steep and that the outcrop records the true thickness of the aureole. Variations in the latter, especially apparent thinning along the northern sector of the northeast contact, are due mainly to extensive outcrop of quartzites, which are insensitive to metamorphism. Mineralogical contact effects are most obvious in the pelitic and calcareous members. Beyond the aureole the former are quartz-

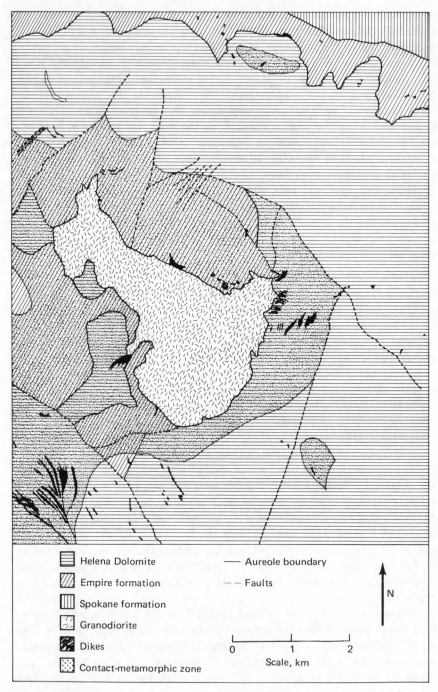

FIGURE 1-1
Aureole of Marysville stock, Montana (after A. Knopf; adapted from J. Barrell).

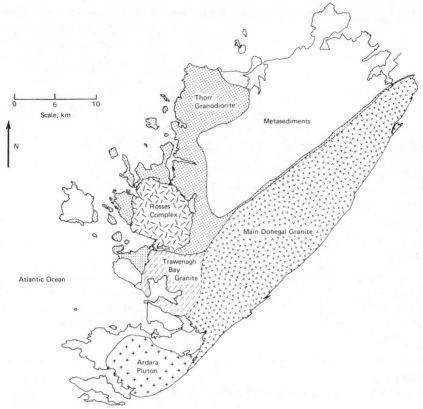

FIGURE 1-2
Donegal granitic complex, northwestern Ireland (after W. S. Pitcher and H. H. Read).

muscovite-chlorite phyllites. Scattered porphyroblasts of muscovite and chlorite, followed inward by biotite, mark the incipient stages of metamorphism, especially in the northwestern sector of the aureole. In the inner zone, within a kilometer or so of the southeastern contact, pelitic rocks have been converted to staurolite-garnet-muscovite-biotite-quartz schists. Many of these contain abundant andalusite with which kyanite or fibrolite are locally associated.[*] Near the northeastern tip of the pluton the principal Al_2SiO_5 phase in the contact zone is kyanite: Cordierite, elsewhere common, is absent from the aureole of the Main Granite. Along the northwestern contact calcareous rocks are prominent in the envelope; they pass inward from an initial calcite-quartz-phlogopite assemblage, through tremolite marbles to sphene-bearing mica-tremolite-quartz schists, some containing diopside. Rafts of metasediments within the granodiorite are of three main types: (1) biotite-muscovite quartzites; (2) pelitic schists consisting of muscovite, biotite, fibrolite, quartz, and newly generated feldspar (andalusite is present in some rocks, but staurolite and garnet are absent); and (3) calcareous skarns consisting of various

---

[*]The genetic significance of associated Al_2SiO_5 polymorphs is discussed on p. 151.

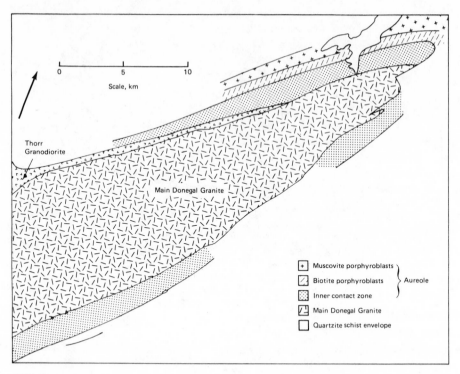

FIGURE 1-3
Aureole of Main Donegal Granite (simplified after W. S. Pitcher and H. H. Read).

combinations of tremoliite, clinozoisite, garnet, wollastonite, vesuvianite, talc, and sphene.

The Ardara pluton is the second member of the intrusive sequence. It has a circular outcrop 8 km in diameter and consists of a central body of granodiorite rimmed continuously with a border of hornblende-biotite-tonalite less than 1 km in width. Contacts with the enveloping schists are sharp and nearly vertical; and the country rocks, tightly folded and bowed around the pluton, bear witness to emplacement of the magma by forceful upward intrusion. Along the northern margin of the pluton the invaded pelitic schists show effects of contact metamorphism as far as 2 km from the contact. Beyond the aureole they are highly deformed rocks consisting of quartz, muscovite, and chlorite. The latter is commonly pseudomorphous after biotite and garnet. The aureole itself is concentrically zoned with respect to the arcuate contact (Fig. 1-4).

1. Outer aureole: Reconstitution of chlorite at the outermost limit of contact metamorphism is followed inward by crystallization of biotite at the expense of chlorite.
2. Inner aureole: 300–550 m wide, consisting of completely reconstituted schists and hornfelses with aluminum silicates (Naggar and Atherton, 1970, pp. 555–556).

a. Kyanite-andalusite zone: Schists with porphyroblastic andalusite and feldspar in a groundmass of quartz, muscovite, biotite, and kyanite (staurolite and garnet are both rare).

b. Andalusite zone: Schists and hornfelses composed of andalusite, biotite, quartz, and plagioclase (with garnet, staurolite, and fibrolite as possible additional minerals).

c. Sillimanite zone: The typical assemblage is sillimanite (fibrolite)-biotite-quartz-garnet, with cordierite in a narrow subzone fringing the contact. Staurolite is sporadic. There is evidence that some of the fibrolite (accompanied by sericitic mica) has directly replaced earlier prisms of andalusite; but most of it, though tending to be concentrated in veinlike metasomatic segregations, shows no textural indication that it replaces preexisting andalusite.

In a detailed chemical study, Pitcher and Sinha (1958) showed that the only chemical changes involved in contact metamorphism were general expulsion of water and possibly slight enrichment in alkalis close to the contact. Surprisingly, it would seem that late conversion of aluminum silicates to muscovite involved no influx of magmatically derived potash, but was accomplished by chemical reaction in a system closed to all chemical components other than water.

Calc-silicate Aureole of the Darwin Mine Area, California

The Darwin mine area (Hall and MacKevett, 1962) lies in the mountainous desert region west of Death Valley in southeastern California. Except where Pleistocene

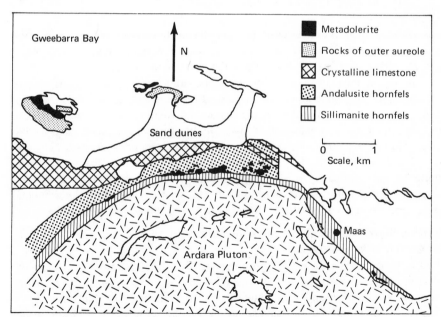

FIGURE 1-4
Aureole of Ardara pluton, Donegal granitic complex (after M. K. Akaad, 1956).

and recent fans cover the lower slopes and the basin floors, exposures of bedrock are excellent and are supplemented by numerous mine workings extending 300 m below the surface. Mississippian to Permian sedimentary rocks, mostly calcareous, are invaded by irregularly outcropping bodies of quartz monzonite. West of Darwin the main pluton is 10–15 km wide. In the mine area itself (longitudinal portion of Fig. 1-5), an outlying mass of quartz monzonite outcrops over an area about 6 km long. Here the Paleozoic sediments show striking effects of contact metamorphism over an area 7 X 2 km around the quartz monzonite outcrop.

The purer limestone beds have been bleached and recrystallized to white marbles. More widely distributed in the Darwin area are impure shaly limestones that have been converted to calc-silicate hornfelses in which the gross bedding is still preserved. Various combinations of diopside, wollastonite, vesuvianite, garnet, calcite, feldspars, quartz, tremolite, and epidote constitute the common mineral assemblages. Forsterite, scapolite, and sphene appear more locally. These rocks (Hall and MacKevett, 1962, p. 47) are believed to have formed by simple recrystallization of impure limestones without significant compositional change other than loss of CO_2. Even a simple change from a carbonate-bearing to a silicate assemblage, such as development of diopside by reaction between dolomite and quartz, must be accompanied by large change of volume—in this case about 35% reduction—or by a corresponding increase in porosity.

$$CaMg(CO_3)_2 + \quad 2SiO_2 \quad \rightarrow CaMgSi_2O_6 + 2CO_2$$

dolomite	quartz	diopside
183 g; 63 cm³	120 g; 41 cm³	215 g; 67 cm³

It is possible therefore that even the calc-silicate hornfelses have been affected by introduction of material from a magmatic source. Alternatively, metamorphism must have been accompanied by a substantial decrease in volume.

In the vicinity of the igneous contacts, later addition of various oxides, presumably from magmatic fluids,[*] has caused the development of skarns (tactites) at the expense of both calc-silicate hornfels and marble. The former has been converted to assemblages dominated by andradite garnet, vesuvianite, and wollastonite. Most skarns derived from marble are rich in andradite and contain epidote.

The latest mineral changes connected with intrusion of the quartz monzonite are exemplified by ore-bearing pipes and veins in calc-silicate hornfels and skarns in the vicinity of the igneous contacts. To this category belong mineral assemblages dominated by sulfides (mainly galena and sphalerite) or scheelite.

Limited Metamorphism Adjacent to Diabase Sill Contacts in Tasmania

Thick sills of Jurassic diabase outcrop over much of the island of Tasmania (e.g., Edwards, 1942). At Mt. Wellington, near Hobart, the lower 300 m of what was once an even thicker and very extensive sheet of diabase and the immediately underlying horizontal Triassic sandstones are continuously exposed. Even within a few meters of the contact, the sandstones show only minor effects of meta-

---

[*]Rich in H_2O rather than CO_2 (cf. p. 281).

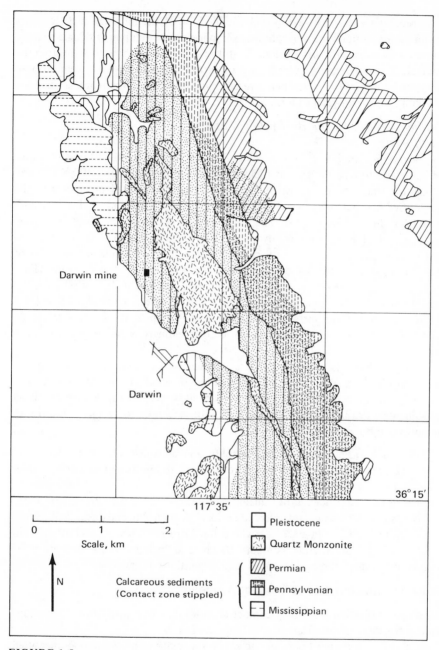

Darwin mine

Darwin

117°35′

36°15′

Scale, km

0   1   2

N

Calcareous sediments
(Contact zone stippled)

Pleistocene

Quartz Monzonite

Permian

Pennsylvanian

Mississippian

FIGURE 1-5

Contact metamorphism, Darwin mine region, southeastern California (after W. E. Hall and
E. M. MacKevett).

morphism. Elsewhere, where the rocks at the base of the intrusion include shales and limestone, contact metamorphism, exemplified by development of calc-silicates in limestone, although more obvious, is still restricted to within 20-30 m from the contacts. Yet the magma at the time of intrusion must have been completely liquid, and therefore at a temperature around 1000°C, for the marginal diabases have a uniformly fine-grained texture.

Contact Aureole of the Bushveld Complex, South Africa

The Bushveld complex of South Africa is an immense sheetlike body of stratified basic and ultramafic igneous rocks outcropping over an area of 400 × 150 km. It "has the shape of an elongated basin which has been tilted downward to the east, so that the bottom of the basin is exposed at the west end of the intrusion" (H. D. Wilson, 1956, p. 290). The maximum thickness of the sheet is at least 8 km and possibly is considerably more. The underlying rocks are late Precambrian shales, slates, and some quartzites. Within them, a spectacular aureole of great but variable width has developed beneath the floor of the intrusion (Hall, 1916, 1932, pp. 386-421). Hall records aureole widths of 100-3000 m, measured normal to the contact projected upward, parallel to the dip of bedding in the floor; but if the intrusion is indeed funnel shaped, the contact would be steeper than the bedding and the aureole correspondingly wider—in places perhaps 5 km or more.

On the basis of pelitic mineral assemblages prominent in the floor rocks, Hall recognized an outer and an inner zone of contact metamorphism. The mineralogical characteristics of these zones are illustrated in a subsequent revision by Willemse (1959, especially pp. li, lxi) with reference to specific localities in the northeastern sector of the aureole.

1. Outer zone (Longsight type): chiastolite and andalusite-chloritoid slates preserving initial sedimentary structures. Local dolomitic limestones contain tremolite or wollastonite.
2. Inner zone (Groothoek type): mainly cordierite-andalusite-biotite-quartz hornfelses, some with abundant microcline; locally, staurolite-andalusite and garnet-andalusite hornfels. In one area where the intrusive body is peridotitic, hornfelses of the inner zone contain abundant sillimanite. Local derivatives of dolomite consist of diopside, spinel, and serpentinized forsterite.

General Characteristics of Contact Aureoles

Certain generalizations regarding contact aureoles may be drawn from observations made in the field (cf. also Harker, 1932, pp. 20-26).

1. Only maximum limits can be set on the width of most aureoles, measured normal to the surfaces of contact. This is because the contact commonly dips gently at the outcrop, and its configuration in depth is rarely known. There are recorded instances, nevertheless, where the aureole must extend at least 2 or 3 km from the nearest plutonic contact.

2. Partly because most large plutons are composed of "granitic" rocks (quartz diorite, granodiorite, quartz monzonite), we tend to associate contact

aureoles mentally with "granites." Many of the aureoles of classic geologic literature do indeed exemplify this association. However, the larger sheetlike intrusions of basic rocks (such as the Bushveld complex) are also bordered by extensive contact aureoles, especially in the floor regions. By contrast, metamorphic effects in the floors of porous sediment that underlie many of the massive sheets and sills of diabase tend to be insignificant or else limited to a few meters from the contacts. At contacts with large ultramafic bodies the only visible effect may be local metasomatism (e.g., albitization or prehnitization) of the country rock—an indication of "cold" intrusion in the solid state (cf. Carmichael et al., 1974, p. 609). Less commonly, the ultramafic body (e.g., that of the Lizard, Cornwall) has developed a high-temperature contact aureole in its envelope (D. H. Green, 1964, pp. 181-182). Blocks of amphibolite and eclogite near the margins of cold intrusions of serpentinite in California may possibly be fragments of disrupted aureoles transported from the depths by the rising serpentinite masses (cf. Essene et al., 1965).

3. Aureoles in argillaceous rocks may be zoned concentrically with respect to plutonic contacts. A common inward sequence from spotted slates and schists to hornfelses is characterized mineralogically by muscovite and chlorite in the outermost zone; biotite with or without andalusite in the next zone; and biotite, cordierite, and sillimanite close to the contact. The aluminous minerals may on occasion include chloritoid (especially in the outer zones), staurolite, almandine garnet, or even kyanite—minerals more familiar in environments of regional metamorphism.

4. Aureoles in calcareous rocks tend to show greater variation and less regularity in mineral paragenesis (cf. Verhoogen et al., 1970, pp. 552, 553). Zoning, except locally and on a small scale, in most cases is obscure. The nature of the mineral assemblage and the distance to which it extends from the contact seems to depend on the chemical composition and the permeability of individual calcareous beds or formations. Near the contact, the appearance of special mineral phases may be correlated with the introduction, presumably from the intrusive magma, of elements that enter readily into volatile compounds, for example, iron (andradite, hematite), fluorine (humite minerals, fluorite, vesuvianite), boron (axinite, tourmaline), chlorine (scapolite), and others.

5. Some mineral assemblages, usually locally developed, express local sequences of events in time. To this category belong skarns (tactites) and sulfide ores, both common in calcareous rocks near igneous contacts. Surprisingly, perhaps, zonal transitions in pelitic rocks seldom show unequivocal textural evidence of direct mutual encroachment involving simple replacement of the outer zone by the inner-zone mineral (e.g., Naggar and Atherton, 1970). Andalusite and fibrolite, for example, may coexist with no sign of mutual reaction; indeed the fibrolite tends to appear in knots formed by breakdown of micas, while associated andalusite persists unchanged as stout porphyroblasts. Evidence of late reactions under the influence of diffusing aqueous fluids during cooling of the aureole is common and widespread: pseudomorphs of micaceous or chloritic aggregates after andalusite, cordierite, or garnet; and serpentinized forsterite and veinlets of brucite in dolomitic marbles.

Thermal Models of Contact Metamorphism

Controlling Conditions and Parameters

For over a century contact metamorphism has been attributed to reactions induced by thermal gradients set up by intrusion of bodies of hot magma into relatively cold rocks. Lyell (1860, p. 593) wrote:

> The precise nature of these altering causes, which may provisionally be termed plutonic, is in a great degree obscure and doubtful; but their reality is no less clear, and we must suppose the influence of heat to be in some way connected with the transmutation, if . . . we concede the igneous origin of granite.

Since we accept the thermal influence as an essential factor in contact metamorphism, we can make further inferences as to the limiting physical conditions in contact aureoles.

Possible patterns of temperature distribution, in space and in time, in aureoles surrounding plutonic intrusions can be set up and evaluated in the light of simple models proposed by Lovering (1936, 1955) and elaborated by Jaeger (1957, 1959). The temperature at any distance from the contact at any given time depends on a number of quantities the limits of which are reasonably well known: size and temperature of the magma body; thermal conductivity, density, specific heat, and diffusivity of country rock and solidified magma; initial temperature and water content of country rock; crystallization temperature and latent heat of crystallization of magma; and heat absorbed or liberated by metamorphic reactions.

Complicating factors more difficult to assess include the pattern of magmatic flow—rate of intrusion, possible multiple injection, and postintrusive convection—and the regime of water circulation in the envelope. Jaeger simplifies the problem by postulating instantaneous intrusion; and he shows that the time taken for a pluton to solidify then depends essentially on conduction in the envelope, effects of internal convection being relatively small (Jaeger, 1957, p. 317), and therefore neglected. Even with such simplifications, Jaeger's models show that the dimensions and thermal history of natural aureoles must be determined principally by the minimum dimension D of the pluton (thickness of a sheet, diameter of a stock) and the maximum temperature developed in the envelope at the intrusive contact. From Jaeger's models emerge geologically significant inferences, probably valid within rather narrow quantitative limits.

Maximum (Initial) Contact Temperature

The simplest model postulates instantaneous intrusion of a body of magma at a fixed liquidus temperature T_m into country rocks initially at T_0. At the contact, the temperature immediately rises to some intermediate value T_c, the principal governing parameter being

$$\sigma = \frac{K_1 k_0^{1/2}}{K_0 k_1^{1/2}}$$

where K_0 and K_1 are the respective conductivities, and k_0 and k_1 the respective diffusivities of the country rock and the solidified igneous rock. Where $\sigma = 1$, a condition approximated by intrusion of granitic magma into mixed sandstone and shale, $T_c = \frac{1}{2}(T_m + T_o)$, if the heat of magmatic crystallization is neglected. However, the effect of this latter factor proves to be significant: If a reasonable value of 80–100 cal g^{-1} is assumed, T_c is thereby raised by over 100°. Values computed on this basis by Jaeger (1959, p. 46) or from his data are given in Table 1-1.

In natural systems heat is transferred outward by conduction and becomes dissipated for some distance from the contact by vaporization of pore water and by endothermic metamorphic reactions (dehydration, decarbonation). Both processes tend to reduce contact temperatures by a few tens of degrees; and this trend will be somewhat enhanced by the influence of pore water in raising the effective conductivity of the country rock and by the inward flux of water controlled by the escape of steam along the contact and absorption of water into undersaturated magma.† The values T_c^* in the right-hand column of Table 1-1 reflect the influence of water saturation in a country rock with a porosity of 0.2 (Jaeger, 1959, p. 49, Table 2).

Temperature Gradients

Aureole temperatures for any given intrusive system are a function of time and of distance X from the contact. At any point the temperature rises from the moment of intrusion, reaches some maximum value (less than T_c), and then falls more gradually toward T_o. Figure 1-6 shows temperature–time gradients in the aureoles of two granodioritic plutons, respectively, 10 and 4 km in diameter, generating a maximum contact temperature $T_c = 540°C$ in country rock initially at $T_o = 100°C$.

---

†Most magmas at depths greater than 3–4 km probably are undersaturated in water (Carmichael et al., 1974, p. 326). Moreover, the evidence of oxygen-isotope composition trends suggests that, contrary to views long generally held, even in granite aureoles the flow of water may be toward and into the cooling pluton (Verhoogen et al., 1970, p. 556). Jaeger (1959, p. 52) argues that the thermal effect of an inward flux would be relatively slight.

TABLE 1-1

Initial Contact Temperatures T_c Computed for Instantaneous Intrusion of Magma at T_m into Dry Country Rock Initially at T_o

Igneous rock	Country rock	σ	Temperature, °C			
			T_m	$T_o{}^a$	T_c	T_c^{*b}
		1	800	100	560	520–540
		1	1000	0	622	573
Granodiorite	Shale	2	800	100	685	
Granodiorite	Shale	2	800	200	710	
Granodiorite	Sandstone	0.8	800	100	~500	
Gabbro	Shale	1.54	1000	0	750	
Gabbro	Sandstone	0.66	1000	0	~460	
Gabbro	Sandstone	0.66	1000	100	~500	

[a] Heat of magmatic crystallization is 100 cal g^{-1}.

[b] T_c^* is computed for a water-saturated envelope.

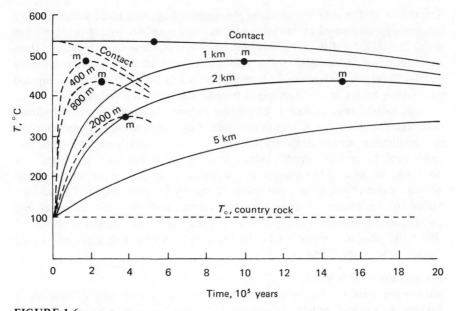

FIGURE 1-6
Gradients of temperature in time at specified distances from contacts with granodioritic plutons 10 km (full curves) and 4 km (dashed curves) in diameter. Initial temperature of country rock 100°C; initial magmatic temperature 800°C; heat of crystallization 80 cal g^{-1} (computed from Jaeger, 1957, p. 311, Fig. 1).

Figure 1-7 shows temperature–distance (X) gradients for the same 4-km pluton at successive intervals of time ($100 \times 10^3 - 500 \times 10^3$ years) following intrusion. Gradients of maximum temperature, against X, for granitic plutons of different dimensions are given in Fig. 1-8. Metamorphic T-X gradients inferred from mineralogical data and geothermometry are generally equated with curves such as those of Fig. 1-8.

Other things being equal, the main controlling factor for each kind of gradient is the dimension D of the pluton normal to the contact (diameter of a cylindrical body, thickness of a sheet). The maximum temperature at distance X (Fig. 1-8) is a function of D/X. Thus, a value of 400°C is reached where $D/X = 3.3$ at 300 m from the contact of a 1-km pluton (A), at 3 km from that of a pluton 10 km in diameter (B). The thermal histories, however, are very different because the time taken to reach any given temperature (D/X being constant) is a function of D^2. This is illustrated in Fig. 1-6, in which, for $D/X = 5$ ($X = 800$ m, $D = 4$ km; $X = 2$ km, $D = 10$ km), the temperature reaches 400°C at time $0.006D^2$ (D measured in meters)—6×10^5 years for the larger, and almost 10^5 years for the smaller pluton. On both curves, the maximum, 430°C, is reached at $0.015D^2$ years (1.5×10^6 and 0.24×10^6, respectively). The maximum on both the 1-km ($D = 10$ km) and 400-m ($D = 4$ km) curves of Fig. 1-6 is at 490°C, reached, respectively, at 10^6 and 0.16×10^6 years, that is, in both cases at $0.01D^2$ years.

Temperature Gradients and the Kinetics
of Metamorphic Reactions

Most metamorphic reactions are known to be very slow. Their rates decrease exponentially with falling temperature (cf. p. 79). Assuming, as is generally done, that the temperature of metamorphism at any point in the aureole is close to the maximum there attained, it is appropriate to examine the times involved in heating and cooling through a small interval on either side of the maximum. Here are some inferences, drawn from Jaeger's models, that may have a bearing on kinetics of metamorphic reactions.

First, for a given value of D/X, temperatures are maintained close to the maximum (say, within $20°$) for a time that is a function of D^2. In Fig. 1-6, take $D/X = 10$ ($X = 1$ km, $D = 10$ km; $X = 400$ m; $D = 4$ km). Temperatures remain between $470–490°C$ for $0.012D^2$ years—1.2×10^6 years in the larger and 0.19×10^6 years in the smaller aureole.

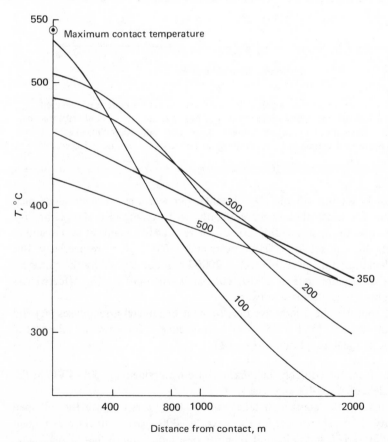

FIGURE 1-7
Gradients of temperature against X, distance from contact, at times after intrusion specified in multiples of 1000 years. Same intrusive system (pluton 4 km in diameter) as Fig. 1-6.

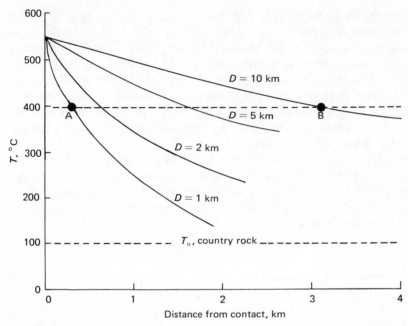

FIGURE 1-8
Gradients of maximum temperature against distance from contact for plutons of specified
diameter D. Intrusive system closely similar to that of Figs. 1-6 and 1-7: Granodioritic magma
initially at 800°C (crystallization range 800–600°C, heat of crystallization 800 cal g^{-1}) emplaced in water-saturated sediments ($\sigma = 1$) initially at 100°C (computed from Jaeger, 1959,
pp. 46 and 47, Fig. 1).

Second, in a given aureole (D constant), temperatures are maintained near
the maximum for times that increase slightly with X. Fig. 1-6 shows that for
$D = 4$ km, temperatures stay within 20° of the respective maxima at 400 m and at
2000 m from the contact for 190,000 years and 260,000 years, respectively. But
the greater length of time available at $X = 2000$ km is outweighed by the exponential decrease of reaction rate at 350°C compared with 490°C. The effectiveness
of metamorphism must decrease outward.

Third, consider the alternative development of mineral assemblages (A) and
(B), stable at 400–450° and at 450–500°C, respectively, for different values of X
in the aureole of the 4-km pluton of Fig. 1-6.

1. At 800 m from the contact, temperatures are maintained at 400–440°C in the
   stability field of A for 400,000 years.
2. At 400 m from the contact, it takes only 30,000 years to cover the full span
   of stability of A. Thereafter, for the next 240,000 years, temperatures remain
   between 450–490°C in the field of B before returning again to that of A.
3. Within 20 m or so of the contact, heating is so rapid that the residence time in
   the stability field of A is geologically negligible; thereafter, temperatures exceed
   450°C for over 300,000 years.

Application to Natural Systems

Jaeger's thermal models are generally consistent with accepted inferences drawn from the minerology and chemistry of contact aureoles. In some cases, they place quantitative limits on these; in others, they provide plausible explanations for what otherwise seem anomalous aspects of time and temperature in metamorphism. Some geologically significant applications follow.

Maximum contact temperatures in an aureole are several hundred degrees below temperatures of intrusive magmas. Reasonable values for many situations might be 500–700°C.

Many of the classic examples of contact metamorphism are aureoles generated by postkinematic plutons emplaced shortly after the climax of regional metamorphism of the envelope. Two factors combine to make metamorphism conspicuous under these conditions: Country rock temperatures at depths of 10 km or so are likely to exceed 200°C, thus correspondingly raising the contact temperature T_c above the values quoted in Table 1-1. The dimensions of the plutons, usually several kilometers in diameter, are appropriate for the development of wide aureoles (cf. Fig. 1-8). An outward flux of water from the cooling pluton could produce the same effect (Hori, 1964), but the oxygen-isotope patterns of at least some wide aureoles strongly suggest the reverse circulatory system.

A converse explanation applies to what seem at first sight to be anomalously slight contact effects at the floors of great intrusive sheets of diabase such as the Mt. Wellington Sill in Tasmania. These presumably are emplaced at temperatures close to 1000°C. But maximum contact temperatures are likely to have been lowered to perhaps 500°C or even less by a combination of factors including near-surface emplacement into cold country rocks, which are dominantly water-saturated porous sandstones with high conductivity (cf. Table 1-1). Impressive though these intrusive bodies are in the field, their minimum dimensions (D commonly 400–700 m) are normal to the contact. At 40 m below the floor of the 400-m Mt. Wellington Sill, the temperature could have been maintained above 400°C for perhaps no more than 4000 years.

Temperature-time gradients (Fig. 1-6) offer an explanation for what appears to be a general phenomenon of contact metamorphism: virtually direct derivation of inner-zone phase assemblages from the incipiently reconstituted country rock, without intervening formation of assemblages and textures now found in zones more distant from the contact. The controlling factor must be the kinetics of the outer-zone reactions. We have seen that the residence times in the temperature interval of effective metamorphism is many times greater in the outer than in the innermost zone. It is obvious, too, from previous discussion that reactions in the vicinity of 400°C must be excessively slow, perhaps being poorly effective over periods computed to be of the order of 5000 or 10,000 years. Perusal of Fig. 1-6 also suggests that a metamorphic assemblage, once formed, can survive with but minor change periods of prolonged postmetamorphic cooling; for they must have remained within 200° or so of the temperature of metamorphism for periods measured in hundreds of thousands of years.

In some natural situations, contact metamorphism occurs under conditions far removed from Jaeger's models. Xenoliths completely immersed in magma and wall-rocks of conduits for fast-flowing basic magma can reach temperatures close to that of the magma itself. The resulting patterns of mineralogical change, in some cases accompanied by partial fusion, have been termed pyrometamorphism (cf. "sanidinite facies").

REGIONAL METAMORPHISM

General Character

Over much of the Precambrian shields and in eroded Phanerozoic fold belts margining or cutting across present continents, metamorphic rocks extend for thousands of square kilometers. Even where granitic plutons are exposed within the metamorphic terrane—as they commonly are—intrusion of magma and metamorphism seem to be partially independent manifestations of some broader crustal disturbance. Emplacement of some plutons may be roughly synchronous with metamorphism; others postdate metamorphism by tens of millions of years; still others seem to have been formed by partial melting of the crust—the very culmination of the metamorphic process. Metamorphic rocks have also been recovered in dredge hauls from the ocean floor, and there is every indication that here too metamorphism has been recently active over very large areas, without direct magmatic influence.

The processes responsible for such rock transformations on an extensive scale have come to be known collectively as *regional metamorphism.* The term is used here in the time-honored sense without prejudice as to tectonic location, possible heat sources, or the structural character of the imprint.

The most conspicuous feature of regionally metamorphosed rocks in the classic regions to be described shortly is a pervasive foliated (schistose) structure seen on all scales from the microscopic to that of the outcrop (mesoscopic). It is an essential feature of the commonest completely metamorphic rocks—slates, phyllites, schists, amphibolites, and many granulites. Foliation (schistosity) is the result of flow under high nonhydrostatic stress—a strain phenomenon expressing irreversible structural rearrangement of rock materials, penetrative down to the scale of ionic groups and atoms. Thus, it is a structure (texture) of great tectonic significance, and much effort has been spent on unraveling strain history (commonly prolonged and episodic) and in interpretation of strain effects in dynamic and kinematic terms (cf. Turner and Weiss, 1963).

It has become increasingly apparent in recent years that there are great areas of rocks in fold belts, Precambrian basins, and beneath the ocean floor that completely lack foliation but that nevertheless bear a partial mineralogical imprint of metamorphism. These, once classed as nonmetamorphic, clearly express a pattern of regional metamorphism. There are many tectonic belts in fact where they grade in the field into foliated rocks of similar parentage. We shall meet them repeatedly in later chapters when we discuss problems of ocean-floor, burial, and geothermal metamorphism.

There is great variety in the mineral assemblages of regionally metamorphosed rocks, even among rocks of the same general chemical composition. Thus, the metamorphic derivatives of basalt in various situations include chlorite-albite-epidote schist, amphibolite (hornblende-plagioclase), glaucophane-lawsonite-chlorite schist, and pyroxene granulite. Some of the common minerals of the schists are also widely distributed in hornfelses of contact aureoles. These include the micas, pyroxenes, hornblende, epidote, and feldspars. Minerals that are more widespread in schists than in contact aureoles are almandine and staurolite; others never formed by contact metamorphism include glaucophane, jadeite, pumpellyite, lawsonite, and stilpnomelane. On the other hand, wollastonite, forsterite, vesuvianite, andalusite, which are all widespread in contact aureoles, are rarely or less commonly found in products of regional metamorphism.

Field characteristics, structure, and mineral paragenesis of regionally metamorphosed rocks vary from one province to another and usually within any large single province. Each case is unique in detail. Yet within the total range of mineralogical variation one can perceive broad recurrent patterns and trends. This we shall now demonstrate through a few well-documented classic examples.

Dalradian Schists of the Southeastern Highlands of Scotland

The southern geologic limit of the Scottish Highlands is a dextral transform fault trending NE-SW known as the *Highland Boundary Fault*. North of it lies a belt of strongly deformed regionally metamorphosed rocks, 50–80 km wide, known as the *Dalradian* series (Fig. 1-9). This belt, which also trends NE-SW, is margined along its northwestern border by another series of regionally metamorphosed rocks: the Precambrian metasediments of the *Moinian series*. The Dalradian metamorphics are derivatives of geosynclinal sediments with some intercalated basic volcanic rocks and sills of diabase. The period of sedimentation extended through the latest Precambrian and at least into middle Cambrian times. Locally, the Dalradian metamorphics are overlain uncomformably by nonmetamorphic upper Devonian sandstones. Metamorphism of the Dalradian is now assigned to the Grampian orogeny (Lambert and McKerrow, 1976). The same metamorphism left an imprint on the already metamorphosed Moinian series of the western Highlands. Granitic rocks in the Dalradian terrane fall into two structurally defined categories. Migmatitic and foliated granites, which tend to be concentrated in regions of most intense metamorphism, are concordant with the metamorphic envelope. These are the *Older Granites* of classic literature, generally believed to be synchronous with the climax of metamorphism. Much more extensive are cross-cutting *Newer Granites*, which, though now known from radiometric dating to have a considerable collective time span (possibly 50 million years), individually postdate the culmination of metamorphism in their immediate surroundings.

Dalradian metamorphism has a special place in classic petrology. In the Dalradian terrane south of Aberdeen, Barrow (1893, 1912) first demonstrated the progressive nature of regional metamorphism by mapping successive zones (Fig. 1-10) based on mineralogical and textural changes observed in pelitic rocks in passing from slates to coarse-grained sillimanite-garnet-mica schists of approximately the same chemical composition. Each zone is named after an index mineral. The outer limit of any zone is mapped where the corresponding index mineral

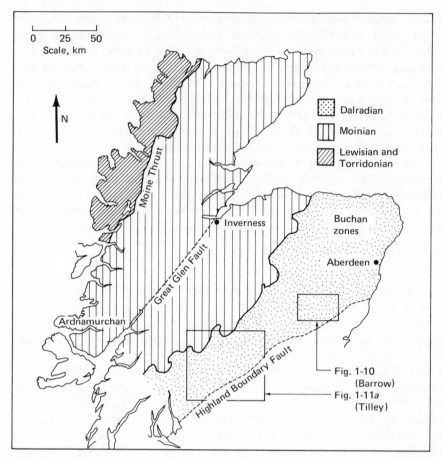

FIGURE 1-9
Outline map showing distribution of main metamorphic units in the Highlands of Scotland
(simplified after M. R. W. Johnson).

first appears in the direction of increasing metamorphism. <u>Barrow's (1912) zonal
sequences</u>, in order of increasing metamorphism, is:

1. Zone of digested clastic mica, now termed (following Tilley, 1925, p. 102)
   the *chlorite zone*. The typical pelitic assemblage is quartz-chlorite-muscovite-
   albite.
2. Zone of biotite: Marked by the appearance of red-brown biotite at the expense
   of muscovite-chlorite.
3. Zone of garnet: The critical assemblage is quartz-muscovite-biotite-almandine
   (-albite or oligoclase).
4. Zone of staurolite: Quartz-biotite-muscovite-almandine-staurolite (-oligoclase).
5. Zone of kyanite: Quartz-biotite-muscovite-oligoclase-almandine-kyanite.
6. Zone of sillimanite: Quartz-biotite-muscovite-oligoclase-almandine-sillimanite.

Barrow's zones were later extended southwest (Tilley, 1925a; Elles and Tilley, 1930) across the full width of the southern Highlands and still later by W. Q. Kennedy (1949) to cover much of the Moinian terrane to the north (cf. Fig. 1-12). Tilley termed the zonal boundaries *isograds*, implying thereby that each represents a change, recognizable in the field, in the *grade* or degree of metamorphism. Progressive mineralogical changes in diabasic sills were correlated by Wiseman (1934) with the zonal sequence already established for pelitic rocks. These are summarized in Table 1-2 (possible additional minerals are given in parentheses). W. Q. Kennedy (1949, p. 53) suggested that isograds could also be drawn on the basis of calc-silicate indices in progressively metamorphosed, thin calcareous interbeds in the western Moinian. His correlation with pelitic zonal assemblages has since been modified by Tanner (1976) as shown in Table 1-2.

Structural analysis of bedding and metamorphic foliations in many parts of the Highlands more recently has revealed a succession of episodes of folding collectively covering 100 million years or more (e.g., Sutton, 1960; McKerrow, 1962; Johnson, 1963). All have left their imprints on the Dalradian terrane. A relatively simple isograd pattern has been superimposed on much more complex large-scale structures dating from the first two episodes of folding, which indeed have deter-

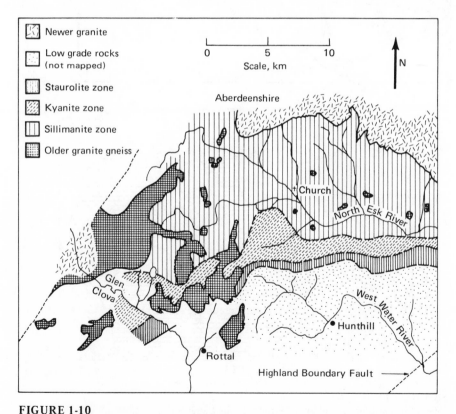

FIGURE 1-10
Zones of progressive regional metamorphism in a portion of the Dalradian of the southeastern Scottish Highlands (mapped by G. Barrow, 1893).

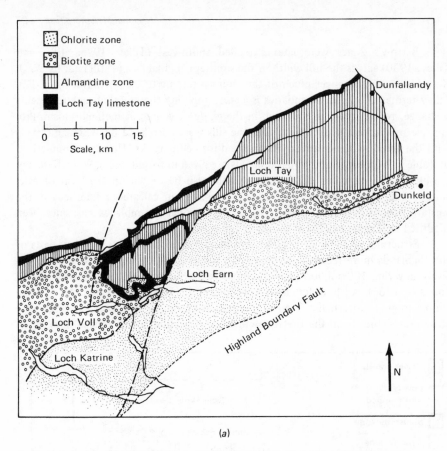

(a)

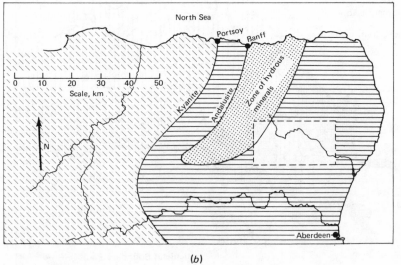

(b)

FIGURE 1-11

Zones of regional metamorphism in portions of the Dalradian in the eastern Scottish Highlands.
(a) Portion of lower and middle grade zones, Barrovian type (after C. E. Tilley, 1925);
(b) Al_2SiO_5 isograds, eastern Dalradian, Buchan type; outcrop of postmetamorphic gabbro and newer granite (plutons omitted) (after G. A. Chinner, 1966, and W. C. Porteous, 1973). Dashed rectangle gives site of H. H. Read's map (1952).

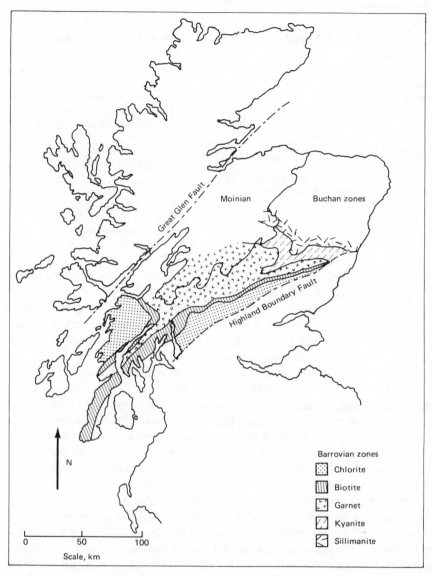

FIGURE 1-12
Barrovian metamorphic zones of the Dalradian in the southern Scottish Highlands (after data of
W. Q. Kennedy and M. R. W. Johnson).

mined the main features of outcrop geometry and of mapped formational trends
(cf. Fig. 1-11*a*). For this reason, and from supporting textural evidence on the
microscopic scale, it is thought that the metamorphic mineral assemblages were
established during and immediately following the second episode of folding in early
Ordovician (Arenig) times. This period of mineral reconstitution is customarily
termed the *culmination of metamorphism*. It was followed by still later, more
localized deformation and retrogressive metamorphism (chloritization of biotite

TABLE 1-2
Correlation of Mineral Assemblages in Zones of Progressive Metamorphism
in Scotland

Zonal index (pelitic)	Basic rocks	Calc-silicate rocks
Chlorite Biotite	Chlorite-albite-epidote-sphene (calcite, actinolite)	Albite-zoisite-calcite-biotite-garnet
Almandine		Andesine-zoisite-garnet biotite-(and/or hornblende)
Staurolite Kyanite	Hornblende-plagioclase (epidote, almandine, diopside)	Bytownite (anorthite)-hornblende-garnet
Sillimanite		Bytownite (anorthite)-diopside-garnet

and garnet; sericitization of kyanite) that, for the most part, only slightly effaced
the mineralogical record of the culmination.

The total stratigraphic thickness of the Dalradian has been obscured by
repeated folding, but may have been 10-20 km. There is no relation between
Barrow's zones and stratigraphic depth. The metamorphic zones, even throughout
the whole Dalradian and Moinian terrane between the Highland Border Fault and
the Great Glen Fault, cut across the mapped large-scale structures (Fig. 1-11a)
and conform to a simple pattern (Kennedy, 1948; Sutton, 1960; Johnson, 1963).
This is a broad arch whose axis plunges southwest, with the grade of metamorphism
increasing with tectonic (not stratigraphic) depth. During the culmination of metamorphism, the depth of cover of Barrow's sillimanite zone may have been on the
order of 12 km (Johnson, 1963). The northeastern segment of the Dalradian in
Banffshire (Fig. 1-11b), 60 km or so north of the region mapped by Barrow, was
buried much less deeply, perhaps to a depth of only 3-4 km (Johnson, 1963,
p. 140). Here the sequence of zones of progressive regional metamorphism in pelitic
schists, generally referred to today as the *Buchan type* of metamorphism, is not
the same as in the southeastern region mapped by Barrow (*Barrovian type*).[*] The
highest grades in the Buchan type are marked by mineral assemblages containing
kyanite or the pair andalusite-cordierite as well as garnet and/or staurolite; the
sillimanite present in some of these rocks seems to have formed in a more localized,
slightly later overprint (Chinner, 1966).

The picture of Dalradian metamorphism just presented is simplified and far
from complete. As an introduction to the more tangible direct manifestations
of regional metamorphism it concentrates on the demonstrated existence, mineralogical character, and field distribution of metamorphic zones delineated by
mineral isograds, and it illustrates the progressive nature of the zonal sequence.
But specific features of the field and mineralogical picture, while capable of being

---

[*]In this book, the terms *Barrovian* and *Buchan* have a purely local connotation, referring
only to British Grampian metamorphism.

described in objective terms, nevertheless raise questions that are at the same time intriguing and at first sight difficult to answer. These will be discussed in a general context in later sections of this book—particularly in the final chapter. In the meantime, while the field and mineralogical data—albeit in simplified outline—are before us, it is appropriate to note for future reference some of the broad problems and questions that these implicitly raise:

In a region of protracted and complex history, covering at least 150 million years of early Phanerozoic time, what may be the relations in time and perhaps some direct genetic relations as well—between episodic deformation and the mineralogical culmination of the metamorphic event? Is there any general connection, either direct or indirect between regional metamorphism and massive upsurges of granitic magma during the same broad orogenic cycle? What role, if any, did large-scale influx of basic magma play in shaping the character of regional metamorphism in the Buchan province? Are the migmatitic "Older Granites" the ultimate product of metamorphism that culminated in partial fusion of meta-sediments? Or do they represent intrusive masses of magma rising from the depths and so exercising a direct and independent influence on the thermal regime of metamorphism?

Dalradian metamorphism has unique interest by virtue of its classic status in the historic development of tectonic-metamorphic concepts. For more than twenty years it remained the sole example and the very prototype of progressive regional metamorphism. And when other instances of comparable phenomena became recognized and described (e.g., Goldschmidt, 1915, 1921) they were closely comparable in general pattern; for they were located in the Scandinavian segment of the same orogenic belt—the Caledonian fold system of northern Europe. However, as work on similar lines progressed in other metamorphic belts of other ages, not only variations on the Dalradian theme but mineralogical patterns of an entirely different character began to emerge. To illustrate something of this variety—as well as analogies with the classic Dalradian pattern—we now turn to other examples in different geographic, tectonic, and chronologic settings.

Paleozoic Metamorphism, Northern Appalachians, U.S.A.

The Appalachian belt of eastern North America, like the Dalradian of Scotland, was the site of prolonged Paleozoic tectonic activity with accompanying regional metamorphism and episodes of plutonism. Metamorphic zones were first mapped on a combined textural and mineralogical basis in Pennsylvania (Knopf and Jonas, 1929) and by mineral isograds in New York State (Barth, 1936). Here we concentrate on the New England sector of the northern Appalachians; for this region has become one of the most fully investigated metamorphic provinces in the world (Billings, 1937; Heald, 1950; White and Billings, 1951; Lyons, 1955; Zen, 1960; Zen et al., 1968).[*]

Although the respective patterns of regional metamorphism in New England and in the Scottish Dalradian have a good deal in common, they are by no means

---

[*]This set of review essays brings together a great deal of information covering several aspects of Paleozoic geology of New England.

identical.[*] In New England, the Paleozoic rocks affected are mostly Ordovician to mid-Devonian sediments and intercalated volcanics. The main metamorphic event is correlated with the Acadian orogeny and is middle Devonian, but the older rocks also retain the structural (and perhaps locally metamorphic) imprint of earlier deformation during the middle and later Ordovician Taconic orogeny. Granite plutonism in New England was largely synchronous with the metamorphism: Not only are the plutons of New Hampshire and Vermont concentrated where the grade of regional metamorphism is high but the sillimanite zone locally is restricted to narrow belts concordantly ringing the individual intrusions (Figs. 1-13 and 1-14).

Metamorphic zones have been mapped on the basis of pelitic mineral assemblages, the sequence of index minerals being parallel to that already established for the Dalradian of Scotland (J. B. Thompson and S. A. Norton, in Zen et al., 1968, pp. 319–327). These, together with distinctive minerals in both pelitic and associated calcareous rocks, are set out in Table 1-3. Compositional differences between Appalachian and Dalradian pelites account for distinctive features in the mineralogical pattern of progressive metamorphism. Ankeritic dolomite, widely present as a minor constituent in rocks of the chlorite zone, participates in reactions leading to the first appearance of biotite at the biotite isograd. The composition of Appalachian rocks favors much more widespread crystallization of chloritoid at the biotite isograd and later of staurolite. As a result, the staurolite zone is more sharply developed in New England than in Scotland. Other distinctive features probably relate to the thermal regime itself: andalusite is rather widespread, kyanite more restricted, and sillimanite so widely developed in some parts that two sillimanite isograds can be drawn. The first marks formation of sillimanite by reactions involving almandine, staurolite, and muscovite and by direct inversion of kyanite; the second occurs where quartz-muscovite breaks down to sillimanite and K-feldspar.

The outcrop extent of individual metamorphic zones varies greatly from place to place. About one-third of the state of Vermont lies in the biotite zone (Fig. 1-14); in western New England and adjoining parts of New York State, the chlorite zone occupies a N-S belt many kilometers wide and over 400 km in length. In New Hampshire and adjacent parts of Maine, the two sillimanite zones plus enclosed outcrops of granitic plutons cover an area of about 20,000 km². On the other hand, in eastern Massachusetts, probably because of postmetamorphic disturbance, the combined width of the biotite, garnet, and staurolite zones is only 5 km.

Haast Schist Group, Southern New Zealand

Geologic Setting

From early Permian to late Jurassic times, much of New Zealand was the site of continuous sedimentation, with subordinate intermittent volcanism, in a trough known as the New Zealand Geosyncline. Early in the Cretaceous, the sediments—

---

[*]Seen in the light of plate tectonics, the two regions are severed sectors of a once-continuous tectonic belt with similar but not identical histories of subduction, metamorphism, and plutonism.

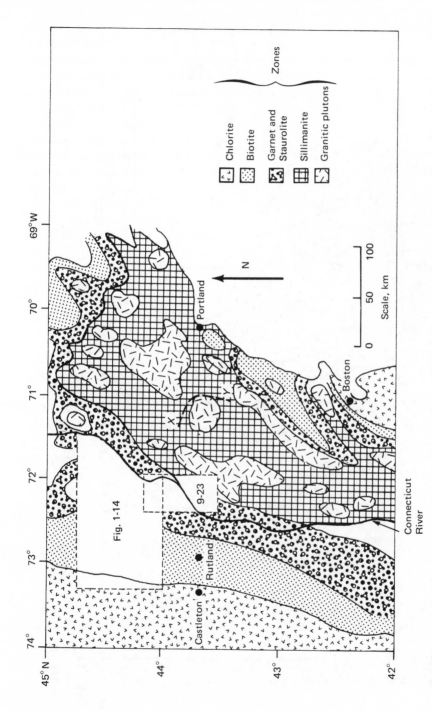

FIGURE 1-13

Metamorphic zones and associated post-Ordovician granitic plutons, central New England, U.S.A. (simplified after J. B. Thompson and S. A. Norton, p. 320, and W. S. White [general map] in Zen et al., 1968). In sillimanite zone, K-feldspar is present mostly south of *XY*.

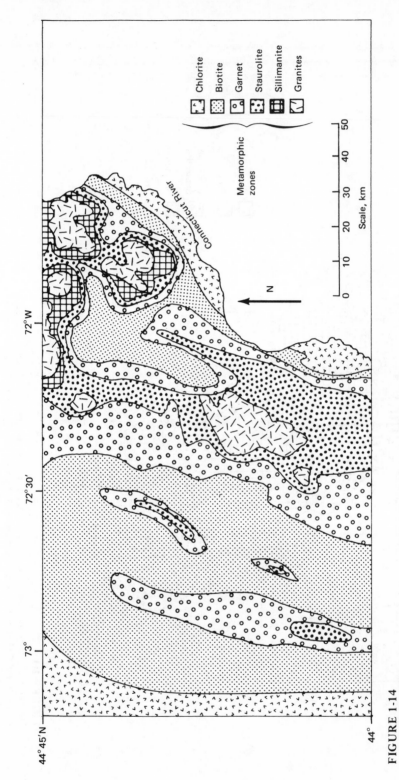

FIGURE 1-14
Metamorphic zones, northern Vermont, U.S.A. (simplified after A. L. Albee, in Zen et al., 1968, pp. 319–328).

Legend — Metamorphic zones:
Chlorite, Biotite, Garnet, Staurolite, Sillimanite, Granites

34

TABLE 1-3
Zonal Indices and Typical Minerals in Regionally Metamorphosed Rocks, New England, U.S.A.

Zonal indices	Typical minerals	
	In quartz-bearing pelites	In dolomitic limestones
Chlorite	Chlorite, muscovite, albite, ankerite	
Biotite	Biotite, muscovite, chlorite, chloritoid, albite	Talc, phlogopite
Garnet	Almandine, biotite, muscovite, chloritoid, oligoclase	Tremolite, actinolite, epidote, zoisite
Staurolite	Staurolite, almandine, kyanite, andalusite, biotite, muscovite, plagioclase	Diopside
Sillimanite	Sillimanite, muscovite, biotite, almandine, plagioclase	Grossularite, scapolite
Sillimanite K-feldspar	Sillimanite, K-feldspar, biotite, almandine, plagioclase	Forsterite

After J. B. Thompson and S. A. Norton.

largely graywacke—were repeatedly folded during a profound tectonic disturbance called the *Rangitatan orogeny*. Everywhere, and especially in the south, the geosynclinal filling now shows, at least to an incipient degree, the effects of regional metamorphism, the culmination of which outlasted the second of the two principal episodes of folding. Present discussion is confined to the southern two-thirds of the South Island (Fig. 1-15).

Metamorphism is most pronounced in rocks comprising the Haast Schist Group, which covers some 30,000 km² in the southern province of Otago (Otago schists) running some 400 km along the western flank of the southern Alps (Figs. 1-15 and 1-17). The Otago schists grade northward, the Alpine schists eastward, into nonfoliated but incipiently metamorphosed Permian-Triassic graywackes comprising the Torlesse Group or Terrane of current literature (e.g., B. L. Wood, 1978). This shows, though only to a slight degree, the mineralogical imprint of Rangitatan metamorphism. The same may be said also of a Permian ophiolite belt and fossiliferous Triassic and Jurassic sediments of a different lithologic and depositional facies west and southwest of the Otago schists, which for present purposes we term "rocks of the southwestern borderlands." Rocks of the Haast Group and transitional metasediments on its southwestern margin terminate abruptly on the west against major postmetamorphic dislocations, one of which is the transform Alpine Fault with right-lateral displacement of nearly 500 km. Beyond these faults lie remnants of an earlier Paleozoic geosynclinal filling (Tasman Geosyncline) that bear the imprints of at least two metamorphic–plutonic episodes (one possibly Precambrian, one mid-Paleozoic) and have yielded a few other radiometric dates that could record effects of the Rangitatan orogeny (Landis and Coombs, 1967).

Mineral Isograds

The fullest spectrum of metamorphism is in the west. Here, in east–west sections 30–50 km long across the Southern Alps between Mt. Cook and the Haast River,

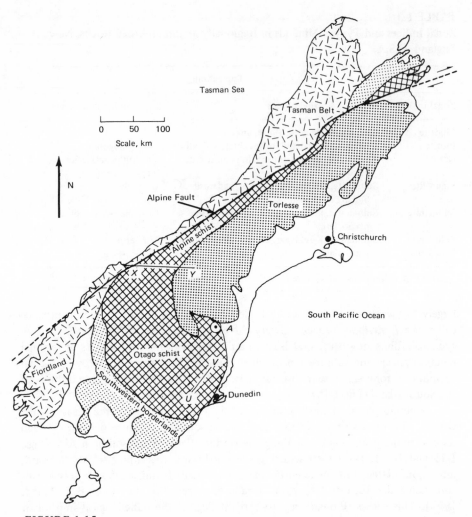

FIGURE 1-15

Metamorphic rocks of the New Zealand Geosyncline east of the Tasman Belt, South Island, New Zealand (after C. A. Landis and D. G. Bishop, 1972). *XY*, Haast River section; *A*, Dansey Pass. Western marginal area (dashed) from Fiordland northward is the more ancient Tasman Belt.

the grade rises steadily westward to the Alpine Fault (Fig. 1-16). Elsewhere in the Otago schist, terrane and adjacent rocks of the New Zealand Geosyncline metamorphism, with local variations, follow the same general pattern, but are restricted to the lower grades (Fig. 1-17). Metamorphic zones are based on mineral assemblages developed in rocks of metagraywacke lithology. At the lowest grade, the newly crystallized metamorphic* minerals appear only as joint fillings and as constituents of a fine-grained base developing between predominant relict clastic

---

*Equally appropriate is the term *diagenetic*; as realized so long ago by Van Hise (1904), the distinction between diagenesis and incipient metamorphism is purely semantic.

grains. Once reconstitution becomes well advanced, the metamorphic assemblage is dominated by quartz, sodic plagioclase, micas, and chlorite accompanied by smaller amounts of epidote and sphene. Isograds, in order of increasing grade, are marked by appearance and then successive elimination of prehnite and pumpellyite; by later appearance first of biotite, then of almandine, and finally by the elimination of albite. Corresponding zones of progressive metamorphism are as follows (Turner, 1933; Hutton, 1940; Coombs, 1960; Mason, 1962; Landis and Coombs, 1967; Bishop, 1972):

1. Prehnite-pumpellyite
2. Pumpellyite (-actinolite)
3. Chlorite (-clinozoisite)
4. Biotite
5. Almandine
6. Oligoclase

By far the greater part of the New Zealand Geosyncline as presently exposed is occupied by low-grade rocks outside the biotite isograd. Their general distribution in the South Island east of the Alpine Fault is shown in Fig. 1-17. While the metagraywackes of the Torlesse and the schists of the Haast Group together comprise a coherent sedimentary-tectonic-metamorphic unit, the rocks of the southwestern borderlands are in many respects distinct. They consist of a Permian to Jurassic marine sequence of a different sedimentary facies and include a prominent ophiolite band that takes its name—Dun Mountain ophiolite (Coombs et al.,

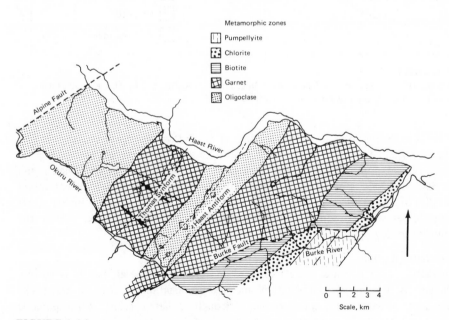

FIGURE 1-16
Metamorphic zones in Haast Group, section *XY*, Fig. 1-15 along Haast Valley (after A. F. Cooper and J. F. Lovering, 1970).

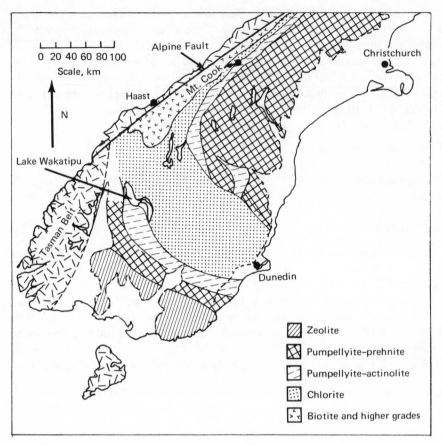

FIGURE 1-17
Metamorphic zones, New Zealand Geosyncline, southern sector, east of Alpine Fault and Tasman belt (slightly modified and simplified after C. A. Landis and D. G. Bishop, 1972).

1976)—from the classic dunite locality in the offset northwestern segment of the geosyncline west of the Alpine Fault. Zeolitic assemblages, of lower grade than typical pumpellyite-bearing paragenesis, are prominent in the Triassic and Jurassic volcanic sands of the southwest borderlands (they also appear rather locally in the Torlesse). Of considerable interest in subsequent discussion are assemblages with lawsonite in partially recrystallized Permian rocks outside the chlorite zone.

Textural Zones
Increasing metamorphic grade expressed in terms of mineral indices is accompanied by progressive deformation and recrystallization as massive graywacke becomes converted to coarse-grained, strongly foliated schist. Corresponding successive stages in textural evolution are easily recognizable on the mesoscopic scale in the field. These have long been used to map four textural

zones* covering the complete graywacke-schist transition (Turner, 1935; Hutton and Turner, 1936; Turner, 1948, p. 38; Grindley, 1963; Bishop, 1972). The zonal boundaries—lines of comparable textural evolution—have been called *isotects*. In any limited province, their configuration is closely related to that of the mineral isograds. Evidently, mineralogical and textural development were controlled in part by the same physical conditions. Even for large areas, it is possible to generalize rather crudely in this fashion.

1. Textural zone T1 embraces most of the prehnite-pumpellyite zone of the Haast and adjacent Torlesse groups and generally overlaps the prehnite-disappearance isograd.
2. In the Otago Schist terrane, the pumpellyite-actinolite zone occupies T2 and much of T3. One tends to equate the chlorite zone with T4, but the pumpellyite-disappearance isograd in most places falls well within T3.
3. North of Mt. Cook, the T3-T4 boundary obliquely intersects the biotite isograd. There, in marked contrast with conditions in Otago, schists first develop segregation laminae typical of T4 only within the biotite zone (cf. Reed, 1958).

Configuration of the Isogradic Surfaces

As seems so commonly to be the case elsewhere, the metamorphic zonal pattern in New Zealand, imprinted relatively late in the tectonic cycle, is simple compared with gross geologic structure. In the western sector of the Haast Schist Group (Alpine schists; Fig. 1-16), where topographic relief exceeds 3000 m, the isogradic surfaces and the surfaces bounding the textural zones are approximately vertical. Individual zonal outcrops are but a few kilometers in width. By contrast, over much of central and east Otago, the chlorite zone† is very extensive, even though the whole terrane is broken by Tertiary faults of great displacement and relief is 1500–2000 m. This suggests regional development of a thick zone of chlorite bounded in depth by a subhorizontal isogradic surface still unexposed. Mapping along the northern margin of the schist block, at least in one area (*A*, Fig. 1-15), indicates steep but by no means vertical isogradic and isotectic surfaces in rocks affected by low-grade metamorphism (Bishop, 1972).

Synchronous Granite Plutonism

Nowhere in the Haast Schist and adjoining Torlesse groups, in spite of extensive outcrop in areas of high relief, is there any sign of granite plutonism synchronous with metamorphism.‡ However, in now-adjacent sections of the Tasman meta-

---

*Before the individual identities of the zones of prehnite-pumpellyite and pumpellyite-actinolite had been recognized, these zones were designated Chl 1–4—subzones of the then all-inclusive chlorite zone. Here, in following Bishop's (1972) reevaluation, I substitute the prefix T (signifying textural zone) for Chl.

†Biotite has been reported to occur sporadically over much of the chlorite zone of Otago and has been interpreted as a possible relic of an earlier high-grade phase of metamorphism (Means, 1963). Much, perhaps most, of this "biotite" proves to be highly birefringent vermiculite formed by oxidation (weathering) of chlorite (E. H. Brown, 1967).

‡Except for pegmatite veins of limited extent in parts of the oligoclase zone of Westland.

morphic belt, which was tectonically dead before the onset of sedimentation in the New Zealand Geosyncline, granitic plutons are conspicuous. Radiometric dates on some of these perhaps overlap the early Cretaceous span of metamorphism recorded in the Haast Schist Group.

Paired Metamorphic Belts, Japan

The islands of Shikoku and Honshu in Japan are traversed longitudinally for 800 km by a pair of metamorphic belts in mutual contact throughout most of their length along a major dislocation, the *Median Tectonic Line* (Fig. 1-18). The two belts differ strikingly in metamorphic pattern, but radiometric dating indicates that metamorphism in both probably was of Cretaceous age (Banno, 1964a; Miyashiso, 1961, p. 287).

Sanbagawa Belt

In the Bessi mining district of Shikoku, Banno (1964a) has mapped an area 300 km² typical of the southwestern or Sanbagawa belt (Fig. 1-19). Here along the northern

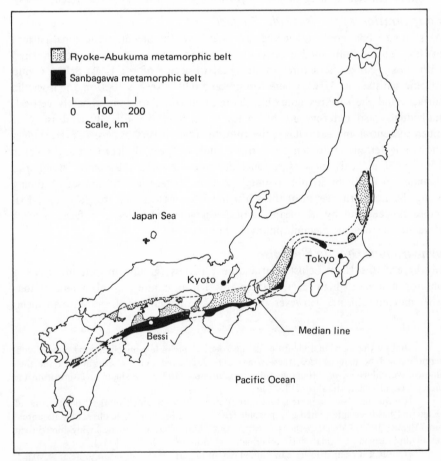

FIGURE 1-18
Sanbagawa and Ryoke metamorphic belts, Japan (after A. Miyashiro).

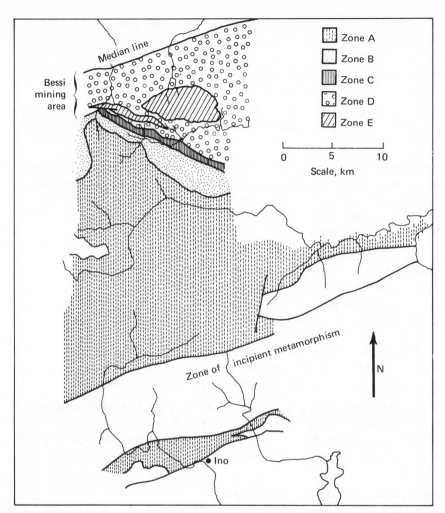

FIGURE 1-19
Zones of progressive regional metamorphism in vicinity of Bessi mine, Japan (after S. Banno).

margin, the Median Line terminates the Sanbagawa schists against nonmetamorphic late Mesozoic sediments. The schists themselves are part of a late Paleozoic geosynclinal filling that is part sedimentary and part volcanic. Within the Sanbagawa belt, the grade of metamorphism increases northward toward the Median Line. Banno (1964a) has defined five metamorphic zones (A to E in order of increasing grade) on the basis of coexisting mineral assemblages in pelitic rocks and derivatives of basic lavas.

A–C. The pelitic assemblage is quartz-muscovite-chlorite-albite-epidote; manganese garnet comes in as an additional phase in C. The metabasaltic assemblage is albite-chlorite-epidote-actinolite, with glaucophane and pumpellyite (rarely lawsonite) in A, glaucophane only in B; in C, hornblende is the sole amphibole.

D. A transitional zone in which manganese garnet gradually gives way to almandine in pelitic rocks.
E. Oligoclase takes the place of albite in both rock types. The typical pelitic assemblage is quartz-muscovite-biotite-almandine-oligoclase. Metabasites are amphibolites with diminished chlorite and epidote.

The Sanbagawa schists of Shikoku are cut by ultramafic intrusives, the largest of which, occurring at Bessi, is enclosed in schists of zones D and E and itself contains lenses of eclogite.

Ryoke Belt

Suwa's (1961) studies of progressive metamorphism in the Ryoke belt reveal a completely different pattern of paragenesis. Moreover, more or less synchronous intrusion of granitic plutons is characteristic of much of the metamorphic terrane. Pelitic and basic assemblages in order of increasing grade are as follows:

1. Pelitic: Quartz-albite-chlorite-muscovite (-biotite)
   Basic: Albite-epidote-actinolite-chlorite (-calcite)
2. Pelitic: Quartz-oligoclase-biotite-muscovite
   Basic: Andesine-hornblende (-epidote-sphene)
3. Pelitic: Quartz-andesine-biotite-muscovite (-cordierite or -andalusite or almandine)
   Basic: Labradorite-hornblende-diopside
4. Pelitic: Quartz-andesine-orthoclase-biotite-sillimanite (-almandine or cordierite)
   Basic: Bytownite-hornblende-diopside (-cummingtonite or hypersthene)

In calcareous rocks, actinolite is characteristic in zone 1; hornblende-diopside-grossularite in zones 2 and 3; and wollastonite-diopside-grossularite in zone 4.

Metamorphism in the Ryoke and in Sanbagawa belts, although approximately synchronous, was evidently effected under very different physical conditions.

Gneisses of the Northwest Adirondacks, New York State

Intimate association of metamorphic rocks and gneissic granite is characteristic of the Precambrian the world over. A detailed account of field and chemical aspects of metamorphism of this type in a section of the Adirondack Mountains has been given by Engel and Engel (1958, 1960). The rocks that most closely retain their original chemical identity are quartzofeldspathic gneisses derived from graywackes, with less abundant marbles and some amphibolites. On the mesoscopic scale, the metasedimentary gneisses, which themselves contain little or no potash feldspar, are everywhere streaked to some degree with granite. On the macroscopic scale (Fig. 1-20), such rocks occur in elongate areas of a few square kilometers interfingering with similar areas of microcline-rich granite gneiss. Between the two are transitional zones of migmatite: gneisses of sedimentary origin, intimately layered with thin seams of granite or studded with microcline porphyroblasts on the mesoscopic scale.

Along a 50-km traverse, a single zonal boundary has been mapped on the

FIGURE 1-20

Distribution of Precambrian gneiss, granite-gneiss, and migmatite, Emeryville area, New York State (after A. E. J. Engel and C. E. Engel).

43

basis of the mineral assemblages in the nongranitized metasedimentary gneiss (Fig. 1-21). To the west, representing the lower grade of metamorphism, the characteristic assemblage is quartz-biotite-oligoclase-muscovite. Hornblende-andesine is the assemblage in interlayered amphibolites. To the east of the iso-grad, the gneiss is composed of quartz-andesine-biotite-garnet, and in associated amphibolites the assemblage is andesine-hornblende-diopside-hypersthene. Al-though only one isograd has been drawn, the increasing grade of metamorphism along the whole section can be traced by regular chemical changes in the prin-cipal minerals: that is, TiO_2/MnO changes from 16 to 520 in biotites, and from 0.003 to 0.06 in garnets; in both minerals, the ratio Mg/Fe varies systematically along the metamorphic gradient. The range of temperature involved has been estimated from mineralogical data, such as Mg/Ca ratios in dolomite and Na/K ratios in muscovite, as $500-600°C$; but these values are subject to considerable uncertainty.

With the increase in grade of metamorphism, the metasedimentary gneiss becomes somewhat "basified" by depletion in K and Si and complementary enrich-ment in Al, Fe, Mg, and Ca. The liberated K and Si are partly retained in newly developed granitic veins in migmatite. Parts of the gneiss, on the other hand, are granitized by "several processes, especially mechanical injection of magma, per-meation, and replacement of the gneiss by magma, by fluids from magma, or by ichors and ions" (Engel and Engel, 1958, pp. 1411–1412). In the eastern area of maximum metamorphic grade, granitic rock "clearly of igneous origin" is abundant in the gneiss complex. The picture presented by Engel and Engel is one in which high-temperature metamorphism involves the beginning of differential fusion and is associated in time and place with large-scale intrusion of granitic magma, probably itself the result of fusion of crustal rocks at no great distance from the site under consideration.

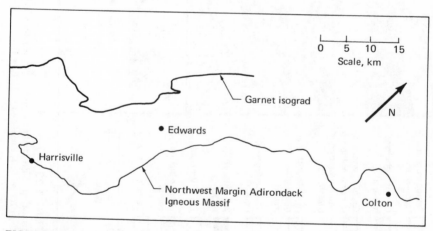

FIGURE 1-21

Simplified map of Precambrian metamorphic and migmatitic terrane, northwest Adirondacks, New York State, showing the garnet isograd (after A. E. J. Engel and C. E. Engel).

General Character of Regional Metamorphism

Progressive and Retrogressive Metamorphism

Regional metamorphism is generally thought of today, in a rather loose way, as a progressive process. The zonal sequence, marked by any mapped series of isograds, records the pattern of mineralogical progression. The existence of partially reconstituted rocks at one end of the sequence usually defines the sense of increasing grade which is confirmed texturally by elimination of premetamorphic structures, strengthening of foliation, and coarsening of grain as the grade increases. Mineralogical changes are striking. Yet in rocks of given composition, apart from the volatile components, H_2O and CO_2, the relative proportions of the principal oxide components as shown in a chemical analysis seem, except in suboceanic metamorphism, to remain constant over the full gamut of progressive metamorphism, at least until the onset of fusion in migmatite zones.

It has become customary to equate a rising grade of metamorphism in any progressive sequence with increasing temperature. Yet changing pressure, especially when the collective width of zonal outcrop is extensive, must also play some role (cf. Harker, p. lxxix; Tilley, 1924b, pp. 168–170). In most geologic situations, temperature and pressure simultaneously rise with increasing depth. But as we shall see shortly, progressive metamorphism does not necessarily imply simultaneous increases in temperature and pressure; for the observed metamorphic gradient is recorded on the tangential surface of existing topography.

Largely from classic studies of metamorphic crystallization in relation to structure,[*] amplified by modern isotopic studies, it has become obvious that, in any given terrane, temperatures and pressures conducive to metamorphism must have been maintained for millions rather than thousands of years. At any particular site, temperatures and pressures must have risen and fallen in each metamorphic cycle, and there is evidence that repeated cycles are the rule rather than the exception. In spite of such changes and fluctuations in metamorphic gradients, it is usually possible to recognize in a regular zonal progression the "frozen in" expression on a single gradient. It is to this gradient that we refer when speaking of the culmination of metamorphism. Superimposed on the progressive sequence of mineral assemblages, there are almost invariably traces of partial reaction in response to the falling temperature gradient that must have been maintained for long intervals after the climax had been reached. There are even regions where the zonal sequence now preserved has been attributed to different degrees of retrogressive reaction in response to waning temperatures. This is the interpretation placed by Wyckoff (1952, p. 25) on metamorphic zones developed in the Wissahickon schist near Philadelphia.

> The most intense metamorphism took place, not at the time of highest temperatures, but during a period of declining temperatures, when mineral changes were facilitated by copious hydrothermal solutions and

---

[*]A classic essay on the time relations of deformation, crystallization, and granite emplacement is H. H. Read's (1949) "A Contemplation of Time in Plutonism."

strong regional deformation. The decipherable history is therefore largely one of retrograde metamorphism.

One of the most provocative questions relating to regional metamorphism is this: Considering the great length of time available, why are not all regionally metamorphic rocks reduced to the mineral assemblages characteristic of the chlorite zone? To this question, too, we shall return later.

Relation to Granitic Magmas

Granite intrusions are not invariably directly associated with regional metamorphism, even of high grade. But the association of granitic magma with high-grade metamorphism is widespread. To recognize the association is more important than to decide whether uprise of magma on a regional scale is the primary cause of the metamorphic gradient, or whether differential fusion of crustal rocks, with granitic magma as the product of fusion, is the culmination of the metamorphic process. In either case, we are left with the still unsolved problem of the means by which, from time to time in different parts of the crust, heat becomes concentrated to the point where it constitutes the driving force of orogeny, generation of magma, and regional metamorphism.

Problems Related to Metamorphic Gradients

The pattern of regional metamorphism in any province has important implications regarding the regional temperature–pressure regime prevailing there over some finite interval of past time. The zonal sequence of mineral assemblages in rocks of the same general composition, in fact, constitutes a record of some particular temperature–pressure gradient. This concept is generally accepted; but a fallacy, not always explicitly stated underlies a good deal of current reasoning along these lines. Crudely stated, this fallacy views the metamorphic gradient as a fossil depth-controlled geothermal gradient. Critical examination of this proposition is postponed until the final chapter of this book. Here we simply list some of the issues that render such an oversimplified concept untenable.

    1. Factors other than pressure and temperature may exert some influence on recorded patterns of regional metamorphism. One such, considering the importance of dehydration and decarbonation reactions in the metamorphic process, is the composition of the pore fluid. In any province, this is likely to vary both regionally and in time.

    2. It is surely unlikely that a topographic section 50 km long transverse to the isograds could even approximate a fossil depth gradient. Nor is it generally likely, although possible in individual cases, that such a section everywhere crosses a regionally developed uniform geothermal gradient. More likely, high-grade zones represent loci of accelerated heat flow compared with low-grade zones of the same province.

    3. Obviously, the culmination of metamorphism when the pattern of metamorphic mineralogy was "frozen in" need not have been synchronous at opposite ends of the metamorphic gradient. Radiometric dating, in fact, indicates time differences measured in tens of millions of years for the setting of the radiometric clock (cf. Dewey and Pankhurst, 1970). Intervals of this magnitude, permitting

differential uplift and erosion, could result in corresponding sharp changes in the recorded metamorphic gradient.

However the mineralogical patterns are interpreted, it is abundantly clear that metamorphic gradients collectively cover a wide spectrum of crustal temperatures and pressures. Some gradients will be similar, some obviously dissimilar. No gradient can be regarded as normal*; each is to some degree unique. Their quantitative evaluation in terms of temperature and pressure is the ultimate task of the metamorphic petrologist, and to this we shall address ourselves in Chs. 8 and 11. First, however, there is the simpler, although still difficult, problem of placing numerical limits on temperatures and pressures recorded by some of the commonly recurring metamorphic mineral assemblages. To this topic we now turn.

*Some of us perhaps have tended to regard the Barrovian pattern as the norm of regional metamorphism simply for the inadequate reason that it was the first to be recognized.

2

Metamorphic Facies and the Concept of Metamorphic Rocks as Systems in Stable Equilibrium

HISTORICAL BACKGROUND

Nineteenth-Century Concepts

Charles Lyell, in developing his concept of metamorphism, attributed the accompanying mineralogical and structural changes to elevated temperatures acting at depth or in proximity to granitic intrusions. He recognized the essential roles of time and of aqueous fluids in metamorphic processes, and he visualized granitic magma as a product of rock fusion in the culmination of metamorphism. With reference to the genesis of schist from mudstones and of marble from limestone, he wrote (Lyell, 1847, p. 171):

> The transmutation has been effected apparently by the influence of subterranean heat, acting under great pressure, or by chemical and electrical causes operating in a manner not yet understood, and which have been termed *plutonic* action. . . . To this plutonic action the fusion of granite itself in the bowels of the earth, as well as the superinducement of the metamorphic texture into sedimentary strata, must be attributed; . . .

It is to G. H. Williams in particular that we owe the more sophisticated notion of metamorphism as the response of a rock to imposed progressively changing conditions of temperature and pressure, under the influence of which the meta-morphic mineral assemblage tends to a state of internal equilibrium in the thermo-dynamic sense. Commenting on the small number of chemical components (MgO, SiO_2, etc.) that enter into the comparatively large number of known metamorphic mineral assemblages, Williams (1890, p. 39) wrote:

> It seems to be oftentimes more a matter of external condition rather than of chemical composition, which determines what particular mineral is formed; and the equipoise between the existence of a certain silicate and the external conditions is often so delicate that a mere change in the latter alone is sufficient to destroy the mineral as such and to cause it to change to some other modification or compound. . . . Rocks whose component minerals are so delicately balanced to accord with the particular set of conditions under which they were formed [the reference is to igneous rocks] must be peculiarly subject to altera-tion when these conditions are changed; . . .

Meanwhile Sederholm (1891), in an account of the Precambrian migmatites of Finland, recognized the profound differences in style of metamorphism, struc-tural as well as mineralogical, between ancient gneisses of Finland and the schists of younger eroded fold-mountain systems in the Harz and Taunus (Sederholm, 1891, p. 140).

> The . . . uniform type of transformation within the main thoroughly crystalline reconstitution occurs predominantly in Archaean rocks whose layers have a nearly vertical attitude, and which accordingly were once exposed to the activity of uniform long-sustained lateral pressure in relatively deep regions of the earth's crust. On the other hand the nonuniform rocks transformed by crystallization of "weathering minerals" [sericite, chlorite, epidote, calcite] mostly belong to the higher levels of the younger mountain chains. Here tangential move-ments extend themselves in more irregular eddies.

Here the emphasis is upon depth as the principal factor controlling conditions of metamorphism and accompanying deformation. Sederholm (1891, p. 139) also recognized the important indirect role of stress and resulting strain in accelerat-ing metamorphic reactions by increasing "almost ad infinitum" the area of the reacting surfaces of the crushed mineral grains.

Metamorphism as a Function of Depth: Turn-of-the-Century Concepts

By the opening of the present century, the concept of metamorphism as a process controlled primarily by depth was thoroughly ingrained in geologic thinking. Becke (1903) and Grubenmann in Europe and Van Hise (1904) in the U.S. all fitted the phenomena of regional metamorphism to some postulated sequence of depth zones in the crust. So simple and comprehensive a concept inevitably has proved inadequate, and geologists of today no longer speak of progressive metamorphism in terms of depth zones. Yet, the influence of Grubenmann in particular lasted long in Europe and can still be traced in intuitive speculation the world over on the significance of metamorphic gradients in mapped isograd sequences.

Depth Zones of Van Hise

Van Hise's *Treatise on Metamorphism* covered a wide diversity of topics in addition to metamorphism in the strict sense—for example, weathering, diagenesis, ore deposition, and crustal geochemistry. Perhaps because its ponderous nature contrasted with more concise and explicit treatment by European contemporaries, Van Hise's book had little influence on metamorphic petrology outside North America, and its impact was not much felt beyond World War I.* Two depth zones were postulated with a mutual boundary estimated as between 2 and 12 km. In the upper zone of "katamorphism" (weathering and cementation), reactions were seen as exothermic—typified by hydration and carbonation. Their diagenetic (cementation) products were said to include zeolites and prehnite, chlorites, epidotes, and serpentine and talc. "Anamorphism" in the lower zone was seen as a series of endothermic reactions involving decrease in volume, and so initiated and controlled essentially by hydrostatic pressure (Van Hise, 1904, p. 656). Today's growing interest in regional metamorphism of the lowest grades (cf. Coombs, 1961, 1971; Kisch, 1969; Frey, 1970; Miyashiro and Shido, 1970; Kubler et al., 1974) revives a concept familiar to and expounded at length by Van Hise: Processes and products (artificially separated by some as diagenetic and metamorphic, respectively) completely overlap in nature. Exclusion of cementation (diagenetic) processes from the field of metamorphism as some of us have done in the past (e.g., Turner, 1948, p. 3) is no longer realistic. Van Hise's account of katamorphism in the "zone of cementation" contains much that is pertinent to metamorphism at the lowest grades.

Depth Zones of Becke

In 1903, Becke presented to the Vienna Academy of Sciences a paper (Becke, 1913) in which he treated metamorphic assemblages as systems in thermodynamic equilibrium. He recognized that temperature and pressure, both of which increase with depth, have opposite effects upon most metamorphic reactions. In modern terms, the slope of the curve of univariant equilibrium drawn for such a reaction on a pressure–temperature field is positive (Fig. 2-1). In other words, the reaction proceeds with simultaneous increase (or decrease) both in entropy and in volume.

On the above basis, Becke proposed two depth zones of regional metamorphism:

1. In the upper zone, reactions were said to proceed with decreasing volume and to conform to a *volume law* (for example, $Q \rightarrow P$ in Fig. 2-1). Among the typical reaction products are dense minerals such as garnet, and many hydrous silicates (chlorites, micas, epidotes, amphiboles) that are dense compared with chemically equivalent minerals plus water as a separate phase. The conversion of gabbro (plagioclase-pyroxene) plus water to garnet amphibolite or to chlorite-epidote-albite schist would exemplify a reaction of Becke's upper zone. But other

---

*Van Hise's ideas were more concisely treated by Leith and Mead (1915).

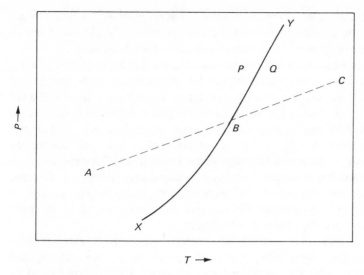

FIGURE 2-1
Curve of univariant equilibrium (XY) for a hypothetical metamorphic reaction $P \rightleftharpoons Q$. ABC is a segment of a depth gradient.

reactions in the upper zone, such as those concerned in the low-grade metamorphism of pelitic sediments, involve progressive expulsion of water. On a diagram such as Fig. 2-1 they would proceed, contrary to Becke's generalization, from left to right in opposition to the volume law.

2. In the lower zone reactions proceed, according to Becke, in the sense opposite to that required by the volume law ($P \rightarrow Q$ in Fig. 2-1). The influence of increasing temperature was said to overshadow that of increasing pressure. Today we visualize the reaction products simply as the result of progressive dehydration or decarbonation under increasing temperature. They include feldspars, pyroxenes, garnets, sillimanite, olivine, etc.

Depth Zones of Grubenmann

Grubenmann's (1904) great work on *The Crystalline Schists*, later rewritten and modified by P. Niggli (Grubenmann and Niggli, 1924), has strongly influenced European conceptions of metamorphism, especially during the first four decades of this century. Like Sederholm and Becke, Grubenmann stressed mineralogical and textural differences that were supposed to exist between "Archaean" metamorphic rocks and the schists of younger fold-mountain chains. Again the principal factor controlling the observed differences was thought to be depth. Accordingly, Grubenmann assigned metamorphic rocks to three depth zones. But apart from the original supposed distinction between "Archaean" and younger metamorphic rocks, the criteria of depth are purely textural and mineralogical.

1. *Upper or epi zone.* Typical minerals are muscovite, chlorite, chloritoid, stilpnomelane, talc, actinolite, epidotes, glaucophane, carbonates, and others. Cataclastic textures with structural relics of an earlier state are characteristic; folded, finely schistose and lineated structures are common. The inferred physical

conditions are relatively low temperatures and pressures combined with high non-hydrostatic pressure (stress). The epi zone is exemplified by the chlorite zones of regions such as the Highlands of Scotland and southern New Zealand.*

2. *Middle or meso zone.* Typical minerals include biotite, muscovite, staurolite, kyanite, hornblende and other amphiboles, plagioclase, epidote, garnet and calcite. Characteristic, too, are mineral assemblages including minerals of the epi and of the meso zone. Widely prevalent is a regular planar foliation (*crystallization schistosity*) marked by parallel dimensional orientation of micas and other tabular minerals, which were thought to have crystallized with their long dimensions normal to the axis of maximum principal stress. Laminated and linear fabrics are common. Metamorphism in the meso zone was envisaged as chemical reconstitution governed by moderate temperatures and pressures, with highly variable nonhydrostatic pressures. The meso zone of Grubenmann would embrace all of Barrow's zones in the Dalradian except the zone of sillimanite.

3. *Lower or kata zone.* Characteristic minerals are biotic, K-feldspar, calcic plagioclase, sillimanite, hornblende, pyroxenes, garnets, and others. The typical texture is granulitic, with thin elongate lenses of quartz and feldspar aligned to give a planar foliation. Migmatitic structures are common. Metamorphism in the kata zone was conceived to be a protracted process of chemical reconstitution under high pressure and temperature, with nonhydrostatic pressure relatively weak or lacking. The kata zone was said to be exemplified chiefly by Archaean rocks. This is true of high-grade Archaean granulites; but the mineral assemblages of many Archaean rocks turn out to belong to the meso zone (Eskola, 1939, p. 340); and even more extensive in some of the shields are very old "greenstone" belts whose mineralogy is typical of the epi zone.

Grubenmann framed a general classification of regionally metamorphosed rocks on a dual basis: the threefold division in terms of depth, and a twelvefold subdivision based on bulk chemical composition (Al-silicate rocks, Mg-silicate rocks, marbles, and so on). Thus he clearly demonstrated the twofold dependence of every common metamorphic assemblage upon its present chemical composition and the physical conditions of metamorphism. Of course, there were anomalies in the classification. Some low-temperature–high-pressure minerals such as jadeite and some high-temperature–low-pressure minerals such as periclase and cordierite were assigned to the kata zone. Other low-temperature–high-pressure minerals, notably lawsonite and glaucophane, were placed in the epi zone.† The complete gamut of physical conditions encompassed by metamorphism is too wide and varied to be expressed by any single parameter such as age or depth.

In Grubenmann's scheme the individual mineral is the index of metamorphism. Today the emphasis has shifted to the mineral assemblage as an entity. K-feldspar is a constituent of metamorphic rocks formed over a wide range of conditions. The same may be said of sillimanite, and of almandine. But the assemblage orthoclase-sillimanite-almandine is found only in the highest grades

---

*Today generally assigned to considerable crustal depth.

†The anomaly is even greater in Niggli's revision (Grubenmann and Niggli, 1924), which forces the products of low-pressure contact metamorphism into the kata zone.

of metamorphism; and on this fact rests the subdivision of the sillimanite zone in New England (cf. Chap. 1). It remained for Goldschmidt, P. Niggli, and Eskola to demonstrate the significance of the metamorphic mineral assemblage; and so arose the concept of metamorphic facies.

METAMORPHIC FACIES

The Facies Concept

In the Oslo region of Norway (Goldschmidt, 1911), a mixed series of pelitic, sandy, and calcareous sediments of Paleozoic age has been invaded by igneous plutons ranging in composition from alkali gabbro to granite. Close to the igneous contacts in the resulting aureoles the hornfelses show a remarkably uniform paragenesis. In spite of their wide diversity in chemical composition the common mineral assemblages are relatively simple. Each consists essentially of four or five out of ten widely prevalent minerals: quartz, K-feldspar, plagioclase, andalusite, cordierite, hypersthene, diopside, wollastonite, grossularite, and biotite. Certain pairs of these appear consistently to the exclusion of chemically equivalent pairs; thus anorthite-hypersthene is common, but the equivalent pair andalusite-diopside is unknown.

$$CaMgSi_2O_6 + Al_2SiO_5 \rightarrow CaAl_2Si_2O_8 + MgSiO_3$$

Moreover, for a given range of chemical composition, the mineral assemblage in the Oslo hornfelses is always the same; e.g., quartz-orthoclase-andalusite-cordierite in pelitic rocks, diopside-wollastonite-grossularite-calcite in calcareous hornfelses.

Shortly after the publication of Goldschmidt's work on the Oslo hornfelses, Eskola (1914, 1915) described the effects of metamorphism and mineralization associated with Proterozoic granites of the Orijärvi mining region of Finland. Again the mineral assemblages were found to be simple and consistently related to rock composition. Some assemblages such as diopside-grossularite and andalusite-cordierite-plagioclase are common to the two regions. But there are consistent mineralogical differences between chemically equivalent assemblages as shown in Table 2-1. These differences Eskola attributed to different physical conditions of metamorphism. He considered it likely that temperatures were higher and pressures

TABLE 2-1
Chemically Equivalent Mineralogical Assemblages in Metamorphic Rocks of Oslo and of Orijärvi

Oslo	Orijärvi
K-feldspar + andalusite	Muscovite + quartz
K-feldspar + cordierite	Biotite + muscovite
K-feldspar + hypersthene + anorthite	Biotite + hornblende
Hypersthene	Anthophyllite

lower in the Oslo aureoles than at Orijärvi—a conclusion that has been upheld by subsequent experimental work.

On the basis of the above comparison, Eskola (1915, pp. 114, 115) proposed the term *metamorphic facies* to include any association of metamorphic rocks within which there is constant correlation between mineral and chemical composition. The rocks of Orijärvi constitute one facies, those of the Oslo aureoles another. Each facies has since been recognized in other parts of the world. In Eskola's original definitions, in his subsequent writings on facies, and in later discussion of the same topic by many writers, there is a good deal of confusion as to the relative significance of observed petrologic data and inferred physical conditions of metamorphism as criteria for defining facies (cf. Fyfe, Turner, and Verhoogen, 1958, pp. 8-10, 18). Facies refer to mineral assemblages of associated rocks—not to inferred metamorphic conditions. Accordingly, any definition of facies in general, or of individual facies such as that of Oslo, must be framed in terms of criteria that may be observed in metamorphic rocks. A definition of facies proposed by Fyfe and Turner (1966) is here adopted:

> A metamorphic facies is a set of metamorphic mineral assemblages, repeatedly associated in space and time, such that there is a constant and therefore predictable relation between mineral composition and chemical composition.

This definition requires amplification in several respects:

1. Any facies is recognized on the basis of a set of mutually associated rocks collectively covering a wide range of composition. It cannot be defined in terms of a single rock type, even though each facies is customarily named after some characteristic rock: greenschist, amphibolite, and so on. Contrary to a view repeatedly expressed in the literature (e.g., Becke, 1921; Tilley, 1924b), the facies concept is unsuited for use in developing a comprehensive classification of individual rock types.

2. The relation between the mineral and the chemical composition of rocks belonging to any facies is such that, given the chemical analysis, it is possible to predict the corresponding mineral assemblage. Thus in the greenschist facies rocks having the composition of basalt will always be represented by one of the assemblages

Albite-chlorite-actinolite-epidote-sphene
Albite-chlorite-epidote-sphene
Albite-chlorite-epidote-calcite-sphene

Which of these three assemblages is developed and whether quartz is present as a minor additional phase, depends upon the particular chemical composition within the general basaltic range. Typical pelitic assemblages in the same facies are

Quartz-muscovite-chlorite (-albite-epidote)
Quartz-muscovite-chlorite (-biotite-garnet)
Quartz-muscovite-biotite (-garnet)

All three may have virtually identical chemical compositions. Which of the three develops in any particular locality depends upon some factor other than composition—almost certainly the values of temperature and pressure within some restricted range.

3. What determines the mineral assemblage in a given rock within any facies is the present composition as shown by a chemical analysis. The facies concept throws no light upon the initial state of the rock nor upon any change in bulk composition that may have accompanied metamorphism. For instance, rocks of one composition in the greenschist facies are composed of actinolite and calcite. The parent rock may have been a pure dolomite, a siliceous dolomite, or a peridotite. The initial state can be reconstructed only on the basis of chemical, textural, and field data.

During his lifetime, Eskola increased the number of facies he recognized from five to eight. More have been added by other writers. Some of these have later been abandoned or redefined. Many have been divided into subfacies. For example the greenschist facies was originally defined to include rocks of the chlorite and biotite zones of regional metamorphism. The diagnostic assemblage in greenschists (derivatives of basic igneous rocks) is albite-epidote-chlorite-sphene-quartz, with or without actinolite or calcite. It was later redefined and divided into subfacies on the basis of pelitic assemblages (Turner and Verhoogen, 1960, p. 533). More recently Lambert (1965) has criticized the use of subfacies as having become both confused and cumbersome. Accordingly it is now proposed to discontinue attempts to divide facies into minor units of more than local significance (Fyfe and Turner, 1966), and to revert to Eskola's original usage regarding the greenschist facies. It seems that ten or a dozen facies will prove sufficient to encompass the complete gamut of metamorphic rocks; this number is small enough to permit the general petrologist to remain familiar with their essential characteristics.

The confusion that still exists regarding nomenclature arises mainly from differences in opinion as to where arbitrarily to draw boundaries between facies that necessarily show transitional relations to one another. Such transitions, of course, reflect the gradational relations that are now recognized to exist between mineral assemblages on either side of any of the generally recognized isograds. In current literature, this situation has been met in three different ways depending partly on the interests and prejudices of the authors, partly on the scale on which they treat metamorphism.

Winkler (1970), who views metamorphic rocks on a small scale (hand specimen or thin section) as chemical polyphase systems in thermodynamic equilibrium, has "abolished" metamorphic facies, and substituted a classification of metamorphic rocks in terms of reactions inferred from isograds.

Miyashiro (1961, pp. 277, 278), who looks at regional metamorphism on the broadest possible scale in relation to tectonism, takes as the most significant unit, the complete sequence of metamorphic assemblages displayed in successive zones of regional metamorphism. This comprehensive unit he has termed a *facies series.**

---

*The term was originally used by Vogt (1927, pp. 412, 514–516) and adopted by Eskola (1939, p. 359) in quite a different sense: to denote a standard sequence of more or less isochemical mineral assemblages resulting from progressive metamorphism of some selected rock type such as basalt (gabbro). Greenschist → amphibolite → pyroxene granulite is such a series. In this book Migashiro's usage is adopted.

Thus, the Barrovian facies series of the Scottish Dalradian includes the complete gamut of the greenschist and amphibolite facies, as there displayed, with emphasis on the subfacies that define the individual zones and isograds. In the locally developed subfacies, Eskola's criterion of constant correlation between rock chemistry and mineral assemblages is strictly met. And in these, too, will be found characteristics unique to the Barrovian facies series.

In this book, as in the previous edition, we prefer to retain the facies as the general unit, the subfacies as a variant of local significance. Each such sequence we shall term a facies series in the strict sense of Miyashiro's usage, with emphasis on the uniqueness of every such series (cf. Turner, 1970, pp. 343-345).

If we no longer attempt to set up standard subfacies of worldwide significance, nomenclature becomes simplified to the point where metamorphic phenomena can be discussed with a minimum of ambiguity by any geologist. In any given region it will still be possible to define locally significant subfacies corresponding to the various metamorphic zones that can be mapped between the isograds that limit the facies in question in the field. But to attempt any rigid application of such a series of subfacies to phase assemblages in the same facies as it is developed elsewhere is to ignore the differences, which are just as important as the resemblances, between the respective metamorphic parageneses of the two regions.

More serious divergences of opinion are apparent with regard to what metamorphic conditions may be inferred from the combined mineral assemblages of any given facies. Even in this area, however, opinion is much more nearly unanimous on some questions than was the case a dozen years ago. This growing consensus reflects the influence of laboratory experiment and thermodynamic reasoning in clarifying the conditions of critical metamorphic reactions.

The Metamorphic Assemblage as a System in Stable Equilibrium

General Definition

The related concepts of equilibrium and stability as applied to metamorphic rocks are rather subtle ones capable of unequivocal definition only in thermodynamic terms (see later in this chapter). Consider a system of several specific phases A, B, C, D, at constant temperature T and pressure P. The system is in a state of *stable equilibrium* when under these conditions there is no tendency (thermodynamic possibility) for internal reaction tending toward elimination of any phase, e.g.,

$$A + B \to C \quad \text{or} \quad C \to D$$

or toward generation of some new phase, e.g.,

$$A + B \to E + F$$

When such a transformation is possible, but fails for reasons of reaction kinetics to materialize, the system is said to be *metastable.*

Prevalence of Metamorphic Stable Equilibrium:
General Evidence

Ever since G. H. Williams (e.g., 1890, p. 39) wrote of the "equipoise" or "delicate balance" between metamorphic mineral assemblages and the physical conditions of metamorphism, the classic writers on metamorphic petrology have seen each common mineral assemblage as a system approximating stable equilibrium controlled by some limited range of temperature and pressure conditions (e.g., Becke, 1913, p. 4; Goldschmidt, 1911, p. 118; Eskola, 1915, pp. 114-115; Harker, 1932, pp. 10-11). There is abundant cumulative petrographic evidence to support this contention *as a first approximation*. Minerals belonging to most isomorphous series tend to be remarkably uniform in composition within domains ranging from a thin section to a metamorphic zone. Optical measurements made on hundreds of grains of plagioclase in schists of the chlorite and biotite zones of Otago, New Zealand (an area 30,000 km^2 in extent) indicate compositional variations no greater than An_0 to An_5. Even this limited range probably reflects error in measurement rather than variation in anorthite content. Perhaps the true range is no greater than An_0 to An_1 (cf. Evans, 1964, pp. 175, 177). The chlorite series is one in which there is a wide range of possible substitution between Mg^{2+}, Fe^{2+}, Al^{3+} and between Al^{3+} and Si^{4+}. Yet such chlorites of New Zealand and Japanese greenschists as have been analyzed are highly restricted in compositional range: they are prochlorites in which the ratio FeO/MgO is about 0.8-1.1. Optically recognizable zoning in plagioclase and amphibole crystals, although by no means unknown, is relatively rare in metamorphic rocks. Garnet of pelitic schists, however, is commonly zoned.

The rapidly growing analytical data on metamorphic minerals have already demonstrated many consistent and widely prevalent correlations between composition of mineral series and paragenesis (i.e., facies). For example, in coexisting ferromagnesian silicates of any facies, the partitioning of Fe and Mg follows consistent patterns. Thus the respective distribution coefficients for Mg and Fe in the pairs diopside-hypersthene and hypersthene-garnet in granulites have been shown to be constant (Kretz, 1961; Davidson, 1968; Scharbert and Kurat, 1974). Francis (1964, pp. 177-178) found that in a group of associated, high-grade pelitic schists from Scotland, the biotite of biotite-muscovite-kyanite-almandine schists has a Mg/Fe ratio of about 0.6; in biotite of biotite-almandine-kyanite schists, Mg/Fe < 0.6; in that of schists lacking almandine the ratio Mg/Fe > 0.6. The almandine, as is usually the case in high-grade pelitic schists, has a consistently low Mg/Fe ratio (not greater than 0.3). Distribution of Ca between coexisting garnet and plagioclase is regularly related to grade of metamorphism (Kepezhinskas, 1973; Ghent, 1976). White micas in low-grade chlorite and glaucophane schists usually contain significant amounts of MgO, FeO, and Fe_2O_3 and have been called phengites (Tilley, 1926; Ernst, 1963). In biotite-muscovite schists of higher grade, on the other hand, the white mica more closely approximates the ideal composition of muscovite.

A strong tendency for regularity in the chemistry of coexisting metamorphic minerals was perceived long ago by Becke; and he interpreted it as evidence of general prevalence of equilibrium in metamorphic rocks. Today, as microprobe data become increasingly available, the picture is much more comprehensive and more convincing than in Becke's time. Chemical consistency in coexisting solid solutions in equilibrium indeed is demanded by thermodynamic theory. It is the basis of modern geothermometry and geobarometry (see Chap. 3).

Thermodynamically predictable, too, is conformity to the phase rule of Willard Gibbs—a topic to be developed later in this chapter. This rule restricts the *number* of phases in any system of a given number of chemical components in a state of equilibrium under stated variance with respect to temperature, pressure, and composition variables (in solid solutions and in the fluid phase). In any metamorphic rock, the chemical components, however they are designated (e.g., SiO_2, Al_2O_3, CaO, . . .) are many. Yet, the principal associated mineral phases are few. This does not prove equilibrium—either in any particular case or in general. But, the petrographic evidence is highly suggestive since it is in accord with general thermodynamic prediction as stated in the phase rule. This extremely important generalization was perceived by Goldschmidt (1911b) and by P. Niggli (1912). In fact, it led both men to expose metamorphic petrology to the light of thermodynamic appraisal—the first and most significant step in setting the geochemical trend that pervades the science today.

In no way invalidating the proposition that thermodynamic equilibrium is generally approximated in common metamorphic mineral assemblages is the fact that many metamorphic rocks show textural and mineralogical evidence of more than one episode of metamorphism. A new mineral assemblage may be seen in process of development from an older one. Biotite and garnet are commonly partially chloritized; kyanite or andalusite may be partly converted to white mica; crystals of plagioclase or of amphibole may show optically recognizable simple zoning. Here indeed is evidence of disequilibrium resulting from partial conversion of an older to a newer equilibrium assemblage. Moreover on a very small scale compositional variation within optically homogeneous grains is being increasingly revealed by means of the electron microprobe analyzer (cf. Evans, 1964). Some of this variation probably represents the expectable small-scale adjustments to postmetamorphic conditions in microsystems sufficiently small for ionic diffusion to be effective during postmetamorphic time. On the other hand, zoning in garnet crystals appears commonly to have been inherited from the culmination of metamorphism. Here is evidence that equilibrium was never attained, even in small domains, at maximum metamorphic temperatures.

Spatial Limits of Natural Systems

Petrologists treat rocks on all scales—from individual outcrops to parts of thin sections. So, to apply to rocks the concept of thermodynamic equilibrium one must first define the spatial limits of the system in question, and these will depend on the purpose of the study and on the techniques available for procuring the requisite data.

1. Classic discussion centers around data obtained from samples of a few cubic centimeters, on which scale the rock is chemically homogeneous in that samples of comparable size have identical chemical composition (cf. Blackburn, 1968). This is the bulk chemical composition of the system on this scale.

Physically, the system is heterogeneous in that it consists of mechanically separable phases (minerals). If each phase is homogeneous on the scale of the individual crystal, its composition and its thermodynamic properties can be determined on a mechanically separated pure fraction or its composition obtained by averaging microprobe analyses. Systems on this scale constitute much of the subject matter of this book; for they provide the material for translating the mineralogical data of facies and facies series into field gradients in temperature and pressure.

2. Effects of postmetamorphic exsolution in once-homogeneous crystals are widespread: lamellar structures in pyroxenes and amphiboles; perthitic feldspars; calcite crystals with exsolved blebs of dolomite in high-grade marbles. Provided that the operative diffusion process is strictly intragranular and that the analyzed mineral sample consists of grains that are large compared with the scale of exsolution, heterogeneity of this kind in no way affects conventional treatment of the system in terms of bulk compositions of separate mineral fractions, each of which includes the host and the exsolved phase. Such treatment refers to the system at the culmination of metamorphism. To investigate the exsolution process itself, however, requires treatment on a much smaller scale in which a single crystal comprises the system and its mineral components—the host and its enclosed exsolved products—are the phases.

3. Certain textures clearly reveal the imprint of a late episode of retrograde metamorphism at some stage during cooling from the temperature of culmination: symplectites, coronas, pseudomorphs, and some cases of optically recognizable zoning (e.g., tremolite rimmed with glaucophane). To unravel the retrograde process the problem is to distinguish the respective complete phase assemblages of the two successive metamorphic episodes; for reaction and ionic diffusion between nearby (not necessarily contiguous) crystals of different phases of the first assemblage seems to be general. Only thus, for example, can one explain pseudomorphous replacement of garnet by chlorite in some crystals, by lawsonite or albite in others nearby, in conversion of Californian eclogite to glaucophane schist. The pertinent system is microscopic, but nevertheless covers a multigranular domain limited by kinetics of ionic diffusion and exchange.

4. The advent of the microprobe has shown compositional zoning of metamorphic crystals to be more widespread than was once suspected. Not all of this can be attributed to retrograde reactions. Zoned crystals of almandine in pelitic schists commonly have manganese-rich cores inherited from a stage of nucleation and initial growth prior to the culmination of metamorphism. The core material, effectively isolated by unfavorable diffusion kinetics, played no part in development of the ultimate high-grade assemblage (cf. Atherton, 1968). In this, the garnet participant is represented by the composition of the outer zone of each crystal.

5. Metamorphic facies are based on end products of progressive metamorphism, regardless of the nature of the process itself. But the latter also is significant to our understanding of the whole phenomenon, one aspect of which concerns the path by which, with changing conditions, one assemblage of phases gives way to another. Here, the pertinent system is microscopic. Attention focuses on kinetics of ionic diffusion and crystal nucleation in domains consisting of a few closely associated grains (cf. D. M. Carmichael, 1969).

Closed and Open Systems

Facies are defined in terms of mineral assemblages, which are the end products of what may have been a complex and protracted metamorphic process. It is the individual assemblage that is the system to which we apply the concept of equilibrium. This takes no account of the path, in most cases only vaguely revealed, by which the bulk composition of the system as we now see it and its presumed state of equilibrium were ultimately attained. There is a good deal of evidence that most metamorphic rocks, on the scale of a hand specimen, retain the essential bulk composition (expressed in terms of common oxides) of the parent material; for example, shales are transformed to metapelites, basalts to metabasalts. There is nevertheless an important omnipresent exception relating to inward or outward diffusion of a pore fluid with the potential for exchange of soluble ions (as well as H_2O, CO_2, and other "volatile" components) with some external reservoir extending far beyond our metamorphic "system." This brings up the vexed topic of open versus closed systems, of mobile versus immobile (inert) components, which figures prominently in the thermodynamic treatment of metamorphic systems by Korzhinskii (1936, 1949, 1967) and by J. B. Thompson (1955, 1959, 1970).[*] Such considerations are essential for understanding the element of metasomatism in the actual process of metamorphism (a topic, however, that is largely beyond the scope of this book).

The question nevertheless cannot be completely bypassed. There can be no doubt that during progressive metamorphism water is progressively expelled from pelitic rocks, and carbon dioxide from limestones and their derivatives. Equally obvious is the effect of an inward flux of water from an oceanic reservoir during spilitization of basalts or serpentinization of peridotites in the environment of ocean-floor spreading. Diffusion of this kind may lead to an unmistakable exchange of ions between the metamorphic system and its enveloping chemical environment. One possibility may be equal-volume replacement of one phase by another, as in albitization of plagioclase in spilites. Or there may be positive volume changes of indeterminate magnitude as in serpentinization of peridotite, or of forsterite in retrograde metamorphism of forsterite marble. Because of such uncertainty, in the absence of definite pseudomorphs, to write a quantitative chemical equation usually is simply to postulate one possible model of chemical exchange (metasomatism).

There are some cases where the path and degree of ionic exchange are revealed by textural evidence. Thus, zoned diffusion skarns a few centimeters wide that developed at granite-dolomite contacts or around flint nodules enclosed in limestone represent units in a sequence of mosaic equilibria as the term is used by Thompson. In the Broadford area of Skye, dolomitic limestone encloses nodules of flint. In the inner aureole of an intrusive granitic pluton, individual flints and immediately enclosing dolomite domains have been converted to successive shells composed of the following assemblages, listed in order from within outward (Tilley, 1951a, pp. 623-624).

Quartz-diopside	Diopside-forsterite
Diopside	Forsterite-calcite

---

[*]For a critical appraisal of this approach see Weill and Fyfe (1964).

These collectively constitute a mosaic of four equilibria controlled by the inward diffusion of Mg and Ca and the outward diffusion of Si, along a gradient in chemical potential.*

To return to the problem of metamorphic mineral assemblages as systems in thermodynamic equilibrium: to evaluate the metamorphic temperature-pressure gradient expressed by any facies series, we postulate that the mineralogical makeup of each assemblage was determined predictably by the final bulk composition and some finite narrow range of temperature and pressure conditions prevailing at the culmination of metamorphism. No assumption is made as to the path by which the system reached its present bulk composition. There is, however, one inescapable difficulty: one of the participatory phases, the pore fluid, has escaped from the system. Its composition, expressed by concentrations, partial pressures, or fugacities of its components, must be postulated either from indirect mineralogical evidence (presence of carbonates, hydrous phases, graphite, iron oxides, etc.) or on the basis of microscopic fluid inclusions. To this topic we return in the ensuing section.

Pressure Variables of Metamorphic Equilibrium

A large rock mass undergoing metamorphism is in a state of stress induced by external forces. These include the vertical load of the overlying rock pile, and lateral forces of tectonic origin, which are structurally expressed by contemporary folds and foliations. From a thermodynamic standpoint, a mineral assemblage is usually considered on a small scale, that of a hand specimen or a thin section. On this scale, the state of stress is likely to vary from one such small domain to another. But, as a first approximation, we may conceive the local stress system as controlled principally by load and influenced to some degree by lateral constraints imposed by the surrounding rock which is itself in a state of stress.

One component of any stress system is hydrostatic. This is the pressure P postulated in thermodynamic argument. It has usually been equated with a hydrostatic pressure that would develop in a viscous body under the weight of an overlying column of rock (about 300 bar km^{-1} of depth). The other component is a shear stress whose magnitude is limited by the rheologic state of the body. The prevalence of isostatic compensation and the widespread occurrence of flow structures (foliations and lineations) in regionally metamorphosed rocks indicates that a rock mass, during protracted recrystallization in the deeper levels of the crust, behaves essentially as a viscous body except probably at low temperatures (see below). Within it, shear stresses of high magnitude could not be sustained for the long periods ($>10^7$ years) required for a cycle of regional metamorphism. We therefore write the thermodynamic pressure variable P as a hydrostatic load pressure P_l, in some cases augmented by an increment of "tectonic overpressure." Since the equivalent viscosity of a rock increases exponentially with decreasing temperature (cf. Heard,1963, pp. 182, 192-194), the increment of "tectonic overpressure" may possibly be considerable at temperatures of 200 or 300°C even

---

*Mosaic equilibrium can be envisaged on all scales. The controlling gradient may be one of temperature and pressure as in the large-scale mosaic comprising a sequence of mapped zones of progressive metamorphism.

at very low rates of strain. Networks of veinlets filled with such minerals as preh-nite, pumpellyite, aragonite, lawsonite, or glaucophane in low-grade schists and nonfoliated metagraywackes indeed are consistent with brittle fracture at tempera-tures below $300°C$ under long-sustained stress.

In a thermodynamic system, the pressure P acts uniformly on all the asso-ciated phases. In a porous rock saturated with a fluid phase, the hydrostatic pres-sure P_f within the fluid is not necessarily the same as the hydrostatic component of the stress system within the continuous aggregate of mineral grains (sometimes distinguished as the pressure on solids P_s). The difference is likely to be substantial at shallow depths, where the rock is strong and where the fluid in the pores extends continuously through joints and fissures to the earth's surface. At depths of a few kilometers, however, experience in deep drilling for petroleum and gas shows a strong tendency for the fluid pressure P_f to approach the load pressure P_l. In our simplified model of metamorphism, we therefore assume that at depths of 10 km or more, $P_f = P_l$. This is consistent with our earlier assumption that the rock undergoing metamorphism is essentially viscous.

Finally we turn briefly to the role of shear stress as an independent pressure variable. First the free energy of a stressed solid phase at constants P_l and T is increased by an amount proportional to its molar volume (Turner and Verhoogen, 1960, p. 475). The stability fields of individual metamorphic minerals may be changed significantly by shear stress. Sixty years ago Grubenmann (1904, p. 43) wrote:

> The modification of a mineral incompatible with the influence of stress dissolves and goes over to the corresponding heteromorphous com-plementary form. Augite is transformed into finely fibrous uralite or hornblende, andalusite into pinacoidal kyanite . . .

Harker (1919, pp. lxxvii, lxxviii; 1932, pp. 147-151) noted that certain minerals, such as kyanite, almandine, epidotes, and staurolite occur mainly in schists whose foliated structure bears witness to metamorphic deformation. These he termed *stress minerals* in the belief that their fields of stability on a *P-T* diagram are extended under the influence of shear stress. This extension might even be a necessary condition for the stability of some species. By contrast, other minerals, such as andalusite, cordierite, and forsterite, which occur mainly in undeformed rocks such as hornfelses, were classed as *antistress minerals.* It was thought that shear stress reduces their stability fields, perhaps in some instances even to zero. This hard-and-fast distinction has not been substantiated by the growing mass of petrographic data on associations and distribution of metamorphic minerals. There may be a very few minerals—clinoenstatite of peridotite mylonites is one—that have no field of true stability except under high shear stress. But for the most part shear stress is assessed simply as an increment, perhaps not a substantial one to the load pressure.[*]

Shear stress, especially at low temperatures, appears to have a more signifi-

---

[*]For a general discussion of the thermodynamic role of shear stress in relation to geo-logic problems, see Paterson (1973).

cant role in triggering and accelerating metamorphic reactions. The free energy of a strained crystal, by virtue of accumulated newly generated lattice defects (dislocations), is higher than that of an unstrained crystal of the same phase. Similarly the free energy of a phase is enhanced by reduction of grain size and consequent increase in surface energy per unit volume. Cataclastic flow induced by high shear stress not only reduces grain size but renews surfaces of contact between grains of different phases and may intermittently increase local permeability to fluids. Thus shear stress may indirectly supply the activation energy necessary for nucleation and growth of new phases, thus promoting reactions that otherwise would be too sluggish to be effective. Long ago, Grubenmann (1904, p. 41) spoke of the "work of stress . . . in stimulation and encouragement of chemical and mineralogical rock transformations." Today there is abundant field and petrographic evidence that metamorphism at lower grades is initiated mainly by the accelerating influence of shear stress. Thus in the Southern Alps, New Zealand (Lillie and Gunn, 1964), indurated graywacke has been transformed into quartz-albite-chlorite-muscovite schist in sharply limited, intensely deformed zones a kilometer or so wide. Although the stability field of the metamorphic assemblage there was determined by the standard temperature and pressure variables, the trigger that locally set the reaction in motion appears to have been shear stress.

Role of Pore-Fluid Composition

Most metamorphic reactions involve participation of one or more components of the pore fluid which is assumed to diffuse freely within, from, or into the metamorphic system as dictated by the nature of the reaction and by the nature, dimensions, and rheology of the system and its envelope (cf. J. B. Thompson, 1955). The pore fluid—except in the case of water in near-surface hydrothermal systems ($T < 374°C$, depth < 750 m)—is a gas. Because gas is highly compressible, the thermodynamic properties (molar volume and entropy) of its components are much more sensitive to pressure variation at any given temperature than are solid phases in the same system; although this difference becomes less marked as pressure increases. Consequently, the course of metamorphic reaction and the pressure-temperature fields of stability of resulting mineral assemblages are profoundly influenced by the composition of the pore fluid and its thermodynamic response to variations in fluid pressure P_f.

Goldschmidt's (1912) calibration of the wollastonite equilibrium—which provided the sole quantitative P-T datum employed for several decades in metamorphic petrology—was based on an equation expressing the response of pure CO_2 to variation in pressure at any given temperature. In Korzhinskii's writings of the 1930s (e.g., Korzhinskii, 1937) there is a strong emphasis on the role of CO_2 pressure in decarbonation reactions, a topic elaborated by Bowen (1940) in his classic discussion of progressive metamorphism of siliceous dolomites. Bowen thought it likely that the gas phase in most natural reactions in this sequence approached pure CO_2; but the possibility of dilution by some other component (such as H_2O) comes into his discussion, thus implying that it is the partial pressure p_{CO_2} rather than P_f that is the essential controlling condition. To Yoder (1952, 1955) especially we owe the parallel concept concerning the dominant role of P_f and p_{H_2O} in metamorphic reactions of hydration and dehydration. This was the approach adopted in the previous edition of this book. It is in some respects only an approximation, which, however, can now be greatly improved upon by utilizing currently available data on fugacities of H_2O, CO_2, and some minor but influential components such as CH_4 and O_2.

In the flood of newer experimentally based contributions on the chemistry of metamorphism—especially those relating to systems with CO_2 and H_2O as gas components—data are usually presented in terms of molar fractions X_i, such that

$$X_{H_2O} + X_{CO_2} + \cdots X_i = 1$$

For ideal mixing of gas components

$$p_{H_2O} + p_{CO_2} + \cdots p_i = P_f$$

and

$$X_{H_2O}P_f + X_{CO_2}P_f + \cdots X_iP_f = P_f$$

Relevant fugacity data are given by Burnham et al. (1969), for water; Price (1975), Majundar and Roy (1956), and Ryzhenko and Valkov (1971), for carbon dioxide.

In well-designed experiments, molar fractions of the gas components are predetermined or directly measured. In thermodynamic models, values of partial pressures and corresponding known fugacities can be postulated. To apply conclusions so reached to a natural metamorphic system, we are obliged to infer, from mineralogical and petrographic evidence, the composition of the gas. There can be no doubt, for example, that water was a principal component in serpentinization of peridotite or in conversion of quartz-tremolite marble to diopside marble. But were these the only gas components involved, and in multicomponent gases what values are to be assigned to individual concentrations X_{H_2O}, X_{CO_2}, etc.? Surprising to many of us was Touret's (1971) discovery that microscopic fluid inclusions entrapped in constituent mineral crystals of some Norwegian granulites are relatively rich in CO_2—suggesting that correspondingly low X_{H_2O} (and so f_{H_2O}) rather than very high temperature may have been the dominant influence in reactions leading to crystallization of the anhydrous granulite assemblages. Fluid inclusions in adjacent amphibolites are essentially aqueous. Fluid inclusions indeed may provide valuable independent evidence of the composition of a metamorphic gas phase (e.g., Poty et al., 1974), attended, however, by uncertainty as to the stage (early or late metamorphic, or even postmetamorphic) at which the gas was trapped.

With due caution as to possible uncertainties involved, it is convenient to consider the role of gas composition in shaping metamorphic equilibria in terms of a few specific models. Though oversimplified, these presently appear realistic with respect to certain common chemical patterns of metamorphism. Here are some examples:

$$X_{H_2O} = 1 \qquad p_{H_2O} = P_f$$

Some metamorphic reactions appear from mineralogical evidence to involve simple hydration or dehydration, with water the sole or dominant component of the gas phase. Ocean-floor metamorphism in an environment permeated by sea-water—so important in the light of plate-tectonics theory—can be viewed in this category (conversion of basalt to spilite or to greenschist). It is customary to apply this model to progressive metamorphism of pelitic rocks; but here the fugacity of water may have been reduced below that of pure water by presence of CO_2 (as in ankerite-bearing pelites of New England) or by CH_4-CO-CO_2 mixtures in the presence of graphite (cf. French, 1966; Ghent et al., 1970; Ghent, 1975).

$X_{CO_2} = 1$ $p_{CO_2} = 1$

This model is appropriate to metamorphism of siliceous dolomitic marbles in the absence of any hydrous phase (assemblages such as calcite-wollastonite and calcite-fosterite-diopside are typical end products). It appears realistic, too, for higher grades of metamorphism of similar rocks after elimination of low-grade hydrous phases—and for massive anhydrous carbonate rocks not readily permeable to water from external sources.

$X_{CO_2} + X_{H_2O} = 1$ both variable

Hydrous silicates, notably talc and tremolite, are characteristic of the earlier stages of metamorphism of calcareous rocks and subsequently become eliminated in favor of anhydrous calc-silicates. Values of X_{CO_2} and X_{H_2O} for reactions leading to talc or tremolite cannot be postulated with any certainty; for there is no way of knowing whether the water component was indigenous to the parent rock or was supplied from external sources such as pelitic interbeds. For dehydration-decarbonation reactions, models can be set up with greater confidence, especially where the rocks concerned occur in massive beds as in the Lepontine Alps (Trommsdorff, 1972). The assumption is that the equilibrium assemblage of participating phases buffers the gas to the composition dictated by the reaction in question: For example, in what appears to be a common reaction

$$Ca_2 Mg_5 Si_8 O_{22}(OH)_2 + 3CaCO_3 + 2SiO_2 \rightarrow 5CaMgSi_2 O_6 + \underbrace{3CO_2 + H_2O}_{gas}$$

$$\text{tremolite} \qquad \text{calcite} \quad \text{quartz} \quad \text{diopside}$$

the gas composition could be maintained at the stoichiometric level

$X_{CO_2} = 0.75$ $X_{H_2O} = 0.25$

Here the buffer is the full assemblage tremolite-calcite-quartz-diopside.

Many reactions involve ferriferous silicates and oxides—biotite, garnet, staurolite, magnetite and so on. A potent control in such cases is exercised by minute concentrations of oxygen in the pore fluid maintained at some specific level (at a given temperature) by internal buffers consisting of various combinations of participating phases such as iron and titanium oxides, ferrous silicates, and graphite. These buffers can be calibrated experimentally for metamorphic temperatures and pressures and provide the basis for one of the most valuable types of geothermometer. Though f_{O_2} values in natural systems are extremely low, they vary through several orders of magnitude. Herein lies the potency of their influence. For example, in the range $T = 500\text{--}700°C$, the magnetite-ilmenite pair (depending on the ratio Mg/Fe in the oxide system) buffers the value of f_{O_2} at about 10^{-15} to 10^{-25} bars (cf. Buddington and Lindsley, 1964). Because the quantity of oxygen involved in any buffer reaction such as $3Fe_2SiO_4 + O_2 \rightarrow 2Fe_3O_4 + 3SiO_2$ is minute, metamorphic systems may be effectively buffered internally even when permeable (open) to major gas components such as water from outside sources.

Interpretation of Facies and Facies Series: General Propositions

In this book, quantitative interpretation of metamorphic facies and of facies series is based on the following general propositions, with due allowance for considerable departures and uncertainties in specific cases.

1. Every common metamorphic mineral assemblage, on the scale of a few cubic centimeters (cf. Blackburn, 1968), approximates a system in stable equilibrium within some finite range of temperature and pressure.
2. Pressure can be expressed as $P_s = P_f$. It is visualized essentially as hydrostatic pressure controlled by the load of superincumbent rock. An increment of "tectonic overpressure" may possibly be significant under conditions (notably low temperature) favoring brittle rather than ductile failure of rock under shear stress.
3. For most metamorphic reactions, the composition of the pore-fluid phase plays an essential role. Ideal specific conditions, each believed to be realistically approached in some instances for common reactions are $X_{H_2O} = 1$; $X_{CO_2} = 1$; $X_{CO_2} + X_{H_2O} = 1$; X_{H_2O} and X_{CO_2} internally buffered by the reaction itself; and f_{O_2} internally buffered by iron and titanium oxides, ferriferous silicates, graphite, and so on. Nevertheless it must be stressed that thermodynamic evaluation of specific metamorphic systems is beginning to reveal significant departures from ideal models such as $X_{CO_2} + X_{H_2O} = 1$ (e.g., Ferry, 1976).
4. The equilibria represented by the mineral assemblages that define any facies have a broad field of stability (in terms of T and P) in common. Within this broad field are narrower, possibly overlapping fields of stability of constituent subfacies represented by zonal assemblages.
5. A mapped sequence of facies and subfacies bounded by isograds—i.e., a specific facies series—expresses a field gradient in temperature and pressure with the possibility, too, of a gradient or breaks in time.

THERMODYNAMIC CONSIDERATION OF STABILITY AND EQUILIBRIUM

The General Problem

Some metamorphic transformations, real or postulated, can be represented approximately by simplified equations of the type

$$SiO_2 + KAl_2(AlSi_3O_{10})(OH)_2 \rightleftharpoons KAlSi_3O_8 + Al_2SiO_5 + H_2O$$

quartz   muscovite   K-feldspar   sillimanite

and

$$4SiO_2 + 3Mg_3Fe_2Al(AlSi_3O_{10})(OH)_8$$

quartz   prochlorite

$$\rightleftharpoons 3Fe_2MgAl_2(Si_3O_{12}) + Mg_6(Si_4O_{10})(OH)_8 + 8H_2O$$

almandine   antigorite

More usually, to accommodate the many oxide components of typical rocks and to express precise equivalence of phase assemblages representing different grades of metamorphism, the corresponding equation is much more complex and can be developed only by analysis based on linear programming. Thus, H. J. Greenwood showed that the mineral assemblages of two pelitic schists from different parts of the northern Appalachian region are chemically equivalent in terms of the equation

0.2018 chlorite + 0.2484 chloritoid + 0.5403 muscovite

+ 0.0095 rutile $\rightleftharpoons$ 0.5269 biotite + 0.0125 quartz

+ 0.4034 kyanite + 0.0170 albite + 0.0402 H_2O

To write any such equation, simple or complex, poses questions fundamental to the problem of assessing possible physical conditions of metamorphism. What are the stability fields, in terms of pressure and temperature, of the ideal assemblages participating in the simplified postulated reactions? How will these fields be affected by solid-solution phenomena emerging from microprobe analyses of the minerals themselves? What will be the effect of variation, within realistic limits, in gas composition? How will the reaction be affected by additional phases present in the analogous metamorphic rock? Under what specific *P–T* conditions is the reaction possible or likely to occur? Thermodynamics provides the ultimate answers to such questions, subject to limitations imposed by availability and accuracy of data on pertinent thermal and pressure-related properties of all participating phases. And it is only within the framework of thermodynamics that the concepts of equilibrium and stability can be discussed and their criteria rigorously defined.

Thermodynamic reasoning was introduced into general metamorphic petrology by Goldschmidt (1911, 1912) and P. Niggli (1912) both of whom were influenced by Van't Hoff's earlier treatment of natural salt equilibria (cf. Eugster, 1971) and by W. Nernst's *Theoretical Chemistry*. The same approach figures, too, in Johnston and Niggli's (1913) early essay and in Niggli's elaborate introductory revision of Grubenmann's classic treatise (Grubenmann and Niggli, 1924). Nevertheless it was only after World War II that thermodynamic appraisal of metamorphic systems became incorporated into petrologic texts in the English language (e.g., Turner and Verhoogen, 1951). Today much of current literature in the field of metamorphic geochemistry would be unintelligible without some appreciation of thermodynamic principles and reasoning; and demands in this respect upon the nonexpert reader are growing.

It is assumed that most readers of this book have an adequate background for this approach to critical analysis of current problems in metamorphic chemistry. For fuller and more sophisticated comprehensive treatments than that provided in this book see J. B. Thompson (1955), Turner and Verhoogen (1960), Pippard (1966), and Kern and Weisbrod (1967). Nevertheless it is perhaps in order at this point to remind ourselves of fundamental concepts and relations underlying rigorous definition of stability and equilibrium as these terms may be applied to metamorphic minerals and rocks.

Reversible Process

Consider a process expressed by the chemical equation

$$A \rightleftharpoons B$$

By definition, this is reversible at some stated P and T if an infinitesimal change in either pressure or temperature permits the reaction to proceed in one sense (say, from left to right), while an infinitesimal change of opposite sign reverses the sense of reaction. The rate of any reversible reaction at P and T is infinitesimally small; so the reversible process is an idealized concept. Reversibility can be closely approached in the laboratory, sometimes, as in the case of ice $\rightleftharpoons$ water at 1 bar, $0°C$, within a small fraction of a degree. But it is never actually attained. All real (spontaneous) reactions are irreversible at constant P and T; i.e., reaction is then possible in one sense only.

Entropy of Reaction ΔS_r

The entropy S of a system (a quantity reflecting the degree of internal disorder in the system) is defined by the statement that in any *reversible* reaction

$$\Delta S_r = \frac{\Delta q}{T} \tag{2-1}$$

where q is the quantity of heat absorbed and T is the temperature, Kelvin (T K). The third law of thermodynamics assumes that, with certain qualifications (cf. Fyfe, Turner, and Verhoogen, 1958, pp. 27–28), the entropy of a perfect crystal at 0 K is zero. From measurements of molar heat capacity C_p at $P = 1$ bar over the interval 0–298.15 K, the molar entropy S of any phase at room temperature (298.15 K) and pressure (1.018 bar) is given by

$$S = \int_0^{298.15} \frac{dq}{T} = \int_0^{298.15} \frac{C_p\, dT}{T} = \int_0^{298.15} C_p\, d\ln T \tag{2-2}$$

To calculate S for mineral phases at metamorphic pressures and temperatures, it would be necessary to have additional data over the appropriate range of conditions—specific heats, molar volumes, compressibilities, and coefficients of thermal expansion. These are lacking for many minerals. However, in the realm of inorganic chemistry, values of entropy from room temperature to several hundred degrees centigrade at atmospheric pressure are known for many compounds, some minerals among them (Kelley and King, 1961; Kelley, 1960, 1962; Robie, 1966; Robie and Waldbaum, 1968[*]). Especially valuable are accurate data for H_2O (Burnham et al., 1969) and CO_2 (Price, 1955) covering a wide range of pressure as well as temperature.

Without exception in any *irreversible* (i.e., spontaneous) reaction

$$\Delta S_r > \frac{\Delta q}{T} \tag{2-3}$$

where ΔS_r and Δq are the resultant changes in entropy and heat. This important relation follows directly from and is equivalent to statements of the second law of thermodynamics framed in terms of heat exchange. For example, consider the equation

$$NaAlSi_2O_6 + SiO_2 \rightarrow NaAlSi_3O_8$$
$$\text{jadeite} \qquad \text{quartz} \qquad \text{albite}$$

At $25°C$ (298.15 K), 1.018 bars, standard tabulated data give

$$\Delta S_r = +8.4 \text{ cal mole}^{-1} \text{ degr}^{-1}$$

Measurements of heats of solution of all three phases in hydrofluoric acid (Kracek et al., 1951) give

$$\Delta q = 600 \text{ cal mole}^{-1}$$

So $\Delta q/T = 600/298.15 \approx 2$ cal mole^{-1} degr^{-1} ($<\Delta S_r$) and the reaction from left to right is irreversible (i.e., possible). This is true even though no one has succeeded in directly converting jadeite + quartz to albite at room temperature and pressure.

Again consider dissociation of dolomite

$$CaMg(CO_3)_2 \rightarrow CaCO_3 + MgCO_3$$
$$\text{dolomite} \qquad \text{calcite} \qquad \text{magnesite}$$

At 298.15 K, 1.018 bars, standard data give

---

[*]Amended and greatly amplified since this went to press by R. A. Robie, B. C. Hemingway, and J. R. Fisher, *U.S. Geol. Surv. Bull.*, 1452, 1978.

$$\Delta S_r = +0.9 \text{ cal mole}^{-1} \text{ degr}^{-1}$$

$$\Delta q = +3.429 \text{ cal mole}^{-1}$$

$$\frac{\Delta q}{T} = 11.5 \text{ cal mole}^{-1} \text{ degr}^{-1} > \Delta S_r$$

Dissociation is not possible since the reaction from right to left is irreversible.

Gibbs Free Energy of Reaction ΔG_r

The Gibbs free energy G of a system at constant temperature T and pressure P is written

$$G = E + PV - TS \tag{2-4}$$

where E is the internal energy,[*] V the volume, and S the entropy of the system. For any reaction within the system

$$\Delta G_r = \Delta E + P \Delta V_r - T \Delta S_r$$

$$= (\Delta q - P \Delta V_r) + P \Delta V_r - T \Delta S_r$$

$$= \Delta q - T \Delta S_r$$

For a reaction at constant pressure, this may be written

$$\Delta G_r = \Delta H_r - T \Delta S_r \tag{2-5}$$

where ΔH_r is the enthalpy of reaction at constant pressure.

For a reaction

$$A + B \rightarrow C + D$$

if ΔG_r is negative, the reaction is irreversible and may occur spontaneously; if ΔG_r is zero, the reaction is reversible.

Chemical Potentials

A most important aspect of equilibrium in a polyphase system concerns the partitioning of common independent chemical components $i, j, \ldots, q$ between coexisting phases $\alpha, \beta, \ldots, \gamma$. The chemical potential μ_i of a component i in the system as a whole was proposed by Willard Gibbs to define the effect of changing the number n_i of moles i on the internal energy of the system, entropy, volume, and other molar concentrations $n_j, \ldots, n_q$ being held constant. If we consider any phase α as a self-contained system, it is easy to show from this definition (cf. Turner and Verhoogen, 1960, p. 15) that

[*] By definition, $dE = dq - P\,dV$, where $-P\,dV$ is the work done on the system.

$$\mu_i^\alpha = \left(\frac{\delta G^\alpha}{\delta X_i^\alpha}\right)_{P,T} \tag{2-6}$$

where X_i^α is the molar fraction of component i in α.

From the definition of free energy and Eq. (2-6), it can also be shown how the chemical potentials of $i, j, \ldots, q$ in phase α change in response to any change in P and T. This is expressed by the Gibbs-Duhem relation (cf. Turner and Verhoogen, 1960, p. 19).

$$S^\alpha \, dT - V^\alpha \, dP + \Sigma X_i^\alpha \, d\mu_i^\alpha = 0 \tag{2-7}$$

Molar fractions such as X_i^α and X_j^β thus yield intensive variables ranking with P and T in defining the state of the system—a property that as we shall presently see is significant in discussion of the phase rule as it applies to equilibria involving fluid or solid solutions.

The chemical potential μ_i^α, like the partial pressure p_i of a gas component, expresses the tendency for component i to migrate to any adjoining phase β. For this to occur spontaneously, ΔG of the diffusion process must be negative, i.e.,

$$\mu_i^\alpha > \mu_i^\beta$$

By analogy with the expression for chemical potentials of components of a perfect gas as a function of P and T, we can write for components of condensed (liquid or solid) phases at given P and T (cf. Turner and Verhoogen, 1960, pp. 20–21)

$$\mu_i^\alpha = \mu_i^0 + PT \ln a_i^\alpha \tag{2-8}$$

where μ_i^0 is the chemical potential of pure i in the appropriate condensed phase at P and T; and a_i^α is the activity of i in $\alpha = \gamma_i X_i^\alpha$, the activity coefficient γ_i being dependent on both temperature and pressure. *Ideal* solution of i in α is defined as the condition for which $\gamma = 1$ for i and all other components of α.

Equilibrium and Stability Defined

The general condition that defines equilibrium at given uniform P and T in a system of several components $i, j, \ldots, q$ in phases $\alpha, \beta, \ldots, \gamma$ is that the chemical potential of any component is the same in all phases in which it is present.

$$\mu_i^\alpha = \mu_i^\beta = \cdots = \mu_i^\gamma$$
$$\mu_q^\alpha = \mu_q^\beta = \cdots = \mu_q^\gamma \tag{2-9}$$

Otherwise components would tend to migrate spontaneously from one phase to another. Thus, a crystal of garnet continuously zoned, as commonly is the case, with Mg/Mn increasing outward is in a state of disequilibrium in that μ_{Mn} is variable in a single phase. A microcline-albite perthite will be in equilibrium only at the moment of exsolution, when $\mu_{albite}^{micr} = \mu_{albite}^{plag}$ in the intergrown phases.

Some natural systems and many that have been experimentally investigated or theoretically proposed consist of essentially pure phases in which solid solution is negligible so that Eq. (2-9) is redundant. Equilibrium and reversibility of reaction between coexisting phases are essentially synonymous. When any reaction that can be postulated completely in terms of coexisting stoichiometrically defined phases is reversible, the participating phases are in equilibrium ($\Delta G_r = 0$; $\Delta H_r = T \Delta S_r$). For the reaction

$$CaMg(CO_3)_2 + 2SiO_2 \rightleftharpoons CaMgSi_2O_6 + 2CO_2$$
$$\quad\ \text{dolomite} \qquad \text{quartz} \qquad \text{diopside} \qquad \text{gas}$$

ΔG_r is computed as zero at $200 \pm 40°C$ and $P_{CO_2} = 1$ bar (Turner, 1967). Under these conditions—which as we shall see later are not unique—the assemblage dolomite-quartz-diopside-CO_2 is by definition in equilibrium.

By definition, a system is stable when its free energy is minimal. For any of the many chemical reactions between its phases that can be postulated for a stable system of fixed chemical composition, under given physical conditions, $\Delta G_r > 0$ at the pressure and temperature of stability.* Between 400–450°C at $P_{CO_2} = 1$ bar, the system calcite-diopside-quartz-CO_2, is stable because $\Delta G_r > 0$ for all possible reactions between its phases, such as

$$CaCO_3 + SiO_2 \rightarrow CaSiO_3 + CO_2$$
$$\text{calcite} \qquad \text{quartz} \qquad \text{wollastonite} \qquad \text{gas}$$

or

$$CaCO_3 \rightarrow CaO + CO_2$$
$$\text{dissociation of calcite}$$

Clearly, all stable systems are in equilibrium. But some equilibria are unstable. Consider the assemblage dolomite-quartz-forsterite-calcite-CO_2 for which an internal reaction can be written

$$2CaMg(CO_3)_2 + SiO_2 \rightleftharpoons Mg_2SiO_4 + 2CaCO_3 + 2CO_2$$
$$\quad\ \text{dolomite} \qquad \text{quartz} \quad \text{forsterite} \quad \text{calcite} \qquad \text{gas}$$

From standard data ΔG_r for reaction from left to right (at 25°C, 1 bar) = 11.36 kcal (Turner, 1967, p. 9); so the complete five-phase assemblage is unstable and in disequilibrium. However at about 290°C, 1 bar, $\Delta G_r = 0$, and the full assemblage is in equilibrium. But it is unstable in that under these conditions, the chemically equivalent four-phase assemblage dolomite-quartz-diopside-CO_2 has lower free energy.

---

*The reader may care to verify from standard tabulated data the statement that calcite-dolomite-quartz-CO_2 is stable at 25°C (298.15 K) 1.018 bars.

   While stability is a clear-cut condition, instability from a petrological viewpoint is a matter of degree. The rate at which an unstable system is transformed
to a stable system depends upon other factors than the magnitude of negative ΔG_r.
It varies from explosively rapid to almost infinitely slow. When an unstable system
fails to change appreciably within time limits appropriate to a given situation, it is
said to be *metastable*—a few days in some experiments, years in a museum draw,
thousands or millions of years in a geologic situation. Orthoclase or orthoclase-
perthite in a granite specimen is metastable: the equivalent phase combination
with minimal free energy under room conditions is a perthitic intergrowth of
microcline and low albite. Unstable equilibria postulated on the criterion $\Delta G_r = 0$
may be completely unrealistic in that the velocity of conversion to a stable state
proves to be virtually instantaneous. As shown in Fig. 2-2, the system ice $\rightleftharpoons$ steam
is in equilibrium at about 82°C at atmospheric pressure. This equilibrium is mani-
festly unstable since for both reactions ice $\rightarrow$ water and steam $\rightarrow$ water ΔG_r is
strongly negative (~ -430 cal mole^{-1}). It is unreal moreover because both reactions yielding liquid water take place so rapidly that steam and ice cannot be held
together at 82°C. On the other hand, as experimental geochemists are aware, there
are some unstable equilibria that are reversible in the laboratory, while others
survive in nature and in the museum simply because of infinitely slow rates of

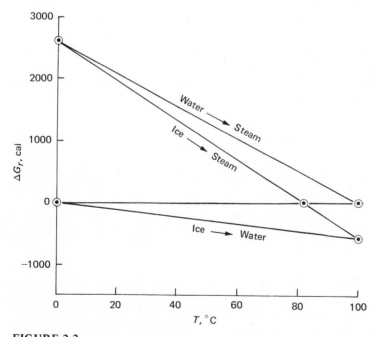

FIGURE 2-2
Variation of ΔG_r with temperature at atmospheric pressure for two-phase transitions in the
H_2O system, given $\Delta S_r^{ice \rightarrow water}$ at 0°C = 5.27 cal mole^{-1} degr^{-1}, $\Delta S_r^{water \rightarrow steam}$ at
100°C = 26.05 cal mole^{-1} degr^{-1} (making use of Eq. (3-7) and assuming that ΔS_r for each
reaction is constant over the interval 0–100°C—an approximation close enough for present
purposes).

phase interaction. Most high-grade metamorphic rock specimens belong to this category. All such unstable equilibria are metastable.

Finally we note that both in nature and in the laboratory, phases or phase assemblages may be metastable from the moment of origin. In all cases, ΔG_r for reactions leading to their appearance must be negative; but kinetic factors of nucleation and growth favor development of the metastable rather than the truly stable system. Because of greater available time, direct crystallization of metastable phases is not quite so common in metamorphic as in igneous systems. On the other hand, laboratory experiments, especially if highly unstable reactive starting materials are employed,* are especially prone to yield metastable products.

Henceforth, discussion of stability and equilibrium in metamorphic minerals and rocks will be limited by the rigorous thermodynamic constraints set out in this section.

Coupled Reactions

Much of the currently available experimental data relating to metamorphic reactions refers to simple transformations such as polymorphic inversions, breakdown and synthesis of pure mineral phases (wollastonite, tremolite, muscovite, phlogopite, and so on), and equilibria involving a few pure phases (e.g., muscovite-quartz-sillimanite-H_2O). Most metamorphic reactions however, involve participation of more numerous phases. They generally involve transformation of one multiphase assemblage into another, with active participation of all phases present (cf. Tilley, 1926). Moreover, since many metamorphic minerals are members of isomorphous series, survival of a phase such as biotite or ilmenite (present in both assemblages) more often than not is accompanied by marked change in its chemical composition.†

The application of experimental data to problems of metamorphic paragenesis is limited by three axiomatic principles.

1. The stability field of any phase assemblage $(A + B)$ must encompass the stability fields of all other assemblages $(A + B + C)$ of which A and B are both members. Thus the temperature-pressure range over which jadeite has been found by experiment to be stable cannot be extended in nature by the presence of additional associated minerals such as lawsonite or glaucophane.

2. There are certain conditions such that the stability field of $(A + B)$ is reduced by introduction of an additional phase C into the system, now $(A + B + C)$. Consider the three equations

$$a.\ A + B \rightarrow D + E \qquad b.\ C + D \rightarrow F + H \qquad c.\ A + B + C \rightarrow E + F + H$$

and let the respective free energy changes involved at some specified P and T be

---

*This practice unfortunately was common in many laboratories during the exploratory period of the 1950s.

†The nature and widespread incidence of such compositional changes in isomorphous series is only now beginning to be appreciated as a result of detailed studies of mineral compositions made possible by modern methods of separation and analysis and especially by use of the electron microprobe analyzer.

ΔG_a, ΔG_b, and ΔG_c. Equation c is the summation of $a + b$ and represents a corresponding *coupled reaction.* Let ΔG_a be positive ($A + B$ stable) and ΔG_b negative ($F + H$ stable). Then $\Delta G_c < \Delta G_a$; there will be a range of temperature, still at pressure P over which ΔG_a is positive and ΔG_c is negative. The stability field of $A + B + C$ is thereby reduced compared with that of $A + B$. The stability field of jadeite, as we shall see later, is reduced by coexisting quartz.

3. In a solid-solution series α–β the stability field of any member is reduced compared with that of one end member α by an amount that increases with molar fraction X_β of the other end member β.

Returning to proposition 2 above, we see that reduction of the temperature range over which $A + B$ is stable at given P is especially marked when the additional phase C is SiO_2; for dissociation of silicates into oxides at high temperature involves—especially if one of the oxides is a fluid phase—large entropy changes ΔS_r. Consider two specific examples.

1. Effect of quartz on the stability of muscovite:

    a. $KAl_2(AlSi_3O_{10})(OH)_2 \rightarrow KAlSi_3O_8 + Al_2O_3 + H_2O$
         muscovite   K-feldspar   corundum   water

    b. $Al_2O_3 + SiO_2 \rightarrow Al_2SiO_5$
       corundum   quartz   andalusite

    c. Muscovite + quartz $\rightarrow$ K-feldspar + andalusite + H_2O

    At $P_{H_2O} = 2$ kb muscovite alone was found to be stable at temperatures less than $670°C$, but in the presence of quartz, the breakdown temperature is lowered to $600°C$ (Evans, 1965).
2. Effect of quartz on the stability of calcite:

    a. $CaCO_3 \rightarrow CaO + CO_2$
       calcite

    b. $CaO + SiO_2 \rightarrow CaSiO_3$
             quartz   wollastonite

    c. Calcite + quartz $\rightarrow$ wollastonite + CO_2

    At atmospheric pressure ($p_{CO_2} = P_f = 1$ bar), the dissociation temperature of calcite is about $870°C$, but calcite and quartz react spontaneously to yield calcite at temperatures greater than about $270°C$ (Turner, 1967).

Phase Rule

A century ago, Willard Gibbs derived from first thermodynamic principles equations such as Eq. (2-7) that, together with expressions designed to eliminate interdependence of chemical components, provide the machinery for quantified descriptions of specific systems in equilibrium. The controlling intensive variables so defined are P, T, and the molar fractions X_i^α, ..., X_q^φ, of all independent chemical components in all coexisting phases. Obviously, there is great potential here (cf. Rumble, 1974) for solving the type of problem that most interests the metamorphic petrologist—to assign specific values to P, T, and pertinent variables relating to gas composition involved in metamorphic paragenesis. Currently, this potential is only imperfectly realized. For most metamorphic systems, data for entropy and molar volume of participating phases (except at room pressure), and especially data relating to chemical potentials in solid-solution series, are still inadequate.

Fortunately, however, from Gibbs's treatment of the problem, there emerged a much simpler, somewhat qualitative, but very useful numerical relation applicable to any system in a state of equilibrium. This has become known as the *phase rule*, and its derivation is a matter of simple algebra:

> For a system of c independent components in φ phases, the number of unknowns—the intensive variables, P and T, together with X_i^α, ..., X_q^φ—totals $(2 + c\varphi)$. Between them are φ relations of the type $\Sigma_i X_i^\alpha = 1$. Equilibrium requires $c(\varphi - 1)$ additional relations (cf. p. 71, Eq. 2-9) of the type $\mu_i^\alpha = \mu_i^\beta$. In all, there are $\varphi + c(\varphi - 1)$ separate relations between $(2 + c\varphi)$ variables. It is necessary to assign arbitrary values to only a minimum number ω of unknowns in order to determine the values of the remainder. This number ω, the *variance of the system*, is given by the number of unknowns less the number of relations between them.

$$\omega = 2 + c\varphi - [\varphi + c(\varphi - 1)]$$

$$\omega = c + 2 - \varphi$$

(2-10)

There is a special case—common in inorganic chemistry, specifically designed in some experiments, and approximated in some simple metamorphic systems—where equilibrium is not complicated by solid solution. Simple inversions and some Ca-Mg silicate equilibria belong to this category. Compositional variables are now eliminated (or negligible), and variance ω cannot exceed two. Components can be counted in the usual way as oxides CaO, MgO, or can simply be identified as the phases themselves. In either case the condition of independence must be satisfied by reducing c by the number of exact stoichiometric relations between components. The variance then is correspondingly reduced below two.

Example 1

$$CaMg(CO_3)_2 + 2SiO_2 \rightleftharpoons CaMgSi_2O_6 + 2CO_2$$

dolomite   quartz   diopside   gas

For the four-phase system dolomite-quartz-diopside-CO_2, the value of c for the four oxide components CaO, MgO, SiO_2, and CO_2 is reduced to three by the requirement that in any phase where either CaO or MgO *occur,* $X_{CaO} = X_{MgO}$. *Alternatively, the three components (CaO, MgO), SiO_2, and CO_2 define the composition of all phases, and again* c = 3. *Alternatively again, let the components be identified as the four coexisting phases; c is again reduced to three by the relation expressed by the above equation. However it is viewed, the system is in univariant equilibrium ($\omega = 1$).*

Example 2

$$2CaMg(CO_3)_2 + SiO_2 \rightleftharpoons 2CaCO_3 + Mg_2SiO_4 + 2CO_2$$
$$\text{dolomite} \qquad \text{quartz} \qquad \text{calcite} \qquad \text{forsterite} \qquad \text{gas}$$

Conventional treatment in terms of the four oxide components gives

$$\omega = 4 + 2 - 5 = 1$$

And again, if the five phases themselves are counted as components, the relation implicit in the above equation reduces c to four, so that again $\omega = 1$.

Example 3

Consider the six-phase assemblage dolomite-calcite-quartz-diopside-forsterite-CO_2. Again, there are four oxide components

$$\omega = 4 + 2 - 6 = 0$$

and the system is invariant. If all six phases are identified as components, the two independent relations given by the above two equations reduce c from six to four, and the solution is the same.

Example 4

Consider the seven-phase assemblage dolomite-calcite-quartz-diopside-forsterite-wollastonite-CO_2. This introduces the additional relation

$$CaCO_3 + SiO_2 \rightleftharpoons CaSiO_3 + CO_2$$

By whatever choice c = 4 and $\omega = 4 + 2 - 7 = -1$. The system is in disequilibrium.

Early in the century, the phase rule was invoked in a rather crude way to explain igneous rocks as equilibrium systems of half a dozen chemical components.[*] But it was not long before trivariant, bivariant, and univariant silicate-melt equilibria experimentally investigated in two- and three-component silicate-melt systems were being rigorously tested and expounded graphically in terms of the phase rule. It is through phase diagrams of this type, used so effectively in the

[*] E.g., T. T. Read, *Econ. Geol.*, vol. 1, pp. 101–118, 1905 (criticized by A. L. Day and E. S. Shepherd, *ibid.*, pp. 286–289, 1906).

Geophysical Laboratory of Washington, that most petrologists first become familiar with implications of the phase rule.

From the outset the compositional evolution of igneous melts and of crystallizing silicates was studied by analogy with simple systems in which ω, c, and φ were all fixed by experimental conditions, and compositional variables of the type $X_{Mg_2SiO_4}^{olivine}$ were evaluated by direct observation. However, by reason of experimental difficulties, this approach was delayed for several decades in the field of metamorphism. But Goldschmidt (1911b) and P. Niggli (1912) already had seen how, even in the absence of precise data, the phase rule might be applied to put constraints upon and to illustrate diagrammatically the treatment of metamorphic rocks as systems in equilibrium. Goldschmidt thought it likely, and most of us would agree today, that any mineral assemblage that is commonly repeated in nature must be stable over a range of both T and P. The variance in such cases must be at least two. For equilibria postulated for the combined assemblages on either side of an isograd, the variance would be reduced by one. So in the absence of any information but the number of phases (essential mineral constituents) and the value of c—usually reduced for convenience of diagramming to three or at the most five—metamorphic rocks were treated qualitatively as bivariant equilibria. The compositional variables X_i^α, etc., were unknown and so perforce were neglected as was the composition of the all important, once present but now inaccessible, gas phase. Compliance with the phase rule could be assumed but never demonstrated unequivocally.

With the advent of experimental techniques for calibrating T and P of solid-gas equilibria at high pressure and new methods of mineral analysis, the situation is completely changed. The phase rule is being applied to metamorphic systems with increasing sophistication. Graphic representations of phase relations and combinations by means of triangular composition diagrams, and by the now-fashionable Schreinemakers "web" on P-T diagrams (introduced by P. Niggli, 1912, p. 67) remain much as they were inherited from the second decade of the century. But quantification of such diagrams marks the main contribution of modern metamorphic geochemistry. The phase rule nevertheless cannot of itself provide numerical solutions to the problem that most concerns us. All it can tell us is the variance of any equilibrium under consideration. Fortunately, this alone provides a partial test of equilibrium. The phase rule moreover narrows the scope of experiment that may be directed profitably toward quantification of metamorphic equilibria; it points up current needs for thermodynamic data, especially in the realm of solid–solution mineralogy; and the validity of the whole field of geothermometry and geobarometry is subject to rigorous compliance with the phase rule.

PROBLEMS RELATED TO REACTION KINETICS

Controls of Metamorphic Reaction Rates

On the basis of free-energy data, thermodynamics can predict whether a reaction is possible. To predict further whether a possible reaction is likely to occur spontaneously under given conditions, we turn to experimental experience on reaction rates interpreted in terms of theory in which the system is viewed on the molecular scale.

Any reaction between minerals involves relative motion and regrouping of ions and atoms. Before this can occur, bonds must be broken and ions must be able to diffuse through intergranular fluids, along grain boundaries, or even through crystal structures, to reach favorable sites where nucleation of new phases is in progress. Obviously, there are energy barriers that must be surmounted before a thermodynamically possible reaction becomes a reality. Moreover, nucleation of new phases plays an important role in reaction. The new nuclei must be able to grow to sufficient size to be truly stable if the reaction is to be effective. Ions must be able to diffuse (through fluid or solid) sufficiently fast for nuclei to develop to stable proportions before they spontaneously break down because of instability inherent in very small size.

In order to treat rigorously the problem of whether the velocity of a possible reaction will be appreciable under given conditions, we need to take account of molecular fluctuations within microscopically homogeneous phases. Essential to reaction is the transient development of particles of high free energy (the *activated complex*) which spontaneously regroup or break down to yield stable nuclei of the newly growing phases of minimal free energy. A full treatment of the problem is beyond the scope of this book, but it is helpful to note some general conclusions drawn from more rigorous discussion elsewhere and verified by experiment (Fyfe, Turner, and Verhoogen, 1958, pp. 53–103; Turner and Verhoogen, 1960, pp. 48–49, 478–484).

A metamorphic reaction involves three interdependent processes: liberation of particles from the structural networks that make up crystals of the initial phases, diffusion of particles to sites where regrouping is possible, and nucleation of the new stable phases at such sites. The rate of a given reaction is the rate of the slowest of these processes.

Reaction rates have been found by experiment to increase exponentially with temperature. A general equation relating the experimentally measured rate K to temperature, and to energy or heat of activation E, is

$$K = Ae^{-E/RT} \tag{2-11}$$

E is a measure of the energy barrier that separates the initial form from the final state. A is a "frequency factor" representing the number of activated particles that enter into reaction in unit time. E may be determined experimentally by measuring K at different temperatures (over a range for which A varies slightly) and plotting $\ln K$ against $1/T$. It is found that K is not greatly affected by pressure. A good deal is known about rates of dehydration reactions (Fyfe et al., 1958, pp. 86–96) and of cation substitution in sheet silicates (e.g., Eberl and Hower, 1976), but because of greater experimental difficulties, information about other solid–solid transformations of special significance in metamorphism is rather meager. Lacy (in Pitcher and Flinn, 1965, p. 146) lists experimentally determined values of activation energy E ranging from 20-30 kcal mole^{-1} for movement of divalent cations, to between 50 and 200 kcal mole^{-1} for reactions involving the breakdown of anionic structures. From Eq. (2-11), the higher the value of E, the more profound will be the effect of temperature on arithmetic change in reaction rates.

Reaction rates increase exponentially with the activation entropy ΔS_r^*. This usually has the same sign as the entropy of reaction ΔS_r.

Rates of diffusion through ionic crystals are extremely slow. They may be significantly accelerated by lattice defects due to strain or impurities and by increase in the total proportion of disorganized surface matter due to small grain size in an aggregate.

Nucleation tends to be slow since a small nucleus, by the very nature of its large ratio surface/volume, is unstable compared with a larger grain. The nucleus, presumably as a result of fluctuations, must reach a critical size before it becomes stable and can survive under given conditions.

Because of high activation energies necessary to disrupt crystal lattices and slow rates of solid diffusion and nucleation, reaction between solids is very slow in the range of metamorphic temperatures and pressures.

Most reactions are accelerated by the presence of water; it must be remembered that in metamorphism an aqueous intergranular film is widely prevalent. The equilibrium temperature T_E must be overstepped to a temperature T at which solution, diffusion, and nucleation are rapid enough for the reaction to proceed spontaneously. The degree of overstepping $\Delta T = (T - T_E)$ increases with temperature but varies inversely with the reaction entropy ΔS_r.

Example 5: The aragonite → calcite inversion

At room temperature and pressures below $3\frac{1}{2}$ kb the stable form of $CaCO_3$ is calcite; in the absence of water aragonite is metastable, the rate of inversion to calcite being imperceptible. However at temperatures around 400°C, aragonite, even in dry air, spontaneously changes to calcite in the course of a few hours or days. The effect of temperature on the rate of inversion can be studied conveniently at atmospheric pressure in the range 380–440°C; and this has been done by W. H. Brown, Fyfe, and Turner (1962).

In any experiment the percentage of calcite formed by inversion is directly proportional to time. So a rate constant

$$k = \frac{dy}{dt}$$

where y is the fraction of calcite formed at time t *(conveniently expressed in hours). The constant k expresses the combined influence of K and A in Eq. (2-11). In Fig. 2-3, y is plotted against* t *for five sets of experiments, each conducted at constant temperature (varying from 380°C to 460°C) in dry air at atmospheric pressure. The slope of each curve defines k for that temperature (Table 2-2).*

From these data a plot of ln k against 1000/T K proves to be rectilinear (Fig. 2-4a), implying that over the limited temperature span

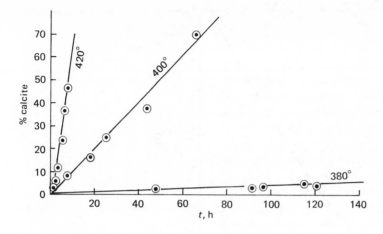

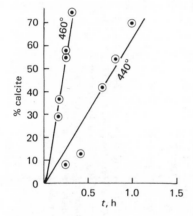

FIGURE 2-3

Aragonite → calcite inversion in dry air at atmospheric pressure. Fraction y of newly formed calcite in time t (hours); temperatures in °C (data from W. H. Brown, W. S. Fyfe, and F. J. Turner, 1962, p. 576).

TABLE 2-2

Experimental Data on Rate of Inversion Aragonite-Calcite in Dry Air at Atmospheric Pressure

Temperature			Inversion rate k: fraction per hour	$\ln k$	Time t for 0.1 inversion (h)	$\ln t$
°C	K	$1000/T$				
460	733	1.364	2.2	0.788	0.045	−3.10
440	713	1.403	0.65	−0.431	0.154	−1.871
420	693	1.443	0.065	−2.733	1.54	0.432
400	673	1.486	0.01	−4.605	10	2.303
380	653	1.531	0.00043	−7.751	234	5.46

From W. H. Brown, Fyfe, and Turner, 1962, p. 576.

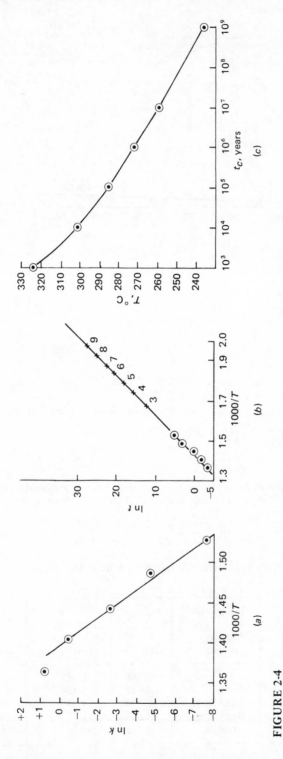

FIGURE 2-4

Aragonite → calcite inversion; rates in dry air at atmospheric pressure (data from Fig. 2-3 and Table 2-2): (*a*) graphic determination of activation energy *E* (see text); (*b*) time *t* (hours) for 0.1 inversion as an exponential inverse function of temperature *T* (K). Circled dots from experimental data; crosses computed for 10^3–10^9 years are numbered accordingly; (*c*) time t_c (years) for complete inversion as an inverse function of temperature (°C); computed from curve *b*.

involved, A *in Eq. (2-11) remains essentially constant. The slope of the ln* k *curve defines the activation energy* E *of inversion. Thus from Eq. (2-11),*

$$-\frac{E}{RT} = ln\ k$$

and

$$E = \frac{-1000R\ ln\ k}{(1000/T)^*}$$

where the denominator is (1000/T) minus the value 1.39 at which ln k *is zero. The value of* E *obtained from Fig. 2-3a is 110 kcal mole^{-1}. The ln* k *curve extrapolates to 79 at 1000/T = 0. Here Eq. (2-11) reduces to ln* A = ln K = 79−A *having the dimensions of rate on the same scale as* K.

The time required for some given degree of inversion decreases exponentially with increasing temperature, as illustrated in Fig. 2-4b and c. Times for complete elimination of dry aragonite are 10^9 years at 235°C, 10^6 years at about 270°C, and 10^3 years at 325°C. At 400°C, dry aragonite could not survive 100 years in the pressure field of calcite stability (below 8 kb, curve 2, Fig. 4-13). These times are greatly reduced by the presence of water, which lowers the value of E *by a factor of 4 (cf. W. H. Brown et al., 1962, Fig. 4b). Even at 50°C, aragonite would still be eliminated completely in about 10^6 years in accordance with the well-known rarity of aragonite in cements of ancient rocks.*

Metastable Metamorphic Minerals

From time to time the question has been raised as to whether common metamorphic minerals, especially the index minerals of metamorphic zones and subfacies, ever crystallize as metastable phases or persist metastably from an earlier stage and so survive as constituents of the later and principal stage of metamorphism. If this were indeed so, our treatment of standard metamorphic assemblages as equilibria would be seriously at fault.

We have seen that solid ⇌ solid reactions among anhydrous silicates are usually accompanied by only slight changes in entropy and free energy. This fact has been referred to (Fyfe, Turner, and Verhoogen, 1958, p. 22) as "the plague of small ΔG's" in metamorphic reactions. Simple instances are certain first-order polymorphous transitions such as andalusite ⇌ sillimanite ⇌ kyanite, anthophyllite ⇌ cummingtonite, and calcite ⇌ aragonite. So the possibility arises that, in some spontaneous reactions, other factors than minimization of free energy may determine which of two polymorphs crystallizes. Chemists have long recognized a principle known as Ostwald's step rule, which states that there is a tendency for preference of that reaction that involves minimum ΔS_r rather than minimum G. Such is the crystallization of cristobalite from silica glass within the temperature range over which α-quartz is the truly stable phase. Again, adularia, crystallizing in low-temperature veins, usually has the structure of sanidine, the high-temperature polymorph of $KAlSi_3O_8$. The coexistence of andalusite, sillimanite, and kyanite in some pelitic schists, and perhaps the association of cummingtonite and antho-phyllite in magnesian hornfelses, possibly reflects the metastable condition of one or more of the phases concerned. It is not unlikely, then, that kyanite, sillimanite, or andalusite may be a metastable member of the metamorphic assemblage even when occurring alone. The well-known tendency for sillimanite to replace mica suggests that crystallization of this particular phase, rather than andalusite or kyanite, conceivably may be due in some instances to a smaller value of ΔS_r in the breakdown of mica to sillimanite as contrasted with andalusite or kyanite. Silli-manite could then be metastable from the moment of its formation.

Crystallization of metastable phases is indeed likely in the earliest stages of metamorphism, represented by the zeolite facies and by rocks of the chlorite zone. Here, low temperatures slow down metamorphic reaction rates. At temperatures of perhaps $200-300°C$, a parent aggregate of clay minerals, feldspar, and quartz in a mudstone is highly unstable. The respective values of ΔG_r for a number of possible metamorphic reactions are all correspondingly high. When the tempera-ture rises to a point where reaction velocities become appreciable, the nature of the product is likely to depend upon such factors as minimal change in entropy or favorable conditions of nucleation, rather than attainment of minimal possible free energy. Moreover, even within an isochemical rock series, the temperature and products of reaction will depend partly upon the mineralogical nature of the parent material, especially the nature of the clay minerals (cf. Yoder, 1955, p. 513). On these grounds one might expect considerable mineralogical variation among the zeolites, chlorites, micas, etc. that appear in the earlier stages of meta-morphism. Some such variety is indeed encountered. But, perhaps surprisingly, there is a remarkable degree of uniformity among the reaction products: the common zeolites are analcite, heulandite, and laumontite; the mica is phengitic muscovite; and the chlorite is at first celadonite, later a prochlorite.

Other questions relating to metastability may be raised. One concerns the possible survival of metastable phases from early episodes of metamorphism. For example, in eastern Otago, New Zealand, the common metamorphic assem-blage in derivatives of graywacke is quartz-albite-chlorite-muscovite-epidote. But there are local areas in which the same minerals are accompanied by biotite and almandine garnet (Brown, 1963, p. 858). Is one or both of these a metastable survival from an earlier episode of crystallization at relatively high temperature? Or are they comembers, along with quartz, albite, chlorite, and muscovite, of an equilibrium assemblage? Progressive chloritization of garnet and biotite in poly-metamorphic rocks elsewhere may supply an answer, testifying to the metastable status of the partly destroyed phases. In the Otago rocks, there is no such un-equivocal textural evidence, and garnet and biotite therefore are assumed to be members of an equilibrium assemblage that also included albite, chlorite, and muscovite as constituent phases. It is emphasized that evidence of internal dis-equilibrium in metamorphic rocks is largely textural. Consequently, our basic assumption that most common metamorphic mineral assemblages represent once-stable equilibria rests heavily on the general data of classic petrography.

Significance of Isograds in Prograde Metamorphism

Concept of Metamorphic Grade

When Tilley (1924b, pp. 168-169) introduced the concept of *metamorphic grade* or degree of metamorphism, he assigned a joint controlling role to temperature and pressure. However, the tendency today is to equate grade rather loosely with temperature and to treat isograds essentially as isotherms. For example, calcite-diopside-forsterite is generally considered to represent a higher grade of metamorphism than calcite-diopside-tremolite, the inference being that the former assemblage necessarily crystallized at a higher temperature than the latter. This may be true in some situations, especially where, as in some aureoles, it is likely that both assemblages crystallized under similar conditions of pressure at constant $X_{CO_2}^{gas}$. But where we are comparing rocks formed under different pressure regimes—the general situation—implications as to comparative temperature are equivocal. The high-grade assemblage may have crystallized at the lower temperature if f_{CO_2} were also lower. A further anomaly arises where two sets of isograds mapped on different interbedded lithologies have been found to intersect (D. M. Carmichael, 1970). Clearly grade cannot here be controlled by temperature alone (cf. P. H. Thomson, 1970).

To remove such anomalies, we now define grade in terms of the sign of entropy change of metamorphic reactions concerned. Increasing grade involves an increase in entropy of the metamorphic system (including, of course, the postulated gas phase). Seen in this light, the calcite-diopside-forsterite assemblage does indeed represent a higher grade than calcite-diopside-tremolite; for the left-to-right reaction equating the two assemblages

$$3Ca_2Mg_5Si_8O_{22}(OH)_2 + 5CaCO_3 \rightarrow 11CaMgSi_2O_6$$
$$\text{tremolite} \qquad\qquad \text{calcite} \qquad\qquad \text{diopside}$$

$$+ 2Mg_2SiO_4 + 3H_2O + 5CO_2$$
$$\text{forsterite} \qquad \text{gas}$$

has a large positive ΔS_r.

Problem of Possible Kinetic Influences

Most isograds are drawn in the field where some index mineral first appears, in the prograde sense, in rocks of uniform composition. Biotite, almandine, and staurolite, in that order, are familiar examples in pelitic schists. At other isograds, an index mineral prevalent in lower-grade zones disappears. Such are pumpellyite and stilpnomelane in low-grade metagraywackes, staurolite in pelites at a higher grade. From the first, the inferred chemical transformations have been expressed by chemical equations—at one time necessarily simplified, today taking into account all the main chemical components of the two equivalent mineral assemblages. The next step (see Chap. 3) is to assign *P-T* values to such equations treated as equilibria (usually univariant in terms of P and T). Since this approach lies at the heart of much current investigation in metamorphic petrology and geochemistry, its validity deserves critical appraisal. The fundamental question involved must have occurred to every petrographer who has mapped an isograd. Is regional metamorphism truly progressive? Is the critical mineral assemblage of each zone the end product of a chronological sequence of steps corresponding to the series of isochemical assemblages displayed, in order of increasing grade, in preceding metamorphic zones? The orthodox answer is in the affirmative: as in so many geologic situations we believe it valid to extrapolate into time what is preserved for observation in space. But this view has been repeatedly challenged on the basis of experimental anomalies (Yoder, 1955, pp. 620-623) and on grounds of petrographic experience (e.g., Atherton, in Pitcher and Flinn, 1965, pp. 169-202; Chakraborty and Sen, 1967, pp. 222-223); and the challenge deserves serious attention. If substantiated it would raise the possibility that isograd reactions, proceeding from highly unstable starting materials, might be controlled as much by kinetics as by thermodynamic constraints on equilibrium. Certainly this possibility cannot be discounted with respect to successive important reactions that lead gradually to elimination of the parent mineral assemblage (e.g., plagioclase-pyroxene-ilmenite in basalt) in the earlier stages of metamorphism.

Kinetic Implications of Experimental Synthesis

During the 1950s, experiments designed to calibrate directly the temperature-pressure fields of simple metamorphic phase assemblages customarily employed as starting materials highly unstable mixtures of oxides, glasses, and even organic metallic salts. Not surprisingly, many of the results obtained were obviously anomalous. Some products were metastable from the outset. In other cases chemically similar mixtures would yield a variety of products over much the same narrow interval of temperature and pressure. Such anomalies caused Yoder (1952) to suggest that initial water content rather than temperature and pressure is responsible for critical phase assemblages diagnostic of facies, and that some at least of the classic isograds are determined by kinetics of reaction and crystal growth. The importance of water fugacity (whether internally or externally controlled) as one of the definitive parameters of the "petrogenic grid" soon became generally realized (e.g., J. B. Thompson, 1955; Yoder, 1955). But the role of reaction kinetics as an explanation of experimental anomalies must surely be reversed: with a single possible exception, it is not in nature but in the laboratory—where available time is necessarily short—that rates of nucleation and growth determine the nature of the product.

The exception concerns metamorphism at the lowest grades. Here the initial materials—e.g., clay sediments or basaltic lavas—were highly unstable at the outset, and reaction kinetics could have affected the nature of the first metamorphic products and fixed the outer field limit of recognizable metamorphism. With this in mind it would be unwise to assign any fixed temperature (at given pressure) for initiation of metamorphism at what Yoder (1955, p. 513) termed the "chlorite isograd."

Kinetic Implications of Rock Textures

The key to the nature and paths of metamorphic reactions lies, however, not in experiment but in the textures of rocks close to isograds. Evidence of simple prograde reactions involving pairs of chemically similar phases—e.g., chlorite →

garnet; chloritoid → staurolite; diopside → tremolite; or kyanite → sillimanite–is not unknown (e.g., Tilley, 1925b, p. 318; 1926, p. 43; Harker, 1932, pp. 192, 193; Trommsdorff and Evans, 1974, p. 337); but in most rocks of medium and high grade it is strikingly lacking. This generalization is the basis of the repeatedly expressed inference that isograds do not represent direct transformation of a lower-grade to the adjoining higher-grade isochemical mineral assemblage. The evidence cited is entirely negative. The underlying fallacy in the argument seems to be an oversimplification of the nature of metamorphic reactions and a failure to appreciate flexibility in the paths by which they are achieved.

In metamorphism, textural and mineralogical evolution must proceed hand in hand. Processes of ionic diffusion, nucleation, and crystal growth that shaped the texture are responsible too for contemporaneous transformation of the lower- to higher-grade mineral assemblage. Development of segregation laminae controlled by mechanically induced foliation, growth of porphyroblasts, segregation of minerals in "pressure shadows," and general coarsening of grain size with rising grade all testify to the universal role of ionic diffusion on a microscopic scale. The overall gross chemical composition on the scale of a hand specimen may, and apparently usually does, remain unchanged. But on the microscopic scale metasomatism must be ubiquitous. A large porphyroblast of garnet or staurolite must be a product of metasomatism of preexisting material of different composition at the same site. It is small wonder that direct prograde pseudomorphism of a high-grade phase is a rare phenomenon.

A realistic and sophisticated approach to the problem of the path of progressive metamorphism is that of D. M. Carmichael (1969). He used the evidence of existing textures in pelitic schists to frame possible models of chemical reaction paths consistent with well-substantiated chemical concepts of large-scale metasomatism developed by students of ore genesis (e.g., Meyer and Hemley, 1967). Mineral transformations are envisaged as a series of complementary "metasomatic cation-exchange reactions which proceed in different microscopic domains of the rock but which add up on the scale of the whole thin section to give the balanced metamorphic reaction." Basic to Carmichael's reaction models is the assumption, based on geological and experimental experience, that aluminum is relatively immobile (cf. Morey, 1957; Fyfe et al., 1958, p. 79; Meyer and Hemley, 1967, p. 210). Exchange of other cations is effected via an intergranular aqueous phase; and water, as well as H^+ ions, is an important participant. Here are two examples both based on observed textural relations between phases in rocks close to individual isograds.

The simplest case is development of sillimanite and elimination of kyanite at the first sillimanite isograd (where muscovite plus quartz is still stable). Muscovite in one microdomain becomes converted to sillimanite-quartz, absorbing H^+ ions and releasing K^+ ions and H_2O in the process.

$$2KAl_2(AlSi_3O_{10})(OH)_2 + 2H^+ \rightarrow 3Al_2SiO_5 + 3SiO_2 + 2K^+ + 3H_2O$$
$$\text{muscovite} \qquad\qquad\qquad \text{sillimanite} \quad \text{quartz}$$

At a nearby site a reverse reaction occurs: kyanite is eliminated in favor of a growing porphyroblast of muscovite, releasing H^+ ions to and utilizing H_2O and K^+ ions from the first site. Textural evidence is seen in newly developed quartz grains crowded with needles of sillimanite (fibrolite) and nearby, but typically not contiguous, large muscovites enclosing kyanite relics. The only thermodynamic constraint on the exchange reaction is that ΔG_r be negative for the reaction kyanite $\rightarrow$ sillimanite.

At another stage of metamorphism, staurolite becomes eliminated, with a complementary influx of sillimanite (in other provinces, kyanite) and garnet. The corresponding reaction defining a sillimanite-garnet isograd can be written

$$9(Mg,Fe)Al_4Si_2O_{10}(OH)_2 \ + \ KAl_2(AlSi_3O_{10})(OH)_2 \ + \ 5SiO_2$$

staurolite   muscovite   quartz

$$\rightarrow 17Al_2SiO_5 \ + \ 2(Fe,Mg)_3Al_2Si_3O_{12}$$

sillimanite   garnet

$$+ \ K(Mg,Fe)_3(AlSi_3O_{10})(OH)_2 \ + \ 9H_2O$$

biotite

Carmichael has proposed a complex model consistent with the mineralogy and textures of several kinds of microscopic domains:

1. Staurolite and quartz become replaced by biotite and oligoclase.
2. Oligoclase is locally eliminated in favor of sillimanite, biotite, and quartz.
3. Oligoclase and biotite elsewhere become replaced by garnet.
4. Biotite, muscovite, and quartz become replaced by oligoclase.

Metasomatism in each type of domain involves exchange of cations (H^+, K^+, Na^+, Mg^{2+}, Fe^{2+}) with the other three. Water also participates in the exchange process and in part diffuses out of the total system. The net result, after elimination of staurolite, is a six-phase assemblage—quartz-oligoclase-muscovite-biotite-garnet-sillimanite. The last three collectively define the higher grade zone; all but sillimanite occur in staurolite-bearing assemblages on the low-grade side of the isograd.

No cation-exchange reaction model can be unique. However, Carmichael has shown that plausible reactions of this kind are consistent with familiar textural patterns; to explain this consistency otherwise one must invoke chronologic sequences of crystal growth and relatively large-scale metasomatism for which there is no direct evidence. In so doing, Carmichael has demolished the argument, based on absence of intuitively expected textures of another kind, against the strictly progressive character of prograde regional metamorphism. The way is now open to set up other models for other metamorphic situations that need not, perhaps, involve relative immobility of aluminum. One such is progressive development of alternating quartz-albite and chlorite-epidote-actinolite-sphene laminae in meta-graywackes at the isograd separating the pumpellyite-actinolite from the chlorite zone proper in southern New Zealand (Turner, 1941).

If we are correct in assuming that partition of elements common to coexisting metamorphic phases obeys the constraints of the phase rule, cation exchange in metamorphic reactions is inescapable. But it would seem that exchange of ions goes on at an even more pervasive level. Partition of oxygen isotopes ^{16}O and ^{18}O between phases such as quartz and muscovite strongly suggests equilibration at the maximum temperature locally attained. Herein is the basis of one of our most widely used geothermometers. Implicit in this generalization is high local mobility of oxygen ions and the fact that 90% of the volume of any common rock is occupied by oxygen atoms.

Finally, the role of reaction kinetics in prograde regional metamorphism must be severely limited by long duration of the metamorphic cycle. We have seen that in the innermost zone of a contact aureole temperatures may perhaps rise so rapidly that low-grade reactions might be bypassed (cf. p. 22). However, thermal evolution must surely follow a very different regime where accelerated heat flow from the depths induces a cycle of regional metamorphism. Because of the low conductance of common rocks, a rise in temperature in any zone must be a long-protracted process. This view finds general support in chronologic studies of regional metamorphism of repeatedly folded terranes.

Collectively viewed, the textural evidence of petrography rules out the possibility that isograds are significantly influenced by reaction kinetics. The proposition that regional metamorphism is a strictly progressive phenomenon remains unchallenged and is consistent with inferences regarding reaction paths that may legitimately be drawn from rock texture.

Survival of High-Grade Metamorphic Phase Assemblages

The Problem

During unloading by erosion, any medium- or high-grade mineral assemblage that has crystallized in the depths passes continuously through a regime of decreasing temperature and pressure. Yet such rocks typically show little or no sign of response to lower temperatures and pressures that elsewhere have given rise to the familiar products of prograde metamorphism in the zones of chlorite and biotite. Survival of metamorphic assemblages is an indisputable fact, but it seems paradoxical and so is scientifically intriguing. The same problem is raised by survival of igneous mineral assemblages during unroofing of a pluton. Why does the assemblage plagioclase-pyroxene-olivine in gabbro survive postconsolidational cooling from 800°C, when it can be converted by regional metamorphism at perhaps 300–400°C to the low-grade assemblage albite-epidote-chlorite-actinolite-sphene?

At the root of the problem must be fundamental differences in rates of reaction, paths of temperature-pressure change, and availability of fluids (water especially) during the postmetamorphic cooling phase as contrasted with the heating phase of the metamorphic cycle.

Kinetics of Prograde-versus-Retrograde Reactions

Becke (1903, p. 34) long ago suggested that reaction rates are faster with rising than with falling temperature over the same interval, and this view found general intuitive acceptance (e.g., Harker, 1932, p. 11; Eskola, 1939, p. 318; Turner, 1948, p. 301). In fact, it is virtually implicit in our general interpretation of high-grade mineral assemblages as records of maximum temperatures attained in any meta-morphic episode. There is abundant supporting evidence drawn from experimental experience, and some theoretical justification too (Fyfe et al., 1958, pp. 97–98), for a generalization to the effect that the rate of a given transformation $A \rightleftharpoons B$ is faster in the sense of increasing reaction entropy (ΔS_r positive). For example, ice cannot be superheated above $0°C$, though liquid water can be significantly undercooled below $0°C$. Homogenization of perthite and inversion of microcline to sanidine are readily accomplished in a matter of hours or days above 800–1000°C, but the reverse transformations involving ordering of structure (ΔS_r negative) cannot be induced in experiments of ordinary duration.

The difference between forward (prograde) and corresponding backward (retrograde) reaction rates is most pronounced when the degree of "overstep-ping" of the temperature of actual reaction T_r beyond the true equilibrium tem-perature T_E is significant—a condition favored by low values of ΔS_r. Most solid $\rightleftharpoons$ solid transformations are in this category; this helps to explain survival of high-temperatue polymorphs such as sillimanite. Most prograde reactions, however, involve expulsion of H_2O or CO_2. For these, ΔS_r is high, and overstepping tends correspondingly to be reduced. Nevertheless, even here backward reaction may be significantly slowed. For example, Harker and Tuttle (1955) found that while dolomite readily decomposes to periclase-calcite-CO_2 on heating to 800°C at $P_{CO_2} = 2$ kb, cooling to lower temperatures fails to induce a reversal of the reac-tion in experiments of a few hours' duration.

Temperature-Pressure Regime
of Postmetamorphic Unloading

Thermal conductivities of silicate rocks are low: at temperatures up to 300°C, about $5-7 \times 10^{-3}$ cal cm^{-1} s^{-1} degr^{-1} for most plutonic rocks, twice as much for quartzite (Clark, 1966).[*] Consequently, if premetamorphic burial or postmeta-morphic unloading is rapid, there must be a significant time lag in adjustment of temperature toward any regional geothermal gradient that can be recognized. The metamorphic P-T gradients that develop during loading and unloading will neces-sarily be transient to a degree that depends on the rates of tectonic processes con-cerned. Complete smoothing out to a steady-state gradient implies a lengthy period of static conditions at maximum pressure before unloading begins. Such a con-dition probably was approximated during metamorphism in Barrow's classic zones, but blueschist metamorphism appears to be characteristic of transient conditions of low temperature and high pressure inconsistent with any plausible steady-state model.

In most cases, the respective P-T paths of loading and unloading must be considerably different, as illustrated by a hypothetical example in Fig. 2-5. And this as we shall now see could have a significant bearing on the problem of prograde-versus-retrograde reaction rates. Most curves of univariant equilibrium on which isograds are based have a positive slope dT/dP (or in terms of depth D, dT/dD): Values for solid $\rightleftharpoons$ solid inversions may be high; for kyanite $\rightleftharpoons$ sillimanite,

---

[*]Values for good conductors range from 60 to 90×10^{-3} cal for sulfides to between 150 and 900×10^{-3} cal for metals.

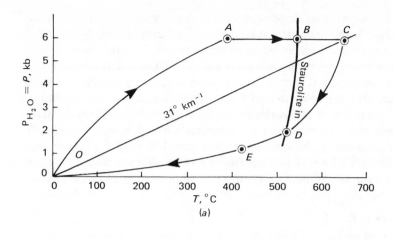

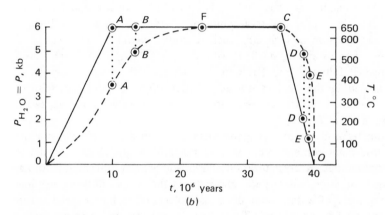

FIGURE 2-5

Diagrams to illustrate a single hypothetical case (see text) of the possible relations between pressure, temperature, and time in some local domain during a complete tectonic-metamorphic cycle. Postulated regional uniform geothermal gradient, $31°$ km^{-1}. (*a*) *P-T* paths during loading ($O \rightarrow A$), static constant-pressure conditions ($A \rightarrow C$), and unloading ($C \rightarrow D \rightarrow O$). Univariant curve for crystallization of staurolite at the expense of chloritoid (at staurolite isograd), *BD* (see also Fig. 4-4). (*b*) Paths of *P* (full line *OACO*) and *T* (dashed line) in relation to time. Dotted vertical lines connect synchronous *P* and *T* values corresponding to similarly lettered points in diagram (*a*). *FC* represents a period of uniform steady-state heat flow at the culmination of metamorphism. (Note: Radiometric dating based on *K-A* or *Rb–Sr* measurements would yield values on the cooling curve close to 40×10^6 m.y.)

for example, about $50°$ kb^{-1} or $15°$ km^{-1} (cf. Fig. 4-2); those for dehydration reactions at moderate pressures much lower ($10°$ kb$^{-1} = 3°$ km^{-1}). So the temperature at which an equilibrium curve is cut by the cooling path may be significantly lower than that of intersection with the path of previous heating. For the staurolite curve in Fig. 2-5*a*, the difference is only $30°$, but even this degree of lowering could perhaps reduce the rate of backward reaction by an order of magnitude.[*]

[*]By analogy with rates of the aragonite → calcite inversion (Fig. 2-3).

Figure 2-5 represents a single hypothetical, much simplified situation: Loading by combined burial and tectonic influences proceeds uniformly for 10×10^6 years (along $0 \to A$) and is succeeded by a lengthy period, 25×10^6 years, of static load $(A \to C)$, followed by rapid unloading (along $C \to 0$) at a uniform rate (uplift at 4 mm per year) over the final 5×10^6 years of a tectonic cycle occupying 40×10^6 years. The staurolite isograd is cut by the heating and cooling paths at B and D, $30°$ apart. The time available for staurolite to crystallize (B to D) is about 25×10^6 years; and during most of it temperatures would be between $50-100°$ above that of equilibrium. By contrast it takes only 10^6 years for temperatures on the cooling path (D to E) to drop $100°$ below equilibrium temperature; and long before this the rate of backward reaction would be reduced to zero effectiveness [cf. Eq. (2-11)].

Role of Water and CO_2

Progressive metamorphism of sediments involves continuous expulsion of water[*] and/or CO_2. An aqueous gas phase indeed figures as a principal product of most reactions that have been proposed to account for isograds in regions of pelitic and semipelitic rocks. Because of high ΔS_r, such reactions should be relatively rapid and the degree of overstepping small. If we accept D. M. Carmichael's models of cation exchange, it follows, too, that water accelerates and indeed is essential to reactions expressed in the field as isograds. Participation of water should tend, then, to minimize the contrast between respective rates of forward and backward reactions at given P and T.

The ultimate products of high-grade metamorphism are coarsely crystalline rocks with a low water content: quartzofeldspathic schists, granulites, calc-silicate rocks, and amphibolites. Recrystallization and crystal growth outlasting deformation have sealed the intergranular pores and reduced the permeability to very low values. In the absence of water, the mineral assemblages of such rocks tend to survive subsequent cooling unchanged. There may be microscopic evidence of incipient changes along grain boundaries, e.g., growth of amphibole by hydration of pyroxene or the partial serpentinization of forsterite. Probably more general are exsolution in pyroxenes and feldspars, partial oxidation of titaniferous magnetite, and microscopically invisible marginal redistribution of cations resulting from diffusion across grain boundaries, e.g., zonal variation in ratios Fe/Mg/Mn revealed in crystals of garnet and iron ores by the electron microprobe. Coronas of hypersthene around olivine grains and of garnet, pyroxene, and spinel around iron ores in metamorphosed gabbro and anorthosite are similarly interpreted as products of incomplete reaction between dry mineral grains. Here, however, the high-temperature parent assemblages are igneous.

Summary

Postmetamorphic survival of high-grade mineral assemblages undoubtedly is the rule rather than the exception. And this fact strengthens rather than weakens the

---

[*]Flow of water during progressive metamorphism is the main topic of an early essay by Yoder (1955) in which, however, he was inclined (contrary to this writer's view) to stress quantity of available water and reaction kinetics as factors contributing to the isograd pattern.

concept of such assemblages as high-temperature equilibria, "frozen in" against destruction during unloading, and cooling to surface conditions. The explanation lies in a number of influences all tending to retard or prevent retrograde reactions. First and foremost is absence or difficulty of access of essential pore fluids (especially water) in rocks already rendered impermeable by the metamorphic crystallization process. Other factors concern reaction kinetics: the known and thermodynamically predictable contrast between faster prograde and slower retrograde reactions at constant temperature; temperature differences between the respective intercepts of heating and cooling paths on a given univariant curve effective especially when the dT/dP gradient of the latter is high (as in the kyanite $\rightleftharpoons$ sillimanite inversion); and the brief duration of the cooling interval covering temperatures below a univariant curve but still high enough to permit effective backward reaction.

Postmetamorphic Survival of Low-Grade Phase Assemblages

Glaucophane schists and their associates are now known to be products of metamorphism at temperatures of perhaps 250-350°C and very high pressures (6 to possibly 12 kb). Their most characteristic mineral constituents include dense low-entropy phases such as aragonite, lawsonite, and the pair quartz-jadeite. Reduction of pressure during unloading (cf. Fig. 4-13) will bring such rocks into the stability fields of phases with *higher* entropy so that spontaneous reaction would be in the prograde sense:

Aragonite $\rightarrow$ calcite

Jadeite + quartz $\rightarrow$ albite

Where such reactions fail to materialize, as commonly is the case, survival of the high-pressure phases can be attributed only to low temperature,[*] aided perhaps by limited available time during rapid unloading.

To accept the above explanation is to pose a kinetic problem in reverse. How in the first place could metamorphism bring about crystallization of aragonite and jadeite-quartz, when subsequently, at much the same temperatures, these phases survived destruction by potential reactions in the forward sense? The key to the problem lies in the nature of the initial materials—clay assemblages in shales, plagioclase-quartz-clay in graywackes, plagioclase-pyroxene in basalts—all in the presence of pore fluids rich in H_2O and/or CO_2. We can visualize reactions such as

Plagioclase + H_2O $\rightarrow$ jadeite + quartz + lawsonite

or

Plagioclase + H_2O + CO_2 $\rightarrow$ albite + pumpellyite + quartz + aragonite

These would all involve large negative changes in free energy—sufficient it would

[*]As experimentally demonstrated for aragonite (cf. Fig. 2-4c).

seem to render reaction effective. No doubt an additional catalytic influence is provided by synchronous deformation. A characteristic textural feature of quartz-jadeite metagraywackes in California is ubiquitous shear foliation (Bloxam, 1956, p. 489).

Reactions of Hydration and Carbonation

General Conditions

Many igneous and high-grade metamorphic rocks are essentially anhydrous silicate assemblages: e.g., plagioclase-pyroxene-olivine in basalt and diabase, plagioclase-hypersthene-diopside-garnet, and quartz-feldspar-garnet-sillimanite in granulites. Continuous penetrative permeation of such rocks by externally supplied water or CO_2 at temperatures in the low and medium range of metamorphism can convert them, completely or in part, to metamorphic assemblages that include hydrous silicates and carbonates. Where this occurs on a regional scale, it has usually been aided or even instigated by shear failure or hydraulic fracturing under high shear stress. Typically, the end products are schistose and lineated rocks, in some cases localized in shear zones cutting or enclosing bodies of nonschistose unaltered parent material.

Low-Grade Metamorphism of Igneous Rocks

Particularly vulnerable are ash beds, basic flows and sills, and peridotite lenses enclosed in pelitic and simpelitic geosynclinal sediments. Partial dehydration of such sediments (and in some cases decarbonation) affords the necessary continuous supply of water (and/or CO_2) by which basic rocks become converted to familiar greenschist assemblages and peridotites to antigorite and talc-tremolite-carbonate schists.

Low-grade metamorphism of igneous rocks has the thermodynamic character (ΔS_r negative) of a retrograde reaction. Under premetamorphic conditions, the temperature from the first is far below the equilibrium value for hydration so that ΔG_r (negative) for the potential reaction is correspondingly high. As temperature increases, the magnitude of ΔG_r—the driving force of reaction—decreases. But this tendency is eventually outweighed by exponentially increasing reaction rates until, at perhaps 200–300°C, reaction becomes effective, and metamorphism sets in. The kinetic factor being crucial to the process, the catalytic potential of strain induced by shear stress is obvious. Another condition that aids reaction as a self-perpetuating process is the heat generated by the mineralogic transformations themselves; both hydration and carbonation are strongly exothermic processes.

Once a low-grade assemblage becomes established, a further rise in temperature induces a succession of prograde reactions, involving the expulsion of water and CO_2, that lead to rocks such as amphibolites and ultimately to granulite assemblages. Many basic granulites have been through just such a cycle, ultimately returning (through a hydrated stage) to anhydrous assemblages having much in common with the initial igneous material.

Retrograde Metamorphism

In some situations, a high-grade metamorphic rock either fails to survive post-metamorphic cooling or is remetamorphosed at lower temperature in some later metamorphic episode. In either case, since the product is an assemblage of lower metamorphic grade, the process is called *retrograde* (retrogressive) *metamorphism* or *diaphthoresis* (Becke, 1909; E. B. Knopf, 1931; Harker, 1932, pp. 342-356). The process can be traced in all stages, from incipient to complete. Where far advanced, retrograde metamorphism can be recognized only by the persistence of undestroyed relic high-grade mineral grains (e.g., of garnet and staurolite in phyllonite) or of enclosed bodies of unaltered parent rock, or again by regional transition between high-grade rocks and their retrograde derivatives. So arises the possibility that some low-grade intensely foliated schists may in reality be products of retrograde metamorphism that has eliminated all traces of a previous high-grade metamorphic condition (cf. Wycoff, 1952, p. 25).

Becke and Knopf attached great importance to the role of synchronous deformation in retrograde metamorphism, with reference especially to phyllonite formations in the Alps and New England. "If adjustment to the new pressure-temperature field is to take place, the instigating force or trigger of the reaction must be furnished by a strong differential movement of the constituent parts before or together with diaphthoresis" (E. B. Knopf, 1931, p. 7). Later writers (e.g., Schwartz and Todd, 1941) emphasized the role of water and CO_2. Both are essential to extensive development of retrograde phyllonites and schists.

High-grade Precambrian granulites in many parts of the world show regional transition into amphibolites of lower grade. Radiometric dating in some instances indicates that metamorphism at all grades was synchronous, the mineralogical differences being due to gradients in temperature or in some other condition such as p_{H_2O} in the pore fluid—as in southern Norway where fluid inclusions in amphibolites are rich in water, those in contemporary granulites in CO_2 (Touret, 1971). Elsewhere the transition is due to localized overprinting of a late retrograde metamorphism upon high-grade assemblages developed in some earlier episode.

A classic example of this second pattern is afforded by the Lewisian gneisses of northwestern Scotland. On the basis of field, structural, and petrographic evidence, Sutton and Watson (1951) recognized the individual imprints of two major Precambrian metamorphic episodes separated by a "great interval of time." These two episodes "produced in two separate periods of metamorphism, migmatization and deformation" they named Scourian and Laxfordian, respectively—and so they were long referred to in Scottish literature (cf. Craig, 1965, pp. 69-75). The time interval has since been shown to be long indeed (Park, 1970; Moorbath and Park, 1971): culmination of the first episode has been dated at 2900-2600 million years ago,[*] the second at 2200 million years. To resolve nomenclatural difficulties arising from confusion between chronologic spans and specific episodes occurring within them, the first metamorphic episode is now generally termed Badcallian, the second Invernian (Park, 1970). But such semantic niceties and bickering that arises from them (e.g., discussion in Evans and Lambert, 1974, pp. 149-150) in no way detract from the originality and value of the initial contribution based purely on classic observation and reasoning. Large tracts of the Lewisian, one in the type Scourie area (Fig. 2-6), consist of high-grade rocks ranging from

---

[*]The earlier date given by Pb data, the later (a cooling date) by K-Ar and RbSr data.

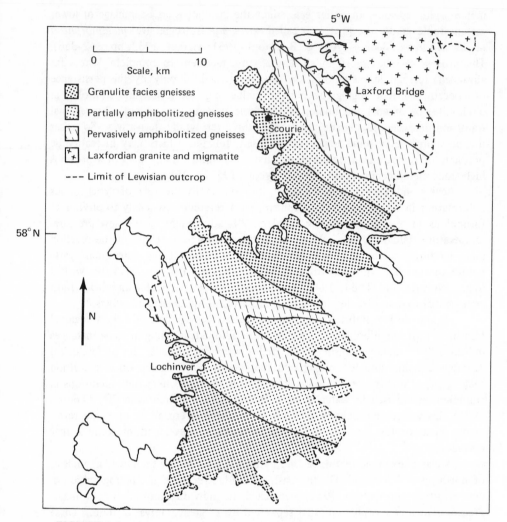

FIGURE 2-6
Distribution of rocks showing respective imprints of Scourian and Laxfordian metamorphism, northwestern coast of Scotland (after A. Beach).

siliceous to basic, even to ultramafic granulites. They are products of the earlier episode: assemblages of plagioclase, clinopyroxene, orthopyroxene, and garnet (with quartz in siliceous and olivine in ultramafic rocks). Elsewhere over areas of 100 km² or more, as well as in narrow zones of late deformation, the early mineralogical pattern has been obliterated by the later imprint, and a facies of lower grade has been substituted. The reconstituted products of retrograde metamorphism are quartz-biotite-feldspar gneisses, amphibolites, and ultramafic schists (with serpentine, magnesian amphiboles, and talc). Structural effects of strong synchronous deformation characterize those areas of Lewisian rocks that bear the later mineralogical imprint.

Retrograde metamorphism is generally thought of as a broadly isochemical process with respect to major chemical components: amphibolites retain the basic composition of the parent granulites; quartz-feldspar-biotite schists that of their high-grade siliceous counterparts. Nevertheless, since the process involves continuous permeation by externally derived fluids, some detectable changes in chemistry are to be expected, particularly with respect to trace elements. This aspect of two Lewisian areas affected by Laxfordian (Invernian) retrograde metamorphism has been discussed by Beach (1974) and Drury (1974). Beach found that amphibolitization of granulites in the type Scourie–Laxford area has resulted in some loss of Ca and Mg and a gain in Na. Much further south, Drury recorded an influx of K, Rb, and Th, and simultaneous depletion in Ba, Sr, P, and rare-earth elements during the Laxfordian episode.

Critics of the facies concept from time to time have raised the objection that phase assemblages of two facies may sometimes coexist in a single outcrop or even hand specimen. This situation does indeed occur where the imprint of a retrograde episode has only locally obliterated the mineral assemblages resulting from an earlier high-grade metamorphism. It was in fact by recognizing such a relation on all scales that Sutton and Watson first established the different entities of what they termed Scourian and Laxfordian metamorphism in Lewisian rocks.

FACIES AND THE PETROGENIC GRID

Goldschmidt's thermodynamic calibration of the wollastonite reaction and Eskola's (1915) general proposition that the mineralogical character of metamorphic facies is determined by equilibrium within limited fields of temperature and pressure set the stage for modern investigation in metamorphic geochemistry. The general pattern is inherent in Bowen's (1940, pp. 272-274) proposed goal of a "petrogenic grid" comprising a network of univariant equilibrium curves for relevant reactions plotted against pressure-temperature coordinates. At the time the sole line on the embryonic grid was Goldschmidt's curve. In the four following decades many other curves have been added, and those first to appear have subsequently been displaced or modified in the light of new data and with the advent of new techniques and changes in fashion of thinking. Complications in pattern have been introduced, too, by taking into account the crucial role of water and CO_2 in many reactions. For simple hydration or carbonation equilibria, pressure-temperature coordinates can still be used by setting P_{H_2O} or $P_{CO_2} = P_s$ (e.g., Albee, 1965; Turner, 1967; Evans and Trommsdorff, 1970). For equilibria with both water and CO_2 as active components of the gas phase it is convenient to use isobaric plots (e.g., at $P_f = 1$ or $P_f = 2$ kb) against T and X_{CO_2} (e.g., Wyllie and Hass, 1966; Metz and Trommsdorff, 1968; Johannes, 1969; Kerrick, 1974). The petrogenic grid of today has become too complex to be represented in totality by a single plot.

Some geochemists (e.g., Winkler, 1970, 1974, p. v) would deemphasize or even discard the facies concept as obsolete, preferring to view metamorphic mineralogy solely in terms of inferred reactions still tentatively calibrated with varying precision on a petrogenic grid. This is not the approach adopted in this book. Metamorphic facies and, in specific provinces, subfacies are in fact firmly established broad entities that are readily recognizable on the basis of mineralogical criteria. They still comprise the most convenient units for discussion of petrologic evidence relating to thermal and depth regimes of metamorphism. Only in terms of facies can one grasp in totality the broad spectrum of metamorphic phenomena. To each facies provisional limits of temperature and pressure may be assigned from the petrogenic grid in its current status—for the grid itself must always be a tentative frame of reference. Whichever view the individual reader may favor, he or she must comprehend something of the experimental background of quantitative evaluation of metamorphic reactions and must appreciate the nature of the uncertainties involved in this all-important approach and the degree of precision in numerically expressed conclusions. This is the topic of the immediately ensuing chapters.

3

Quantitative Appraisal
of Metamorphic Equilibria:
General Methodology

PHYSICAL CONDITIONS OF METAMORPHISM

Regional metamorphism is a phenomenon of the deeper levels of the earth's crust. Metamorphism in contact aureoles may occur relatively close to the surface—at depths of 1 or 2 km—while rock fragments enclosed in dikes and lava flows may show striking metamorphic effects brought about at magmatic temperatures and near-surface pressures. The total range of metamorphic pressure, calculated as load pressure P_s thus lies between a few bars and 10 or 12 kb.

The upper limit of metamorphic temperatures is set by partial or complete fusion of more fusible rocks such as graywacke and shale. This is generally assumed to be 650–700°C at pressures of a few thousand bars, for these are the minimal temperatures of melting in granite systems in the presence of excess water. However, rocks such as granulites, from which all water has been expelled during progressive metamorphism, will remain unfused up to considerably higher temperatures. So also will xenoliths enclosed in magma at near-surface pressures. Thus metamorphic temperatures in the depths probably extend to 800°C or more, and near the surface perhaps occasionally reach or exceed 1000°C. The lower limit is the temperature at which reaction rates in common rocks first become high enough for effective metamorphism within periods on the order of a million years. There is some experimental evidence on this point (Fyfe, Turner, and Verhoogen, 1958, pp. 93-95, 100). Studies of rates of dehydration of clay minerals suggest that metamorphism is unlikely to be effective at temperatures below 200°C. This figure agrees with observations that sediments may remain almost unaltered apart from diagenetic changes such as conversion of smectites to illite (e.g., Eberl and Hower, 1976) after burial for millions of years at depths consistent with temperatures of 100–150°C.

Our task, then, is to explore the behavior and stability relations of common metamorphic minerals and mineral assemblages at $T = 200$–$1000°C$, and $P = 100$ bars to 12 kb. Most significant will be experiments on hydrous minerals with $P_{H_2O} = P_s$, on carbonate minerals with $P_{CO_2} = P_s$, and on combinations of carbonates and hydrous silicates with $(p_{H_2O} + p_{CO_2}) = P_f = P_s$. It is also desirable, particularly in systems with FeO, Fe_2O_3, MnO, or Mn_2O_3 as components, to explore the buffering effect of familiar natural combinations of graphite, ilmenite, magnetite, and hematite upon oxygen fugacity.

SCOPE OF EXPERIMENTS

The aim of most experiments in the chemistry of metamorphic reactions is to determine the respective stability fields of individual minerals and simple assemblages upon a temperature-pressure diagram. The boundary of any field is a curve of univariant equilibrium between chemically equivalent phase assemblages expressible by a reversible reaction

$$A + B \rightleftharpoons C + D$$

e.g.,

$$\underset{\text{muscovite}}{KAl_2(AlSi_3O_{10})(OH)_2} + \underset{\text{quartz}}{SiO_2} \rightleftharpoons \underset{\text{microcline}}{KAlSi_3O_8} + \underset{\text{sillimanite}}{Al_2SiO_5} + \underset{\text{water}}{H_2O}$$

There are two broad approaches to the problem. Each is simple in principle but difficult in execution. The first approach is to observe directly the conversion of $A + B \rightarrow C + D$, and also the reversed reaction, at a number of temperatures and pressures. The equilibrium curve lies between the respective fields of the reactions $A + B \rightarrow C + D$ and $C + D \rightarrow A + B$. The second approach is to use standard thermodynamic data for the participating phases, from which the free energy of the reaction ΔG_r may be calculated for a range of conditions in the vicinity of the equilibrium curve. The curve itself connects all points for which ΔG_r is zero. The final step is synthesis of results independently obtained by the two methods—both for any specific equilibria and for different equilibria sharing one or more phases in common. Herein is revealed not only the potentiality of certain equilibria as metamorphic indices but also inconsistencies pointing to error and deficiencies in the thermodynamic data, the experimental methods, or both.

Any equilibrium, whether established by experiment or calculated from thermochemical data, may prove to be metastable. Thermochemical calculation gives the equilibrium temperature of the reaction

Dolomite + 2 quartz $\rightleftharpoons$ diopside + $2CO_2$

at $P_{CO_2} = 1$ bar as 200°C. The equilibrium temperature at the same pressure similarly calculated for the alternative reaction

2 dolomite + quartz ⇌ forsterite + 2 calcite + 2CO$_2$

is 290°C. At this temperature and pressure all five phases (dolomite, quartz, forsterite, calcite, and carbon dioxide) can coexist in equilibrium. But the equilibrium is metastable; for at $T = 290$°C and $P_{CO_2} = 1$ bar, the most stable known chemically equivalent assemblages are diopside-dolomite-CO$_2$ and diopside-quartz-CO$_2$ (cf. Turner, 1967, p. 9). Contrary to the statement of Fawcett and Yoder (1966, p. 373, footnote) "that any heterogeneous reaction can take place only within the stability limits of the reactants and their products," many experimentally investigated reactions involving mineral phases represent metastable equilibria and can be reversed at temperatures and pressures over which one or more of the participating phases is not stable. For example, the metastable equilibrium

Muscovite + quartz ⇌ sanidine + kyanite + H$_2$O

as determined by Evans (1965) at $P_{H_2O} = 2$ kb and $T =$ about 670°C is well outside the stability field of kyanite (cf. Fig. 4-3).

Also accruing from experimental work are data concerning reaction rates. From these something may be predicted regarding the possibility that some minerals or assemblages may appreciably overstep the limits of their stability fields. It has been found, for example, that over much of the range of metamorphic temperatures and pressures mutual inversions of the three polymorphs of Al$_2$SiO$_5$ are impossible or difficult to induce. Geologists should watch for instances in which andalusite, sillimanite, or kyanite occur as metastable minerals. On the other hand, the inversion of aragonite to calcite, especially in the presence of water, has been found to be so rapid that aragonite, crystallized at high pressure, cannot be expected to survive reduction of pressure to near-surface values except when cooled from initial temperatures below 200–300°C (Brown, Fyfe, and Turner, 1962).

DIRECT DETERMINATION OF EQUILIBRIUM CURVES

The difficulties that beset experimental determination of equilibrium curves by the direct method are many. For some reactions, especially in the lower temperature range where rates are low, they have not yet been surmounted. For this reason some so-called "curves of univariant equilibrium" are valueless or dubious. Those that appear acceptable are constantly being revised in the light of new experiments. The geologist must therefore scrutinize with care the experimental procedure and the nature of the data presented in order to evaluate the published curves referring to any particular reaction. He must ask himself questions such as these: Was the reaction really reversed; that is, were the initial phases used for the backward reaction identical with the phases formed as the products of the forward reaction? How were the reaction products identified? If X-rays alone were used for identification, is it possible that a critical phase present in small amount passed unnoticed? Was the quenching procedure such that products of reaction at high temperature and pressure have survived unchanged to laboratory temperature and pressure at which they were identified? Is it possible—especially in complex high-pressure equipment such as squeezers—that strong pressure-temperature gradients develop within the charge, and that the instrumentally recorded values of P and T differ from those at which reaction actually occurred?

Some of the grounds upon which published "equilibrium" diagrams are subject to criticism or even outright rejection have been summarized for the benefit of the geologist by Fyfe (1960). To his remarks may be added a warning that the latest set of data is not necessarily the best—especially if there is reason to suspect defective instrumental recording of P and T values, or where the author of new data fails to give a critical appraisal of earlier records. Against this background we can now review briefly some of the methods currently used in determining curves of univariant equilibrium by direct observation of the reactions concerned.

Experimentally Reversed Reactions

Figure 3-1 shows the curve of univariant equilibrium established by Harker and Tuttle (1955, p. 218) for the reaction

$$MgCO_3 \rightleftharpoons MgO + CO_2$$
magnesite periclase

The plotted points represent runs in which the starting materials were the participating phases magnesite or periclase in an atmosphere of CO_2. Two dubious points, at $T > 800°C$ and $P = 20{,}000$ psi, were rejected because the final products included magnesite formed during slow quenching. The reaction was reversed over narrow temperature intervals at pressures ranging up to 3 kb. So the curve can be regarded as satisfactorily established within a few degrees. It is consistent, too, with available thermodynamic data.

The stability relations of three Al_2SiO_5 polymorphs, because of their obvious potential as indices of temperature and pressure independent of fluid composition, have been the subject of repeated and intensive experimental investigation over two decades. The conclusions that have emerged in some respects are disappointingly conflicting (cf. Zen, 1969). At this point we shall consider only the most completely investigated of the three two-phase equilibria, namely, kyanite $\rightleftharpoons$ sillimanite.

First efforts at reversal (Clark, Robertson, and Birch, 1957; Clark, 1961) were successful only at temperatures and pressures far beyond the normal metamorphic range—T between 1200 and 1400°C; $P > 18$ kb. Subsequent experiments by Richardson et al. (1968) and Newton (1969) have given mutually consistent reversals in the 700–1000°C range. Other reported reversals (e.g., Althaus, 1969) depart significantly from these results. Figure 3-2 shows the univariant equilibrium curve of Holdaway (1971) based on critically selected mutually consistent experi-

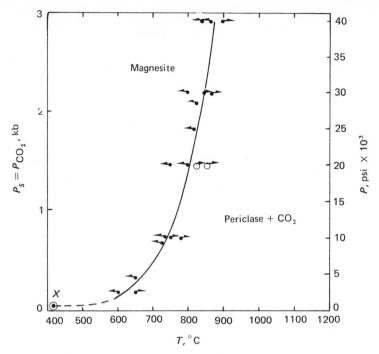

FIGURE 3-1
Curve of univariant equilibrium for magnesite ⇌ periclase + CO_2 reaction experimentally established by R. I. Harker and O. F. Tuttle (1955). Projected to calculated point X for 1 bar. Solid circles show experimentally determined points, with arrows indicating directions of reaction. Open circles are dubious points rejected because of imperfect quenching procedure.

mental data (excluding those of Althaus). It can be regarded as fairly satisfactorily established; but there are still appreciable discrepancies (to be discussed later) relative to existing thermodynamic data (Holdaway, 1971, p. 114).

The sluggish nature of many reactions stems from failure of stable nuclei of new phases to form spontaneously, close to the reaction temperature. To overcome this difficulty it is now customary to start with mixes of all participating phases, and to hold these at constant temperature and pressure for long periods until the reaction, in one or other direction, has proceeded to completion. Nuclei of all phases are thus already provided in the initial charge, and one of the principal kinetic barriers to reaction is thus removed. In their classic investigation of the system $MgO\text{-}SiO_2\text{-}H_2O$, Bowen and Tuttle (1949, p. 450) were unable to synthesize anthophyllite. They concluded, and on the basis of his own experiments Yoder (1952, p. 587) agreed, that pure magnesian anthophyllite has no stability field in the presence of water. The chemically equivalent stable assemblages at $P_{H_2O} = 1$ kb and $T = 700\text{-}800°C$ were thought to be enstatite-talc and enstatite-quartz. Fyfe (1962) found that at $P_{H_2O} = 1\text{-}2$ kb, talc-anthophyllite-quartz and enstatite-anthophyllite-quartz mixes can be converted largely to anthophyllite by prolonged heating over this range of temperature. He concluded that

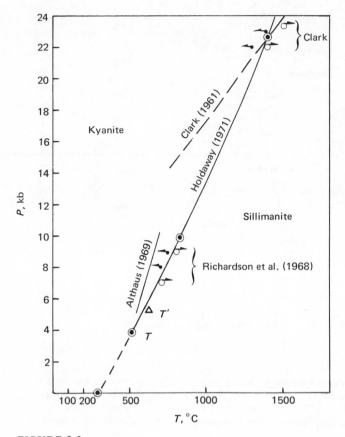

FIGURE 3-2

M. J. Holdaway's (1971) preferred curve of univariant equilibrium for kyanite ⇌ sillimanite (*T* is triple point). Experimental reversal points shown for crystallization of kyanite (solid circles) and sillimanite (open circles): high-temperature points from Clark (1961), low-temperature points from Richardson et al. (1968). For comparison are given Althaus's (1969) curve of experimental reversal, and Clark's (1961) curve (dashed) based on synthesis in the range 900–1200°C. The triple point preferred by Richardson et al. (1969) is shown as *T'*.

anthophyllite is stable with respect to talc and to enstatite-quartz over a temperature range of 100°C, with 760 ± 10°C as the upper limit, at $P_{H_2O} = 2$ kb. An independent and more detailed study by Greenwood (1963, p. 325), using the same technique, gave the stability range at the same pressure as 675–760°C. Curves generated from the best available thermodynamic data (Helgeson et al. 1978, Fig. 26c,d) have further narrowed the stability limits of anthophyllite at this point to 725–750°C—values virtually in harmony with the original opinion of Bowen and of Yoder.

One-Way Reactions

Many reactions proceed too slowly in the direction of decreasing entropy for reversal to be achieved except possibly in experimental runs of very long duration. For this reason there are a number of published curves based solely or largely on points representing only the "forward" reaction with increasing entropy. These are useful as they set upper limits to reaction temperatures; but they are not curves of univariant equilibrium.

The accepted "equilibrium" curve for the reaction

$$CaMg(CO_3)_2 \rightleftharpoons CaCO_3 + MgO + CO_2$$
$$\text{dolomite} \qquad \text{calcite} \quad \text{periclase}$$

is that of Harker and Tuttle (1955, pp. 216–219) shown in Fig. 3-3. Their data include no records of reversal, that is, of synthesis of dolomite from a calcite-periclase mix. Runs in which dolomite recrystallized unchanged were interpreted as indicating stability of dolomite; but this conclusion has no thermodynamic justification. Of no significance are runs in which a calcite-magnesite mix was employed as starting material. Where this was converted to dolomite the latter was assumed to be truly stable; but where the end product was periclase and calcite, periclase was pronounced metastable if the plotted point fell to the left of the reaction curve based on the other data. An unexplained anomaly is raised by two points (*t* in Fig. 3-3) in which small amounts of calcite and periclase were detected in prolonged runs starting with natural dolomite.

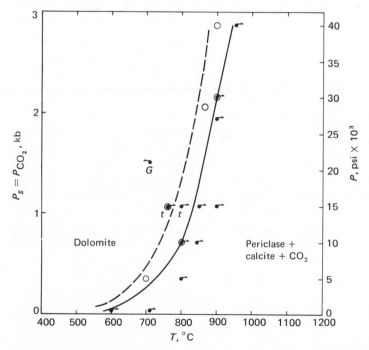

FIGURE 3-3
Dissociation curve for upper temperature limits of the dolomite $\rightleftharpoons$ calcite + periclase + CO_2 reaction experimentally established by R. I. Harker and O. F. Tuttle (1955). Open circles indicate recrystallization of dolomite unchanged. Broken curve is the magnesite $\rightleftharpoons$ periclase + CO_2 curve of Fig. 3-1. Point *G* corresponds to a reversal of the dolomite-dissociation reaction by D. L. Graf and J. R. Goldsmith (1955, p. 123).

Reactions of Synthesis

At relatively low temperatures covering much of the metamorphic range, reactions among silicates, even many in the presence of water, tend to be notoriously slow. In early attempts it was often found impossible to induce some reactions of meta-morphic significance, even in runs of weeks' or months' duration. In this dilemma some experimenters reverted to alternative reactions by which the desired mineral phases could be synthesized under controlled conditions from reactive materials such as glass or oxide mixes. Unfortunately such reactions can yield no direct information as to the primary metamorphic reaction (cf. Fyfe, 1960, pp. 553–562).

Suppose that the primary reaction to be investigated is

$$A \rightleftharpoons B$$

and that the synthesis reactions that are actually studied, starting with a glass or an oxide mix C are

$$C \rightarrow A \quad \text{and} \quad C \rightarrow B$$

Near the $A \rightleftharpoons B$ equilibrium conditions, ΔG_r for the primary reaction is small compared with ΔG_r for either reaction starting from C. Thus, there is a strong potential favoring crystallization of both A and B. Which of the two actually crystallizes depends less on the sign of ΔG_r for the $A \rightarrow B$ reaction than on kinetic factors favoring preferential nucleation and growth of A or B. Clearly an important influence is exerted by the very nature of the starting material. For example, at $375°C$ and $P_{H_2O} = 2$ kb, kaolinite-quartz crystallizes from a mixture of amorph-ous Al_2O_3 and quartz, while pyrophyllite-cristobalite crystallizes from a mixture of kaolinite and amorphous silica of the same bulk composition (Carr and Fyfe, 1960). In the absence of direct data relating to the reaction $A \rightleftharpoons B$, it has been ten-tatively concluded by some workers that A is likely to be stable in a temperature-pressure field where it can be synthesized from different starting materials. Such conclusions must be viewed with skepticism when found to conflict with geologic evidence, and must be rejected outright when results of synthesis are inconsistent with one-way data relating directly to $A \rightarrow B$ or to $B \rightarrow A$ or with reliable thermo-dynamic data. For example, curves once proposed for the reaction (Yoder and Eugster, 1955, pp. 235–242)

Muscovite $\rightleftharpoons$ K-feldspar + corundum

and for the inversion (Clark, 1961)

Kyanite $\rightleftharpoons$ sillimanite

between 800–1200°C are in conflict with thermodynamic data and have finally been discarded in favor of curves e.g., Fig. 3-2) based on successful reversals (Evans, 1965; Richardson et al., 1968; Newton, 1969).

Solubility Measurements

Weill and Fyfe (1961) proposed an experimental approach to delineation of the stability fields of the three Al_2SiO_5 polymorphs by measuring their respective solubilities over a suitable range of temperature and pressure. The first solvent to be employed was fused cryolite (Na_3AlF_6); and from solubility measurements so obtained, Weill (1966) calculated an equilibrium point for andalusite $\rightleftharpoons$ sillimanite at about 700°C, 1 bar. G. C. Brown and Fyfe (1971) determined the solubilities of kyanite and andalusite in steam in the range $P = 1$–3 kb, $T = 400$–500°C. Equilibrium points so obtained were 398°C, 1 kb; 472°C, 2 kb; 534°C, 3 kb. These lie on a curve with a slope $dP/dT = 14.7$ bar degr^{-1} as compared with 12.0 bar degr^{-1} calculated (Fyfe, 1967b) from entropy-volume data (cf. p. 151). This intersects the kyanite-sillimanite curve at a triple point (see Fig. 4-2) 460°C, 2 kb, subject to error due to obliquity of the intersection (compared with 410°C, 2.4 kb calculated from solubility and free energy data by Weill; 622°C, 5.5 kb given by reversal data of Richardson et al., 1969; and 501°C, 3.76 kb preferred by Holdaway, 1971). Solution of Al_2SiO_5 in either medium is incongruent. For water the solution reaction may be written

$$Al_2SiO_5 + nH_2O \rightarrow \underset{\substack{\text{corundum} \\ \text{precipitate}}}{Al_2O_3} + \underset{\text{solution}}{SiO_2 nH_2O}$$

Nevertheless the thermodynamic argument by which solubility data may be applied to the andalusite $\rightleftharpoons$ sillimanite equilibrium is simple: A dilute aqueous solution of a component i approximates ideal behavior and so may be treated by analogy with mixing in a perfect gas. Its chemical potential, μ_i^{soln}, as a dissolved component at any P and T is given by Eq. (2-8).

$$\mu_i^{soln} = \mu_i^0 + RT \ln X_i$$

where μ_i^0 is the chemical potential of pure fluid i at P and T, and X_i is the molar fraction of i in solution. Since X_i is much less than 1, μ_i^{soln} is much less than μ_i^0 and decreases with X_i. For equilibrium between crystalline i and its solution (saturated)

$$G_i^{cryst} = \mu_i^{cryst} = \mu_i^{soln}$$

Applying this relation to the dilute solutions (soln A) of silica in equilibrium with crystalline andalusite,[*] ΔG_r for the solution reaction

$$\underset{\text{andalusite}}{Al_2SiO_5} + \underset{\text{gas}}{nH_2O} \rightarrow \underset{\text{corundum}}{Al_2O_3} + \underset{\text{solution A}}{SiO_2 nH_2O}$$

is given as

---

[*]Values of $X_{\text{silica}}^{\text{soln A}}$ for the experiments of Brown and Fyfe range from $\sim 10^{-3}$ to 10^{-4}.

$$\Delta G_r = G_{cor} + G_{silica}^{soln\ A} - G_{and}^{cryst}$$

At equilibrium $\Delta G_r = 0$, and

$$G_{and}^{cryst} = G_{cor} + \mu_{silica}^0 + RT \ln X_{silica}^{soln\ A}$$

Similarly for solutions (soln K) in equilibrium with kyanite,

$$G_{ky}^{cryst} = G_{cor} + \mu_{silica}^0 + RT \ln X_{silica}^{soln\ K}$$

For the spontaneous inversion of andalusite $\rightarrow$ kyanite,

$$\Delta G_r = G_{ky}^{cryst} - G_{and}^{cryst} = RT \ln \frac{X_{silica}^{soln\ K}}{X_{silica}^{soln\ A}}$$

The argument so far has neglected the possibility that dissolved silica may be polymerized. But, in any case, the relations for equilibrium between andalusite and kyanite

$$\Delta G_r = 0 \qquad X_{silica}^{soln\ A} = X_{silica}^{soln\ K}$$

must hold, provided the same species of silica exist in the same proportions in both solutions (as indeed would seem most probable).

USE OF THERMODYNAMIC DATA

Nature and Sources of Data

If accurate data were available for molar entropy S of all common metamorphic minerals and for ΔH_f, the heat of formation (enthalpy) of each phase from its component elements, covering the complete range of metamorphic P and T, it would be a simple matter to construct the curves of univariant equilibrium for all metamorphic reactions. In Goldschmidt's day scarcely any such information was available for compounds analogous to metamorphic minerals—only enough in fact for him to compute the curve for the wollastonite reaction from the best value of ΔH_r° then available. This was only a rough approximation. But it provided a single datum for metamorphic conditions and it demonstrated the possibility of what in the past two decades has become the most powerful tool for calibration of metamorphic gradients of pressure and temperature.

Today we have abundant data pertinent to many metamorphic reactions at surface P and $T-V^\circ$, S°, ΔH_f°, and ΔG_f° for participating phases at $P = 1.013$ bars (one atmosphere) and 298.15 K (25°C). Also available are supplementary values for many phases covering the range of metamorphic temperature at atmospheric pressure. In the rest of this chapter we use comprehensive tables compiled by Robie and Waldbaum (1968)[*] together with much more accurate and comprehensive data for water and CO_2 over a wide range of P and T (Robie, 1966, pp. 454–458; Burnham et al., 1969; Ryzhenko and Volkov, 1971).[†] Information compiled for standard conditions could be extrapolated from heat-capacity, thermal-expansion, and compressibility data to cover any desired range of P and T. However, at the present time such data tend to be inadequate for common minerals. For some such as almandine, staurolite, and common hornblende they are virtually lacking.

A serious current weakness in the purely thermodynamic approach stems from uncertainties, commonly of the order of 500–1000 cal mole^{-1}, in ΔH_f^o and ΔG_f^o values [compare sets of data compiled by Robie and Waldbaum (1968) and by Helgeson et al. (1978)], and lesser but still significant possible error in S^o. Some of the error relating to the entropy of silicates can be eliminated (or at least recognized) by estimation based on Kelley's rule[‡] elaborated to take into account such factors as density, crystal structure, and order-disorder (e.g., Helgeson, 1969, 1978). But errors in ΔH_f^o based on direct calorimetric measurement remain serious and can lead to uncertainty of ±30–$50°$ in thermodynamically computed equilibrium temperatures. Added complications arise from differences relating to solid solution and order-disorder phenomena between metamorphic minerals and their standard counterparts (cf. p. 125).

In spite of such deficiencies the outlook gives grounds for cautious optimism. It has long been possible to draw geologically significant broad conclusions from thermodynamic data then available (e.g., Fyfe et al., 1958; Miyashiro, 1960; Ramberg, 1964). Today the situation has improved to the point where curves of univariant equilibrium for some reactions have been computed within rather narrow limits of accuracy. In other cases thermodynamic data place strict constraints on the geometric configuration (dP/dT) of equilibrium curves, predict the effects of compositional variation in the gas phase, and delimit areas of P and T within which specific equilibria may be profitably explored by direct experiment.

We now proceed to demonstrate the nature of simple computations and approximations that can be used to construct equilibrium curves and to examine the accuracy and limitations of results based on standard tabulated data. In some cases we shall find serious discrepancies between such results and conclusions reached by direct experiment; and this poses problems that can be resolved only

---

[*]These supersede previous compilations such as that of Robie (1966), are readily available in any library, and have the advantage that values of ΔH_f and ΔG_f of all phases (silicates included) refer to formation from component elements. Since this book went to press the calorimetric data of Robie and Walbaum have in turn been updated and greatly extended (Robie, Hemingway, and Fisher, 1978), and an alternative set of data has been computed by Helgeson et al. (1978). Use of either of the newer sets of values would refine but in no way invalidate the thermodynamic argument presented in this and the ensuing chapter. A useful student exercise would be to compare results obtained in individual cases from the three sets of basic data.

[†]Of interest to many students will be some of the fundamental work leading to development of today's standard tables (e.g., G. C. Kennedy, 1950, 1954; Kelley (1960, 1962).

[‡]K. K. Kelley proposed an approximation equating the entropy of an anhydrous compound with the sum of the entropies of component oxides (cf. Fyfe et al., 1958, pp. 25–34).

by more comprehensive and sophisticated treatment to be mentioned, without elaboration, at the close of this section (pp. 126-127).

Stability Relations at Surface Temperatures and Pressures

Given $S°$ and $\Delta H_f°$ (at 298.15 K, 1.013 bars) for all phases in two chemically equivalent assemblages, it is easily seen which is the more stable at surface temperature and pressure. Consider, for example,

$$CaCO_3 + SiO_2 \rightleftharpoons CaSiO_3 + CO_2$$

  calcite   quartz   wollastonite   gas

Pertinent data per mole of each phase (Robie and Waldbaum, 1968, pp. 16-23) are

Calcite: $\Delta H_f° - 288{,}592$ cal $S° = 22.15$ cal degr^{-1}

Quartz: $\Delta H_f° - 217{,}650$ cal $S° = 9.88$ cal degr^{-1}

Wollastonite: $\Delta H_f° - 390{,}640$ cal $S° = 19.60$ cal degr^{-1}

CO_2: $\Delta H_f° - 94{,}051$ cal $S° = 51.06$ cal degr^{-1}

For the reaction from left to right,

$$\Delta H_r = -390{,}640 - 94{,}051 + 288{,}592 + 217{,}650 = 21{,}551 \text{ cal}$$

$$\Delta S_r = 19.60 + 51.06 - 22.15 - 9.88 = 38.63 \text{ cal}$$

$$\Delta G_r = \Delta H_r - 298.15 \, \Delta S_r = 10{,}033 \text{ cal}$$

Clearly the stable assemblage is (calcite + quartz). Since this is the low-entropy assemblage, the equilibrium temperature must be greater than 25°C, and the large value of ΔG_r indicates that it must be at least a few hundred degrees Celsius.

For most simple minerals the recorded values of $S°$ are accurate to ±0.5-1%; for oxides the error is much less than this. Values of $\Delta H_f°$ for most oxides and carbonates are accurate to ±0.5-1%, but the error for silicates may be as high as 3 or 4%. Against this background it is possible to generalize as follows:

1. For reactions involving a change of state, notably those of dehydration and decarbonation, both ΔH_r and ΔS_r are commonly large compared with possible errors. Equilibrium conditions calculated from such data can be accepted as close approximations with some confidence. Fortunately, many metamorphic reactions fall into this category. Accuracy of the calculated equilibrium temperatures is likely to be ±30-50°.

2. For reactions between solids when one or more is an oxide phase, although ΔS_r is small, ΔH_r may be large enough to permit meaningful inferences

to be drawn from thermodynamic data. For example, for the reaction

$$CaSiO_3 \rightarrow CaO + SiO_2$$

at $T = 298.15$ K and $P = 1.013$ bars, $\Delta H_r^\circ = 21.2 \pm 0.7$ kcal mole^{-1}, $\Delta S_r^\circ = 0$ (within limits of error), and ΔG_r° is thus 21.2 ± 1 kcal mole^{-1} (data from Robie and Waldbaum, 1968).

3. For reactions between solids exclusive of oxides, ΔS_r again is commonly insignificant, and ΔH_r may be so small that the value of ΔG_r and even its sign are in doubt. Such is the case for some polymorphic inversions such as sillimanite $\rightleftharpoons$ andalusite and calcite $\rightleftharpoons$ aragonite. At $T = 298.15$ K and $P = 1.013$ bars (several kilobars below the equilibrium pressure), ΔG_r° for the aragonite $\rightarrow$ calcite transition is only -250 cal mole^{-1}, and the possible error is around ± 400 cal mole^{-1}.

Equilibrium at High Temperatures and Atmospheric Pressure

Given ΔH_r and ΔS_r for any temperature T and pressure P, it is possible to compute the approximate value of T_E at P, provided that $T_E - T$ is not more than 200 or 300 degr. The underlying assumption is that $\Delta H_r / \Delta S_r$ varies only slightly over the interval $T_E - T$. This is plausible since increments in S and ΔH_f of any phase depend on the same measured heat-capacity values; and it is borne out by the standard data for atmospheric pressure. Since at equilibrium

$$\Delta H_r = T_E \, \Delta S_r \quad \text{and} \quad T_E = \frac{\Delta H_r}{\Delta S_r}$$

then at any pressure P, in close approximation

$$T_E = \left(\frac{\Delta H_r}{\Delta S_r} \right)_{P,T} \tag{3-1}$$

where T is within a few hundred degrees of T_E. Another expression of the same approximation is to rewrite the well-known relation

$$\left(\frac{\delta \, \Delta G_r}{\delta T} \right)_P = -\Delta S_r$$

as

$$(T_E - T)_P = \left(\frac{\Delta G_r}{\Delta S_r} \right)_P \tag{3-1a}$$

Consider again the reaction calcite + quartz $\rightarrow$ wollastonite + CO_2 at room temperature ($25°C$) and pressure. From data already given on p. 110, Eq. (3-1) gives

$$T_E = \frac{21,551}{38.63} = 558 \text{ K } (285°\text{C})$$

Eq. (3-1a) gives

$$T_E = 25 + \frac{10,033}{38.63} = 285°\text{C}$$

At one time there was some difference of opinion (e.g., Bowen, 1940; Harker and Tuttle, 1956, pp. 250-255) as to the relative temperatures at which wollastonite and periclase appear during progressive metamorphism of dolomitic limestones. Today the problem is clearly resolved by thermodynamic argument. The pertinent reactions are

Calcite + quartz → wollastonite + CO_2

Dolomite → calcite + periclase + CO_2

Additional data required to evaluate the second reaction are

Dolomite: $\Delta H_f° = -557,613$ cal $S° = 37.09$ cal degr^{-1}

Periclase: $\Delta H_f° = -143,800$ cal $S° = 6.44$ cal degr^{-1}

$\Delta H_r° = -288,592 - 143,800 - 94,051 + 557,613 = 31,170$ cal

$\Delta S_r° = 22.15 + 6.44 + 51.06 - 37.09 = 42.56$ cal degr^{-1}

$$T_E = \frac{31,170}{42.56} = 732 \text{ K } (459°\text{C})^*$$

Computation thus clearly shows that at low pressures periclase can form only at temperatures some 170° higher than those marking the appearance of wollastonite. This conclusion agrees with the experimental findings of Harker and Tuttle who place the dolomite-periclase curve about 130° beyond the wollastonite curve at $P_{CO_2} = 1000$ bars, and it accords with geological experience that periclase is a much rarer mineral than wollastonite in shallow contact aureoles.

Referring again to the periclase reaction, tabulated data for the approximate equilibrium temperature just computed are as follows:

At 732 K, 1.013 bars, from standard data

$\Delta H_r = -94,182 - 143,599 - 287,292 + 555,387 = 30,314$ cal

$\Delta S_r = 60.41 + 15.91 + 43.90 - 79.09 = 41.13$ cal degr^{-1}

$\Delta G_r = 30,314 - (732 \times 41.13) = 207$ cal

---

*An earlier estimate, 470°C (Turner, 1969, p. 9), was based on $\Delta H_f°$ data since superseded.

$$T_E = \frac{30,314}{41.13} = 737 \text{ K } (464°\text{C})$$

The discrepancy between the two calculated values is only $5°$ and has no real significance. Both values are subject to error of at least $\pm30°$ reflecting uncertainties of ±1000 cal in ΔH_r and ±0.3 cal degr^{-1} in ΔS_r. Apparently insignificant are possible errors inherent in the approximation [Eq. (3-1)] on which the value 732 K is based and in heat-capacity measurements that would affect only the 737 K value.

Equilibrium at High Temperatures and Pressures

Influence of Pressure: Basic Equations
The change of free energy of a phase with variation in P at constant T is simply related to molar volume, thus

$$\left(\frac{\delta G}{\delta P}\right)_T = V_T \tag{3-2}$$

So for a reaction at constant temperature and variable pressure

$$\left(\frac{\delta \Delta G_r}{\delta P}\right)_T = \Delta V_r \qquad \Delta h = P \delta V \tag{3-2a}$$

It follows that the free energy of formation of a phase at P and T is

$$(\Delta G_f)_{P,T} = (\Delta G_f)_{1.013,T} + \int_{1.013}^{P} V_T \, dP \tag{3-3}$$

and for a reversible reaction at P and T

$$0 = (\Delta G_r)_{1.013,T} + \int_{1.013}^{P} (\Delta V_r)_T \, dP \tag{3-4}$$

The slope of the corresponding P-T curve of univariant equilibrium at any point is given by the Clausius-Clapeyron equation

$$\frac{dP}{dT} = \frac{\Delta S_r}{\Delta V_r} \tag{3-5}$$

Solid-Solid Equilibria
Volume data for metamorphic minerals include $V°$ measured at 298.15 K, 1.013 bars (Robie and Waldbaum, 1968, pp. 11–25), and coefficients of thermal expansion (Skinner, 1966) and of compressibility (Birch, 1966). These are the bases for

computing ΔV_r, ΔG_r, and (given heat-content data) ΔS_r for reactions at metamorphic temperatures and pressures. However, for most solid $\rightleftharpoons$ solid reactions, ΔG_r is small and subject to a wide margin of error due to inherent uncertainties in available ΔH_f values. Compared with this error, the effects of compressibility and thermal expansion on ΔG_r at pressures up to 10 or 15 kilobars and temperatures up to 1000°C in nearly all cases are negligible. So for practical purposes, Eq. (3-4) reduces to the approximation

$$P_E = \frac{-\Delta G_r^\circ \times 41.84^*}{\Delta V_r^\circ} \qquad \qquad \Delta G + P \Delta V = 0 \ , \ P = \frac{-\Delta G_r}{\Delta V_r} . \qquad (3\text{-}6)$$

For most solid $\rightleftharpoons$ solid reactions, P_E values so estimated are subject to wide limits of uncertainty. Consider for example the reaction

$$\underset{\text{jadeite}}{NaAlSi_2O_6} + \underset{\text{quartz}}{SiO_2} \rightarrow \underset{\text{low albite}}{NaAlSi_3O_8}$$

From Robie and Waldbaum's tables, at 298.15 K, 1.013 bars,

$$\Delta G_r^\circ = -883{,}988 + 677{,}206 + 204{,}646 \ = -2136 \pm 2000 \text{ cal}$$

$$\Delta V_r^\circ = 100.07 - 60.40 - 22.69 = 16.98 \pm 0.23 \text{ cm}^3$$

$$P_E = 2136 \times \frac{41.84}{16.98} \text{ bar} = 5.3 \pm 5 \text{ kb}$$

This result (though far from accurate!) is by no means valueless. It shows that albite is the stable phase at surface temperatures and pressures. Moreover, since ΔS_r° is high (8.42 ± 0.7 cal mole^{-1} degr^{-1}), it follows from the well-known relation

$$\left(\frac{\delta \Delta G_r}{\delta T} \right)_P = -\Delta S_r \qquad (3\text{-}7)$$

that, even at low metamorphic temperatures (300–400°C), ΔG_r at atmospheric pressure will have a high negative value and the computed value of P_E will significantly exceed any possible error.

Tabulated data for 700 K (427°C) give

$$\Delta G_r = -811{,}555 + 618{,}959 + 187{,}176 = -5420 \pm 2000 \text{ cal}$$

$$\Delta V_r^\circ = 16.98 \pm 0.23 \text{ cm}^3$$

$$P_E = 5420 \times \frac{41.84}{16.98} \text{ bars} = 13.4 \pm 5 \text{ kb}$$

---

*1 cal = 41.84 bar cm^3.

Despite the possibility of such large errors this simple calculation was enough to show that the assemblage jadeite-quartz, so widely distributed in glaucophane-schist terranes, can be stable in the crust only in regions of low thermal gradient (dT/dD) and at depths probably well above 30 km (cf. Fig. 4-13).

Values of S° and V° for most solid phases are less subject to error than ΔH_f° (and hence ΔG_f°) values. So even where $(P_E)_T$ estimates based on Eq. (3-6) are valueless, the *slope* of a curve of a univariant equilibrium can be determined from Eq. (3-5) provided ΔV_r and ΔS_r are significantly large. Consider for example the much-investigated kyanite $\rightleftharpoons$ sillimanite equilibrium (Figs. 3-2 and 4-2). ΔG_r°, from Robie and Waldbaum's tables is so small compared with possible error (800 ± 1300 cal, left to right) as to have no real value. But ΔS_r° (2.95 ± 0.2 cal mole^{-1} degr^{-1}) and ΔV_r° (5.81 ± 0.1 cm^3) are large and relatively accurate and fix the slope of the equilibrium curve as

$$\frac{dP}{dT} = 2.95 \times \frac{41.84}{5.81} = 21.2 \pm 1.5 \text{ bars degr}^{-1}$$

This value strictly is applicable only at temperatures and pressures close to 25°C and 1 bar. However, it can safely be extrapolated over a few kilobars and hundreds of degrees without significant error provided the compressibilities and thermal expansions of participating phases do not differ appreciably among themselves. Such is the case with kyanite and sillimanite. So the slope of 21.2 bars degr^{-1} combined with Clark's experimental reversal of the reaction at high temperatures (Fig. 3-2) has fixed the equilibrium curve between narrow limits and renders untenable some earlier experimentally based estimates that placed the triple point at impossibly high pressures.

There is a general inverse relation between density and entropy of chemically and structurally comparable minerals—e.g., among carbonates or among the aluminosilicates of Ca, Na, and K. It follows that the slope dP/dT of most equilibrium curves is positive—commonly in fact being +15-22 bars degr^{-1}. However, when ΔV_r° and ΔS_r° are small this generalization fails. For the andalusite $\rightleftharpoons$ sillimanite inversion standard tables give $\Delta S_r^\circ = 0.69 \pm 0.2$ cal degr^{-1}; $\Delta V_r^\circ = -1.63 \pm 0.08$ cm^3; the slope of the corresponding equilibrium curve is negative and its value highly uncertain (-18 ± 6 bars degr^{-1}).

Finally, it should be noted that use of V° and S° data to compute P_E or dP/dT at high temperatures and pressures will be subject to large error if compressibilities and thermal expansions of participating phases differ significantly among themselves. A notable example is the inversion diamond $\rightleftharpoons$ graphite,[*] for which I. S. E. Carmichael et al. (1974, p. 102) have computed a curve that takes into account compressibilities and thermal expansions of both polymorphs (thermal expansion of graphite is nearly three times that of diamond, its compressibility larger by an order of magnitude). From Eq. (3-6), P_E at 25°C = 15.4 kb, compared with the more accurate value 16.8 kb computed by Carmichael et al.; and at that

---

[*]This inversion is one of the few geologically significant solid $\rightleftharpoons$ solid reactions for which ΔG_T° is accurately known.

point dP_E/dT_E is about 18.5 bar degr^{-1}. If this were extrapolated, without correction for compressibility and thermal expansion, to a mantle temperature of 1500°C, it would give $P_E = 43$ kb. The accurately computed curve, which steepens as ΔV_r decreases with increasing pressure, places P_E at 1500°C at about 58 kb.

Solid-Fluid Equilibria
with a One-Component Fluid

Many prograde metamorphic reactions can be modeled on simple dehydration or decarbonation equilibria, the gaseous component being pure H_2O or CO_2 as the case may be. For a gas phase V varies markedly with both temperature and pressure, and, by contrast with solids, S also is highly sensitive to pressure, especially in the low-pressure range. So approximations neglecting effects of compressibility and thermal expansion of the gas are totally inapplicable. Fortunately, specific volumes of both H_2O and CO_2 have been accurately measured over a wide range of temperature and pressure; and these data, combined with measured heat capacities (and hence S values) at atmospheric pressure up to 1000°C have been used to compute accurate values of ΔG_f, S, and the fugacity coefficient γ, covering the whole metamorphic range of pressure and temperature for H_2O and pressures up to 1400 bars for CO_2 (Price 1955; Robie, 1966, pp. 454–458; Burnham et al., 1969).

The readily available data of Robie and Waldbaum (1968) combined with gas tables of Robie (1966, pp. 454–458) suffice for computing P_E up to 1400 bars at temperatures in the metamorphic range. For higher pressures one must turn to Burnham et al. (1969) for data on water, and for fugacity of CO_2 and some other gases to tables compiled by Ryzhenko and Volkov (1971).[*]

For any specific reaction at temperature T ($>$ the equilibrium temperature T_E) first compute $(\Delta G_r)_{1.013,T}$ at atmospheric pressure. Increase in pressure at constant T causes an increment in ΔG_r, which at P_E on the equilibrium curve reduces the negative $(\Delta G_r)_{1.013,T}$ to zero. Thus, the increment of ΔG_r (sign positive) is numerically equal to $(\Delta G_r)_{1.013,T}$ (sign negative). From Eq. (3-4)

$$(\Delta G_r)_{P,T} = 0 \quad \text{at } P_E$$

and

$$\int_{1.013}^{P} \Delta(V_r)_T \, dP = -(\Delta G_r)_{1.013,T}$$

The left-hand side of the equation (the free-energy increment) can be divided into two fractions: ΔG_r^{sol} contributed by the solid phases, ΔG_r^{gas} contributed by the fluid phase. If compressibility of the solid phases is neglected,

---

[*]These tables give values of γ to 1000°C and 10 kb computed from equations of state based on volume data determined experimentally in the low-pressure range (to 1.4 kb).

$$(\Delta G_r^{sol})_{P,T} = \int_{1.013}^{P} (\Delta V_r^{sol})_T \, dP = P(\Delta V_r^{sol})_T^0$$

$$(\Delta G_r^{gas})_{P,T} = \int_{1.013}^{P} (\Delta V_r^{gas})_T \, dP$$

$$= RT \ln \gamma P$$

So at equilibrium pressure P_E, writing all terms expressed as calories

$$\frac{P_E(\Delta V_r^{sol})^0}{41.84} + RT \ln (\gamma P_E) = -(\Delta G_r)_{1.013,T} \tag{3-8}$$

The calcite-wollastonite equilibrium illustrates the potentiality and also the limitations of the purely thermodynamic approach to a reaction (considered outside the context of other reactions with participating phases in common).

Basic data are set out in the upper half of Table 3-1. Below these are given corresponding values of ΔG_r^o, and values of P_E derived therefrom by Eq. (3-8), taking $(\Delta V_r^{sol})^0 = -19.692$ cm^3. For example, at 1100 K, Eq. (3-8) gives

$$1100 \, R \ln (\gamma P_E) - 0.47 P_E = 19,106 \text{ cal}$$

P_E is obtained from fugacity tables[*] by successive approximation:

[*]At lower pressures and temperatures G^{CO_2} increments at constant temperature (Robie, 1966, p. 458) can be used instead of $RT \ln \gamma P$.

TABLE 3-1
Values of ΔG_f, cal (Robie and Waldbaum, 1968) and Corresponding Computed ΔG_r for Reaction calcite + quartz → wollastonite + CO_2 at Atmospheric Pressure (Computed Values of P_E also Shown)

	Temperature, K				
	700	800	900	1000	1100
CO_2	−94,495	−94,539	−94,577	−94,609	−94,636
Wollastonite	−342,983	−336,282	−329,599	−322,935	−316,294
Quartz	−187,176	−182,905	−178,680	−174,494	−170,325
Calcite	−245,239	−239,245	−233,275	−227,343	−221,499
ΔG_r, cal	−5,063	−8,671	−12,221	−15,707	−19,106
P_E, bars	<100	260	960	2,400	4,500

At 4 kb, $\gamma = 3.05$: calculated ΔG_r increment = 18,686 cal

At 5 kb, $\gamma = 4.09$: calculated ΔG_r increment = 19,345 cal

So, at ~4.5 kb, calculated ΔG_r increment at 1100 K = 19,106 cal

$$= -(\Delta G_r)_{1.013,1100}$$

This and similarly computed points are shown as circled dots in Fig. 3-4.

Figure 3-4 shows three curves that have repeatedly been cited for the calcite-wollastonite equilibrium.

1. V. M. Goldschmidt's (1912) curve computed from an approximation developed by the chemist W. Nernst.

$$\ln P_E = \frac{-H_r^\circ}{RT_E} + 1.75 \ln T_E + 7.4$$

He used a ΔH_r° value of 25,300 cal (compared with 21,550 cal from current data), and CO_2 was treated, for want of other information, as a perfect gas.[*] This curve, for so long used as a classic standard, is now superseded.

---

[*]There are obvious analogies between the approximation employed by Goldschmidt and our Eq. (3-8), rewritten thus ($R = 1.987$):

$$\ln (\gamma P_E) = \frac{-(\Delta H_r)_{1.013,T}}{RT} + \frac{T(\Delta S_r)_{1.013,T}}{RT} \quad \frac{-P_E(\Delta V_r^{sol})^\circ}{41.84\,RT} \qquad \text{[a small positive number]}$$

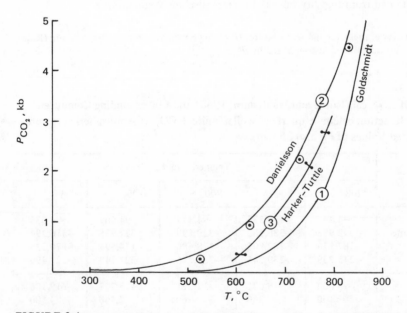

FIGURE 3-4
Three independently developed univariant equilibrium curves for the reaction calcite + quartz ⇌ wollastonite + CO_2. (1), (2), computed; (3) from experimental reversals (see text).

2. Danielsson's (1950) curve based on rigorous treatment using ΔH_f° and S values available from K. K. Kelley's tables of 1949, and taking into account departure from ideal behavior of CO_2 evaluated from compressibility data. Possible error in T_E was estimated as $\pm 20^\circ$. Points plotted from Eq. (3-8) using current data for ΔG_r and for CO_2 fugacity fall very close to Danielsson's curve.

3. Harker and Tuttle's (1956) curve determined by direct experimental reversals indicated by bracketed dots.

Agreement between curves 2 and 3 is close enough to demonstrate the validity of both the thermodynamic and the direct experimental approach. But differences are significant and in the low-pressure range give rise to considerable ambiguity in evaluating conditions in contact aureoles. The two curves in fact are seriously incompatible. Which is the more "acceptable" for petrological purposes? We are still faced with a dilemma that is not likely to be resolved simply by refining current approaches to the problem.

Solid-Fluid Equilibria with a Two-Component Fluid

In many metamorphic reactions the participating fluid consists of two main components. Familiar examples are seen in the earlier stages of progressive metamorphism of siliceous dolomites and of serpentinite and soapstones where the gas phase consists essentially of CO_2 and water. Tremolite* is the most widespread hydrous phase to appear in low-grade metamorphism of magnesian limestones, and with increasing grade it gives way to diopside by the reaction

$$\tfrac{1}{4}Ca_2Mg_5Si_8O_{22}(OH)_2 + \tfrac{3}{4}CaCO_3 + \tfrac{1}{2}SiO_2 \rightleftharpoons 1\tfrac{1}{4}CaMgSi_2O_6 + \underbrace{\tfrac{3}{4}CO_2 + \tfrac{1}{4}H_2O}$$

| tremolite | calcite | quartz | diopside | gas |

The complete assemblage of reactants plus products is a system of five components (CaO, MgO, SiO_2, CO_2, and H_2O) and five phases. So, for equilibrium, the variance is 2. There are now three independent variables—P, T, and X_{CO_2} (or X_{H_2O}).† Complete graphic representation is possible, therefore, only by a three-dimensional figure (cf. Wyllie, 1962); and this is difficult to construct and to read quantitatively. To meet this difficulty it is customary to consider separately a series of plane sections in which one variable is held constant. Experimental geochemists favor isobaric sections, since pressure is readily controlled in the laboratory. On such a section the trace of the bivariant equilibrium surface appears as a curve that is univariant with respect to the remaining variables T and X_{CO_2}. Perhaps more generally useful to a geologist are P–T diagrams for the special case where X_{CO_2} is held constant at the stoichiometric value appropriate to the equation of equilibrium—in the case under consideration, at 0.75. Diagrams of this kind apply to self-buffering systems; and this model seems commonly to be appropriate to dehydration of tremolite- or talc-bearing marbles even where these have subordinate pelitic interbeds in which the gas phase is more aqueous (cf. Greenwood, 1967; Trommsdorff, 1972; Kerrick, 1974, pp. 751–753; Rice, 1977).

---

*In more aluminous rocks, edenite (Rice, 1977).
†$X_{CO_2} + X_{H_2O} = 1$.

Thermodynamic appraisal of metamorphic systems with two-component fluids has been developed particularly by Greenwood (1962, 1967) and has been reviewed in the context of comprehensive discussion of experimental and geologic aspects of the same broad problem by Kerrick (1974). Here we confine ourselves to two useful relations [Eqs. (3-9) and (3-10)], illustrating them by reference to the tremolite-calcite-quartz-diopside equilibrium.

We start with the simplifying assumption that mixing of CO_2 and H_2O in the gas phase is ideal. This is certainly not true at low temperatures and high pressures (cf. Walter, 1963; Kerrick, 1974, p. 736); but corrections may be made as more experimental data on CO_2–H_2O mixtures become available. We also neglect the influence of compressibility of solid phases upon ΔG_f. By analogy with Eq. (3-8),

$$(\Delta G_r)_{P,T} = (\Delta G_r)_{1.013,T} + \frac{P(\Delta V_r^{\text{sol}})^\circ}{41.84} + uRT \ln (PX_{CO_2}\gamma_{CO_2})$$

$$+ \upsilon RT \ln (PX_{H_2O}\gamma_{H_2O}) \tag{3-9}$$

where u and υ are the respective numbers of moles of CO_2 and of H_2O in the equation of equilibrium, and γ is the fugacity coefficient of each gas component as pure gas at P and T.

Example

Tremolite-calcite-quartz-diopside equilibrium, self-buffered (u = X_{CO_2}; v = X_{H_2O}) at T = 700 K. Pertinent data from standard sources are given in Table 3-2. From these,

$$(\Delta G_r)_{1.013,700^\circ} = -6595 \; cal$$

$$(\Delta V_r^{sol})^\circ = -24.67 \; cm^3$$

Estimate ΔG_T for 700 K, 300 bars: By substitution in Eq. (3-9)

TABLE 3-2

Thermodynamic Data for the Appraisal of Reaction $\frac{1}{4}$ tremolite + $\frac{3}{4}$ calcite + $\frac{1}{2}$ quartz → $1\frac{1}{4}$ diopside + $\frac{3}{4}$ CO_2 + $\frac{1}{4}$ H_2O at 700 K

	$(\Delta G_f)_{1.013,700^\circ}$, cal	V°, cm^3	$\gamma_{300,700^\circ}$	Gas
$1\frac{1}{4}$ diopside	−837,052	82.61		
$\frac{3}{4}$ CO_2	−70,871		1.024	CO_2
$\frac{1}{4}$ H_2O	−12,479		0.671	H_2O
$\frac{1}{4}$ tremolite	−636,290	68.23		
$\frac{3}{4}$ calcite	−183,929	27.70		
$\frac{1}{2}$ quartz	−93,588	11.35		

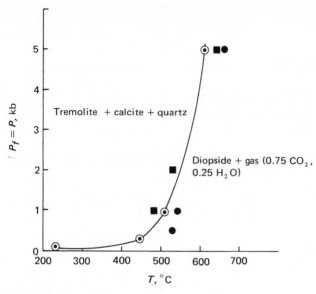

FIGURE 3-5

Thermodynamically computed equilibrium curve for reaction $\frac{1}{4}$ tremolite + $\frac{3}{4}$ calcite + $\frac{1}{2}$ quartz $\rightleftharpoons 1\frac{1}{4}$ diopside + $\frac{3}{4}$ CO_2 + $\frac{1}{4}$ H_2O, at $X_{CO_2}^{gas}$ 0.75, $X_{H_2O}^{gas}$ 0.25. Points experimentally determined by Metz (1970, Fig. 6), solid circles; by Slaughter et al. (1975, Fig. 8), solid squares.

$$(\Delta G_r)_{300,700°} = -6595 - \frac{24.67 \times 300}{41.84}$$

$$+ 0.75R \times 700 \ln (0.75 \times 300 \times 1.024)$$

$$+ 0.25R \times 700 \ln (0.25 \times 300 \times 0.671)$$

$$= -6595 - 177 + 5675 + 1363 = 266 \ cal$$

Then from the relation

$$\left(\frac{\delta \Delta G_r}{\delta T}\right)_P = -\Delta S_r \approx -15 \ cal \ mole^{-1} \ degr^{-1}$$

$$T_E - 700 \approx \frac{266}{15} \approx 18°$$

$$T_E \approx 718 \ K \ (455°C)$$

Figure 3-5 is the P-T curve for equilibrium ($X_{CO_2}^{gas}$ = 0.75) constructed from similarly estimated values of T_E for 300, 100, and 7000 bars. (The equilibrium temperature approximately 235°C at P = 1.013 bars was estimated from standard data: $T_E = \Delta H_r° / \Delta S_r° = 19,268/37.92 = 508 \ K$.)

All equilibria in which the gas phase consists of CO_2 and water can be written in the form

$$A \rightleftharpoons B + u_{CO_2} + v_{H_2O}$$

where A and B represent the solid phases and, disregarding sign, the sum $|u| + |v| = 1$. For example the reaction 3 dolomite + 4 quartz + H_2O $\rightleftharpoons$ talc + 3 calcite + $3CO_2$ is rewritten

$$\tfrac{3}{4} \text{ dolomite} + \text{quartz} \rightleftharpoons \tfrac{1}{4} \text{ talc} + \tfrac{3}{4} \text{ calcite} + \tfrac{3}{4}CO_2 - \tfrac{1}{4}H_2O$$

The topology of a "univariant" curve on an isobaric $X_{CO_2}^{gas}$-T_E plot is completely defined by a relation developed by Greenwood (1962, 1967).

$$\left(\frac{\delta T_E}{\delta X_{CO_2}^{gas}}\right)_P = \frac{RT}{\Delta S_r}\left(\frac{u}{X_{CO_2}^{gas}} - \frac{v}{X_{H_2O}^{gas}}\right) \tag{3-10}$$

Among other things this requires that the curve for a reaction of combined decarbonation and dehydration rise to a maximum value of T_E where $X_{CO_2}^{gas} = u$ and $X_{H_2O}^{gas} = v$—where the gas phase is internally buffered by the specified reaction. Figure 3-5 corresponds to a plot of such maxima, at $X_{CO_2}^{gas} = 0.75$, transferred from several isobaric projections each topologically similar to Fig. 3-6. Curves for reactions in which only the CO_2 component of the gas phase actively participates necessarily are asymptotic with respect to the T_E coordinate as $X_{CO_2}^{gas}$ approaches zero; on the other extreme where $X_{CO_2}^{gas} = u$, the slope of the curve is given by

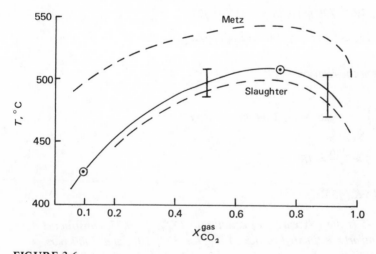

FIGURE 3-6

Isobaric plot, at $P = 1000$ bar, of computed equilibrium curve (full line) for the reaction $\tfrac{1}{4}$ tremolite + $\tfrac{3}{4}$ calcite + $\tfrac{1}{2}$ quartz $\rightleftharpoons 1\tfrac{1}{4}$ diopside + $\tfrac{3}{4}$ CO_2 + $\tfrac{1}{4}$ H_2O. Dashed curves based on experimental data (after P. Metz, 1970, and Slaughter et al., 1975).

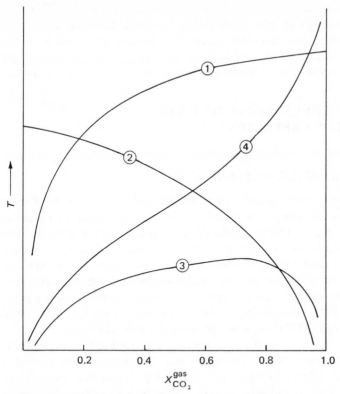

FIGURE 3-7
Some topological variations (diagrammatic) in isobaric equilibrium curves for reactions involving CO_2 and other gases (after D. M. Kerrick, 1974). (1) Calcite + quartz $\rightleftharpoons$ wollastonite + CO_2. (2) Zoisite + quartz $\rightleftharpoons$ anorthite + grossularite + H_2O. (3) Tremolite + calcite + quartz $\rightleftharpoons$ diopside + CO_2 + H_2O. (4) Dolomite + quartz $\rightleftharpoons$ talc + calcite + CO_2 − H_2O.

$RT/\Delta S_r$. Variety of topology of isobaric equilibrium curves for reactions involving CO_2 and H_2O is illustrated in Fig. 3-7.

Figure 3-6 is an isobaric plot (at $P = 1000$ bars) of $X_{CO_2}^{gas}$ against T_E for the equilibrium $\frac{1}{4}$ tremolite + $\frac{3}{4}$ calcite + $\frac{1}{2}$ quartz $\rightleftharpoons$ $1\frac{1}{4}$ diopside + $\frac{3}{4}$ CO_2 + $\frac{1}{4}$ H_2O. At 427°C (700 K) using data from Table 3-2 and values $\gamma_{CO_2} = 1.212$, $\gamma_{H_2O} = 0.315$ at 1000 bars, 700 K (from tables), we write Eq. (3-9) as

$$(\Delta G_r)_{1000,700°} = -6595 - \frac{24.67 \times 1000}{41.84}$$

$$+ R \times 700 \times 0.75 \ln (X_{CO_2}^{gas} \times 1000 \times 1.212)$$

$$+ R \times 700 \times 0.25 \ln (X_{H_2O}^{gas} \times 1000 \times 0.315)$$

$(\Delta G_r)_{1000,700°}$ becomes zero where $X_{CO_2}^{gas} = 0.12$. The value of $X_{CO_2}^{gas}$ for $T_E = 800$ K has already been established as 0.75 (Fig. 3-5). The rest of the curve can be extrapolated from Eq. (3-10).

For comparison the curves of Metz (1970) and Slaughter et al. (1975) based on experimental reversals are also shown in Fig. 3-6. Note that once again we are confronted with significant discrepancy reflecting possible influence of factors such as nonideal mixing of CO_2 and H_2O, error in ΔH_f° values used in computations and error in experimental reversals (cf. Slaughter et al., 1975, pp. 160–162).

SYNTHESIS OF THERMODYNAMIC DATA AND RESULTS OF EXPERIMENTAL REVERSALS

Basic Proposition and Related Problems

The topology of any curve of univariant equilibrium and its location with reference to P-T coordinates are completely described by the thermodynamic properties of the participant phases. Ideally, therefore, any curve generated from standard thermodynamic data should be identical with that obtained from direct experimental reversals or from solubility measurements pertinent to the same equilibrium. And in the absence of reliable calorimetrically determined values of ΔH_f° and ΔG_f° (almost universally the case among silicates), experimentally based equilibrium curves can yield valuable independent information regarding these quantities. This is what Zen (1977) has called "phase-equilibrium calorimetry."

We have already seen—and it is very commonly so—that serious discrepancies may exist between experimentally determined and thermodynamically computed curves for even the simplest of equilibria related to problems of metamorphism. So arises a special type of problem—how to resolve such anomalies with respect to specific cases such as the calcite-wollastonite equilibrium.

There are also more general problems, wider in scope, related to the same issue: Within a broader system such as CaO-MgO-SiO_2-H_2O-CO_2, there will be a number of univariant equilibria each involving a different combination of phases belonging to the same set—e.g., quartz, calcite, dolomite, brucite, talc, tremolite, diopside, wollastonite, forsterite, and others. It has been general practice to investigate each equilibrium experimentally as an entity without reference to other equilibria in the same set. Yet all must be interdependent; for each must be consistent with a common set of thermodynamic data. The general problem, then, is to test the set of experimentally based equilibria for internal consistency, as well as to reconcile differences between each curve and its thermodynamically computed counterpart. And finally, with the petrogenic grid in mind, there is the ultimate goal of eliminating all inconsistencies between partially overlapping sets of equilibria (such as those of the systems CaO-MgO-SiO_2-H_2O-CO_2 and CaO-Al_2O_3-SiO_2-H_2O), thus leading toward construction of a self-consistent standard grid embracing all metamorphic equilibria.

It is easy to visualize the nature and importance of such problems, stated as above in the simplest terms. But to appreciate fully the variety of possible factors underlying ever-present anomalies, let alone to attempt resolution of a particular problem, requires a degree of geochemical sophistication beyond the scope of this book. Yet the topic is fundamental to critical assessment of P-T

values assigned to metamorphic equilibria. The reader who wishes to pursue the matter more deeply is referred particularly to two recent contributions by Zen (1977) and Helgeson et al. (1978) and to the many pertinent publications cited therein (e.g., Zen, 1972; Chatterjee and Johannes, 1974; Ulbrich and Merino, 1974; A. B. Thompson, 1974; Zen and Chernosky, 1976).

Significance of the Numbers

The stability relations of any specific mineral sample are controlled precisely and predictably by its thermodynamic properties. These vary however—at least slightly, in some cases significantly—among different samples of the same mineral; depending on factors relating to solid solution, order-disorder, submicroscopic heterogeneity, structural imperfections, even grain size and shape. Thus uncertainties stemming from experimental technique are compounded by real variation in thermodynamic properties among different samples of the same mineral or fluid phase.

To familiarize himself with the nature and complexity of the problem, the serious student of mineral equilibria should examine the experimental basis on which numbers assigned to a few common phases in standard tables have been founded (appropriate references are cited in the tables themselves). He should also familiarize himself with the elements of high-temperature calorimetry and attendant inherent sources of uncertainty. Zen's (1972) discussion of related problems in general terms will prove a valuable and stimulating aid. Thus equipped, one readily perceives that the numbers cited in thermodynamic tables, though extremely useful in constructing a broad picture of mineral stability (such as the petrogenic grid) are neither divinely inspired nor immutable. It is true that every mineral sample has precise thermodynamic properties under specified conditions; but these properties remain to some degree elusive, and in some cases must differ significantly from the tabulated numbers.

Causes of Existing Anomalies

At the root of existing anomalies of the kind just discussed are imperfections in accepted data—imperfections which to the nonexpert may be concealed by the impression of accuracy conveyed by any set of numbers. There is of course no certainty that absence of obvious anomalies implies that the equilibrium concerned has been accurately calibrated (cf. Zen, 1972, p. 192). Generally widespread are uncertainties in T_E values based on experimental reversals, wide margins of possible error in standard thermodynamic numbers, and inadequate information as to structural state of crystalline phases.

1. Temperature brackets of experimental reversals are always significant, but are open to more than one interpretation. Is a smooth curve fitted by least squares to a series of such brackets covering a pressure range of a few kilobars a true picture of equilibrium? Is a narrow temperature bracket superior to one of wider span? Should the equilibrium temperature at given pressure be located at the center of the bracket of reversal? These, and other questions still unanswered have been raised and briefly discussed by Zen (1977, pp. 190–192). Then there are questions relating to experimental methodology and instrumentation that

are rarely appreciated by many of us who are not active experimentalists. Obviously to choose a "best value" for T_E of reversal requires critical insight, and the chosen value will still be subject to uncertainty (commonly at least ±20°C).

2. Among standard thermodynamic properties, ΔH_f° based on calorimetric measurements of heats of solution (and hence ΔG_f° as well) is subject to greatest uncertainty—for silicate minerals commonly 500–1000 cal mole^{-1}. Standard values of S° and V° in many cases are accurate enough to permit confidence regarding computed slopes of equilibrium curves. However, listed uncertainties of ±0.2–0.3 cal mole^{-1} degr^{-1} for S° can augment possible error in ΔG_f at metamorphic temperatures by 200 cal mole^{-1} or more, adding to the already large uncertainty (±1000–1500 cal mole^{-1}) stemming from accepted standard values of ΔG_f°.

3. Attention today is being increasingly focused on the influence of structural state upon S° of crystalline phases. Disorder (e.g., as to distribution of Al and Si among alternative sites in pyroxenes and in feldspars), lattice defects introduced by strain, augmented surface area in powdered samples, all tend to increase the entropy of phases used and produced in experimental reversals compared with natural counterparts—especially those samples chosen for their coarse grain for calorimetric measurement.

Present and Future Status of the Petrogenic Grid

All these anomalies and uncertainties compel critical appraisal of the present and future viability of the petrogenic grid as a whole. Helgeson et al. (1978) have presented a comprehensive survey of currently available data at a highly sophisticated level and on this basis have constructed the elements of a tentative all-embracing self-consistent grid. Zen (1977) makes suggestions for possible future refinements.

Because of inevitably high inherent uncertainties involved, Helgeson and his co-workers have virtually discarded calorimetrically based values of ΔH_f and ΔG_f° as listed in standard tables. Except for quartz, periclase, monticellite, magnetite, and gibbsite (for which calorimetric data are retained) they compute new values of ΔG_f° and ΔH_f° for all common metamorphic minerals. For every crystalline phase the requisite data for this procedure are standard values of V°, S° (corrected in a few instances for configurational contributions of disorder, lattice effects and surface effects) and the temperature-independent coefficients a, b, and c of the well-known power function (Kelley, 1960, p. 6) relating heat capacity to temperature (≥298.15 K)

$$C_p = a + bT - cT^{-2}$$

Also required for any set of related equilibria are brackets of experimental reversal selected for superior accuracy and for broad coverage within the set. The test for accuracy is conformity to the Clausius-Clapeyron equation into which has been introduced an approximation (cf. earlier discussion, pp. 116–117) concerning free-energy contributions of the participating *solid* phases; at any point (P_E, T_E) on the univariant curve,

$$\left(\frac{\Delta V_r^{sol}}{\Delta S_r^{sol}}\right)_{P_E, T_E} \approx \left(\frac{\Delta V_r^{sol}}{\Delta S_r^{sol}}\right)_{1.013, 298.15}$$

Given all these data for a set of equilibria, a linear matrix equation is now set up, solution of which yields values of ΔH_f° and ΔG_f° for individual phases, that must then be internally consistent within the set. Similar treatment of partially overlapping matrices eventually leads to an internally consistent comprehensive set of ΔH_f° and ΔG_f° values covering the full range of metamorphic minerals. From these new values, together with known volume and fugacity data for H_2O and CO_2, it is now possible to generate P-T and T-X curves for any desired metamorphic equilibrium. (See Chap. 5.)

No claim is made as to finality regarding the set of data compiled by Helgeson et al. (1978, Table 8); but they have the advantage of internal consistency, and curves generated from them are generally compatible with experimentally based curves. As to future revision, it must be noted that the data tabulated by Helgeson et al. cannot be combined with data on the same phases drawn from independent sources. Any significant change in data relating to one phase treated by Helgeson will be reflected in modifications throughout the whole set. Zen (1977) has proposed that future research be concentrated on refinement of key equilibria, and emphasizes the need for collaboration between laboratories to insure use of standard mineral samples for different types of experimental investigation and measurement. Such efforts, if successful, could lead to refinement of Helgeson's current tentative set of data and of the petrogenic grid that is its graphic expression.

SOLID-SOLUTION GEOTHERMOMETRY

Principle of Geothermometry and Geobarometry

We have been seeing how experimentally established data relating to systems in equilibrium may be applied to common metamorphic mineral assemblages to reconstruct the physical conditions of their origin. The natural system so appraised on classical lines is the complete mineral assemblage viewed on the scale of a small hand specimen. To sharpen and augment conclusions so reached, it has become common practice to attempt independent evaluation of subsystems or auxiliary systems on the microscopic scale: adjoining crystals of different phases with chemical components in common; two- or three-phase fluid inclusions in one or more crystalline hosts (e.g., Roedder, 1972, pp. 14-16); intragranular microdomains of postmetamorphic elastic strain in a host grain peripheral to enclosed crystals of another phase with different piezothermal properties (Adams et al., 1975). Such subsystems are potential indices of temperature (geothermometers) and of pressure (geobarometers) relating to some specific stage of metamorphism.

For practical use, any potential geothermometer requires experimental calibration: its chemical or physical response to change in temperature and pressure must be determined over a range of metamorphic conditions. The results so obtained, moreover, should be tested in the light of theoretical (e.g., thermodynamic constraints. Compositions of coexisting solid solutions are seen as direct or modified records of the principal metamorphic event. Heterogeneity in fluid inclusions or in strain haloes is postmetamorphic; by restoring homogeneity under laboratory-controlled conditions, it is possible to set limits on both temperature and pressure of metamorphism.

Clearly there is a wide range of available potential geothermometers in metamorphic rocks. Many have proved to be too insensitive or ambiguous for practical use. Only a few have been calibrated with sufficient precision to render them practicable instruments applicable to data readily obtained with conventional petrochemical laboratory equipment. Most successful are geothermometers based on partition of one or more elements, or of isotopes of a single element, between coexisting phases. For practical purposes such microsystems should be relatively insensitive to pressure, but sensitive to temperature. We shall confine further discussion to this kind of geothermometry.

Theory of Solid-Solution Geothermometry

Phase-Rule Constraints

In a system of coexisting phases $\alpha, \beta, \gamma, \ldots$, sharing a component i in common, the variables controlling equilibrium are P, T, and the chemical potentials of all components shared by coexisting solid-solution phases, e.g., μ_{MgO} and μ_{FeO} in a system with $Ca(Mg,Fe)Si_2O_6$ and $(Mg,Fe)_2SiO_4$. If the number of known (chemically determined) independent compositional variables equals the variance ω prescribed by the phase rule, the system is a potential geothermometer and geobarometer: for equilibrium the compositions of the phases in question uniquely define both P and T.[*] More commonly in natural systems of this kind the number of known compositional variables is $\omega - 1$, and temperature is uniquely defined only by specifying the pressure or vice versa.

Solution Theory

There is now an extensive literature on application of solution theory to simple mineral assemblages, especially with reference to their potential in geothermometry (e.g., Mueller, 1960; Kretz, 1963; Saxena, 1973, pp. 138-153; B. J. Wood and Banno, 1973; I. S. C. Carmichael et al., 1974, pp. 78-81). Consider a simple case. Mutual substitution of the components Ni and Mg common to coexisting olivine and pyroxene can be represented by an exchange reaction

$$2MgSiO_3 + Ni_2SiO_4 \rightleftharpoons 2NiSiO_3 + Mg_2SiO_4$$
pyroxene   olivine   pyroxene   olivine

The two solid solutions comprise a three-component system, variance 3. Equilibrium between them requires that $\Delta G_r = 0$. By expressing ΔG_r in terms of chemical

---

[*]In silicate-melt systems basic to igneous petrogenesis the same principle customarily is applied in reverse. Values of pressure and temperature uniquely determine the respective compositions of coexisting liquid (melt) and solid (crystalline) solutions in the two-component $NaAlSi_3O_8$-$CaAl_2Si_2O_8$ system (at $P = 1$ bar, $T = 1365°C$, $Ab_{74}An_{26}$ in the liquid, $Ab_{33}An_{67}$ in plagioclase crystals, regardless of the ratio Ab/An in the system).

potentials of both components in both phases it is easily shown from the relation [Eq. (2-9)]

$$\mu_i = \mu_i^{\circ} + RT \ln a_i^{\alpha}$$

that for all compositions within the pyroxene-olivine field at any given pressure and temperature there is an *equilibrium constant K* such that

$$\ln K = \frac{-\Delta G_r^{\circ}}{RT} \tag{3-11}$$

The quantity ΔG_r° refers to reaction between the pure solid phases at $P = 1.013$ bars and T, the temperature of interest, and so is itself a constant. K, like ΔG_r°, is a function of the activities of all components participating in the exchange. For the olivine-pyroxene equilibrium,

$$K^{-1} = \frac{(a_{MgSiO_3}^{pyr})^2 \, a_{Ni_2SiO_4}^{ol}}{(a_{NiSiO_3}^{pyr})^2 \, a_{Mg_2SiO_4}^{ol}} \tag{3-12}$$

The value of a_i in each case, it will be remembered, depends on the molar fraction X_i^{α} and the activity coefficient γ_i^{α} of the component i in the phase α, and so, like γ_i^{α}, depends on both P and T and reflects departure from ideal solution of i in α. Clearly K in any system is a function of molar fractions X_i^{α}, X_i^{β}, X_j^{α}, X_j^{β}, which may be written as—as required by the phase rule—a distribution coefficient K_D for each component (also constant at given P and T)

$$K_D = \frac{(X_i^{\alpha})^u}{(X_i^{\beta})^v}$$

where u and v are the stoichiometric coefficients in the exchange reaction.[*] Again for Ni in the pyroxene-olivine pair,

$$K_D = \frac{(X_{NiSiO_3}^{pyr})^2}{X_{Ni_2SiO_4}^{ol}}$$

The distribution coefficient of i equals the equilibrium constant only in the special case of ideal dilute solution of i in α, which probably applies in many instances to minor and trace elements. Here the activities of the principal components (in the above case Mg_2SiO_3 and Mg_2SiO_4) and the activity coefficients γ of the minor components all approximate unity.

For purposes of geothermometry, the most convenient distribution coefficient is the simple ratio between respective concentrations (weights percent or ppm) of the components in the phases participating in equilibrium.

---

[*]In geothermometry the simple quotient X_i^d/X_i^{β} is commonly employed.

$$K_i^{\alpha/\beta} = \frac{C_i^{\alpha}}{C_i^{\beta}}$$

Regardless of whether the solutions are dilute or ideal, $K_i^{\alpha/\beta}$ in a three-component two-phase system is constant at fixed P and T. A simple geothermometer may be calibrated experimentally in terms of measured $K_i^{\alpha/\beta}$ values. But for more sophisticated treatment of free energy of exchange and to develop models of geothermometry from imperfect data one must take into account the full implications of Eq. (3-12).

Synthesis of Thermodynamic Constraints

For equilibrium in a system of given composition at constant P and T, the chemical potentials (μ_i^{α}, μ_k^{β}, ...) and molar fractions (X_i^{α}, X_k^{β}, ...) of any component in a specific phase are constant. Solution theory relates *ratios* between molar fractions of a component in coexisting phases regardless of its concentration in the system. To compute temperatures from such ratios we need also to know corresponding activity values a_i^{α}, a_k^{β}, ... These are not usually available for simple gases; and again in a natural system, the composition of the gas phase is a matter of inference. Nevertheless, ratios C_i^{α}/C_i^{β} and so on, regardless of the concentration of i in the system, are valid parameters for geothermometry, since they are related to ΔG_r for exchange of i between the phases in question (by Nernst's distribution law). When the pair of coexisting phases lie on opposite ends of a binary solvus, the composition of a single solid solution suffices for use in this connection (since it automatically fixes that of the other phase): e.g., in the calcite-dolomite geothermometer discussed below.

Calibration Requirements and Limitations

Any two-phase solid-solution geothermometer—in the absence of activity data—must be calibrated experimentally by determining compositions of coexisting phases brought to equilibrium over a suitable range of P and T. Logarithms of corresponding distribution coefficients will be found to be inversely proportional to temperature. Consequently, since $d(1/T)/dT$ necessarily increases with decreasing temperature, the geothermometer becomes increasingly sensitive at progressively lower temperatures. In general, then, geothermometry tends to be more precise in the metamorphic than in the igneous temperature range.

Two serious difficulties limit the usefulness of many proposed geothermometers:

1. At least one of the natural coexisting phases employed commonly contains significant amounts of other components than those of experimentally investigated simple solid-solution pairs. O'Hara (1967, pp. 395, 396) has used the Al_2O_3 and excess MgO content of diopsides coexisting with enstatite as combined indices of high temperature and pressure. But to apply his experimentally determined values in the system $CaSiO_3$-$MgSiO_3$-Al_2O_3 to pyroxenes of lherzolite nodules of deep-seated origin he is obliged (O'Hara, 1963, p. 75) to recalculate two of the components of natural diopsides: "Al_2O_3" = $Al_2O_3 + Fe_2O_3 + Cr_2O_3 - Na_2O - K_2O$; and "enstatite" = $MgSiO_3 + MnSiO_3 + NiSiO_3 + FeSiO_3$.

Again, in using the calcite-dolomite pair the possible effect of the $CaFe(CO_3)_2$ component of dolomite has until recently been neglected. The influence of Ca and Al (in alternative sites) on distribution of Mn, Ti, and Fe^{2+} in coexisting pyroxenes, hornblendes, and biotite has been discussed in some detail by Saxena (1968).

2. The object of geothermometry is to measure the temperature at which the metamorphic assemblage as identified under the microscope is assumed to have reached equilibrium. The electron microprobe and electron microscope have revealed, however, that subsequently to equilibration on the microscopic scale, migration of ions, at least on smaller scales, has resulted in almost universal inhomogeneity of individual mineral grains—zoning, exsolution, and so forth. To what extent may intergranular ionic exchange during prolonged postmetamorphic cooling have disturbed the reading of the thermometer? Minerals such as garnet, commonly showing compositional zoning of individual grains, are particularly suspect: it is even possible that the core of any garnet grain was at no time in equilibrium with adjacent grains of other phases as they now exist. Moreover the possibility of more general adjustment to falling temperature is not to be discounted, especially in rocks of high metamorphic grades.

Thus the petrologist, wishing to quantify his mineralogical-geochemical data in terms of temperature, finds himself in a situation all too familiar among geologists. He has additional degrees of freedom within which to fit the model of his choice. If the geothermometer gives a reading consistent with conclusions reached on some other basis—or merely conforming to general expectation—the result tends to be considered acceptable or even definitive. If the reading seems anomalous (e.g., 400°C for a granulite assemblage) it is rejected, and the effect of possible modifying influences such as those just discussed is invoked.

The ideal geothermometer is one involving few components (simple solid-solution series) and few phases. The latter should occur in sharply defined mechanically separable grains whose only detectable internal inhomogeneity can be assigned on textural grounds to postmetamorphic exsolution. Sensitivity in all cases depends on accuracy of experimental calibration, precision of chemical analysis of the solid-solution phases in the system under consideration, and possible effect of pressure on equilibrium.

Illustrative Examples

Calcite-Dolomite Geothermometer

In its simplest form the pair calcite-dolomite, commonly found in magnesian marbles and other calcareous metasediments, is a system of two components ($CaCO_3$ and $MgCO_3$) with variance 2. The composition of calcite coexisting with dolomite departs significantly from stoichiometric requirements in that it contains dissolved $MgCO_3$ (~5% at 500°C, ~15% at 800°C). Departure in the case of dolomite is insignificant except at high temperature; so that only the composition of calcite is of potential use in geothermometry (Graf and Goldsmith, 1955, pp. 177-119; Goldsmith et al., 1955, pp. 225-226; Goldsmith and Newton, 1969). The calcite limb of the solvus as finally determined by Goldsmith and Newton (1969, pp. 174, 177) has been expressed by Bickle and Powell (1977, p. 282) as

$$X_{MgCO_3}^{calc} = e^{0.847-3091/T} + P(0.17 \times 10^{-8}T - 0.33 \times 10^{-6}) \qquad (3\text{-}13)$$

The first term expressing exponential increase of $MgCO_3$ content with temperature is much more significant than the pressure factor; e.g., at $500°C$, 5 kb (X in Fig. 3-8a) Eq. (3-13) becomes

$$X_{MgCO_3}^{calc} = 0.0428 + .0049 = 4.77\%$$

So, as already recognized by Goldsmith and his co-workers, the influence of pressure on temperature estimates is small. Curves drawn for 1, 5, and 10 kb are shown in Fig. 3-8a.

Magnesian calcites cooling from high temperature tend to exsolve perthitically intergrown dolomite clearly recognizable as such beneath the microscope. In geothermometry this exsolved component must be distinguished, in the course of chemical analysis, from any fine-grained dolomite that may be present.

Dolomite of metasediments commonly is ankeritic; and this raises the question of how the additional component $FeCO_3$ may affect the calcite-dolomite geothermometer. This problem has been approached from the thermodynamic standpoint by Bickle and Powell (1977) starting from experimental data available for the binary systems $CaCO_3$-$MgCO_3$, $CaCO_3$-$FeCO_3$, and $MgCO_3$-$FeCO_3$. They propose a regular solution model in which Fe-Mg-Ca distribution is disordered in calcite but ordered in dolomite (Mg and Fe both being confined to one of the two alternative cation sites in the lattice). Their argument develops a model applicable to low concentrations of $FeCO_3$ and $MgCO_3$ in calcite at temperatures below $600°C$. The fundamental equations so deduced (approximations in both cases) lead to two interdependent geothermometers expressed as

$$X_{MgCO_3}^{calc*} = X_{MgCO_3}^{calc} + X_{FeCO_3}^{calc} \, e^{(\omega_{CaFe} - \omega_{CaMg})/RT} \qquad (3\text{-}14)$$

and

$$X_{MgCO_3}^{calc*} = X_{MgCO_3}^{calc} + 2X_{FeCO_3}^{dol} \, e^{-\omega_{CaMg}/RT} \qquad (3\text{-}15)$$

The terms ω_{CaMg} and ω_{CaFe} refer to energy of interaction for Ca with Mg and Fe respectively in regular solution; from the experimentally determined binary solvi (calcite-dolomite and calcite-siderite), their values have been computed as $\omega_{CaMg} = 5360 - 0.032P$ cal mole^{-1} and $\omega_{CaFe} = 3800$ cal mole^{-1}. $X_{MgCO_3}^{calc*}$ is the molar concentration of $MgCO_3$ in calcite in equilibrium with nonferrous dolomite at the temperature of interest.

The variance of the two-phase system is 3, but two independent chemical variables $X_{MgCO_3}^{calc}$ and $X_{FeCO_3}^{calc}/X_{FeCO_3}^{dol}$ reduce the remaining variance to 1. As shown in Eqs. (3-14) and Eq. (3-15), an arbitrarily assigned value of either T or P fixes the value of the remaining variable. Because the value of ω_{CaFe} is independent of pressure, the dual geothermometer, Eqs. (3-14) and (3-15), is even less sensitive to pressure than is the pure magnesium system.

Graphic solutions of Eqs. (3-14) and (3-15) at $P = 5$ kb are shown in Fig.

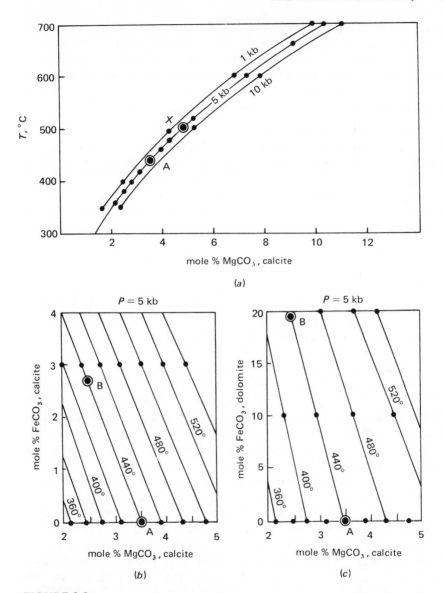

FIGURE 3-8

Calcite-dolomite geothermometers. (*a*) Molar fraction (percent) of $MgCO_3$ in calcite coexisting with nonferrous dolomite as a function of *T* and *P*. Computed from Eq. (3-13) [proposed by Bickle and Powell (1977) to fit experimental data of Goldsmith and Newton (1969, p. 174)]. (*b*) and (*c*) Molar fractions (percent) of $MgCO_3$ and $FeCO_3$ in calcite and of $MgCO_3$ in calcite and $FeCO_3$ in coexisting ankeritic dolomite at *P* = 5 kb and at temperatures (°C) indicated on contours. Computed from Eqs. (3-14) and (3-15) (after Bickle and Powell, 1977).

3-8b and c. For example, at 440°C, calcite with 2.5% $MgCO_3$ and 2.7% $FeCO_3$ is in equilibrium with dolomite carrying 19.7% $FeCO_3$ (points B); the value of $X_{MgCO_3}^{calc*}$ is 3.5% (points A). Possible effects of $MnCO_3$ in molar fractions less than 0.015 have been ignored. For ankeritic dolomite with 10–20 mole% $FeCO_3$, estimated temperatures are 40–60°C higher than would be inferred from the $MgCO_3$ content of calcite alone; they are believed to be accurate within 20–30°C.

Magnetite-Ilmenite Geothermometer

Magnetite and ilmenite coexist in many metamorphic and igneous mineral assemblages. Both phases tend to depart significantly from simple stoichiometric composition. "Magnetite" (the β phase) is a magnetite-ulvospinel solid solution Fe_3O_4-Fe_2TiO_4; "ilmenite" (the α phase) is a titanium-rich member of the ilmenite-hematite series $FeTiO_3$-Fe_2O_3. The two are related by an oxidation-reduction reaction

$$X Fe_2 TiO_4 (1 - X) Fe_3 O_4 + \tfrac{1}{4} O_2 \rightleftharpoons X FeTiO_3 (\tfrac{3}{2} - X) Fe_2 O_3$$

$$\underset{\alpha \text{ phase}}{} \qquad \underset{\beta \text{ phase}}{\phantom{X FeTiO_3 (\tfrac{3}{2} - X) Fe_2 O_3}}$$

In terms of the phase rule, the three-phase system magnetite-ilmenite-oxygen[*] consists of three components (e.g., Fe, Ti, and O) and so has variance 2. Two independent compositional variables—X_{mt}^{α}, X_{hem}^{β}—suffice to determine uniquely the remaining variables T, f_{O_2} (itself a function of P and $X_{O_2}^{gas}$).

The system has been calibrated experimentally for T and f_{O_2} by Lindsley (1963) using standard oxygen buffers such as fayalite-quartz-magnetite or MnO-Mn_3O_4 at controlled temperatures. Buddington and Lindsley's (1964) application of the experimental data to metamorphic and igneous geothermometry nicely illustrates the complications that attend such exercises and the steps that must be taken in attempts to surmount them. Microscopic lamellae of ilmenite in natural grains of titaniferous magnetite prove to be products, not of exsolution, but of late oxidation under falling temperature (α phase $+ O_2 \rightarrow \beta$ phase). So magnetite analyses must be recalculated to magnetite-ulvospinel mixtures representing the initial phase prior to oxidation. An apparent excess of TiO_2 in analyses of ilmenite is attributed to the presence of MgO, not recorded by analysis; so ilmenite compositions must be recalculated to $FeTiO_3$-Fe_2O_3 mixtures, omitting excess TiO_2. Electron-microprobe data so commonly used today do not discriminate between Fe^{2+} and Fe^{3+} and so must be recalculated according to some accepted conventional procedure (e.g., I. S. E. Carmichael, 1967). Such adjustments, however logical and "acceptable" they may be, cannot bring the compositions of the natural oxides into certain equivalence with compositions of phases used in experimental calibration of the geothermometer-oxybarometer. Possible error cited by Buddington and Lindsley for temperatures assigned to iron-oxide pairs is ±50°C; uncertainty for $\log_{10} f_{O_2}$ is ±1.

The magnetite-ilmenite geothermometer is generally applicable to temperatures above 500°C. Variation of oxide compositions with T and f_{O_2} in the upper

---

[*]Oxygen is a minor but critical component ($X_{O_2}^{gas} = 10^{-10}$ to 10^{-25}) of a gas, presumably in most cases aqueous, that otherwise does not affect the iron–titanium oxide equilibrium.

metamorphic range is illustrated in Fig. 3-9. This also shows the magnetite-hematite and fayalite-quartz-magnetite oxygen buffers and plots of temperatures and f_{O_2} values assigned by Buddington and Lindsley (1964, Table 6, p. 337) to five high-grade metamorphic rocks from the Adirondacks. Pertinent data are given in Table 3-3.

Two-Pyroxene Geothermometer

Orthopyroxene and diopsidic clinopyroxene commonly coexist in metamorphic rocks of the granulite facies. The immiscibility gap, calibrated experimentally at 30 kb, 900–1300°C by Davis and Boyd (1966), is the starting point for a geothermometer based on partition of $Mg_2 Si_2 O_6$ between the coexisting phases and developed by B. J. Wood and Banno (1973). To take account of the considerable

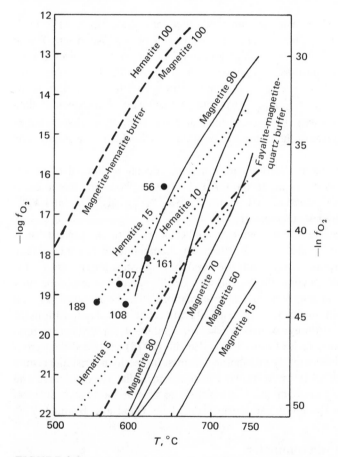

FIGURE 3-9

Metamorphic section of magnetite-ilmenite geothermometer: compositions (mole%) of coexisting magnetite (full curves) and ilmenite (dotted curves) as functions of temperature and oxygen fugacity (after Lindsley, 1963). Heavy dashed curves are drawn for magnetite-hematite and fayalite-magnetite-quartz buffers. Solid circles represent correspondingly numbered analyzed oxide pairs from granulite-facies gneisses in the Adirondacks (taken from Buddington and Lindsley, 1964, p. 337).

Table 3-3

Compositions of Coexisting Magnetite (α Phase) and Ilmenite (β Phase) in Adirondack Metamorphic Rocks and Inferred Values of Temperature and Oxygen Fugacity

Rock number	X^{α}_{mt}, mole%	X^{β}_{hem}, mole%	T, °C	$\log_{10} f_{O_2}$
108	89.8	9.1	590	−19.3
189	95.4	14.9	550	−19.2
56	91.0	17.3	640	−16.3
161	89.1	10.9	620	−18.1
107	92.5	12.3	585	−18.7

content of Fe^{2+} as well as lesser amounts of other ions (Na^+, Mn^{2+}, Al^{3+}, Fe^{3+}, and so on) present in smaller amounts in the natural phases, Wood and Banno resort to a model of ideal two-site solid solution. This of course involves a number of simplifying assumptions. The outcome is a standardized procedure (for which Hewins, 1975, has developed a computer program) for computing activity values $a^{opx}_{Mg_2Si_2O_6}$ and $a^{cpx}_{Mg_2Si_2O_6}$, from mineral analyses. Experimental data from pyroxene systems with Fe^{2+} as a principal component show that presence of Fe^{2+} markedly increases the solubility of $(Mg,Fe)_2Si_2O_6$ in the monoclinic phase.

Taking all these factors into account and introducing additional constants relating to free energies of mixing in the Ca-Mg-Fe system, Wood and Banno come up with a semiempirical equation that relates T_e to $a^{opx}_{Mg_2Si_2O_6}$, $a^{cpx}_{Mg_2Si_2O_6}$ and X^{opx}_{Fe} and that closely fits all experimental data.

The Wood-Banno geothermometer is applicable only to the highest range of metamorphic temperatures (and to magmatic temperatures beyond). Many students of metamorphism may find the level of sophistication necessary for practical use somewhat beyond them. But we can all appreciate the number and nature of underlying assumptions and approximations that are involved, as well as the fact that, given sufficiently precise data for calibration, compositions of coexisting clino- and orthopyroxenes provide the potential for estimating temperatures in the granulite facies (Mori, 1977). Hewins (1975) has tested the pyroxene thermometer, with apparently satisfactory (at least internally consistent) results on hornblende granulites from Australia, Finland, and India. He considered the range of temperature thus obtained (780-860°C) to be not more than 50° too high—which is within the limits cautiously claimed by Wood and Banno (1973, p. 122).

Oxygen-Isotope Geothermometers

Basic Theory

Coexisting minerals of igneous and metamorphic rocks differ appreciably as to isotopic composition of oxygen ($R = {}^{18}O/{}^{16}O$), and fractionation patterns in any pair are found to vary regularly with conditions of petrogenesis, e.g., low- versus high-grade metamorphism or plutonism versus volcanism (Taylor and Epstein,

1962). Equilibrium partition of isotopes depends on exchange reactions such as

$$\tfrac{1}{2}Si^{18}O_2 + \tfrac{1}{4}Fe_3{}^{16}O_4 \rightleftharpoons \tfrac{1}{2}Si^{16}O_2 + \tfrac{1}{4}Fe_3{}^{18}O_4 \tag{3-16}$$

for exchange of one oxygen atom between quartz and magnetite. To simplify use of symbols in subsequent discussion we shall refer principally to the above equilibrium.

In terms of the phase rule, the minimal number of components c—as in all exchange equilibria involving all species s in the system—is $s - 1 = 3$. So the quartz-magnetite equilibrium is trivariant: either P or T as well as the isotopic compositions of both phases must be known in order uniquely to describe the system. The magnitude of ΔG_r and its sensitivity to temperature and pressure depend on ΔV_r and ΔS_r of the exchange. Substitution of ^{18}O for ^{16}O involves slight shortening of bond lengths; but the resulting change in volume—largely compensated on opposite sides of the equation—is thought to be trivial. Consequently, the influence of pressure on isotopic equilibrium is generally neglected. In at least one system—$CaCO_3$-H_2O at 500 and 700°C—any effect of pressure up to 20 kb was indeed found to be below the limits of experimental detection (Clayton et al., 1975).[*] On the other hand, because atomic vibration frequencies—and hence lattice energies—are a function of both atomic mass and strength of bonding, ΔS_r of the isotopic exchange is significant and equilibrium is correspondingly sensitive to temperature. Herein lies the potential of coexisting oxygen compounds, such as the pairs quartz-magnetite and quartz-muscovite, for use as ideal geothermometers virtually unaffected by pressure. The whole topic has been dealt with concisely and clearly by Taylor (1967, pp. 116-127).

Theoretical treatment of isotopic fractionation between condensed phases is hampered by inadequacy of information relating to lattice energies and in any case is beyond the scope of this book. Suffice it to say that by analogy with molecular exchange in a perfect gas some simple approximations emerge that seem to fit experimental data and observations on natural mineral pairs. One of these, proposed by Epstein and Taylor (1961) and elaborated by Bottinga and Javoy (1973) is

$$1000 \ln \alpha = A + \frac{B}{T^2} \tag{3-17}$$

where α is the partition factor R^{qu}/R^{mt} and A and B are constants valid for a fairly large but finite range of temperature (say, 500-800°C). The factor α, like the equilibrium constant to which it is closely related, approaches zero at very high temperatures. The values of A and B must be determined experimentally (see the section on calibration).

Data of Isotopic Analysis

Specialized techniques have been successfully developed to extract the total oxygen from a mineral sample and to determine, by mass spectrometry, its isotopic

---

[*]However, pressures above 8 kb were found to accelerate greatly the rate of equilibration.

composition relative to that of a standard (mean ocean water). The composition is expressed as

$$\delta_{^{18}O/^{16}O}^{sample} = 1000 \left(\frac{R^{sample}}{R^{standard}} - 1 \right) \qquad (3\text{-}18)^*$$

The parameter used to describe isotopic fractionation in a pair (quartz-magnetite) is

$$\Delta^{qu\text{-}mt} = \delta^{qu} - \delta^{mt}$$

Δ values of 2–20 per mil have been recorded for many metamorphic mineral pairs.

Because Δ expresses a small fraction (in ppm) and $(\alpha - 1)$ is also a small fraction, $1000 \ln \alpha \approx \Delta$. For example, a sample of Vermont schist gave $\delta^{qu} = 15$, $\delta^{mt} = 6$; $\Delta^{qu\text{-}mt} = 9$, so $\alpha = 1.015/1.006 = 1.0089$. Thus, $1000 \ln \alpha = 8.9$. For this reason the inverse relation of fractionation to T^2 that is found to exist in products of experimental equilibration and is implicit in Eq. (3-17) is conventionally represented in a plot of $\Delta = 1000 \ln \alpha$, against $1/T^2$.

Necessary Assumptions

Isotopic geothermometry as applied to metamorphism rests on assumptions of an already familiar type: Isotopic equilibrium is attained at the peak temperature of metamorphism and thereafter is preserved "frozen-in" during subsequent cooling and decompression.

Evidence that these assumptions may be well founded in sufficient cases to render isotopic geothermometers widely applicable to metamorphic rock lies in observed regularity in natural isotopic patterns—especially where analyzed samples are small, even grained, and show no sign of retrograde effects (cf. Anderson, 1967).

1. In most provinces of regional metamorphism, Δ values tend to fall regularly with rising metamorphic grade [in conformity with Eq. (3-17)].
2. Respective Δ values for different mineral pairs taken from the same set of samples tend, in spite of some scatter, to vary sympathetically.
3. Values of δ for associated common minerals of both igneous and metamorphic rocks normally decrease in this order: quartz, dolomite, alkali feldspars, plagioclase, muscovite, pyroxenes, hornblende, olivine and garnet, biotite, chlorite, ilmenite, magnetite, and hematite.
4. "Temperatures" registered on the same scale by different mineral pairs in the same specimen commonly but by no means invariably are concordant within 20 or 30° (divergences amounting to 50-60° are also common and may indicate either departure from equilibrium or faults in the thermometric scales employed).

---

*Since all subsequent discussion refers to oxygen, the subscript $^{18}O/^{16}O$ is omitted henceforth in this chapter.

Sets of rock samples that conform to all the above criteria are generally accepted as representing "frozen-in" equilibrium. But do they record maximum temperatures of metamorphism or merely some limiting temperature below which equilibration was too slow to be effective? The fact that so many *igneous* rocks register isotopic "temperatures" appropriate to magmatic crystallization, and much above the metamorphic range gives weight to the peak-temperature interpretation. High-temperature isotopic equilibria do, then, survive in plutonic rocks not obviously affected by postmagmatic alteration and recrystallization. "Temperatures" recorded by oxygen isotopes of metamorphic rocks tend to fit remarkably well with some values conventionally assigned on other evidence to the range of grade in regional metamorphism. As usual in petrology, data that fit the preconceived model are considered "reasonable" or "acceptable." Finally it is hard to imagine any process other than complete recrystallization that could bring about an orderly and complete redistribution of atoms whose collective volume is 90% of the system.

For the above reasons many geochemists (e.g., Garlick and Epstein, 1967; Taylor, 1967, pp. 119–122; Shieh and Taylor, 1969a, p. 326) favor the view that isotopic patterns that conform to all the criteria enumerated above record equilibration at the maximum temperature of metamorphic crystallization. Departures from this pattern are viewed as evidence of postmetamorphic isotopic disturbance such as reequilibration or contamination by surface waters. Other workers in the isotopic field dispute this interpretation at least for certain geothermometers. James and Clayton (1962), for example, suggest that quartz-magnetite continues to reequilibrate during cooling down to perhaps 400°C. Quartz-calcite is another pair that seems to fall in the same category (cf. Schwarcz et al., 1970).

Calibration Problem

The principle of calibration is simple: coexisting phases brought to equilibrium at a series of appropriate temperatures are analyzed for oxygen isotopes. The resulting Δ values are plotted against $10^6/T^2$. The constants A and B of Eq. (3-17) are given by the linear curve of best fit. Thus curve 2 in Fig. 3-10 is a plot for muscovite-water over the interval 300–600°C (O'Neil and Taylor, 1969). Extrapolated to $10^6/T^2 = 0$, it cuts the Δ coordinate at A (−3.89). The difference $(\Delta - A)$ at $10^6/T^2 = 1$ (point B) gives $B \times 10^{-6}$ (2.38).

Solid-water pairs are the most amenable to experimental calibration and form the basis of calibration curves used for most solid-solid isotopic geothermometers. The A and B constants for the latter are simply the differences between the respective A and B values for corresponding solid-water equations. This is illustrated in the upper section of Table 3-4. Curve 3 of Fig. 3-10 has been so constructed for quartz-muscovite, using the constants for quartz-water (1) and muscovite-water (2). Given the A and B constants for such a solid-solid pair, the temperature $T(K)$ for any measured value of Δ is

$$T = \sqrt{\frac{B}{\Delta - A}} \qquad\qquad (3\text{-}19)$$

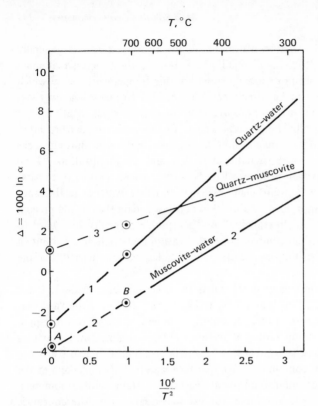

FIGURE 3-10
Reciprocal relation between $\Delta^{18}O/^{16}O$ and temperature (K) for (1) quartz-water (Taylor, 1967; from unpublished data of R. N. Clayton, J. R. O'Neil, and T. Mayeda, 1966); (2) muscovite-water (O'Neil and Taylor, 1969); and (3) quartz-muscovite, derived from (1) and (2).

TABLE 3-4
Some Alternatively Proposed Values for A and B Constants ($1000 \ln \alpha = \Delta = A + B/T^2$) for Oxygen-Isotope Equilibria in Combinations of Quartz, Muscovite, and Water

Curve (Figs. 3-10, 3-11, and 3-12)	Equilibrium	A	$B \times 10^{-6}$	Source
1	Quartz-water	−2.71	3.57	Taylor (1967)
2	Muscovite-water	−3.89	2.38	O'Neil & Taylor (1969)
3	Quartz-muscovite	1.18	1.19	By difference (1 − 2)
4	Quartz-water	−3.7	4.10 ⎫	Bottinga and Javoy
5	Muscovite-water	−3.1	1.90 ⎭	(1973, p. 257)
6	Quartz-muscovite	−0.6	2.20	By difference (4 − 5)
7 (200–500°C)	Quartz-water	−3.40	3.38 ⎫	Clayton et al. (1972)
7 (500–750°C)	Quartz-water	−1.96	2.51 ⎭	
8 (250–500°C)	Quartz-muscovite	0.49	1.00	By difference (7 − 2)
8a (500–620°C)	Quartz-muscovite	1.93	0.13	By difference (7 − 2)
9 (250–500°C)	Quartz-muscovite	−0.3	1.48	By difference (7 − 5)

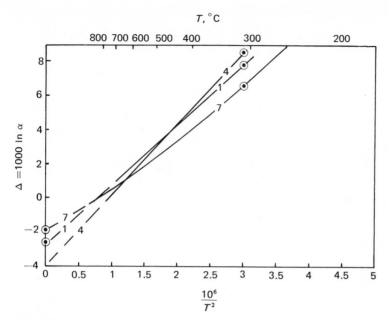

FIGURE 3-11
Alternative curves for reciprocal relation between $\Delta^{18}O/^{16}O$ and temperature (K) for quartz-water. (1) from Taylor, 1967; (4) from Bottinga and Javoy, 1973; (7) from Clayton et al., 1972.

In practice calibration of isotopic mineral geothermometers is fraught with difficulty. Laboratory procedure is time consuming and highly specialized. The output data from one set of experiments show a good deal of scatter and must be smoothed—usually to a least-squares fit. Results obtained in different laboratories do not always agree. Reaction rates below 300°C may be too slow for equilibrium to be established, and then it becomes necessary to resort to some form of extrapolation for which the theory of isotopic equilibrium between condensed phases is still inadequate. So there is a wide margin of disagreement among isotopic geochemists even over the critical quartz-water equilibrium (cf. Table 3-4 and Fig. 3-11). The present upshot of all this uncertainty is that there is no general consensus as to the calibration scales of pairs such as quartz-muscovite (Table 3-4 and Fig. 3-12) and quartz-magnetite. To this topic we shall return later.

Bottinga and Javoy (1974) have approached the problem from a theoretical standpoint. They argue that for all systems consisting of an anhydrous silicate (or magnetite) and water the constant A in Eq. (3-17) should have the same value for a given temperature interval. They suggested a value of -3.7 for 500–800°C. Equation (3-19) for solid-solid pairs (excluding hydrous silicates[*]) would then become

$$T = \sqrt{\frac{B}{\Delta}}$$

(3-19a)

[*]The value of A suggested for muscovite-water is -3.1.

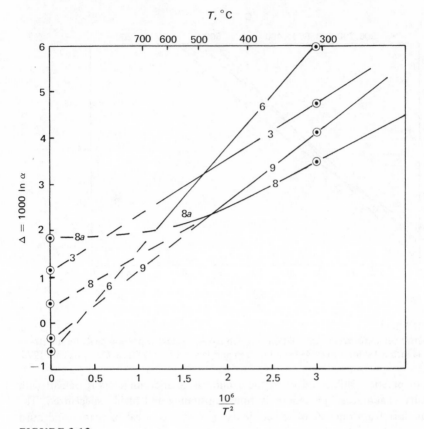

FIGURE 3-12

Alternative curves for reciprocal relation between $\Delta^{18}O/^{16}O$ and temperature (K) for quartz-muscovite. Data derived from experimentally investigated systems of quartz-water and muscovite-water as indicated by reference to numbered curves: (3) from Taylor, 1967, O'Neil and Taylor, 1969; (6) from Bottinga and Javoy, 1973; (8) and (9) from Clayton et al., 1972).

The equations of Bottinga and Javoy give greater concordance—still, however, in some instances imperfect—between "temperatures" recorded for the same rock by different mineral pairs. For some samples the spread is only $30°$, but for others discordances of as much as $70°$ are not uncommon.

Current Status of Oxygen-Isotope Geothermometry

Of all geothermometers in current use, those based on oxygen-isotope fractionation would appear on theoretical grounds to be the most promising. For temperatures between 200–600°C, quartz-muscovite has been widely used. Quartz-magnetite covers a greater range, extending even to volcanic temperatures and is most sensitive, but it is suspect by some as being prone to postmetamorphic disturbance. So also is quartz-calcite (cf. Schwarcz et al., 1970; Black, 1974b) which is complicated by possible fractionation of oxygen between solids and gas during decarbonation reactions (Shieh and Taylor, 1969b, p. 328). Some mineral pairs such as quartz-biotite and quartz-ilmenite have been calibrated only indirectly—by plotting measured Δ values against Δ^{qu-mu} for coexisting muscovite in samples of metamorphic rocks. For example, Shieh and Taylor (1969a, pp. 326–328) use the relation $\Delta^{qu-mu} = 0.49\ \Delta^{qu-bi}$ established in this way.

Obviously of prime importance is accurate experimental calibration of the quartz-water pair. For some time values of A and B (curve 1, Table 3-4) advocated by Taylor (1967) and based on unpublished experimental data of R. N. Clayton and colleagues have been in general use. Combined with O'Neil and Taylor's (1969) experimental calibration of muscovite-water (curve 2, Table 3-4 and Fig. 3-10), these afford what has been accepted as the standard scale for quartz-muscovite (curve 3, Table 3-4 and Figs. 3-10 and 3-12). "Temperature" values so obtained are nicely consistent with those inferred from other geothermometers, phase equilibria, and heat-flow models (cf. Shieh and Taylor, 1969a, pp. 333–339), thus further supporting the hypothesis of "frozen-in" equilibria. Now, as we are about to see, the situation is drastically changed.

The theoretically modified equations (curves 4, 5, 6, Table 3-4) of Bottinga and Javoy (1973) give temperatures significantly different from values based on Taylor's equations (compare curve 6 with curve 3 in Fig. 3-12). Much more serious is the impact of the latest experimental calibration of quartz-water by Clayton et al. (1972) (curve 7, Table 3-4, and Fig. 3-11). Corresponding quartz-muscovite curves (8, 9, Fig. 3-12) yield temperatures 100–150° lower than those obtained from the Taylor curve; and these, moreover, would be rejected by most geologists as unreasonably low. Some examples of such discrepancies are given in Table 3-5 for (1) a schist sample (SRO-22C: Shieh and Taylor, 1969a, p. 331) close to (1.8 m from) a granitic pluton contact, Nevada; (2) a staurolite-kyanite schist (VE-12: Garlick, Bottinga, and Javoy, 1973, pp. 258, 260) from Gassetts, Vermont; and (3) a schist sample (10893: Black, 1974b, p. 200) from the lawsonite zone of New Caledonia. There are anomalies in each set of three temperatures: e.g., the span of 200° or less encompassed in each of columns 6, 8, and 9 is surely insufficient to cover temperatures ranging from the blueschist facies to that of the innermost aureole adjacent to a granodioritic pluton. Again 676°C is well outside the stability limits of quartz-muscovite in a shallow aureole, and temperatures as low

TABLE 3-5
**Alternative Oxygen-Isotope Equilibrium Temperatures for Quartz-Muscovite
in Three Metamorphic Rocks, According to Numbered Equations of Table 3-4
and Corresponding Curves, Fig. 3-12**

Specimen (see text)	Δ^{qu-mu}	$T, °C$			
		Curve 3	Curve 6	Curve 8	Curve 9
SRO-22C, Nevada	2.5	676	569	432	454
VE-12, Vermont	3.0	536	509	358	397
10893, New Caledonia	4.43	332	388	231	286
Total temperature span		344	181	201	168

as 430–450°C conflict with all our ideas regarding heat-flow regimes at plutonic contacts (cf. pp. 18–20).

We conclude that, in spite of intrinsic promise and widespread current use, the present state of oxygen-isotope geothermometry is far from satisfactory. Either calibration is still at fault (certainly it is ambiguous) or isotopic disequilibrium is much more prevalent than most of us would admit. Temperatures based on other evidence can be (and repeatedly have been) *justified* by appealing to patterns of oxygen fractionation; but they cannot be *tested* unequivocally by such means. More reliance perhaps can be placed on temperature differences (e.g., from one zone to another) inferred from sets of oxygen-isotope analysis carried out in the same laboratory.

Finally, to conclude on a pessimistic note, there are disquieting and increasingly numerous, carefully documented instances of marked discrepancy between oxygen-isotope temperatures (whatever the scale of calibration) and temperatures inferred from other geothermometers, from geologic situations, or from thermal models. An illustrative case has been discussed by Floran and Papike (1978, pp. 279–281) with reference to the inner contact aureole of the Duluth gabbro complex. Here and in most other instances temperatures registered on the oxygen-isotope geothermometer are significantly lower than those compatible with other data or reasoning. Can it possibly be that isotopic equilibration of oxygen on a grain-to-grain scale continues during the early stages of postmetamorphic cooling? The possibility of continuing postmetamorphic equilibration down to some "freezing" temperature, determined in each case by kinetic factors, is one that inevitably plagues advocates of geothermometers that are based on partitioning of elements or of isotopes between coexisting phases.

4

Some Key Equilibria
Calibrated by Experiment
and Thermodynamic Computation

BACKGROUND

During the past three decades many simple equilibria relevant to metamorphism have been calibrated numerically by direct experiment and by thermodynamic computation. Much of the earlier experimental work was clouded by faults inherent in methodology: failure (because of unfavorable kinetic factors or low values of ΔG_r) to reverse equilibrium; faulty instrumentation (as in use of squeezer apparatus); choice of highly reactive starting materials such as glass, powdered samples activated by strain and surface energy, even salts of organic acids; equivocal criteria of equilibrium and of reaction sense; failure to heed thermodynamic constraints. Thermodynamic data in use 20 years ago were far from adequate. Past experience, use of laboratory techniques now in vogue, and improved and extended thermodynamic data available today have eliminated or substantially reduced many former anomalies and discrepancies of this kind. So where a general consensus has been reached and past confusion resolved there is no longer a need to recapitulate (as was done in the earlier edition of this book) the pros and cons of alternatives in past controversies.[*] Anomalies and differences of opinion never-

---

[*]Consensus of course is no guarantee of an ultimate solution to any problem. Witness the generally approved value, 5.5 kb, once placed upon the Al_2SiO_5 triple point (cf. Richardson et al., 1969)—a figure now thought by many to be too high by as much as 2 kb (see later in this chapter).

theless remain, and past experience warns us that all numerical calibrations presented in this chapter should be regarded as tentative. Moreover it is unsafe to assume that the latest pronouncement is necessarily superior to earlier views based on simpler experimental techniques. Readers are urged to look more deeply into the literature of geochemistry and form their own opinions as to the validity of calibrations presented below for individual equilibria.

The experimental data that form the factual basis of this chapter are records of direct reversals supplemented in some cases by solubility measurements. An indispensable check is available in standard thermodynamic properties of mineral phases and simple gases (always remembering that calorimetrically determined ΔH_f° and ΔG_f° values are subject to high uncertainty). We shall refer repeatedly to results of the comprehensive synthesis by Helgeson et al. (1978) of experimental with entropy-volume data, which with few exceptions bypasses standard tabulated ΔH_f° and ΔG_f° values.

EQUILIBRIA IN METAPELITES

Current Prospects

Pelitic rocks are specially sensitive to progressive metamorphism—witness the varied detail in recorded zonal sequences of pelitic mineral assemblages. Many actual reactions leading to appearance or elimination of index minerals in nature are complicated by mutual substitution of common elements (notably, Mg, Fe, and Mn) and by the influence of oxygen fugacity internally buffered at different levels. Consequently key equilibria may be difficult to formulate in terms of mass-balanced equations and even more so to calibrate in meaningful terms of pressure and temperature. There are, however, a few simple equilibria on which such influences are minimal: they involve the silicates and hydrosilicates of aluminum and the common metamorphic white mica generally identified as muscovite. These equilibria we shall consider in some detail. They set limits upon the stability fields of paragenetically associated index minerals such as biotite, almandine, staurolite, and cordierite for which existing experimental data alone, for reasons just cited, are inadequate or ambiguous. Physical implications of minerals in this latter category can be treated only in broad terms.

Stability Field of Pyrophyllite-Quartz

The transition from shales to slates and phyllites as diagenesis merges—via what has been termed *anchimetamorphism*—into metamorphism proper is marked by development of a mica-chlorite assemblage from the initial clay paragenesis. A good deal is now known as to the mineralogical character of this transition (e.g., Frey, 1970; Kubler et al., 1974). But the only relevant equilibria that have been experimentally investigated are those defining the stability field of pyrophyllite, a mineral perhaps rather widely distributed in slates and phyllites formed during the first stages of regional metamorphism of aluminum-rich (kaolinite-bearing) clays and shales.

Partly because the free energies of clay minerals are markedly influenced by degree of crystallinity, there was little agreement among early estimates of the limits of the pyrophyllite field in quartz-bearing rocks. Today, however, there is a general consensus among geochemists that at pressures ($P_{H_2O} = P$) of a few kilobars pyrophyllite becomes stable between about 350–400°C. Experimental reversal data would limit the width of the stability field to 50–70°, while the computed equilibria of Helgeson et al. would extend the span to 100° or at pressures of 5–7 kb even more (Fig. 4-1).

Divergence of opinion is greatest with respect to the reaction signaling the entry of pyrophyllite at the expense of kaolinite

$$Al_4 Si_4 O_{10}(OH)_8 + 4SiO_2 \rightleftharpoons 2Al_2 Si_4 O_{10}(OH)_2 + 2H_2 O \qquad (4\text{-}1)$$
$$\text{kaolinite} \qquad \text{quartz} \qquad \text{pyrophyllite}$$

For this A. B. Thompson (1970) has recorded reversals at 345°C, $P_{H_2O} = P = 2$ kb, and at 325°C, 1 kb. Curve 1*a* in Fig. 4-1 has been extrapolated from these points to 7 kb (Haas and Holdaway, 1973). Curve 1*b* has been computed by Helgeson et al. (1978) using selected experimental data in the system $Al_2 O_3$-SiO_2-$H_2 O$ and a value of ΔH_f° for gibbsite calorimetrically newly determined by Hemingway and

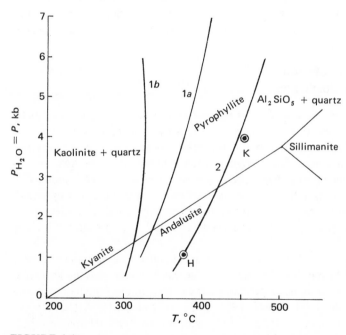

FIGURE 4-1

Experimentally determined pyrophyllite equilibria with kyanite-andalusite boundary (after Holdaway, 1971). 1. Kaolinite + 2 quartz ⇌ pyrophyllite + $H_2 O$ (*a*) Curve extrapolated by Haas and Holdaway (1973) from points of reversal by A. B. Thompson (1970). (*b*) Helgeson's (1978) computed curve. 2. Pyrophyllite ⇌ $Al_2 SiO_5$ + 3 quartz + $H_2 O$ Helgeson's (1978) computed curve. Also shown are points of reversal: *K*, by Kerrick (1968); *H*, by J. J. Hemley (1977, as cited by Helgeson et al., 1978, p. 115).

Robie (1977): $-309,065$ cal mole^{-1}, compared with $-306,380$ cal mole^{-1} given in Robie and Waldbaum's tables.

Pyrophyllite is eliminated, and an Al_2SiO_5 polymorph first appears as a result of the reaction

$$Al_2Si_4O_{10}(OH)_2 \rightleftharpoons \underbrace{Al_2SiO_5}_{\text{andalusite, kyanite}} + 3SiO_2 + H_2O \qquad (4\text{-}2)$$

$$\underset{\text{pyrophyllite}}{} \qquad\qquad \underset{\text{quartz}}{}$$

Reversals by Kerrick (1968) and Hemley are shown in Fig. 4-1 along with a thermodynamically computed curve (2) of Helgeson et al. (1978), which agrees closely with Kerrick's data. Haas and Holdaway (1974), however, would place the pyrophyllite-kyanite equilibrium at significantly lower temperatures, thereby narrowing the pyrophyllite stability field to a span of only 20° (400–420°C) at 7 kb.

In spite of existing uncertainties calibration of the stability field of pyrophyllite has shown that at pressures of a few kilobars the distinctive mica-chlorite paragenesis of low-grade slates and phyllites begins to develop at temperatures of 350–400°C. And the first appearance of andalusite in aluminous rocks in the outer zones of contact aureoles can be placed with some confidence in the vicinity of 400°C. If Helgeson's computed limits of the pyrophyllite field are correct, this mineral should be widespread in aluminous rocks metamorphosed at high pressures and low temperatures in zones of subduction.

Comment on the Evolution of Low-Grade Phyllosilicates

From X-ray studies of shales and slates in the transition from diagenesis to metamorphism (e.g., Frey, 1970; Kubler et al., 1974), a coherent mineralogical picture of evolution of low-grade metamorphic micas and chlorites is beginning to emerge. To put it briefly, illite, mixed-layer phyllosilicates (illite-montmorillonites, corrensite), and kaolin minerals of diagenetic origin give way to phengitic muscovite, aluminous chlorite, and, in the more aluminous rocks, paragonite and pyrophyllite. The only relevant, experimentally tested temperature index is the kaolin-pyrophyllite transition (Fig. 4-1) that suggests 300–350°C at pressures of a few kilobars.

The first isograd based on pelitic assemblages in most metamorphic provinces is marked by the appearance of biotite. This mineral, however, may be generated at this stage by many reactions, depending on the composition of the parent assemblage (cf. Tilley, 1926; E. H. Brown, 1971, 1975; Frey et al., 1973; De Béthune, 1976). Reactants include combinations of phengitic muscovite, K-feldspar, glauconite, stilpnomelane, aluminous chlorites, and carbonates. None of the proposed equilibria has been satisfactorily calibrated; all must be sensitive to variation in oxygen fugacity. The first biotite isograd, easily recognized though it may be in the field, is unlikely to have more than local qualitative value as an index of metamorphic conditions.

The Al₂SiO₅ Polymorphs

Kyanite, andalusite, and sillimanite, all common constituents of metapelites, collectively cover a wide range of metamorphic grades. For this reason, and because their stability fields are unaffected by fluid-pressure variables as distinct from load pressure, their potential as unambiguous indices of metamorphic conditions was appreciated from the first by geochemists interested in calibrating metamorphic gradients.

A glance at the thermodynamic properties of the three polymorphs should have warned that the task would not be easy (cf. Fyfe, 1967). As G. C. Brown and Fyfe (1971, p. 227) have summed up the situation:

> Near equilibrium the ΔS_r of the andalusite-sillimanite reaction is only about 0.3 cal mole^{-1} degr^{-1}. This means that if we wish to know the phase boundary with a certainty of at least $\pm 50°C$ we must also use procedures which will give a free energy $[\Delta G_r]$* with an accuracy of ± 15 cal mole^{-1}. For kyanite reactions, where ΔS_r is about 2 cal mole^{-1} degr^{-1}, again ΔG_r must be known within limits of at least ± 100 cal mole^{-1}. These are trivial quantities when it is noted that the lattice energies of the three polymorphs† are near 5×10^5 cal mole^{-1}.
>
> It is clear when these requirements are considered that small effects, strain energy, surface energy, impurity factors, will be critical in such a system. . . . Thus it seems that the only experiments likely to yield significant results will be those in which unstrained macrocrystalline materials are used.

Looking at the problem slightly differently, overstepping of the equilibrium temperature by 50°C will increase ΔG_r for kyanite → sillimanite by only about 100 cal mole^{-1}; for andalusite → sillimanite the corresponding increment will be a mere 15 cal mole^{-1}. And it will be remembered that ΔG_r is the driving force of reaction, so that within 50°C of equilibrium reaction rates can be expected to be very slow, and reversals correspondingly difficult to accomplish.

Thirty years ago Miyashiro (e.g., 1953, p. 207) was already using a general topology (without numerical calibration) for stability relations between the three polymorphs consistent with field observations and the thermodynamic data available at that time. Subsequent experimental work has confirmed Miyashiro's scheme and provided the necessary calibration with the aid of improved thermodynamic data. Several significant conclusions have emerged from the latter alone (Table 4-1).

*From

$$\left(\frac{\delta \Delta G_r}{\delta T} \right)_P = - \Delta S_r$$

†Values of ΔG_f° (from elements) listed by Helgeson et al. (1978, Table 8) are kyanite, $-580,956$ cal mole^{-1}; andalusite, $-580,587$ cal mole^{-1}; and sillimanite, $-580,091$ cal mole^{-1}.

TABLE 4-1

Thermodynamic Data for Al_2SiO_5 Equilibria: Molar Volumes and Entropies at Atmospheric Pressure, and Computed Slopes of Univariant Curves[a]

Polymorph	V, cm³ mole⁻¹		S, cal mole⁻¹ degr⁻¹	
	800 K	1000 K	800 K	1000 K
Kyanite	44.73		57.91	
Andalusite	52.34	52.76	60.08	70.23
Sillimanite	50.26	50.48	60.48	70.52

Reaction	ΔV_r, cm³ mole⁻¹		ΔS_r, cal mole⁻¹ degr⁻¹		dP/dT bars degr⁻¹ = 41.84 $\Delta S_r/\Delta V_r$	
	800 K	1000 K	800 K	1000 K	800 K	1000 K
Kyanite → sillimanite	5.53		2.57		19.4	
Kyanite → andalusite	7.61		2.17		11.9	
Andalusite → sillimanite	−2.08	−2.28	0.4	0.29	−8.0	−5.3

[a]Molar volumes taken from Skinner et al., 1961; entropies from Robie and Waldbaum, 1968.

1. For the two kyanite inversions values of ΔV_r and ΔS_r are high enough to define the slopes dP/dT of the univariant curves: at $500°C \sim 20$ bars $degr^{-1}$ for kyanite $\rightleftharpoons$ sillimanite, ~ 12 bars $degr^{-1}$ for kyanite $\rightleftharpoons$ andalusite.

2. For andalusite $\rightleftharpoons$ sillimanite, ΔV_r and ΔS_r are too small to fix the slope of the univariant curve with any precision; but the sign must be negative and the slope must decrease significantly in the interval $500–800°C$.

3. The acute intersection of the two kyanite curves and the uncertain slope of that for andalusite $\rightleftharpoons$ sillimanite together give rise to marked uncertainty (perhaps 2 kb or so) as to location of the triple point.

4. Because within $50°$ of equilibrium ΔG_r of all reactions is so low, the value of the triple point as an index of geological conditions is dubious (cf. G. C. Brown and Fyfe, 1971, p. 299). Indeed, this has been suspected from the many records of coexisting polymorphs where one at least appears to have crystallized or survived as a metastable phase within the stability field of another.

Results of experimental investigations in the Al_2SiO_5 system at first led to a good deal of confusion and wide differences in opinion (cf. Zen, 1969). This was perhaps inevitable on thermodynamic grounds. It was heightened by inappropriate methodology (use of "squeezer" apparatus and of activated starting materials), failure to heed thermodynamic constraints, and inherent slowness of reaction rates. Some of this past confusion has now been resolved: in particular, location of the triple point at pressures as high as 8 kb is now generally admitted to be grossly in error. Figure 4-2 shows two versions of the phase diagram (G. C. Brown and Fyfe, 1971; Holdaway, 1971), both consistent with the available data— both experimental (Table 4-2) and thermodynamic (Table 4-1). Other experimentally based phase diagrams with triple points at pressures around 6 kb (e.g., Althaus, 1967; Richardson et al., 1969) have been cited over the past few years in geological contexts. For critical appraisal of these, which brings out the experi-

TABLE 4-2
Selected Experimentally Determined Equilibrium Points for Al_2SiO_5 Polymorphs

Equilibrium	P, kb	T, °C	Source
Kyanite $\rightleftharpoons$ sillimanite	$23\frac{1}{2}-24\frac{1}{2}$	1500	Clark (1961)
	22–23	1400	Clark (1961)
	10	800–820	} Richardson et al. (1968)
	9	750–770	
Kyanite $\rightleftharpoons$ andalusite	1	398 ± 40	} Brown and Fyfe (1971)
	2	472 ± 40	
(metastable)	3	534 ± 40	
Andalusite $\rightleftharpoons$ sillimanite	0.001	775 ± 20	Weill (1966)[a]
	1.8	617 ± 27	} Holdaway (1971)
	3.6	509 ± 18	

[a]Initially reported as slightly below $800°C$; subsequently corrected to $775°C$ as cited by Holdaway (1971, p. 117).

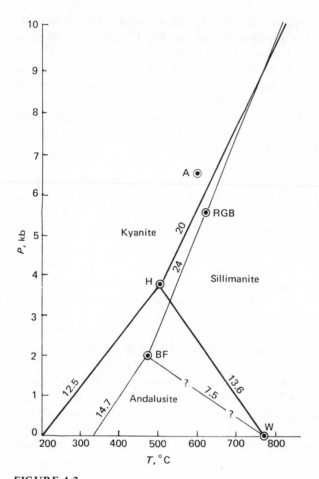

FIGURE 4-2

Experimentally determined stability relations of Al_2SiO_5 polymorphs. Heavy lines after Holdaway (1971); light lines after Brown and Fyfe (1971); numerals indicate slopes dP/dT, bar degr[-1]. Alternative triple points proposed by Brown and Fyfe (BF); Holdaway (H); Richardson, Bell, and Gilbert (RGB); and Althaus (A). Point W is based on solubility measurements by Weill (1966; revised as reported by Holdaway, 1971).

mental difficulties peculiar to the Al_2SiO_5 system, the reader is referred to Richardson et al. (1967, pp. 533–536) and Holdaway (1971, pp. 117–120).

Conclusions applicable to natural occurrences of the Al_2SiO_5 polymorphs are as follows (cf. Fig. 4-2):

1. Extensive development of andalusite implies pressures no greater than about $3\frac{1}{2}$ kb and correspondingly shallow depth (<10 km) of metamorphism.
2. An andalusite-sillimanite isograd indicates temperatures exceeding 500°C, at shallow depths perhaps 600°C.
3. A kyanite-sillimanite isograd ("first sillimanite isograd") indicates temperatures of 500–600°C at relatively high pressures 4–6 kb (10–20 km depth).

Because of potential influences of grain size (as in fibrolite), strain, and Al-Si disorder (in sillimanite) on ΔG_r of natural reactions, greater precision can scarcely be expected of calibrations based on Al_2SiO_5 paragenesis.

Breakdown of Muscovite in the Presence of Quartz

Experimentally Reversed Equilibrium

At the highest grade of metamorphism, K-feldspar and sillimanite (or andalusite) appear in pelitic rocks at the expense of the pair muscovite-quartz, ubiquitous in metapelites of lower grades. The corresponding equilibrium can be expressed in the simplest manner as

$$KAl_2(AlSi_3O_{10})(OH)_2 + SiO_2 \rightleftharpoons KAlSi_3O_8 + Al_2SiO_5 + H_2O \qquad (4\text{-}3)$$
$$\underset{\text{muscovite}}{\qquad} \quad \underset{\text{quartz}}{\qquad} \underset{\text{K-feldspar}}{\qquad} \underset{\text{sillimanite}}{\qquad}$$

This has been successfully reversed in the laboratory by a number of workers— Evans (1965), Althaus et al. (1970), Kerrick (1972), Day (1973), Chatterjee and Johannes (1974); and the corresponding univariant curve has been computed by Helgeson et al. (1978). Figure 4-3 shows Helgeson's curve together with points of reversal by Evans (2–4 kb) and Chatterjee and Johannes ($\frac{1}{2}$ to 5 kb). Agreement could scarcely be closer.[*] Moreover Evans' (1965) reversal point at (2 kb, 600°C) has been exactly confirmed by Kerrick (1972). The curve reproduced in Fig. 4-3 surely must represent one of the most precisely calibrated equilibria available to the student of metamorphic gradients. Presence of a paragonite component in muscovite, in concentrations comparable to that typical of high-grade metamorphic muscovites ($X_{par}^{mus} \approx 0.1$) seems to have little effect upon equilibrium temperatures. Evans and Kerrick both used muscovites of this composition; the mica used by Chatterjee and Johannes was pure synthetic $2M_1$-muscovite, $KAl_2(AlSi_3O_{10})(OH)_2$. Note that the curve in Fig. 4-3 is based on $P = P_{H_2O}$. Kerrick's experiments at $P = 2$ kb show that lowering of $X_{H_2O}^{gas}$ to 0.5 at this pressure reduces the equilibrium temperature by about 50° (to 555°C).

Application to Sillimanite Isograds

Sillimanite isograds have been mapped on the basis of at least three equilibria. That of the Barrovian zonal sequence in Scotland simply marks the kyanite → sillimanite inversion. In parts of the Appalachian province and elsewhere the first appearance of sillimanite coincides with elimination of staurolite by a reaction (cf. D. M. Carmichael, 1969, pp. 256–259) involving muscovite that can be written in its simplest form (neglecting MgO) as:

$$6Fe_2Al_9O_6(SiO_4)_4(O\cdot OH) + KAl_2(AlSi_3O_{10})(OH)_2 + 10SiO_2 \rightleftharpoons 25Al_2SiO_5$$
$$\underset{\text{staurolite}}{\qquad} \qquad \underset{\text{muscovite}}{\qquad} \qquad \underset{\text{quartz}}{\qquad} \underset{\text{sillimanite}}{\qquad}$$

$$+ 3Fe_3Al_2Si_3O_{12} + KFe_3(AlSi_3O_{10})(OH)_2 + 3H_2O \qquad (4\text{-}4)$$
$$\underset{\text{almandine}}{\qquad} \qquad \underset{\text{biotite}}{\qquad}$$

---

[*]Temperatures some 40° higher recorded by Althaus et al. (1970) and by Day (1973) probably reflect the influence of disorder in the K-feldspar phases used and generated in their experiments (cf. Helgeson et al., 1978).

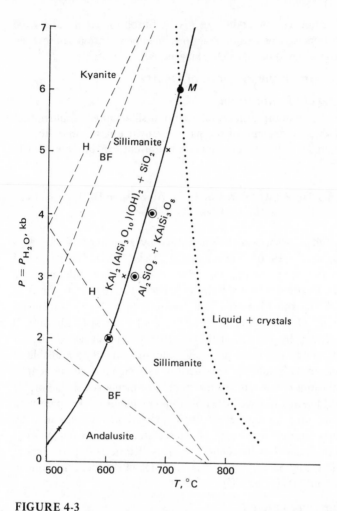

FIGURE 4-3

Curve of univariant equilibrium (full line) for muscovite + quartz $\rightleftharpoons$ K-feldspar + Al$_2$SiO$_5$ + H$_2$O (after Helgeson et al., 1978 [computed]). Points of experimental reversal: circled dots, B. Evans (1965); crosses, Chatterjee and Johannes (1974). Also shown: melting curve, dotted: kyanite $\rightleftharpoons$ sillimanite, and andalusite $\rightleftharpoons$ sillimanite equilibria, dashed (BF; after Brown and Fyfe, 1971; H, after Holdaway (1971).

Thus in the presence of staurolite, the stability field of muscovite-quartz is reduced. Equation (4-4), marking a first sillimanite or sillimanite-almandine isograd, expresses a coupled reaction (cf. p. 74) compounded from

$$\text{muscovite} + \text{quartz} \rightleftharpoons \text{K-feldspar} + \text{sillimanite} + \text{H}_2\text{O}$$

and

$$6 \text{ staurolite} + \text{K-feldspar} + 9 \text{ quartz} \rightleftharpoons 24 \text{ sillimanite} + 3 \text{ almandine}$$

$$+ \text{ biotite} + 2\text{H}_2\text{O}$$

Elsewhere, e.g., in the Oquossoc area of Maine (Guidotti, 1970), the sharply defined sillimanite-almandine isograd corresponding to Eq. (4-4) is preceded by development of sillimanite in small amounts by progressive reduction of the paragorite content of muscovite, albite being a coproduct of the reaction.

The "second sillimanite" or sillimanite-orthoclase isograd of the Appalachian province expresses the breakdown of muscovite-quartz alone. At somewhat lower grades, above that of the sillimanite-almandine isograd, sillimanite is a common constituent, K-feldspar not so common in pelitic assemblages; but the two phases do not coexist in the same assemblage. Nor does the sillimanite-orthoclase isograd mark sudden elimination of muscovite, which indeed can be a widespread constituent of quartz-bearing rocks with coexisting K-feldspar and sillimanite. A more realistic reaction than Eq. (4-3) that expresses observed mineralogical changes at the isograd in western Maine (Evans and Guidotti, 1966, p. 57) is

$$\underset{\text{muscovite}}{K_{0.94}Na_{0.06}Al_2(AlSi_3O_{10})(OH)_2} + \underset{\text{in plagioclase}}{0.1\,NaAlSi_3O_8} + \underset{\text{quartz}}{SiO_2}$$

$$\rightleftharpoons \underset{\text{K-feldspar}}{1.1\,K_{0.86}Na_{0.14}AlSi_3O_8} + \underset{\text{sillimanite}}{Al_2SiO_5} + H_2O \qquad (4\text{-}5)$$

Presumably such a reaction occurs at a somewhat lower temperature than that for corresponding values of P and P_{H_2O} on the curve of Fig. 4-3.

Finally calibration of any isograd in terms of Fig. 4-3 (for which $P = P_f = P_{H_2O}$) is complicated by the fact that, where graphite or pyrrhotite is a member of the metamorphic assemblage, $P_{H_2O} < P_f$. This case has been discussed, with reference to sillimanite isograds in Maine, by Guidotti (1970) and by Kerrick (1972).

Significance of Staurolite

Background Paragenesis

The characteristic milieu of staurolite is in the middle-grade staurolite zone of regional metamorphism: there it is widespread in metapelites (typically quartz-staurolite-almandine-mica schists) of appropriate composition—with high Fe/Mg and Al/K. The staurolite isograd marking the first appearance of the zonal index is not far beyond that of almandine. At maximum grades, beyond the sillimanite-orthoclase isograd, staurolite is no longer present in pelitic assemblages. It has already been eliminated in favor of almandine and sillimanite by reactions involving micas.

In the lower pressure-range of metamorphism, pelitic staurolite-cordierite parageneses take the place of the garnetiferous assemblages so characteristic of higher pressures. Still another set of equilibria are here involved in generation and later elimination of staurolite—complicated by the great disparity between respective Fe/Mg values in the two principal phases (staurolite and cordierite).

Staurolite Isograds

Petrographic evidence shows that any of several possible reactions, depending on rock composition and pressure variables, may be responsible for the first appearance of staurolite in facies series of medium and high pressure (cf. Hoschek, 1967, pp. 141–144; Richardson, 1968; Ganguly, 1972, p. 337). In many of them a principal progenitor is chloritoid; but, rather commonly it seems, staurolite and biotite may form by reactions involving muscovite and iron-rich chlorite. Quartz is a ubiquitous associate of chloritoid and of staurolite in pelitic schists and is a participant in all likely staurolite isograd reactions. Clearly it is impossible to define any unique, universally applicable staurolite isograd in terms of P, T, and other physical variables. Our task is to set quantitative limits upon the range of conditions over which the common quartz-staurolite-almandine-mica paragenesis first develops in metapelites.

A general pattern of the stability field of common staurolite assemblages and some quantitative limits on its boundaries are set by Richardson's (1968) experimental study of the behavior of pure Fe-staurolite and related purely ferrous phases at oxygen fugacities controlled by the quartz-magnetite-fayalite buffer (cf. Fig. 4-4). The practical petrological significance of this work lies in the universally high Fe/(Fe + Mg) ratios of natural staurolites (0.7–0.8) and chloritoids (0.8–0.9). In the purely ferrous system, the stability field of staurolite is limited by three curves of univariant five-phase equilibrium* correspondingly numbered in Fig. 4-4.

*The system has five components; but external buffering of the composition $(X_{O_2}^{gas})$ of the fluid phase reduces the remaining variance of five-phase assemblages to 1.

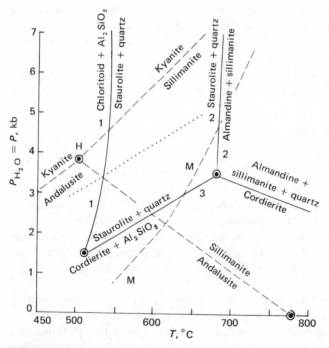

FIGURE 4-4

Experimentally determined stability relations of pure iron end members of the chloritoid, staurolite, almandine, and cordierite series at f_{O_2} buffered by quartz-magnetite-fayalite (after S. W. Richardson, 1968, p. 481). Curves numbered to correspond with equilibria in text. Al_2SiO_5 equilibria after M. J. Holdaway (H), and muscovite-quartz breakdown (M) after B. J. Evans. The dotted line tentative upper limit of natural staurolite-cordierite assemblages.

1. 8 chloritoid + 10 sillimanite $\rightleftharpoons$ 2 staurolite + 3 quartz + $4H_2O$

2. 6 staurolite + 25 quartz $\rightleftharpoons$ 8 almandine + 46 sillimanite + $12H_2O$

3. 2 staurolite + 15 quartz $\rightleftharpoons$ 4 cordierite + 10 sillimanite + $4H_2O$

Curve 1 is the simplified analog of the staurolite isograd. Actual isograd reactions probably occur at f_{O_2} values somewhat above those of the experimental buffer (Richardson, 1968, p. 485), but the resulting increase in temperature of equilibrium 1 will be very slight—according to Ganguly's data (1972, Fig. 2, curve 3) no more than 40° for the full range of f_{O_2} (10^{-21}-10^{-14}), covering the interval between the quartz-magnetite-fayalite and hematite-magnetite buffers at 10 kb and 570 ± 20°C. The effect of adding Mg to the system will be to displace curve 1 slightly into the chloritoid field of Fig. 4-4. Hoschek's (1969) work on the reaction[*]

Chlorite + 3 muscovite $\rightleftharpoons$ staurolite + 3 biotite + 7 quartz + $14H_2O$

demonstrated equilibrium at 540°C, 4 kb and at 565°C, 7 kb—very close to Richardson's curve.

We may conclude then (cf. Ganguly, 1969, p. 939), that the range of temperatures covering common reactions at the staurolite isograd is narrow enough for this to be a useful index of metamorphic conditions—perhaps 520-580°C (increasing with pressure) in the P_{H_2O} range 4-8 kb.

High-Temperature and Low-Pressure Limits
of Staurolite Stability

Curves 2 and 3 define only the extreme limits of staurolite stability at somewhat lower than normal f_{O_2}. They add little to what has long been inferred from petrographic observation.

1. At pressures above perhaps 5 kb staurolite becomes eliminated and almandine and sillimanite appear as reaction products. But natural equilibria include muscovite and biotite [cf. Eq. (4-4)], and they will be sensitive to the magnesium content of the natural systems and possibly to variation in f_{O_2}. Experimental work is consistent with the petrographic observation that staurolite disappears from pelitic assemblages at temperatures below those of the muscovite-quartz breakdown. The temperature span of the staurolite zone is probably less than 100°.

2. At low pressures destruction of staurolite with rising temperature is accompanied by development of cordierite instead of almandine. Curve 3 of Fig. 4-4 represents an equilibrium between purely ferrous phases:

2 staurolite + 15 quartz $\rightleftharpoons$ 4 cordierite + 10 sillimanite + $4H_2O$

There is still some uncertainty, stemming from a lack of knowledge as to the role of water loosely held in cordierite, as to the slope of curve 3. It is clear, however,

---

[*]Stoichiometric coefficients approximate.

that staurolite-cordierite equilibria are sensitive to pressure. In natural systems containing magnesium, which preferentially enters cordierite, the equilibrium shifts significantly to higher pressures—but to a degree still experimentally undetermined. The staurolite-cordierite boundary is also sensitive to variation in f_{O_2}. Ganguly (1972, pp. 348, 349, 365) has discussed an oxidation-reduction equilibrium:

$$27 \text{ cordierite} + 6H_2O + 5O_2 \rightleftharpoons 12 \text{ staurolite} + 10 \text{ magnetite} + 87 \text{ quartz}$$

for which he shows that at $620°C$ increase in f_{O_2} from 10^{-18} to 10^{-17} reduces equilibrium pressure by almost 1 kb. Increase in f_{O_2} thus substantially extends the stability field of staurolite at the expense of cordierite. Taking such factors into account it is clear that there will be a rather wide range of metamorphic conditions—especially pressure—under which staurolite and cordierite may coexist in equilibrium. High $Mg/(Mg + Fe)$ ratios and low f_{O_2} favor increasingly higher equilibrium pressures. Petrographic experience shows that staurolite-cordierite assemblages are indeed not uncommon in nature (as in the Buchan facies series of Scotland); and the Al_2SiO_5 polymorph with which they tend to be associated is andalusite. So the pressure coverage of staurolite-cordierite above curve 3 can be adjusted to individual preference regarding the location of the elusive Al_2SiO_5 triple point [contrast Fig. 4-4 with other tentative diagrams proposed by Richardson (1968, p. 486) and Ganguly (1972, p. 361)].

Cordierite-Garnet Parageneses

A characteristic pelitic assemblage in some granulites at maximum grades of regional metamorphism is cordierite-garnet-sillimanite-quartz-orthoclase, with or without biotite. Partition of Mg-Fe between cordierite, biotite, and garnet is strong, the preference of Mg being for phases in the order just given. Distribution coefficients corresponding to exchange reactions relating natural pairs (cf. Holdaway and Lee, 1977, pp. 188–189) are

1. Cordierite-Biotite

$$K_D = \frac{X_{Fe}^{Cd} X_{Mg}^{Bi}}{X_{Mg}^{Cd} X_{Fe}^{Bi}} \approx 0.54 \pm 0.1$$

2. Cordierite-Garnet

$$K_D = \frac{X_{Fe}^{Cd} X_{Mg}^{Ga}}{X_{Mg}^{Cd} X_{Fe}^{Ga}} \approx 0.16 \pm 0.05$$

During the past decade a good deal of experimental effort and theoretical analysis have been directed toward determining P-T conditions of univariant equilibria involving the pure Fe and Mg end members of all three mineral series, and correlating mineral compositions of coexisting solid-solution pairs with P and T in intervening bivariant fields. The natural systems cannot be treated, even in a simplified manner in terms of fewer than six components (e.g., SiO_2, Al_2O_3, MgO, FeO, K_2O, and H_2O). Even then we ignore CaO and MnO, which can be significant components of high-grade "almandines," and Na_2O, which is ever-present in associated K-feldspar ("orthoclase"). Most of the experimental work has been concentrated on the six-component system, and has ignored the possible influence of water in cordierite on Mg-Fe partition. Not surprisingly, no simple generally applicable conclusion has been reached; in fact, some results obtained by different workers are mutually contradictory. No attempt will be made here to review this work. We shall merely note some conclusions reached and suggestions put forward in two recent critical assessments of available data (B. J. Wood, 1973; Holdaway and Lee, 1977*).

Wood's contribution concentrates on a single problem—the possibility that P_{H_2O} may significantly influence Mg-Fe partition between cordierite and garnet (because of the variable loosely held water content of cordierite). On these terms, and by invoking several reasonable but unsubstantiated assumptions, he resolves the apparent conflict between results of experiments carried out with P_{H_2O} respectively equal to and much less than total pressure; and from natural K_D values he places metamorphic equilibration at P_{H_2O} between 1 and 3 kb.

Figure 4-5 illustrates a tentative comprehensive model put forward by Holdaway and Lee (1977). It is based on new experimental data on equilibria in magnesium-free systems and selected, critically assessed data of other experiments, and also takes into account the melting behavior of quartz-orthoclase in hydrous systems and inferences drawn from a survey of K_D values for natural mineral pairs treated in the manner of A. B. Thompson (1976). The upper pressure limit of the cordierite breakdown is given by univariant curves (similarly numbered in Fig. 4-5) for equilibria between pure ferrous phases.

1. 1.26 Fe-cordierite + 0.84 K-feldspar + $(1 - 1.26n)H_2O \rightleftharpoons 1$ Fe-biotite

  $+ 2.08$ sillimanite + 4 quartz

2. 3 Fe-cordierite $\rightleftharpoons 2$ almandine + 4 sillimanite + 5 quartz + $3nH_2O$

where n represents the water content of cordierite at equilibrium temperatures. Above curves 1 and 2 is a pressure field of bivariant equilibrium, some 3 kb wide above curve 1, where cordierite coexists with its breakdown products. It is terminated above by the upper pressure limit of stability of pure magnesian cordierite. Intervening compositional contours, drawn for maximum Fe in stable

*The interested reader is referred to these papers for references to pertinent experimental work by K. L. Currie, B. J. Hansen and D. H. Green, E. Hoffer, R. C. Newton, W. Schreyer and H. S. Yoder, F. Seifert and W. Schreyer, and A. Weisbrod.

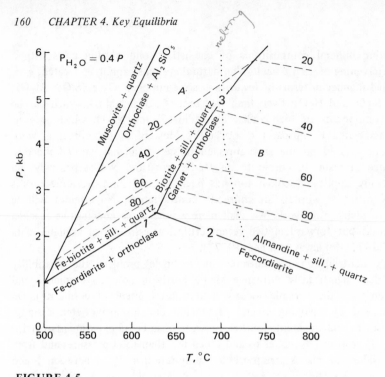

FIGURE 4-5

Model for partitioning of Mg-Fe in natural pairs cordierite-biotite (field A) and cordierite-garnet (field B), at $P_{H_2O} = 0.4P$; dashed lines are contours for molar ratios Fe/(Fe + Mg) in cordierite (after M. J. Holdaway and S. M. Lee, 1977). Dotted curve represents initiation of "granitic" melting in the system.

cordierite, are based on inferences drawn from natural K_D values in relation to presumed grade.

Figure 4-5 reflects conditions postulated by Holdaway and Lee as typical of granulite metamorphism: entry of Ca into garnet and of Na into K-feldspar, and especially a sharp reduction of P_{H_2O} in relation to total pressure (P_{H_2O} arbitrarily fixed as $0.4P$). The collective result is to lower the temperature and pressure of the triple point 1-2-3 by 120° and 0.5 kb, and to raise temperatures of initial melting. Some such stipulation is necessary to bring substantial segments of curves 2 and 3 outside the field of partial melting of assemblages with quartz and K-feldspar.[*] Clearly, although cordierite composition has obvious potential in geobarometry, Fig. 4-5 cannot be regarded as providing a precisely calibrated instrument. In fact considering the expense and effort that have been expended on the problem, progress beyond the long-held, geologically based view that cordierite-almandine granulites represent crystallization at maximum metamorphic temperatures and relatively low pressures has been disappointing.

---

[*]There is independent evidence based on fluid inclusions that some granulite assemblages crystallized in equilibrium with water-deficient fluids (Touret, 1971). And it has been suggested on grounds of bulk composition that cordierite granulites may be water-deficient restites from which a hydrous "granitic" melt has been withdrawn (Harris, 1976).

REACTIONS IN SILICEOUS DOLOMITIC LIMESTONES

Steps in Progressive Decarbonation

Within the range of metamorphic temperatures and pressures, the pairs dolomite-quartz and calcite-quartz tend to become unstable with increasing temperature. In a rock represented by some point in the calcite-dolomite-quartz triangle, progressive metamorphism leads to a series of step reactions, each involving partial elimination of CO_2. Such a series leads to progressive increase in the entropy of the system. For example, a possible sequence, starting from a mixture of equal parts of dolomite and calcite with a small amount of quartz (P in Fig. 4-6), might be

1. Elimination of quartz:

    Dolomite + 2 quartz → diopside + $2CO_2$

2. Elimination of diopside:

    Diopside + 3 dolomite ⇌ 4 calcite + 2 forsterite + $2CO_2$

3. Elimination of dolomite:

    Dolomite → periclase + calcite + CO_2

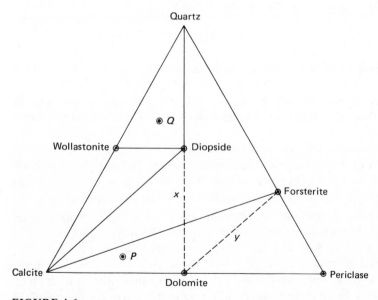

FIGURE 4-6

Possible three-phase assemblages coexisting with CO_2 in the triangle calcite-dolomite-quartz at high temperatures (full lines). The broken lines x and y connect coexisting phases stable at lower temperatures (see text).

The end product is the high-temperature assemblage calcite-forsterite-periclase. The sequence of reactions for other initial calcite-dolomite-quartz mixtures may be different. Thus the sequence for composition Q in Fig. 4-6 might be

1. Elimination of dolomite:

    Dolomite + 2 quartz → diopside + $2CO_2$

2. Elimination of calcite:

    Calcite + quartz → wollastonite + CO_2

The end product would be the assemblage wollastonite-diopside-quartz.

Clearly it is possible to imagine several alternative reaction sequences of increasing entropy for any one initial bulk composition. For example, an alternative sequence of two steps starting from P might be

Dolomite + quartz → calcite + enstatite + CO_2

Enstatite + dolomite → calcite + forsterite + CO_2

Some such reactions must however represent metastable equilibria. For example, as will be shown later, the equilibria

Dolomite + quartz ⇌ calcite + enstatite + CO_2

and

2 dolomite + quartz ⇌ 2 calcite + forsterite + $2CO_2$

are metastable in that for any given P_{CO_2}, their equilibrium temperatures lie beyond the field of stability of dolomite-quartz and within the stability field of diopside.

Almost invariably the metamorphic situation is complicated by the presence of water, so that the lower-grade assemblages contain hydrous phases, notably talc, tremolite, and, less commonly, brucite. So natural equilibria are controlled by T, P, and $X_{CO_2}^{gas}$ (or $X_{H_2O}^{gas}$) as independent variables. The composition of the gas may be buffered externally or internally—the latter a likely situation where one or more of the reactant phases involved in the equilibrium is hydrous.

On the basis of field and mineralogical experience Eskola (1922) listed a general sequence of reactions giving rise successively, in order of increasing grade, to tremolite, diopside, and wollastonite, each in rocks of appropriate silica content. Bowen (1940), using the same approach, formulated his classic sequence of 13 possible steps of progressive metamorphism collectively covering the composition range of the calcite-dolomite-silica system. As later revised by Tilley (1951) to include talc at the first step, this general sequence is marked by successive development, with rising temperature, of the following minerals (each within some limited composition field): talc, tremolite, forsterite, diopside, periclase, wollastonite, monticellite, akermanite, tilleyite, spurrite, rankinite, merwinite, and larnite. The last seven are confined to products of pyrometamorphism in a volcanic or quasivolcanic environment—calibrated experimentally (Walter, 1963) as 800–1000°C at P_{CO_2} not exceeding a few hundred kilobars; for present purposes corresponding equilibria will be considered no further. The relative order of appearance of the first six phases has been tested experimentally and thermodynamically, and as we shall now see has thereby been modified in several important respects.

Calibration of Some Critical Equilibria

Decarbonation Steps in Anhydrous Systems

As input data have become refined and revised, results of rather crude earlier attempts at thermodynamic calibration of the first few steps of decarbonation in the "system" CaO-MgO-SiO$_2$-CO$_2$ (Weeks, 1956; Turner, 1967) have become superseded. Here we use new and mutually consistent values of ΔH_f° and ΔG_f° generated by Helgeson et al. (1978) from a few experimentally reversed equilibria* and standard V and S data of Robie and Waldbaum (1968). These data, by our earlier approximation Eq. (3-1), place the first five steps in the following order (T_E, so computed at $P = 1.013$ bars, is given for each).

1. $\frac{1}{2}CaMg(CO_3)_2 + SiO_2 \rightleftharpoons \frac{1}{2}CaMgSi_2O_6 + CO_2$ 210°C
     dolomite   quartz   diopside

2. $\frac{1}{2}CaMgSi_2O_6 + 1\frac{1}{2}CaMg(CO_3)_2 \rightleftharpoons 2CaCO_3 + Mg_2SiO_4 + CO_2$ 310°C
     diopside   dolomite   calcite   forsterite

3. $CaCO_3 + SiO_2 \rightleftharpoons CaSiO_3 + CO_2$ 310°C
    calcite   quartz   wollastonite

4. $CaCO_3 + \frac{1}{2}CaMgSi_2O_6 + \frac{1}{2}Mg_2SiO_4 \rightleftharpoons 1\frac{1}{2}CaMgSiO_4 + CO_2$ 385°C
    calcite   diopside   forsterite   monticellite

5. $CaMg(CO_3)_2 \rightleftharpoons MgO + CaCO_3 + CO_2$ 450°C
    dolomite   periclase   calcite

Figure 4-7 shows corresponding computed curves of univariant equilibrium (1 and 2), the experimentally determined curve 3 of Harker and Tuttle (1956), and curve 5 (Harker and Tuttle, 1955) for the upper temperature limits of stability of dolomite.† Computed points (circled dots) for pressures >1.013 bars were determined in the following manner, combining the high-temperature data of Robie and Waldbaum with ΔG_f° values given by Helgeson et al. (see Table 4-3).

---

*Only one of which—calcite-quartz-wollastonite-CO$_2$ —corresponds directly to any of our decarbonation steps either in the anhydrous or in the hydrous system.

†Absence of high-temperature data (above 1000 K) for monticellite and dolomite prevents computation of equilibria 4 and 5.

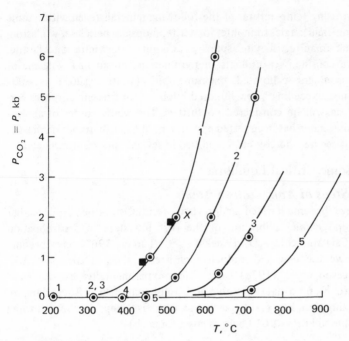

FIGURE 4-7

Univariant curves and computed T_E points at atmospheric pressure for equilibria correspondingly numbered in text. Curves 1 and 2 computed (see text); curves 3 and 5 experimentally determined (Harker and Tuttle, 1955, 1956). Solid squares show points of reversal of equilibrium 1 by Slaughter et al. (1975) at $P_f = 1$ and 2 kb, $X_{CO_2}^{gas} = 0.95$.

TABLE 4-3

ΔG_f Values[a] (cal mole^{-1}) Relevant to Equilibrium $\frac{1}{2}$ dolomite + quartz $\rightleftharpoons$ $\frac{1}{2}$ diopside + CO_2 at Atmospheric Pressure

| Phase | ΔG_f, 298.15 K | | | ΔG_f, 800 K | |
	RW[a]	H	D	RW	H (computed)
$CaMg(CO_3)_2$	−518,734	−517,980[b]	754	−454,372	−453,618
SiO_2	−204,646	−204,646	0	−182,905	−182,905
$CaMgSi_2O_6$	−725,784[c]	−724,000	1784	−655,841	−654,057
CO_2	−94,257	−94,257	0	−94,558	−94,558

[a]RW, from Robie and Waldbaum (1968); H, from Helgeson et al. (1978); D, difference factor (H − RW).
[b]±2190 cal.
[c]Ca, Mg ordered.

Consider equilibrium 1 at 800 K (527°C): To correct Robie and Walbaum's ΔG_f° values at 25°C, 1.013 bars to those tabulated by Helgeson et al. requires positive increments of 754 cal mole^{-1} and 1784 cal mole^{-1} for dolomite and diopside, respectively. The result is an increase of $(1784 - 754)/2 = 515$ cal in ΔG_r°. This increment, transferred to ΔG_r at 800 K, 1.013 bars, raises the value computed from Robie and Waldbaum's high-temperature data from $-12,388$ cal to $-11,873$ cal. $(\Delta V_r^{sol})^\circ$ from standard tables $= -21.82$ cm^3 mole^{-1}. From Eq. (3-8), for equilibrium at P_E, 800 K

$$\frac{-21.82 P_E}{41.84} + 800R \ln (\gamma_{CO_2} P_E) - 11,873 = 0$$

By trial from gas fugacity tables (Ryzhenko and Volkov, 1971): At 2 kb, 527°C $(\gamma_{CO_2} = 1.747)$, the above expression becomes $-1043 + 12,971 - 11,873 = 55$ cal. The corresponding point X on the univariant curve is 530°C, 2 kb.

Coincidence of computed points for the wollastonite equilibrium with the experimentally based curve 3 simply reflects the role of the latter among input data for computing ΔG_f° values. It is significant, however, that points independently determined by experiment for equilibrium 1 (Slaughter et al., 1975) virtually coincide with curve 1 as just computed.

Computed temperatures for equilibrium 2 are much lower than those previously calculated from standard data then available (Turner, 1967). This reflects marked increase in ΔG_f° values[*] here adopted for both diopside and dolomite— the effects being cumulative in reaction 2. Relocation of curve 2, as we shall see shortly—removes previous serious anomalies relating to the natural tremolite-forsterite paragenesis.

Decarbonation Steps in Hydrous Systems

Much more commonly than not, diopside is preceded in the first step of decarbonation by a hydrous phase—tremolite, talc, or, much more rarely, brucite. Here we are dealing with a hydrous general "system" $CaO\text{-}MgO\text{-}SiO_2\text{-}CO_2\text{-}H_2O$. Reactions at first involve simultaneous hydration and decarbonation, and later, as the hydrous phases become eliminated with rising temperature, dehydration, and decarbonation. Most of the relevant equilibria have been experimentally reversed over an appropriate range of P, T, and $X_{CO_2}^{gas}$, and all can be tested thermodynamically using independent ΔH_f° and ΔG_f° data of Helgeson et al. (1978) generated from reversals in the "system" $MgO\text{-}SiO_2\text{-}CO_2\text{-}H_2O$ and of the calcite-quartz-wollastonite equilibrium. With few exceptions, the results of recent experiments (e.g., Gordon and Greenwood, 1970; Skippen, 1971, 1974; Slaughter et al., 1975; Metz, 1976) and thermodynamically computed curves constitute an internally consistent set of data suitable for calibrating some of the most commonly observed metamorphic equilibria. The contributions of Metz and Trommsdorff (e.g., Trommsdorff, 1966, 1972; Metz and Trommsdorff, 1968) provide field and petrographic information for identification of the equilibria themselves as manifested in the Alps.

---

[*]Both, however, within limits of uncertainty of Robie and Waldbaum's data.

Conclusions based on some of Metz's pioneer work (cf. Metz and Trommsdorff, 1968; Metz, 1970) depart significantly from the remaining comprehensive body of data and are here excluded. These and other anomalies have been attributed to a variety of possible causes (cf. Slaughter et al., 1975, pp. 160-162; Helgeson et al., 1978, pp. 107, 108): experimental difficulties, possible disorder in dolomite, uncertainty with respect to f_{CO_2} at high pressures, and so on. Then there are additional inevitable uncertainties arising from close approximation of respective ΔG_T values of some alternative equilibria—particularly those involving first appearance and final elimination of tremolite. It can be virtually impossible in such cases to tell on thermodynamic and experimental evidence which of two equilibria is stable and which metastable over a range of P, T, and $X_{CO_2}^{gas}$ * (cf., for example, 6 and 7).

Some equilibria of potential petrologic significance (cf. Fig. 4-8) are listed below in order of increasing T_E at atmospheric pressure (estimated by approximation from $S°$ and $\Delta H_f°$ data for participating phases).

6. $3CaMg(CO_3)_2 + 4SiO_2 + H_2O \rightleftharpoons Mg_3Si_4O_{10}(OH)_2 + 3CaCO_3$
   dolomite   quartz   talc   calcite

   $+ 3CO_2$ 185°C

7. $5CaMg(CO_3)_2 + 8SiO_2 + H_2O \rightleftharpoons Ca_2Mg_5Si_8O_{22}(OH)_2 + 3CaCO_3$
   dolomite   quartz   tremolite   calcite

   $+ 7CO_2$ 190°C

8. $Ca_2Mg_5Si_8O_{22}(OH)_2 + 3CaCO_3 + 2SiO_2 \rightleftharpoons 5CaMgSi_2O_6 + 3CO_2$
   tremolite   calcite   quartz   diopside

   $+ H_2O$ 240°C

9. $Ca_2Mg_5Si_8O_{22}(OH)_2 + 3CaCO_3 \rightleftharpoons 4CaMgSi_2O_6 + CaMg(CO_3)_2 + CO_2$
   tremolite   calcite   diopside   dolomite

   $+ H_2O$ 280°C

10. $Ca_2Mg_5Si_8O_{22}(OH)_2 + 11CaMg(CO_3)_2 \rightleftharpoons 8Mg_2SiO_4 + 13CaCO_3$
    tremolite   dolomite   forsterite   calcite

   $+ 9CO_2 + H_2O$ 305°C

To draw meaningful petrologic conclusions from data of the kind illustrated in Fig. 4-8, due regard must be paid to the established mineralogical background of petrogenesis and assumptions must be made as to the prevailing value of $X_{CO_2}^{gas}$ during metamorphism. It seems likely—and there is supporting petrographic evidence—that the gas composition commonly tends to be buffered internally (cf.

---

*Experimental reversal by methods currently in use is no guarantee that the reversed equilibrium is stable.

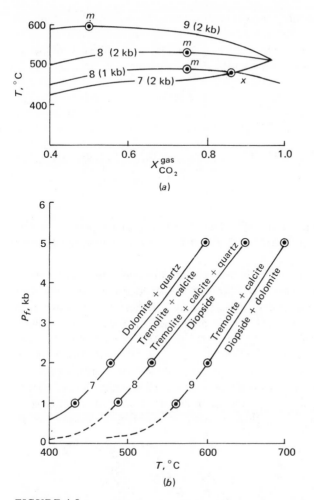

FIGURE 4-8
Three equilibria experimentally reversed by J. Slaughter, D. M. Kerrick, and V. J. Wall (1975, Figs. 8–10), numbered to correspond to equations in text. (*a*) Isobaric plots $X_{CO_2}^{gas}$ against T. (*b*) P-T plots for internally buffered $X_{CO_2}^{gas}$ (point *m* in curves 8 and 9, and *x* in curve 7).

Trommsdorff, 1972); e.g., in reaction 8 $X_{CO_2}^{gas}$ would be maintained close to 0.75. Note that considerable departure from this condition would have little effect upon T_E at constant pressure (cf. Fig. 4-8*a*). An assumption to this effect, as well as our general postulate that metamorphism tends toward a condition of stable equilibrium, underlies the following discussion of specific topics of petrologic interest.

Petrologic experience shows that in some areas talc is the first new phase to appear (equilibrium 6). Elsewhere the first recorded phase is tremolite. The inference is that, under some conditions realized in metamorphism equilibrium 6 is stable with respect to equilibrium 7 (metastable), and under others the reverse is the case. Talc, if initially present in metadolomitic assemblages, later disappears with rising grade, and tremolite comes in in abundance. The proposed reactions are

$$5Mg_3Si_4O_{10}(OH)_2 + 6CaCO_3 + 4SiO_2 \rightleftharpoons 3Ca_2Mg_5Si_8O_{22}(OH)_2 + 6CO_2$$
  talc   calcite   quartz   tremolite

$$+ 2H_2O$$

closely followed by

$$2Mg_3Si_4O_{10}(OH)_2 + 3CaCO_3 \rightleftharpoons Ca_2Mg_5Si_8O_{22}(OH)_2 + CaMg(CO_3)_2$$
  talc   calcite   tremolite   dolomite

$$+ H_2O + CO_2$$

Experimental data (Slaughter et al., 1975, Figs. 8–10) show that appearance of talc at the opening stage of metamorphism is favored by low pressures and by high $X_{H_2O}^{gas}$.

By whatever reaction tremolite is first generated its appearance can be represented on a *P-T* diagram as a narrow band (*b*, Fig. 4-9) encompassing the univariant curve of equilibrium 7 and closely adjacent curves representing the two talc-tremolite equilibria just mentioned. The incoming of diopside associated with tremolite is sharply defined (curve *c*, Fig. 4-9) by univariant curve 8 of Fig. 4-8.

The mineralogy of high-grade metadolomites in the Alps (e.g., Trommsdorff, 1966, 1972) and elsewhere suggests that appearance of forsterite virtually coincides with elimination of tremolite. This is borne out by experimental findings: Metz's (1976, Fig. 8) curve for equilibrium 10 representing generation of forsterite directly from tremolite in fact coincides with that based on the data of Slaughter et al.

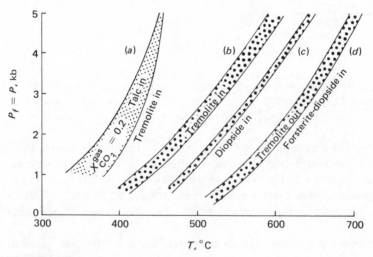

FIGURE 4-9

Possible *P-T* limits for incoming of *b* tremolite, *c* diopside-calcite, and *d* forsterite (coinciding with exit of tremolite) in metadolomites (see text); systems with internally buffered $X_{CO_2}^{gas}$.

Lightly stippled area *a* represents talc-tremolite paragenesis at externally buffered low $X_{CO_2}^{gas}$.

(1975) for equilibrium 9 in which tremolite is eliminated in favor of diopside (cf. Fig. 4-8). The final exit of tremolite, incoming of forsterite, and fresh influx of diopside can thus be represented conveniently as a narrow band on the *P–T* field (*d*, Fig. 4-9).

Once tremolite becomes eliminated from metadolomites,* subsequent decarbonation steps follow the same sequence as in the anhydrous system. A general paragenetic sequence, in which closely consecutive pairs of steps such as 6–7 and 8–9 are telescoped, is given in Fig. 4-10.

EQUILIBRIA IN MAGNESIAN ULTRAMAFIC ROCKS

Background Paragenesis

Bodies of ultramafic magnesian rock, generally considered to have been transported from the upper mantle, are prominent constituents of modern oceanic crust, and of its disrupted, more ancient, metamorphosed equivalent in fold-mountain ranges. In this latter context they have long been known as alpine peridotites and serpentinites—members of the mixed rock associations familiar to European geologists since the turn of the century as ophiolites. In modern parlance, in fact, the terms "ophiolite" and "oceanic crust" have become virtually synonymous. The primary mineral assemblage of typical unmetamorphosed alpine peridotites is olivine-enstatite-diopside (plus chrome spinel); but in the crustal environment most have been converted at least partially to serpentinite. At later stages in the course of orogeny the serpentinites themselves may become remetamorphosed; and it is this later progressive metamorphism (dehydration) of serpentinites that is the topic of present discussion.

Most serpentinites closely approximate the "system" $MgO\text{-}SiO_2\text{-}H_2O$.† The initial mineral assemblage is dominated by a serpentine mineral, accompanied in many cases by brucite or alternatively and less commonly (in more siliceous rocks) by talc. Petrography and field relations (e.g., Evans and Trommsdorff, 1970; Trommsdorff and Evans, 1974; Frost, 1975) have established these successive stages of progressive metamorphism:

1. Chrysotile becomes reconstituted to antigorite, long known as the typical serpentine phase of low-grade magnesian schists.
2. In low-silica serpentinites, brucite becomes eliminated in favor of forsterite. Antigorite itself then disappears and the resulting assemblage is forsterite-talc.
3. Forsterite-talc next gives way to forsterite-anthophyllite.
4. Finally both anthophyllite and any remaining talc are eliminated and the end-product of dehydration is forsterite-enstatite as in the original ancestral peridotite.

---

*Outside the "system," in magnesian schists of the system $MgO\text{-}SiO_2\text{-}H_2O$, tremolite remains stable (as does talc) up to considerably higher temperatures.

†Small amounts of Fe are virtually confined to one phase, magnetite. Ca, when present, is accommodated in either diopside or tremolite.

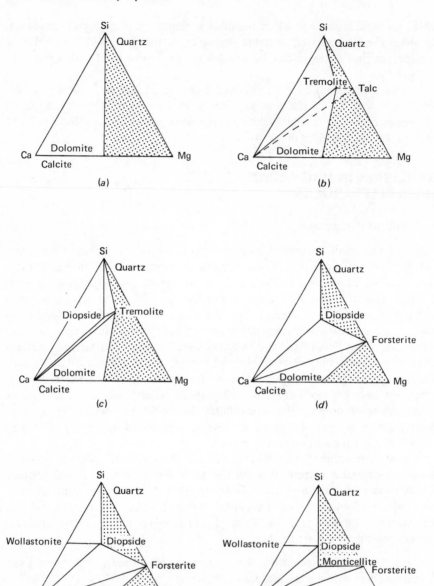

FIGURE 4-10

Successive stages in progressive metamorphism of silica-bearing dolomitic limestones in presence of water: (a)–(f) represents increasing grade at constant $P_f = P$. Phase assemblages in stippled areas (external to the dolomitic system) are not shown. At stage (b), talc may appear before tremolite where $X_{CO_2}^{gas}$ is low. Stage (f) is composite, depicting appearance first of monticellite and later of periclase.

Experimental Calibration of Critical Equilibria in the "System" $MgO-SiO_2-H_2O$

Bowen and Tuttle (1949) set up the general problem and provided the first calibration of three possible steps of metamorphism leading to generation first of forsterite, finally of enstatite. Greenwood (1963),[*] using more reliable experimental techniques directly reversed a number of equilibria—some stable, others metastable—relevant to generation and ultimate elimination of anthophyllite. Later experimenters (e.g., Johannes, 1968, 1969; Chernosky, 1976; Hemley et al., 1977) filled in details and relocated some equilibrium curves using a variety of techniques (Hemley's data for example are based on solution of relevant solids in steam). Finally Helgeson et al. (1978) have presented an internally consistent synthesis of available data.

Temperatures of equilibria involving chrysotile are lower than corresponding antigorite equilibria (cf. curves 2, 2′, Fig. 4-11); and this, together with the general tendency for chrysotile to invert to antigorite at the onset of metamorphism, suggests that from the outset chrysotile is metastable (cf. Dungan, 1977). Here this is assumed to be the case. Fig. 4-11 gives univariant curves for critical reactions

[*]Greenwood's paper is recommended to petrologists inexperienced in experimental geochemistry for its clarity, objectivity, and critical approach.

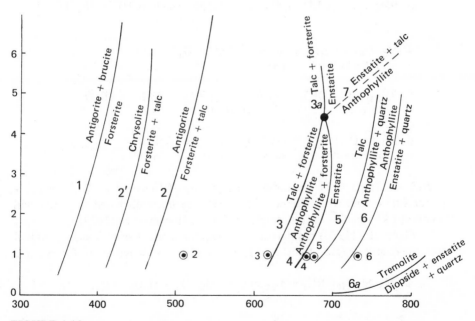

FIGURE 4-11
Univariant equilibria in the "system" $MgO-SiO_2-H_2O$, numbered as in text. [Data from W. Johannes, 1968 (curve 1), H. Helgeson et al., 1967 (curves 2–6), and J. V. Chernosky (metastable curve 2′)]. Dashed upper boundary of anthophyllite (curve 7) uncertain. Curve 6a ("system" $CaO-MgO-SiO_2-H_2O$) represents the ultimate breakdown of tremolite (after F. R. Boyd, 1959). Circled dots correspondingly numbered based on solubility measurements (J. J. Hemley et al., 1977).

marking successive steps of dehydration. The corresponding sequence of mineral assemblages at constant pressure, is summarized in Fig. 4-12.

1. $Mg_3Si_2O_5(OH)_4 + Mg(OH)_2 \rightleftharpoons 2Mg_2SiO_4 + 3H_2O$
    antigorite[*]   brucite   forsterite

Curve 1 is based on reversals by Johannes (1968), employing an unspecified "serpentine" phase, but closely approximates the equilibrium computed by Helgeson for antigorite-brucite-forsterite.

2. $5Mg_3Si_2O_5(OH)_4 \rightleftharpoons 6Mg_2SiO_4 + Mg_3Si_4O_{10}(OH)_2 + 9H_2O$
    antigorite   forsterite   talc

Curve 2, is that computed by Helgeson. It is compatible with scattered early experimental data (Bowen and Tuttle, 1949; Kitahara et al., 1966), but temperatures are some 30–40° lower than those recorded by Evans et al. (1976) at high pressures and than Hemley's point (based on solubility measurements) at 1 kb, 514°C. For comparison, the corresponding metastable chrysotile-forsterite talc equilibrium (Chernosky, 1973) is represented as curve 2'.

3. $9Mg_3Si_4O_{10}(OH)_2 + 4Mg_2SiO_4 \rightleftharpoons 5Mg_7Si_8O_{22}(OH)_2 + 4H_2O$
    talc   forsterite   anthophyllite

4. $Mg_7Si_8O_{22}(OH)_2 + Mg_2SiO_4 \rightleftharpoons 9MgSiO_3 + H_2O$
    anthophyllite   forsterite   enstatite

5. $7Mg_3Si_4O_{10}(OH)_2 \rightleftharpoons 3Mg_7Si_8O_{22}(OH)_2 + 4SiO_2 + 4H_2O$
    talc   anthophyllite   quartz

6. $Mg_7Si_8O_{22}(OH)_2 \rightleftharpoons 7MgSiO_3 + SiO_2 + H_2O$
    anthophyllite   enstatite   quartz

Curves 3–6 (Fig. 4-11) are those computed by Helgeson et al. With minor departures they agree with Greenwood's (1963) experimentally based curves and with points at 1 kb established from solubility data by Hemley et al. (1977).

Chernosky (1976) has determined equilibria alternative to 3 and 5, but with enstatite-quartz instead of anthophyllite as products of dehydration; for example:

3*a*. $Mg_3Si_4O_{10}(OH)_2 + Mg_2SiO_4 \rightleftharpoons 5MgSiO_3 + H_2O$
     talc   forsterite   enstatite

It would seem that these are stable only at pressures above 5 or 6 kb where the anthophyllite-quartz field cuts out along a curve representing the equilibrium

---

[*]Strictly speaking, the composition of antigorite is expressed by this formula minus a small amount of $Mg(OH)_2$.

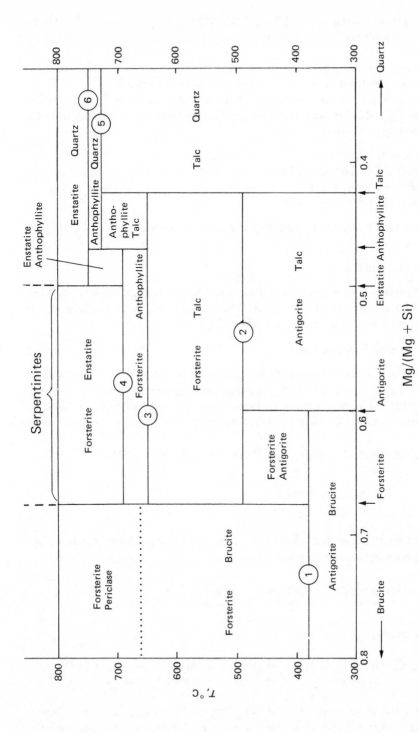

FIGURE 4-12

Stable assemblages in the "system" $MgO \cdot SiO_2 \cdot H_2O$ in relation to temperature and composition at $P_{H_2O} \sim 2$ kb (cf. Fig. 4-11). Heavily dashed vertical lines mark compositional limits of common serpentinites.

173

7. $Mg_7 Si_8 O_{22} (OH)_2 \rightleftharpoons 4MgSiO_3 + Mg_3 Si_4 O_{10} (OH)_2$
    anthophyllite   enstatite   talc

Its location and that of the invariant point 0 are subject to some uncertainty; for its origin is defined by the acute intersection of curves 3 and 4.

Compositions of many serpentinites fall between the forsterite and enstatite points of Fig. 4-12. For such rocks the dehydration steps follow a simple sequence corresponding to reactions 1–4.

1. Brucite out; forsterite in
2. Antigorite out; forsterite-talc in
3. Talc out; anthophyllite in
4. Anthophyllite out; enstatite in

At high pressures where anthophyllite becomes unstable, steps 3 and 4 are telescoped to

3a. Talc out; enstatite in

It will be seen from Fig. 4-11 that for any step the temperature increment between 2 and 6 kb is no more than 50°. Here is useful potential for geothermometry in what seems to be a common situation where $P_{H_2O} \approx P_f$.

Ca-Silicates in Serpentinites

At the earliest stages of metamorphism calcium of serpentinites is accommodated in diopside and/or tremolite, both pairs antigorite-diopside (cf. Evans and Trommsdorff, 1970) and antigorite-tremolite being stable. Just prior to step 2 in the above dehydration sequence diopside becomes eliminated.

2a. $2CaMgSi_2 O_6 + 5Mg_2 Si_2 O_5 (OH)_4 \rightleftharpoons Ca_2 Mg_5 Si_8 O_{22} (OH)_2$
    diopside   antigorite   tremolite

$+ 6Mg_2 SiO_4 + 9H_2 O$
    forsterite

Tremolite-forsterite remains stable into highest grades beyond step 4, when diopside reappears as the result of the reaction

$Ca_2 Mg_5 Si_8 O_{22} (OH)_2 + Mg_2 SiO_4 \rightleftharpoons 5MgSiO_3 + 2CaMgSi_2 O_6 + H_2 O$
    tremolite   forsterite   enstatite   diopside

Finally curve 6a, Fig. 4-11

6a. $Ca_2 Mg_5 Si_8 O_{22} (OH)_2 \rightleftharpoons 3MgSiO_3 + 2CaMgSi_2 O_6 + SiO_2 + H_2 O$
    tremolite   enstatite   diopside   quartz

represents the experimental breakdown of tremolite. Its main interest is that it demonstrates the capacity of nonferrous calcic amphiboles to survive into even the maximum grades of metamorphism; it has not been recorded in nature.

EQUILIBRIA RELEVANT
TO GLAUCOPHANE SCHISTS

Background Paragenesis

Glaucophane schists and associated rocks in what we shall presently call the blue-schist and lawsonite-albite-chlorite facies have a striking mineral paragenesis. Not all the characteristic mineral phases are appropriate to pressure-temperature calibration; for some, like the glaucophanic amphiboles, pumpellyite, stilpno-melane, and epidote have a considerable range of composition and overlap into other low-grade facies. Particularly characteristic, however—virtually diagnos-tic of the facies in fact—are the simple phases lawsonite and aragonite, and sodic pyroxenes—omphacites or diopsidic jadeites associated with quartz. Lawsonite is almost ubiquitous, aragonite and jadeite-rich pyroxenes more restricted in their field occurrence.

Field transitions are known between incipiently metamorphosed rocks con-taining the zeolite laumontite $CaAl_2Si_4O_{12}4H_2O$ and schists with the chemically comparable phase lawsonite $CaAl_2Si_2O_7(OH)_2H_2O$. In low-grade schists of other facies calcite and albite are widespread, to the complete exclusion of aragonite and jadeitic pyroxene; and in these rocks, the prevailing hydrous CaAl silicate is prehnite, pumpellyite, or clinozoisite. Outside the blueschist facies jadeitic pyrox-enes (omphacites) are found only in eclogites of which they are by definition major constituents.

Four simple equilibria relevant to low-temperature, high-pressure meta-morphism have been experimentally and thermodynamically calibrated: analcite-quartz-albite, laumontite-lawsonite-quartz, aragonite-calcite, and jadeite-quartz-albite. Collectively they give valuable information on the P–T limits of blueschists and their associates, thus shedding light on the thermal-pressure regime of sub-duction zones.

Analcite-Albite-Quartz Equilibrium

Albite is the characteristic and almost ubiquitous feldspar in low-grade metapelites, metagraywackes, and metavolcanics. But at minimal grades in the zeolite facies its place is taken by the pair analcite-quartz; and the corresponding ideal univariant equilibrium relation is

1. $\underset{\text{analcite}}{NaAlSi_2O_6 \cdot H_2O} + \underset{\text{quartz}}{SiO_2} \rightleftharpoons \underset{\text{albite}}{NaAlSi_3O_8} + H_2O$

This has been experimentally reversed by A. B. Thompson (1971) and by Liou (1971a). Their respective equilibrium curves differ to some extent, perhaps because of a slight excess of SiO_2 in analcite formed as the reaction product in some of Thompson's experiments (Helgeson et al., 1978, p. 155). Liou's curve is shown (numbered 1) in Fig. 4-13. It is a useful datum within the zeolite facies, and places constraints on temperature gradients leading at higher pressures into the lawsonite-albite-chlorite facies.

Laumontite-Lawsonite-Quartz Equilibrium

This can be expressed as

2. $CaAl_2 Si_4 O_{12} 4H_2 O \rightleftharpoons CaAl_2 Si_2 O_7 (OH)_2 H_2 O + 2SiO_2 + 2H_2 O$
   laumonite   lawsonite   quartz

The reaction has been reversed by Liou (1971b) at pressures ($P_{H_2O} = P_f$) around 3 kb between 200 and 300°C (curve 2, Fig. 4-13). His data agree with an independent reversal at 2.75 ± 0.25 kb, 250°C by A. B. Thompson (1970b) who used a dif-

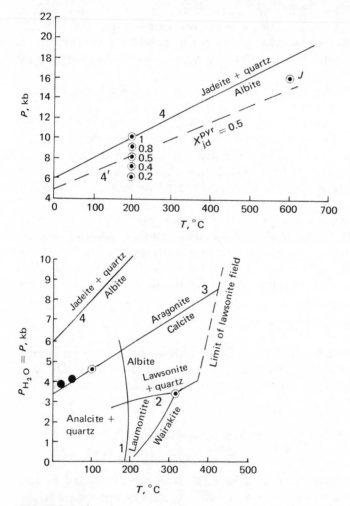

FIGURE 4-13

Selected curves of univariant equilibrium relevant to the lawsonite-albite-chlorite and blueschist facies (curve 1, after J. G. Liou, 1971a; curve 2, after J. G. Liou, 1971b; curve 3, after A. L. Boettcher and P. J. Wyllie, 1967; curve 4, after F. Birch and P. Lecomte, 1961). Curve 4' (approximate only) computed thermodynamically for ideal solid solution $X_{jd}^{pyr} = 0.5$ (see text).

ferent experimental technique. Pressures along curve 2 are lower by about 2 kb than those on a curve tentatively estimated from calorimetrically determined ΔH_f° and S values by Crawford and Fyfe (1965). However, as Crawford and Fyfe predicted, the slope of the curve is remarkably flat for a dehydration-hydration equilibrium—a condition [cf. Eq. (3-5)] reflecting the great difference in density between the two silicate phases and the smallness of ΔS_r accompanying dehydration of zeolites. Thus lawsonite is a most valuable index of pressure in low-grade metamorphic rocks. At temperatures above 300–400° the stability field of lawsonite terminates against the fields of CaAl silicates stable at higher temperatures— wairakite below about 4 kb, clinozoisite or zoisite at higher pressures. Except at temperatures below about 100°C and pressures below 5 kb, albite rather than analcite-quartz is stable in the lawsonite field.

Aragonite ⇌ Calcite Inversion

Aragonite is denser and has a lower entropy than calcite. The slope of the inversion curve is positive and from standard S° and V° data is about 15 bars degr^{-1}; but because of the low value and significant uncertainty of ΔS_r, the slope itself is subject to uncertainty of ±5 bars degr^{-1}.

The curve now generally accepted (in Fig. 4-13) is that established through experimental reversals at about 400°C by Boettcher and Wyllie (1967). It originates from a point close to narrow brackets (solid circles) computed by Jamieson (1953) from solubility measurements and passes directly through a point of experimental reversal (circled dot) by Crawford and Fyfe (1964). The slope, $12\frac{1}{2}$ bars degr^{-1}, is well within limits permitted by uncertainty in the entropy data.

The aragonite-calcite inversion is one of the more accurately calibrated of available petrologically significant equilibria. But its use in petrology is limited by the very condition that has facilitated experimental reversal in the laboratory: reaction rates are so high at temperatures above about 300°C—even in perfectly dry rocks—that aragonite cannot survive cooling across the curve at higher temperatures. Preservation of metamorphic aragonite in glaucophane schists thus strongly implies cooling in the absence of water from a regime of high pressure and temperatures not exceeding about 300°C. Calcite, by far the more widespread of the two polymorphs in metamorphic rocks, has no significance as an index of either temperature or pressure.

Jadeite-Quartz-Albite Equilibrium

The stability of coexisting jadeitic pyroxene and quartz with respect to alternative assemblages with albite can be considered in terms of the simple equilibrium

3. $NaAlSi_2O_6$ + SiO_2 ⇌ $NaAlSi_3O_8$
   jadeite   quartz   albite

Since the system has two components ($NaAlO_2$-SiO_2), the three-phase assemblage jadeite-quartz-albite constitutes a univariant equilibrium. Experimental reversal has been limited, because of difficulties stemming from reaction kinetics, to pressures beyond the normal crustal range—15 kb and upward. But points there established by Birch and Lecomte (1961) and by Johannes et al. (1971), though not in complete agreement, permit extrapolation to lower pressures on the basis of $S°$ and $V°$ data with some confidence. Such a curve is shown as 4 in Fig. 4-13.

Jadeitic pyroxenes associated with quartz (in some cases plus albite) in glaucophane schists are not pure jadeites. Some—especially in metabasalts—are members of the diopside-jadeite solid-solution series (omphacites) with less than 50% molar jadeite. Others contain considerable acmite but have commonly been recorded on optical evidence simply as jadeite. Others again, typically in meta-graywackes, approach jadeite more closely (Jd_{75} to Jd_{90}).

To gain some idea of the effect of such marked departures from the ideal $NaAlSi_2O_6$ composition on which curve 4 is based, Essene and Fyfe (1967, pp. 16-18) considered a model of ideal mixing in the pyroxene series—admittedly only an approximation imposed by lack of activity data for jadeite in pyroxenes at low metamorphic temperatures. The simplest natural system, a three-phase assemblage of jadeite-acmite, albite, and quartz now involves three components ($NaAlO_2$ -$NaFeO_2$ -SiO_2) so that equilibrium is bivariant: P and T must be specified to fix the pyroxene composition, which can be expressed as X_{jd}^{py}. The partial molar free energy of jadeite in ideal solution as a component of pyroxene ($\bar{G}_{jd}^{py} = \mu_{jd}^{py}$) is less than that of pure jadeite ($\bar{G}_{jd} = \mu_{jd}°$) under the same conditions, as shown by the relation [cf. Eqs. (2-6) and (2-8)]

$$\bar{G}_{jd}^{py} = G_{jd} + RT \ln X_{jd}^{py}$$

Substitution of such a pyroxene for pure jadeite in the three-phase assemblage at any point ($P_1 T$) on curve 4 thus disturbs equilibrium: ΔG_r (left to right) now has a positive value, $-RT \ln X_{jd}^{py}$. ΔV_r of reaction in the same sense is negative (standard data give $\Delta V_r° = 16.98$), so that equilibrium can be restored at constant temperature by reducing pressure to P_2 and thus decreasing ΔG_r for reaction involving pure jadeite [cf. Eq. (3-2)] by an amount equal to $\Delta V_r(P_1 - P_2)$. Then for equilibrium in the three-phase assemblage (acmite-jadeite, quartz, and albite)

$$\Delta V_r(P_1 - P_2) = RT \ln X_{jd}^{py}$$

To determine P_2 at 200°C for pyroxene $X_{jd}^{py} = 0.5$: On curve 3 at 200°C, $P_1 = 10$ kb; then from the above relation

$$(10,000 - P_2) = \frac{83.15 \times 473.15 \ln 0.5}{-16.98}$$

and $P_2 = 8390$ bars. Points similarly computed for $X_{jd}^{py} = 0.5$ over a range of temperature plot in Fig. 4-13 as curve 4′ (equilibrium points for different values of X_{jd}^{py} at 200°C are also shown below curve 4).

Solution in the omphacite series is complicated by the possibility of mixing on two cation sites in the structure. This would lower pressures along curve 4′ by as much as 2 kb in the temperature range 200-300°C (Essene and Fyfe, 1967, Fig. 16). Again departure from ideal solution at low temperatures would have effects the magnitude of which though probably not great is still unknown (cf. Ganguly, 1973). And finally disorder of Al-Si distribution in albite at high temperature will affect to some degree extrapolation of high-temperature experimental data to conditions of the blueschist facies where the ordered polymorph, low albite is stable.

In spite of such qualifications equilibrium curves such as 4′, based on a crudely simple model lead inescapably to this important general conclusion: The common jadeitic pyroxenes (especially acmitic jadeite) in quartz-bearing assemblages of the blueschist facies must have crystallized in a unique environment of high pressure and low temperature. At 250–350°C they are almost certain indicators of pressures at least as high as 7–8 kb. Members rich in jadeite, again when coexisting with quartz, indicate even higher pressures, possibly exceeding 10 kb.

CONCLUDING NOTE ON THE PETROGENIC GRID

The material set out in this chapter demonstrates the added significance that has been imparted to the descriptive data of metamorphic mineralogy and petrography by the accumulated results of research in the laboratory on simple mineral equilibria at high temperature and pressure, amplified and tested by thermodynamic appraisal. In the course of time, the classic work of the earlier experimenters has been found faulty in some respects; it has been modified in the light of later and more precise data. The debt of the geologist to the pioneer workers in the Geophysical Laboratory, Washington, is obvious; they inaugurated a new era in metamorphic petrology. Today the geologist is fortunate in having at his disposal an increasingly large amount of internally consistent experimental data, which he may use with some confidence to place limits upon the ranges of temperature and pressure expressed by common metamorphic mineral assemblages. Bowen's (1940, pp. 272–274) concept of the *petrogenic grid* of equilibrium curves relating to metamorphic reactions is abstract no longer. It is now an instrument, still open to further refinement, but already capable of effective use for calibrating temperature-pressure gradients of crystallization in metamorphic belts. There are still obvious lacks, notably a paucity of reliable information on equilibria especially sensitive to pressure by virtue of low $\Delta S_r / \Delta V_r$ ratios. A concensus on the cordierite-garnet equilibrium might help to remedy this deficiency.

The equilibria here reviewed were selected on the basis of simplicity, geologic applicability, mutual compatibility and critical documentation. Modern petrologic and geochemical literature abounds in accounts—all at least to some extent quantitative—of other equilibria related in some degree to metamorphic petrology. Some of these are known to be metastable under metamorphic conditions (e.g., lawsonite-anorthite-water). Some treat ideal end members of what in actual rocks are complex solid solutions—including some of the commonest mineral indices of metamorphic grade such as biotite, hornblende, garnet, and epidote. Studies in this realm have here been ignored, as exercises in geochemistry, which however valuable as such contribute little to clarification of the petrologic question that forms a main theme of this book: What does the mineralogy of a metamorphic facies convey to the geologist regarding the physical conditions of metamorphism?

This and the preceding chapter have set up the frame of reference within which we shall attempt to answer such questions. Our next task is to review the essential mineralogical character of individual facies and facies series within this general context.

5

Chemographic Phase Relations
in Metamorphic Systems

DEVELOPMENT OF THE THREE–COMPONENT
TRIANGULAR DIAGRAMS

The whole range of rock composition within any facies—from limestone to shale to basalt or sandstone—can be expressed in terms of perhaps a dozen principal phases. This number is surprisingly small. Omitted, of course, are accessory minerals such as zircon and apatite, and minerals confined to rocks of unusual chemical composition and limited extent, for example, fluorite and axinite in metasomatically affected limestones.

Now the definitive property of a facies is the constant and therefore predictable relation that exists between the observed combinations of mineral phases (mineral assemblages) and rock composition as expressed by chemical analysis. Five widely distributed minerals in high-grade, quartz-bearing rocks of what we shall call the amphibolite facies are kyanite, almandine, plagioclase, hornblende, and diopside. Rocks of a certain limited range of composition could be expressed equally well in terms of several alternative combinations of these phases: plagioclase-hornblende, plagioclase-diopside-almandine, and plagioclase-diopside-almandine-kyanite. The observed assemblage is always plagioclase-hornblende. Equations such as the following can be written to show the chemical equivalence of these assemblages:

$$9CaMgSi_2O_6 + Fe_3Al_2Si_3O_{12} + 5Al_2SiO_5 + SiO_2 + 3H_2O \rightleftharpoons 3CaAl_2Si_2O_8$$

diopside   almandine   kyanite   quartz   anorthite

$$+ 3Ca_2Mg_3FeAl(AlSi_7O_{22})(OH)_2$$

hornblende

The observed assemblage for rocks somewhat richer in aluminum is plagioclase-hornblende-almandine, never the equivalent trio plagioclase-diopside-almandine. Kyanite is confined to pelitic rocks, and diopside to rocks relatively rich in lime and low in alumina. We have already seen that within any major facies there may be some latitude regarding correlation, but it is always within sharply defined narrow limits. Within the smaller units (the local subfacies), correlation is rigorous.

To express the correlation between mineralogy and chemical composition in any given facies or subfacies, Eskola introduced the now widely practiced procedure of plotting mineral and rock compositions in terms of three chemical components. This treatment can completely express the range of possible variation only in the simplest of rock series. It may be done, for example, using CaO, MgO, and SiO_2 as variables, for metamorphosed siliceous dolomitic limestones, assuming CO_2 to be present as a pore fluid in each assemblage at the time of metamorphism. For more complex systems—metapelites or metabasalts for example—triangular plots have been used since Eskola introduced them early in the century to illustrate gross features of paragenesis in relation to rock chemistry. But to do this it is necessary to resort to approximations and to limit the scope of the chemical field, thus introducing elements of imprecision and inaccuracy that render the diagram itself a qualitative rather than a strictly quantitative expression. Phases common to all assemblages (e.g., quartz and plagioclase in many rocks) are omitted and bulk chemistry is recalculated accordingly by some conventionally agreed procedure. Components that substitute mutually in isomorphous series may be lumped together as compound components: FeO + MgO; in many rocks $Al_2O_3 + Fe_2O_3$.

To complete any diagram, tie lines are drawn between mineral phases found to coexist in different rocks of the same paragenesis (facies or subfacies). These bring out the chemographic relations (cf. P. Niggli, 1954, p. 380) between minerals that collectively define the facies: some degree of chemical equivalence between alternative mineral pairs (not necessarily precise because of the compound nature of some "components" of the system) is indicated by crossed tie lines between mineral pairs, and overlap of three-phase triangles.

It must be emphasized that the triangular diagrams devised by Eskola and elaborated by others to depict the mineral variety within a facies or a subfacies are essentially descriptive. Genetic implications in terms of equilibrium governed by the phase rule are a matter of secondary inference. To this topic we shall return in a later section.

The *ACF* Diagram

Still in general use today are the two three-component diagrams introduced more than a half-century ago by Eskola. Most generally applicable is the *ACF* diagram

(Fig. 5-1 and 5-2) depicting mineralogical and chemical variation in terms of Al_2O_3, CaO, and $(Mg,Fe)O$. In any facies, the effect of variation in SiO_2 upon the possible mineral assemblages can be illustrated by comparing two *ACF* diagrams, one for rocks with excess SiO_2 crystallizing as free quartz (the most widely applicable case), and the other for rocks deficient in SiO_2. In the same way, special diagrams could be constructed for rocks with excess K_2O, deficient H_2O, and so on. The following rules for calculating the percentages of the components *A*, *C*, and *F* from a chemical analysis of the rock are given by Eskola (1939, p. 347):

> To correct for the accessories ilmenite, sphene, and magnetite, the percentages (by weight) of these minerals are first estimated by micrometric analysis as *i*, *s*, and *m* respectively. Then from the percentage of FeO (by weight) subtract 50% *i* and 30% *m*; likewise subtract 30% *s* from CaO and 70% *m* from Fe_2O_3. The percentages of the various oxides, corrected as above, are now calculated as molecular percentages, and CaO is then further corrected for calcite and apatite by subtracting molecular amounts equivalent to $3P_2O_5 + CO_2$. *A*, *C*, and *F* can now be reckoned as follows and are finally recalculated so that $A + C + F =$ 100: $A = Al_2O_3 + Fe_2O_3 - (Na_2O + K_2O)$; $C = CaO$; $F = MgO +$ FeO + MnO. Note that *A* is given by the total alumina and ferric iron, less the quantity that would be required to combine with total alkali as feldspar.

For calcareous rocks containing calcite or dolomite as principal phases, it is customary to omit the CO_2 correction. Clearly the *ACF* diagram is a somewhat

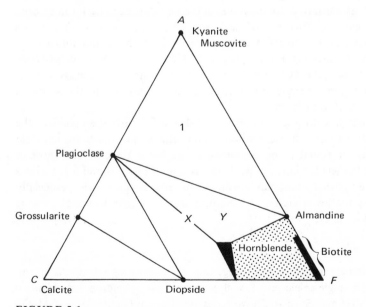

FIGURE 5-1

ACF diagram for quartz-bearing assemblages of the kyanite zone in the Scottish Highlands. Stippled field not recorded.

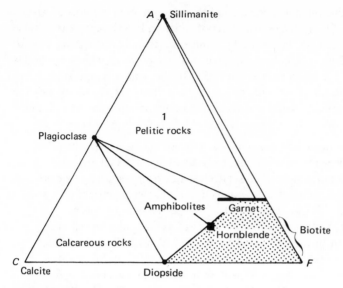

FIGURE 5-2

ACF diagram for mineral assemblages in quartzo-feldspathic gneisses and associated amphibolites in an area of southwestern Quebec (data from R. Kretz, 1959, 1963). Stippled field not recorded.

crude representation of mineral paragenesis. There are many mineral phases in which mutual substitution of Mg^{2+} and Fe^{2+} is far from complete. The same applies to Al^{3+} and Fe^{3+}, as illustrated, for example, in their contrasted behavior in epidote minerals and plagioclase. Partition of such elements between coexisting phases may be highly significant as an index of grade of metamorphism. But this is completely obscured by plotting $(Al,Fe)_2O_3$ and $(Mg,Fe)O$ as single components. In spite of such defects, the *ACF* plot is very useful in illustrating the gross features of correlation between mineralogical and chemical composition in the common mineral assemblages of most facies.

The fact that ties do not cross in Figs. 5-1 and 5-2 further emphasizes the compositional correlation. All rocks whose compositions plot in a triangular field of these diagrams are found to be composed of the same three phases—those at the apices of the triangle in question. While this is true of Figs. 5-1 and 5-2, tie lines between associated phases commonly are found to cross in some facies, especially those representing the lower grades of metamorphism. The significance of crossing ties will be discussed later.

The *AKF* Diagram

To express supplementary information regarding quartz-bearing micaceous assemblages containing a single calcic phase, such as plagioclase or epidote, Eskola introduced the *AKF* diagram. Such rocks were described as containing "excess Al_2O_3 and SiO_2." The analysis is recalculated so that

$$A = Al_2 O_3 - (CaO + Na_2 O + K_2 O)$$

$$K = K_2 O$$

$$F = FeO + MgO + MnO$$

$$A + K + F = 100$$

Figures 5-3 and 5-4 are *AKF* diagrams for pelitic rocks corresponding to triangles 1 in Figs. 5-1 and 5-2, respectively. They bring out the respective roles of micas and of K-feldspar in the pelitic assemblages. Figure 5-3 is based on the observations of Francis (1964), who recorded in pelitic schists of the kyanite zone southwest of Inverness, Scotland, the following assemblages:

Kyanite-almandine-muscovite-biotite
Kyanite-muscovite-biotite
Almandine-muscovite-biotite
Microcline-muscovite-biotite

Quartz and plagioclase are additional phases in each assemblage. A higher grade of metamorphism from another region is illustrated in Fig. 5-4. In pelitic gneisses from a sector of southwestern Quebec, Kretz (1959, 1963) found muscovite absent. In its place appears the equivalent pair K-feldspar-sillimanite. These minerals

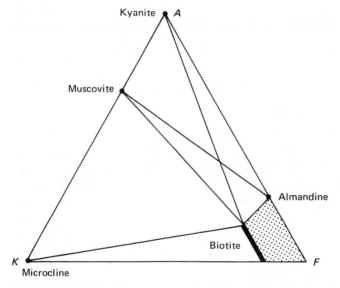

FIGURE 5-3
AKF diagram for quartz-bearing pelitic rocks of the kyanite zone in Glen Urquhart, northeastern Scotland. Data (from G. N. Francis, 1964) correspond to triangle 1 in Fig. 5-1. Stippled field not represented.

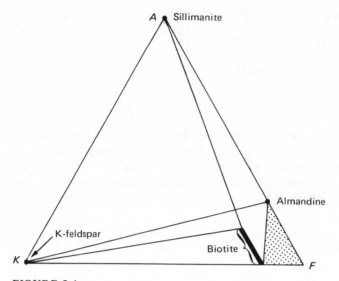

FIGURE 5-4

AKF diagram for pelitic gneisses of triangle 1 in Fig. 5-2 (data from R. Kretz, 1963). Stippled field not recorded.

are typically associated with abundant almandine-rich garnet and biotite, as well as with the ubiquitous quartz and plagioclase.

In both Fig. 5-3 and Fig. 5-4, crossing tie lines correspond to the common occurrence of six-phase assemblages such as quartz-plagioclase-kyanite-almandine-muscovite-biotite or quartz-plagioclase-sillimanite-almandine-biotite-K-feldspar. To elucidate the significance of such assemblages we must turn to yet other projections, such as the *AFM* diagram to be described below. It should be noted, however, that since the *AKF* diagram is used to project systems of many components, crossed ties have no significance as to equilibrium or variance.

Thompson's *AFM* Projection

Among the assemblages that seem to be most responsive to relatively small changes in pressure and temperature are those of pelitic schists. Except at the highest grades of metamorphism, these contain muscovite as the sole white-mica phase. To cover variation in muscovite schists of any subfacies, J. B. Thompson (1957) developed a projection based upon a tetrahedral plot of four components (Fig. 5-5).

$$A = \text{Al}_2\text{O}_3$$

$$B = \text{K}_2\text{O}$$

$$F = \text{FeO}$$

$$M = \text{MgO}$$

$$A + B + F + M = 100$$

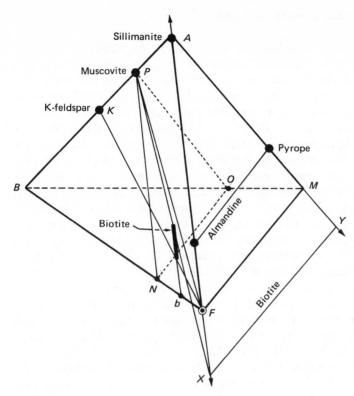

FIGURE 5-5
The *ABFM* projection (after J. B. Thompson).

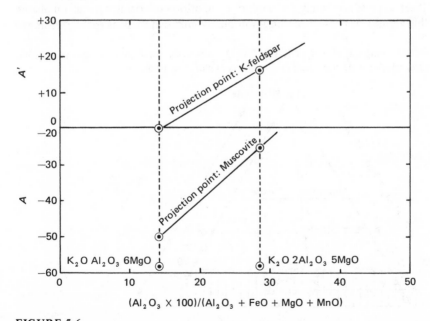

FIGURE 5-6
Data for plotting biotite compositions on *AFM* and *A'F'M'* diagrams, given molecular proportions of Al_2O_3, FeO, MgO, and MnO.

Any muscovite-bearing assemblage can be represented graphically by projecting each pertinent point in the *ABFM* tetrahedron upon the *AFM* plane (Fig. 5-5) by a straight line drawn through the muscovite point *P*.[*] Every such assemblage contains muscovite and may contain quartz and/or plagioclase in addition to the phases connected by the lines in the *AFM* projection. Phases whose compositions lie in the tetrahedral sector *PAFM* (Fig. 5-5) project within the *AFM* triangle itself in Fig. 5-7. Examples are almandine and staurolite. Biotites located in the pyramid *PONFM* plot below *FM*. For these A ($= Al_2O_3 - 3K_2O$) is negative; $A + F + M = 100$. The upward and downward continuations of any line drawn through *A* in Fig. 5-5 (e.g., the *AM* edge) meet at infinite distance. One such line would be projection of K-feldspar, in what Thompson called the positive sense, to *A*. But, for bivariant equilibrium coexistence of K-feldspar, muscovite, and sillimanite, which are colinear on the projection, is forbidden. So K-feldspar is projected in the negative sense to some point at infinite distance. The arrow in Fig. 5-8 shows the direction of a biotite K-feldspar tie so plotted.

Geometrically derived data for plotting biotite compositions on the *AFM* plane (given contents of Al_2O_3, FeO, and MgO) are shown in the lower half of Fig. 5-6. Metamorphic biotites approximate compositions between $K(Mg,Fe,Mn)_3(AlSi_3O_{10})(OH)_2$ and $K(Mg,Fe,Mn)_{2\,1/2}Al_{1/2}(Al_{1\,1/2}Si_{2\,1/2}O_{10})$ $(OH)_2$. So $K_2O/(Al_2O_3 + MgO + FeO + MnO) = \frac{1}{7}$. On the *ABF* face of the fundamental tetrahedron (Fig. 5-5), pure Fe^{2+} biotites plot on the solid bar on the join *Ab*, where $Fb/bB = \frac{1}{8}$. Corresponding *A* values on the *AFM* projection are -50 to -25; $(F + M)$ is -150 to -125.

The *AFM* projection is not practicable for plotting total-rock compositions. But it can express accurately the range of composition of coexisting mineral phases. Possible additional phase assemblages in quartz-muscovite schists (pelitic) from the

---

[*]The composition at *P* is $K_2O + 3Al_2O_3$. Muscovites of medium-grade metamorphic rocks (for which the *AFM* projection was designed) plot close to this point.

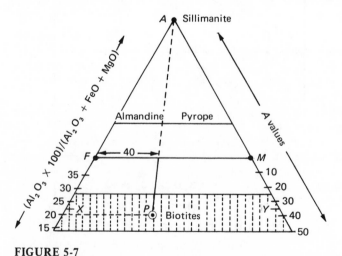

FIGURE 5-7

Plots of biotite and garnet on *AFM* diagram (projection point: muscovite). *P* is biotite $K_2Mg_{2.24}$, $Fe_{3.36}$, $Al_{0.4}$ $(Si_{5.6}Al_{2.4}O_{20})$, $(OH)_4$; $100\ Mg/(Mg + Fe) = 40$ (cf. p. 192).

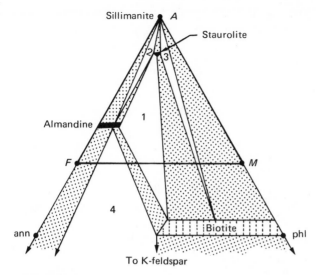

FIGURE 5-8

AFM diagram for mineral phases and possible phase assemblages in quartz-muscovite schists of the muscovite-sillimanite zone, New Hampshire (after J. B. Thompson). Fields of two-phase assemblages stippled; three-phase fields blank: (1) Almandine-staurolite-biotite; (2) Almandine-staurolite-sillimanite; (3) Sillimanite-staurolite-biotite; and (4) Almandine-biotite-orthoclase.

muscovite-sillimanite zone of New Hampshire have been represented by Thompson (1957, p. 581) in the *AFM* projection here reproduced as Fig. 5-8.

To show partition of Fe^{2+}, Mg^{2+}, and Al^{3+} ions between coexisting biotites and garnets of rocks containing K-feldspar but no muscovite, a modified diagram $A'F'M'$ may be drawn by projecting from the K-feldspar point K onto the *AFM* face of the tetrahedron (Fig. 5-5). In the $A'F'M'$ projection $A = (Al_2O_3 - K_2O)$; values for biotite are shown in the upper half of Fig. 5-6 and in Fig. 5-9. Figure 5-10 is an $A'F'M'$ plot of biotites and garnets (using analyses given by Kretz, 1959 and 1963) in quartzo-feldspathic gneisses from southwestern Quebec. This diagram amplifies the paragenesis depicted in more general terms in Figs. 5-2 and 5-4. All these rocks lack muscovite. Many contain K-feldspar. Quartz and plagioclase are additional phases in all assemblages. Some contain sillimanite, some hornblende; but these are mutually exclusive.

Figure 5-10 brings out two points consistent with, but not proving, equilibrium in the various assemblages:

1. Biotites in the assemblages biotite-garnet-sillimanite and biotite-garnet (above *PQ*) are relatively high in Al. Biotites of hornblende-bearing assemblages (whether or not these contain garnet or K-feldspar) are low in Al (below *PQ* in Fig. 5-10).
2. The ratio Mg/Fe in biotite is consistently higher than in associated garnet. The crossing of garnet-biotite ties is insignificant.

Such relations may also be clearly expressed in a simpler manner by plotting some significant chemical parameter such as Mg/(Mg + Fe + Mn) for two coexisting

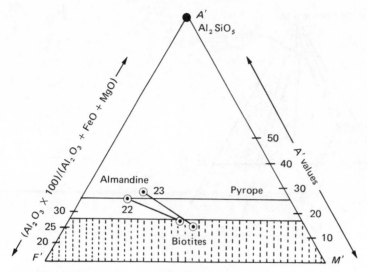

FIGURE 5-9

Plots of biotite-garnet pairs, 22, 23 on $A'F'M'$ diagram (projection point: K-feldspar).

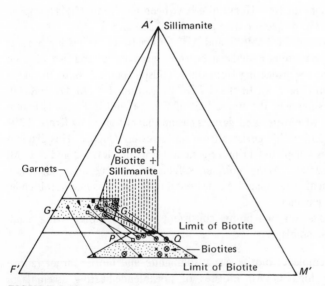

FIGURE 5-10

$A'F'M'$ diagram for mineral phases associated with quartz and K-feldspar in gneisses from southwestern Quebec (see also Figs. 5-2 and 5-4) (data from R. Kretz, 1959, 1963). Circled dots: biotite-garnet-sillimanite; open triangles: biotite-garnet-hornblende; circled crosses: biotite-hornblende; open square: biotite-garnet. Assemblages lacking K-feldspar are biotite-hornblende (crosses), garnet-biotite-hornblende (solid triangles), and garnet-hornblende (solid square). GG is theoretical garnet composition.

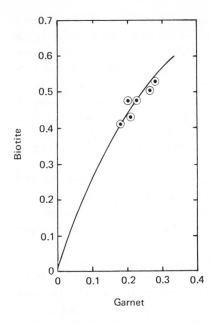

FIGURE 5-11

Plot of Mg/(Fe + Mg + Mn) in coexisting garnets and biotites of quartz-orthoclase-garnet-biotite-sillimanite gneisses from southwestern Quebec (after R. Kretz, 1963, p. 12). Compare with the circled points of Fig. 5-10.

minerals. Figure 5-11 is an example of such a plot for biotite and garnet in the quartzo-feldspathic biotite-garnet-sillimanite gneisses from Quebec (Kretz, 1963). These fall in the lower part of the garnet-biotite-sillimanite field of Fig. 5-10.

GENERAL ALGEBRAIC TREATMENT OF CHEMOGRAPHIC PROJECTIONS

The *AFM* projection represents a geometric solution of a special and commonly recurring problem relating to medium- and high-grade pelitic phase assemblages. Similar solutions could be devised for the graphic analysis of chemographic relations in natural parageneses of a completely different character, e.g., in metavolcanic-metagraywacke assemblages of the blueschist facies. Clearly a general problem of methodology is involved, which encompasses all such possibilities.

This general problem has been elegantly treated by Greenwood (1975) from an algebraic standpoint using simple matrices that express the compositions of all coexisting phases in terms of components selected to suit individual situations. The chosen components are of two kinds: some represent mineral phases of fixed or constantly buffered composition; the remainder, plotted at the apices of the projection triangle, are components whose relative proportions in any given rock determine the nature of the remaining phases that are diagnostic of different equilibrium assemblages. For the *AFM* projection the first category would include quartz, muscovite, and an aqueous phase, with f_{H_2O} buffered at some constant (probably unknown) value; to the second would belong the three "diagnostic" components $A(= Al_2SiO_5)$, $F(= FeO + MnO)$, and $M(= MgO)$.

The first step is to tabulate chemical compositions of all participating phases (including those designated as nondiagnostic components) in matrix form—phases in vertical columns, oxides (or equivalent ions) in horizontal rows. This matrix is then transformed into one with phase compositions expressed in terms of the selected components (horizontal rows). By striking out those rows that denote the contributions of nondiagnostic components, phase compositions are now restated solely in terms of diagnostic components (in the above case, A, F, and M). Compositions of all phases in the new matrix are normalized to a constant sum, say 1 or 100. The three resulting numbers are the coordinates of a phase projected from a point in space representing the nondiagnostic phases (quartz + muscovite + water) onto the AFM plane. Successive steps (for AFM projection) are illustrated by partial matrices in Table 5-1.

Phases with one negative coordinate such as biotites plot outside the AFM triangle: in Fig. 5-7 Ann and Phl (as in Table 5-1) and biotite P with coordinates $A = -0.4$; $F = 0.84$; $M = 0.56$. Phases for which the sum of the coordinates is negative (e.g., K-feldspar) are plotted in the negative sense and cannot be shown on the projection with positive phases.

The above is but an inadequate condensation of Greenwood's lucid exposition, to which the serious reader is urged to turn. He or she is also referred to Brown's (1978) similar treatment of amphibole-pyroxene pairs in the blueschist facies in terms of Ca(Mg,Fe), NaAl, and $NaFe^{3+}$ (Fig. 9-17) starting from compositions of chemically analyzed phases. The algebraic treatment has great

TABLE 5-1

Partial Matrices for Deriving AFM Projection Coordinates of Critical Phases in Pelitic Assemblages of the Sillimanite Zone (Fig. 5-8) from Ideal Chemical Compositions

	Sill	Q	Ms	W	Alm	Ann	Phl	Or
Step 1								
SiO_2	1	1	6	0	3	6	6	6
Al_2O_3	1	0	3	0	1	1	1	1
FeO	0	0	0	0	3	6	0	0
MgO	0	0	0	0	0	0	6	0
K_2O	0	0	1	0	0	1	1	1
H_2O	0	0	2	1	0	2	2	0
Step 2								
Sill	1	0	0	0	1	−2	−2	−2
Q	0	1	0	0	2	2	2	2
Ms	0	0	1	0	0	1	1	1
W	0	0	0	1	0	0	0	−2
FeO	0	0	0	0	3	6	0	0
MgO	0	0	0	0	0	0	6	0
Step 3								
Sill					1 (0.25)	−2 (−0.5)	−2 (−0.5)	−2 (−0.5)
FeO					3 (0.75)	6 (1.5)	0	−2 (−0.5)
MgO					0	0	6 (1.5)	0

Key: Sill, sillimanite; Q, quartz; Ms, muscovite; W, water; Alm, almandine; Ann, annite; Phl, phlogopite; Or, K-feldspar.

Source: Modified and abbreviated from H. J. Greenwood, 1975.

advantages: it is unambiguous, thermodynamically valid (e.g., it obeys the constraints of the phase rule), it obviates the need for rather clumsy graphical constructions such as are embodied in Fig. 5-6, and it gives numerical data that are readily transferable to a graphic plot of the kind familiar to petrologists.

PHASE EQUILIBRIA AND METAMORPHIC PARAGENESIS

Preamble

Much of the collective experimentally established data relevant to metamorphic mineral assemblages concerns simple two-, three-, and four-component systems. These are readily represented on triangular and two-dimensional chemographic diagrams, some analogous to those depicting simple natural assemblages in individual subfacies. Experimentally based diagrams may thus be used to clarify questions relating to equilibrium in common metamorphic mineral assemblages and to set numerical limits on governing physical conditions of metamorphism. To the familiar triangular diagrams employed by Eskola and others to illustrate metamorphic paragenesis they could add dimensions of pressure and temperature.

Triangular Plots of Bivariant Phase Equilibria

Once again a triangular compositional plot covers the complete range of all possible mixtures of the three components represented at its apices. The same graphic treatment can be extended to mixtures of four components provided one of these constitutes a phase common to all assemblages under consideration. Such is CO_2 gas in the "system" $CaO\text{-}MgO\text{-}SiO_2\text{-}CO_2$: the apices of the diagram in this case are CaO, MgO, and SiO_2 (Fig. 5-12). Common usage of the term "system" in this connotation must be distinguished from stricter usage in the context of the phase rule; for this latter applies to a system of specific composition.[*] Any point within the bounding triangle of Fig. 5-12 represents a unique system in the sense of the phase rule.

Equilibria represented respectively by three-phase triangles, two-phase ties, and the unique compositions of plotted phases in Fig. 5-12 are all bivariant. They correspond to natural phases (excluding CO_2 gas) and assemblages formed by metamorphism of siliceous dolomitic limestones at pressures of a few hundred bars and temperatures of $\sim$650–750°C. Each three-phase triangle covers a range of four-phase systems ($\varphi = 4$), e.g., at point X, calcite-diopside-forsterite-CO_2. Since c, the number of components (however reckoned) here is also 4, variance $\omega = 4 + 2 - 4 = 2$. A system Y on the diopside-calcite tie has $\varphi = 3$ (diopside-calcite-CO_2), but the same three entities can be considered as components that completely define the composition of this system, so that $c = 3$, and again $\omega = 2$. At the diopside point c and φ are both reduced to 2 and here the system diopside-CO_2 is bivariant. All such systems with $c < n$, within a comprehensive n-component "system" are said to be degenerate.

---

[*]Henceforth in this chapter where the broader usage is implied we write "system" (in quotes).

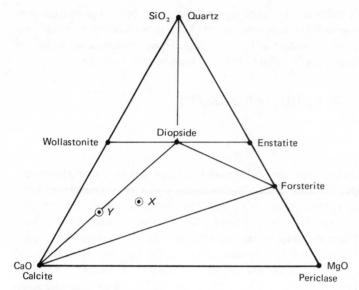

FIGURE 5-12

Equilibrium assemblages of solid phases coexisting with CO_2 gas at high T and low P in the "system" $CaO\text{-}MgO\text{-}SiO_2\text{-}CO_2$.

Where univariant equilibrium curves have been determined for different reactions in a "system" of few components, the overall effect of changing P and T upon equivalent mineral paragenesis can be demonstrated by placing appropriate triangular phase diagrams in the several $P\text{-}T$ fields bounded by the univariant curves. Something comparable has been done in Fig. 5-13 for isobaric equilibria, including a CO_2-rich gas phase, in the "system" $CaO\text{-}MgO\text{-}SiO_2\text{-}CO_2\text{-}H_2O$ over a limited range of temperature (cf. Fig. 4-10*b*). The device of fixing the pressure at some arbitrary value has reduced the remaining variance by one. By this means, a four-phase assemblage with true variance 3, e.g., calcite-talc-quartz-gas in the lowest $CaO\text{-}MgO\text{-}SiO_2$ triangle, becomes "bivariant" in terms of the remaining two variables T and $X_{CO_2}^{gas}$. The "univariant" curves of Fig. 5-13 are traces of bivariant surfaces; the "invariant" point 0, the trace of a strictly univariant curve.

Topology and Geologic Significance of a Set of Univariant Equilibria with Components in Common

Statement of the Case

The family of curves in Fig. 5-13 (cf. discussion pp. 126) provides a relatively simple illustration of the topology of univariant and related invariant equilibria[*] in a comprehensive multicomponent "system." The number of such equilibria and their general topology are determined by limitations of the phase rule, as set out in the next section. Independent experimental or thermodynamic data are needed to establish the slopes and positions of univariant curves in the

---

[*]Remember that in Fig. 5-13 isobaric constraint has reduced the remaining variance by one.

$T\text{-}X_{CO_2}^{gas}$ field; and on these matters opinions still differ (cf. Slaughter et al., 1975).

It is obvious that in a multicomponent "system" such as that represented in Fig. 5-13, a particular phase of fixed composition can be generated under different conditions not only in chemically restricted systems of different composition, but even in a single such system. Thus at constant values of P and $X_{CO_2}^{gas}$ tremolite can be generated in the system M, first by reaction (4) between talc, calcite, and quartz and then, at some higher temperature, by reaction (5) between calcite and talc (dolomite being a co-product of this reaction). In less siliceous systems such as N, tremolite can be generated only by the second reaction. Such behavior has an important bearing on the significance of individual isograds in chemically variable "systems" of many components. Clearly to attach any physical

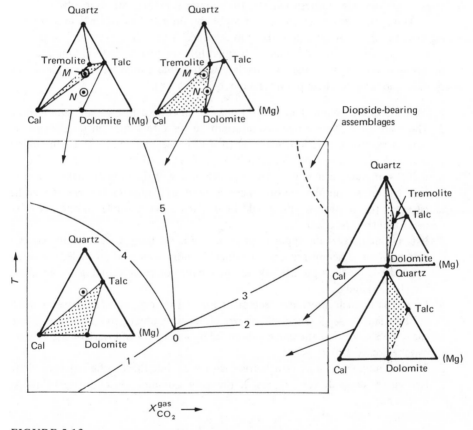

FIGURE 5-13

"Univariant" equilibrium curves (numbered) corresponding to low-grade reactions in siliceous dolomitic limestones ("system" CaO-MgO-SiO$_2$-CO$_2$-H$_2$O) at constant pressure P. Curves and scales are diagrammatic. Calcite (Cal) present in all except ultramagnesian assemblages.
1. 3 Dolomite + 4 quartz + H$_2$O $\rightleftharpoons$ talc + 3 calcite + 3 CO$_2$. 2. 2 Dolomite + talc + 4 quartz $\rightleftharpoons$ tremolite + 4 CO$_2$. 3. 5 Dolomite + 8 quartz + H$_2$O $\rightleftharpoons$ tremolite + 3 calcite + 7 CO$_2$. 4. 6 Calcite + 5 talc + 4 quartz $\rightleftharpoons$ 3 tremolite + 6 CO$_2$ + 3 H$_2$O. 5. 3 Calcite + 2 talc $\rightleftharpoons$ dolomite + tremolite + CO$_2$ + H$_2$O. The "bivariant" three-phase assemblage unique to each P-T field is shown stippled.

significance to a natural isograd, it will be necessary to know the nature of the reaction responsible for it. We shall now consider briefly the theoretical constraints on the topology of diagrams relating phase assemblages to two intensive variables (such as P and T), and the use to which such diagrams have been put in presenting comprehensive experimental data and in illustrating actual parageneses.

Schreinemakers' Treatment of Topology

Between 1911 and 1925 the Dutch chemist F. A. H. Schreinemakers explored in great detail the mutual relations, with variation in P and T, between possible phase equilibria in multicomponent "systems." His treatment is geometric and has been elegantly expounded, along with G. W. Morey's somewhat later analytical solutions of the same problems, by Zen (1966).[*] To this essay we refer the student of geochemistry who wishes to master the geometric manipulations involved.

The basic problem concerns the topology, on a P-T or other field representing two variables, of all equilibria with variance 0 to 2 in a "system" of n components with $(n + 2)$ possible phases. In what follows, unless the term "metastable" is specifically used, we concern ourselves with stable equilibria. From phase-rule considerations alone, these points emerge (cf. Fig. 5-14).

1. At some unique point 0 all $(n + 2)$ phases can coexist in invariant equilibrium.
2. There are $(n + 2)$ univariant equilibrium curves intersecting in 0. Each represents a reversible reaction involving $(n + 1)$ phases—e.g., in a three-component system $1 + 2 + 5 \rightleftharpoons 3$ (where each phase is designated by a numeral); and each curve is uniquely characterized by absence of one of the $(n + 2)$ phases. According to convention the absent phase is used to designate the corresponding curve; in the above case this would be 4. Each curve is stable on one side of 0, metastable on the other.
3. It is axiomatic that on opposite sides of any curve there are chemically equivalent bivariant assemblages one of which is more stable on one side, the other more stable on the opposite side of the curve. For curve 4 of Fig. 5-14b, these are (1, 2, 5) and 3.
4. Equilibria in each intervening sector of Fig. 5-14b, e.g., between curves 4 and 5 are bivariant ($\varphi = 3$). One such, shown stippled, is unique to each sector. It can easily be shown that the angle subtended by any sector of bivariant equilibrium cannot exceed 180°.
5. The full number of univariant curves is $(n + 2)$, but this can be reduced where two curves coincide (i.e., represent the same combination of phases) through degeneracy.[†]

---

[*]Schreinemakers' approach was introduced into geologic literature by Paul Niggli (1912) and illustrated in some detail, as applied to combinations of five phases in a three-component "system," in his classic *De Gesteinsmetamorphose* (Graubenmann and Niggli, 1924, pp. 124–132). It came into vogue in American and British journals after the appearance of an English translation of Niggli's later work on *Rocks and Mineral Deposits* (Niggli, 1954) and an essay by Korzhinskii (1959).

[†]A common case in experimentally studied systems arises through colinearity of three phases in "systems" with $n > 2$: e.g., on the wollastonite-diopside-enstatite join in the "system" $CaO-MgO-SiO_2$ (Fig. 5-12).

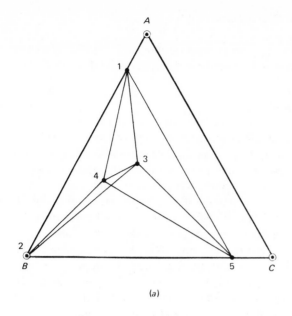

(a)

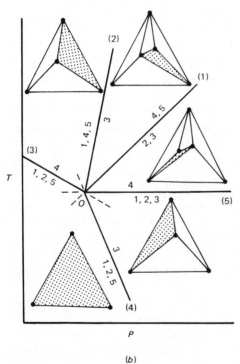

(b)

FIGURE 5-14

Schreinemakers' analysis (diagrammatic) of equilibria in combinations of four out of five phases (numbered) in a "system" of three components (A,B,C) (modified from Zen, 1966, p. 23). (a) One possible chemographic scheme relating phases 1–5. (b) Invariant point O, curves of univariant equilibrium (1)–(5), and chemographic relations in three-phase bivariant equilibria, corresponding to triangle 125, Fig. 5-14a. Three-phase bivalent equilibrium unique to each sector shown stippled.

6. The relative positions of any two nondegenerate univariant curves define the topology of the remaining curves intersecting in an invariant point.

Applications and Limitations
of Schreinemakers' Treatment

Schreinemakers' approach, taken alone, can lead only to a qualitative picture of the topology of equilibria in a multicomponent "system." To use it to clarify or solve some problem in geochemistry or petrology we need considerable additional input data from several independent sources; and on the validity and accuracy of these data depends the value of the outcome: The "system" must be defined in terms of selected components, and the number of possible phases and their chemical compositions stated. The $(n + 2)$ univariant equilibria must be identified by mass-balanced equations, and the relative positions of two of them need to be known. Some combination of experimental reversals and thermodynamic data $(\Delta V_r$ and $\Delta S_r)$ are required to locate each curve and determine its slope.

In experimentally studied "systems" of few components input data in all these categories are usually available and Schreinemakers' analysis is then useful in filling in topological details leading to comprehensive presentation of a set of internally consistent data relating equilibria of any variance between 0 and 2 to any two selected intensive variables (cf. Fig. 5-13).

There are also a very few natural "systems," notably, derivatives of siliceous magnesian limestones and of ultramafic rocks of the serpentinite family, that can be adequately illustrated by Schreinemakers' treatment of experimentally established data.

Figure 5-15, as an example, represents diagrammatically the topology of univariant curves, and the chemographic relations of bivariant phase assemblages, around 0 the invariant point of Fig. 4-11. A five-phase assemblage—talc-anthophyllite-enstatite-forsterite-steam in the three-component "system" MgO-SiO_2-H_2O—is stable at 0 itself. The "system" is degenerate in that, in each of the phases (talc, anthophyllite, and enstatite), $SiO_2/(MgO + SiO_2 + H_2O) = 0.5$, so that the three are colinear in a chemographic plot. By this stipulation c in the phase-rule equation is reduced to 2 for any system on the line TAE, and the three-phase assemblage talc-anthophyllite-enstatite is univariant. It is represented by the curve designated (F, St) which expresses coincidence of the stable segments of curves (F) and (St) in Schreinemakers' notation. The number of univariant curves is thus reduced by degeneracy from $(n + 2) = 5$ to 4.

Schreinemakers' analysis of more complex natural "systems"—notably metapelites and metabasalts that are the basis of most isograd series—has been and perhaps inevitably must remain less fruitful. Reference to some of the more carefully presented studies in this field (e.g., Albee, 1965; Hess, 1969; Brown, 1975[*]) brings out almost insuperable obstacles to any satisfactory quantitative outcome. There is a wide latitude of choice as to components, the nature and number of participating phases and the chemical composition of each. Consequently Schreinemakers' treatment of the same petrologic "system" (e.g., meta-

[*]In no way superseded by the geometrically intricate but chemically less precise study of Kepezhinskas and Khlestov (1977).

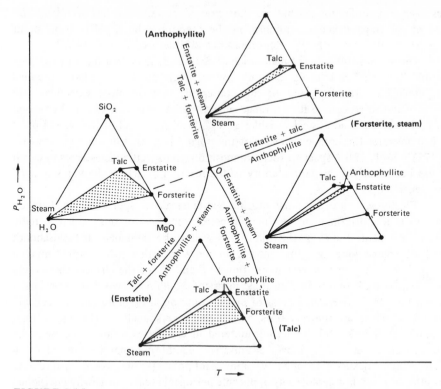

FIGURE 5-15
Univariant curves (diagrammatic) and chemographic plots of bivariant equilibria in intervening sectors around the invariant point O for coexisting assemblages of talc, anthophyllite, enstatite, forsterite, and steam at $T \sim 600$–$750°C$, $P_{H_2O} \sim 3$–7 kb in the "system" MgO-SiO_2-H_2O. Compare Fig. 4-11, curves 3, 3a, 4, and 7. The three-phase triangle unique to each chemographic plot is stippled.

pelites) by different writers can lead to very different topologies involving anything from one to a dozen invariant points. The geometric basis in each case may be sound; but what, if any, is the geologic significance of any such "petrogenic" grid? No uniform composition can be assigned to phases like chlorite, chloritoid, stilpnomelane, biotite, and garnet in which mutual substitution of Fe, Mg, and even Mn is widespread. Compositional variation of such phases across the P-T field destroys the univariant character assigned to reactions represented by sharply drawn curves on the Schreinemakers diagram. To what extent, one wonders, may this discrepancy lead to lateral merging—even to overlap—of adjacent "univariant" curves in a diagram depicting actual paragenesis? And for the most part V and S data for natural phases (solid solutions) are not adequate to define slopes, and in some cases even the sign, of critical curves used to delineate fields of stable bivariant equilibria that (following Goldschmidt's classic dictum) probably constitute the bulk of common metamorphic phase assemblages. Finally, most published "petrogenic grids" that have been developed along the above lines for metapelites and metabasalts understandably lack numerical scales of P and T. Even where calibration has been superposed on a Schreinemakers grid, all too often it has been based on one of the most disputed equilibria in the literature—the Al_2SiO_2 triple point (e.g., Hess, 1969, pp. 196–197; Kepezhinskas and Khlestov, 1977, p. 140).[*]

On the positive side the main value of Schreinemakers' treatment of complex natural "systems" is twofold—on both counts purely qualitative. First it presents an intelligible overall picture of how observed common phase assemblages in rocks of restricted compositional range such as pelites may conceivably be related to P, T, and such additional variables as $X_{H_2O}^{gas}$ and f_{O_2}. And in the second place it demonstrates the unique character of any isograd [e.g., that of biotite in Brown's (1975) study] with respect to rock composition, the specific facies series in which it has been mapped, and the identity of the reaction by which the index mineral was generated.

Finally we must ask what bearing Schreinemakers' approach may have on construction and refinement of a natural petrogenic grid—for this term repeatedly figures in recent studies of this kind. It is well to be reminded, as Goldschmidt (1911b) argued long ago, that most commonly recurring metamorphic mineral assemblages must be bivariant in relation to P and T; for the chances that conditions requisite for univariant, let alone invariant, equilibrium will have been maintained repeatedly over large areas of present outcrop are remote indeed. Yet univariant equilibria are the very topic of Schreinemakers' analysis. The only natural counterpart that is likely to be encountered in any facies series is the isograd,[†] from which the site of an individual univariant equilibrium may be inferred. Complete Schreinemakers nets replete with invariant points (knots) would seem to have no integral place in a geologically applicable petrogenic grid as originally envisioned by Bowen.

[*]In both publications the triple point is located at $P = 5.5$–6 kb, $T = 580$–620°C—values that many of us think unrealistically high (cf. Fig. 4-2).

[†]Even on an isograd the univariant assemblage that defines it is rarely encountered on the scale of a thin section—witness the great rarity of the pair biotite-stilpnomelane in the vicinity of readily mapped isograds where biotite is generated at the expense of stilpnomelane.

6

Synoptic Review of Facies: Nomenclature and Diagnostic Characteristics

INTRODUCTION

The remainder of this book covers the descriptive mineralogical and related chemical data of metamorphic petrology presented within the framework of the facies concept against a background of field occurrence. It leads ultimately to speculative models of P-T regimes of metamorphism in relation to tectonics and time.

This chapter is a preliminary synopsis of material to be elaborated in succeeding chapters. It consists of two sections. The first develops a workable scheme of nomenclature closely following Eskola's classic treatment of the same topic. The second sets out as economically as possible, and insofar as one may generalize from a multitude of data, the essential mineralogical character of each facies.

FACIES NOMENCLATURE

Development and Modification of Classic Ideas

In the decade 1951–1960 we reexamined the facies concept (e.g., Fyfe et al. 1958, pp. 8–20) and developed the nomenclature to the stage finally presented by Turner and Verhoogen (1960). The upshot was a system based on that of Eskola (Table 6-1), retaining much of his terminology with some additions and revision, but

TABLE 6-1
Metamorphic Facies in Relation to Temperature and Pressure (diagrammatic)

	Temperature increasing →			
Pressure increasing ↓				Sanidinite
	Greenschist	Epidote-amphibolite	Amphibolite	Pyroxene-hornfels
				Granulite
		Glaucophane-schist		Eclogite

After Eskola, 1939, p. 345.

expanded, along lines previously initiated by Vogt (1927) and Eskola (1939), by the erection of subfacies. Some of the changes we introduced have found general acceptance. Others have been judged by experienced petrologists to be inadequate, unnecessary, or even tending toward confusion (cf. Lambert, 1965). So we again reappraised the nomenclatural situation (Fyfe and Turner, 1966), recognizing less than a dozen facies, still retaining as much as possible of the earlier terminology. The status of subfacies poses a dilemma. The more narrowly such a unit is restricted (e.g., to cover the overall paragenesis of a single zone in a facies series), the more closely it conforms to the basic requirement of chemical-mineralogical correlation; but the more limited it becomes as a nomenclatural unit relevant to general problems. With this latter limitation in mind we now relegate subfacies to a purely local role as units in specific unique facies series (cf. p. 56). They have no place in the system of nomenclature here adopted.

Preferred Nomenclature

The position here is essentially that stated by Fyfe and Turner (1966), but with an added modification regarding facies transitions. The facies that have been generally recognized on the basis of universally recurring critical mineral parageneses are eleven in number. They are (1) albite-epidote-hornfels, (2) hornblende-hornfels, (3) pyroxene-hornfels, (4) sanidinite, (5) zeolite, (6) prehnite-pumpellyite-metagraywacke (inadvertently not specifically named as such by Fyfe and Turner), (7) greenschist, (8) amphibolite, (9) granulite, (10) bluschist (glaucophane-lawsonite-schist), and (11) eclogite. In the course of the present survey, this writer has become increasingly aware that parageneses transitional between those of some of the above facies not only are known, but are repeated (with minor variation) in many parts of the world and sometimes cover large areas. Such parageneses have, by definition, the full status of facies. To invent new names to cover these transitional facies would not only overtax and complicate unduly the current nomenclature scheme; but in addition it would result in falsely presenting a picture of sharp interfacies boundaries where none exist. This procedure would have all the faults that attended our earlier efforts to multiply and to sharply define universally applicable subfacies.

To meet this situation, it is proposed to recognize transitional facies, where such exist on a more than local basis, and to name them accordingly. In most areas of progressive regional metamorphism, the greenschist facies of the chlorite and biotite zones is clearly distinguishable from the amphibolite facies of the zones of almandine, staurolite, and kyanite or sillimanite. But between the two, in some areas (e.g., the Scottish Highlands) covering much of the almandine zone, in others (e.g., New Hampshire–Vermont) overlapping the high-grade part of the biotite zone, are parageneses combining to some degree the critical characteristics of the other two. These have previously been termed (with considerable attendant confusion) the epidote-amphibolite or albite-epidote-amphibolite facies, or a high-grade subfacies of the greenschist facies. Here they will be described simply as greenschist-amphibolite-transition facies. Similarly, amphibolite-granulite-transition facies will be introduced to replace what we previously termed the hornblende-granulite subfacies of the granulite facies. Other low-grade and transition facies will be introduced where necessary.

Figure 6-1 shows schematically a tentative correlation between facies and the simplest physical controls of metamorphism—temperature and pressure (cf. Fyfe and Turner, 1966). It anticipates conclusions that will emerge in the course of the chapters that follow. In due course we shall find it possible to place more precise limits upon the pressure-temperature fields suggested at this stage in Fig. 6-1. This preliminary presentation should serve, however, to remove from the descriptive survey any false impression that facies fall neatly into pigeonholes whose boundaries conveniently parallel the rectangular coordinates of temperature and pressure or are sharply defined by univariant equilibria.

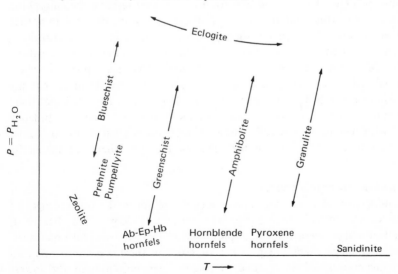

FIGURE 6-1
Schematic relation of facies to temperature and pressure ($P_{H_2O} = P$) (after W. S. Fyfe and F. J. Turner).

MINERALOGICAL CHARACTERISTICS
OF INDIVIDUAL FACIES:
GENERALIZED SYNOPSIS

Mode of Presentation

We now review in the briefest possible terms some generally diagnostic mineralogical characteristics of each facies—the essential criterion of constant predictable relation between mineralogical and chemical composition inherent in definition of facies. In every facies there is some latitude in such relations, and consequent variation in mineralogy, among its constituent local subfacies as developed in one or more facies series. Consideration of such details, which collectively reflect the whole spectrum of metamorphic paragenesis, is postponed until Chaps. 8–10.

The order of treatment of individual facies as separate entities, as is obvious from Fig. 6-1, must necessarily be arbitrary. We have chosen to deal first with low-pressure facies characteristic of contact aureoles. Then follow facies typical of regional metamorphic belts, considered in generalized order of increasing grade— zeolite and blueschist to granulite. Finally there is the eclogite facies, for the most part, it is thought, recording the imprint of metamorphism in the upper mantle or locally in deeply depressed crust. The limitations imposed by this admittedly arbitrary treatment will be set out in the preamble to each section.

Facies of Contact Metamorphism

Arbitrary Stipulations

The four facies to be considered under the above heading are most typically developed in contact aureoles surrounding igneous plutons emplaced independently of and subsequent to deformation and to any associated regional metamorphism of enclosing rocks. This limitation is not just a matter of convenience in presentation. It emphasizes the commonly independent roles of plutonism and regional metamorphism as seen from the viewpoint of students of tectonics. We recognize, nevertheless, that closely similar sets of mineral assemblages may appear elsewhere on a regional scale where the general thermal regime was independent of or at any rate not wholly controlled by igneous intrusion. It must also be noted that there is a widespread pattern of syntectonic "granite" plutonism that is intimately associated with metamorphism and whose products do not fall within the facies we are about to review. Such are the metamorphic components of migmatite complexes.

Albite-Epidote-Hornfels Facies

The first mineralogical effects of contact metamorphism in the outer fringes of most aureoles are difficult to decipher with certainty except in the absence of any imprint of earlier regional metamorphism. Basic and semibasic tuffs and lavas, already in disequilibrium in the presence of water in the lower range of metamorphic temperatures, are susceptible to contact metamorphism of the lowest grade. They recrystallize to the diagnostic assemblage albite-epidote-actinolite, after which the facies has been named. At about the same stage biotite begins to develop in the quartz-muscovite-chlorite matrix of pelitic rocks (spotted slates), so that typical pelitic assemblages include the trio biotite-muscovite-quartz. Andalusite (chiastolite), which also can appear in the more aluminous slates at an early stage (though typically after biotite), probably belongs to pelitic assemblages in this facies.

Albite-epidote-actinolite is widespread also in metavolcanics of the greenschist facies; and for this reason some workers regard the albite-epidote-hornfels facies as a low-pressure variant of the greenschist facies. Mineralogical differences between the two are, at most, rather trivial; but the distinction that we have drawn is useful from the viewpoint of tectonic emphasis.

Hornblende-Hornfels Facies

In most contact aureoles, the bulk of the constituent rocks fall within this facies. Here, as in the pyroxene-hornfels facies, there is a wide variety, largely determined by rock composition, in common mineral parageneses. Diagnostic mineral assemblages are

1. Pelitic: Quartz-biotite-muscovite with andalusite (sillimanite at highest grade) and/or cordierite. K-feldspar mainly in rocks lacking both andalusite (sillimanite) and cordierite.
2. Basic: Plagioclase $(An_{>25})$-hornblende (-diopside).
3. Calcareous: Calcite-diopside-tremolite; calcite-diposide-grossularite (-vesuvianite).
4. Magnesian: Anthophyllite-fosterite; anthophyllite-cordierite.

Almandine and staurolite, widely present in pelitic assemblages of the amphibolite facies are here much less common being restricted to metapelites with high Fe^{2+}/Mg.

Pyroxene-Hornfels Facies

Rocks of the pyroxene-hornfels facies may appear in the innermost zones in shallow contact aureoles, especially where these surround plutons of basic or semibasic rock composition. Characteristic mineralogical features are

1. Association of sillimanite (or andalusite) and cordierite with K-feldspar in pelitic rocks.
2. Absence of muscovite and more restricted occurrence of biotite than in the hornblende-hornfels facies.
3. Presence of diopside-hypersthene and absence of amphiboles in basic hornfelses.
4. Presence of wollastonite in calcic assemblages and of calcite-forsterite-periclase and calcite-forsterite-diopside in silica-poor dolomitic marbles.
5. Almandine garnet when present has a high Fe^{2+}/Mg ratio compared with that of granulite-facies assemblages. The typical magnesian phase is cordierite. Staurolite is unknown.

Sanidinite Facies

Rocks metamorphosed under conditions of maximum temperature and minimum pressure in a volcanic or quasi-volcanic thermal environment are insignificant in total bulk and limited in areal extent. The mineral assemblages present features unique in the field of metamorphism; so, in spite of their limited petrologic significance, Eskola (1939, p. 347) placed them in a special category that he termed the sanidinite facies. The terminology is perhaps unfortunate since sanidinite itself is a volcanic rock—a species of trachyte that, in certain tuff-filled pipes, has served as the vehicle of transport for rock fragments of the facies now under consideration—but time-honored usage warrants retention of the term.

Some of the characteristic mineral phases are common, too, in the pyroxene-hornfels facies—cordierite and wollastonite (though often with significant Fe^{2+} or Mg), anorthite, forsterite, spinel, and corundum. Others—tridymite, mullite, larnite, and rankinite—are more typical of products of quenching from artificial melts. The typical alkali feldspar is sodic sanidine. Micas, amphiboles, and garnets are all absent. Pelitic and semipelitic rocks commonly have been brought to the point of partial fusion (these are termed buchites).

Facies of Regional Metamorphism

Arbitrary Stipulations

We turn now to facies that characteristically develop by regional metamorphism. The reader is reminded in terms of our original definition (p. 24) that there may be no indication of accompanying plutonism; and that where such indeed is in evidence it appears to express local culminations within a regional thermal regime rather than to be the direct control or cause of the metamorphic event. The pattern of facies outcrop may conform locally to the outlines of synmetamorphic migmatite complexes and gneiss domes, as in parts of New England (cf. Fig. 1-13). The overall picture is then one of intensified but locally fluctuating heat flow. It is very different from the thermal setting of what we have called "facies of contact metamorphism," and so too are the respective tectonic implications of the two situations.

The broad configuration of the P-T field of regional metamorphism in the crust is described by the total spans of pressure ΔP and temperature ΔT involved: $\Delta P/\Delta T \approx 15$-$20$ bar degr^{-1}. On the other hand for individual facies, except at the lowest grade, $\Delta P/\Delta T$ is considerably greater (perhaps 30-50 bar degr^{-1}). Thus, individual facies of regional metamorphism—like those of contact metamorphism, but to a lesser degree—can be considered as temperature-sensitive and can be correspondingly designated as low, medium, or high grade.

Low-pressure variants in facies of regional metamorphism may be scarcely distinguishable, on mineralogical grounds alone, from high-pressure parageneses in facies of contact metamorphism. Indeed, in the previous edition a section entitled "Hornblende-Hornfels Facies in Regional Metamorphism" dealt with parageneses now to be considered as representing the amphibolite facies in low-pressure regional facies series. From a geochemical viewpoint the earlier plan is perhaps preferable, for it conforms more strictly to the accepted mineralogical basis of facies. Here, however, it is rejected in favor of treatment that, while admittedly looser, is more in keeping with the dominant tectonic bias in current geological thinking. Incipient metamorphism of low grade at depths no greater than a few kilometers poses a similar problem: zeolitic assemblages of one kind or another may appear on a regional scale or else locally, as revealed by drilling in geothermal areas, above recently emplaced hot igneous bodies. The principal development of what we shall call the zeolitic facies, however, is regional;

and in this category it is listed below. Such ambiguities are inescapable in any scheme of presentation involving division between merging geologic phenomena.

Facies now to be considered in the regional category are as follows:

1. Facies of low grade; loosely in order of increasing depth (pressure):
   a. Zeolite
   b. Prehnite-pumpellyite
   c. Pumpellyite-actinolite
   d. Lawsonite-albite-chlorite
   e. Blueschist
   f. Greenschist
2. Facies of high grade:
   g. Amphibolite
   h. Granulite
   i. Eclogite

Zeolite Facies

This is the facies characteristic of incipient metamorphism at minimal grade corresponding to temperatures and pressures induced by burial at depths of only a few kilometers. For the most part the products of metamorphism are confined to vein and amygdale fillings and fine-grained matrices enclosing relic grains surviving from the parent rock.

The diagnostic and most widespread assemblage is laumontite-quartz-chlorite. In some situations, the place of laumontite is taken by some other calcium zeolite: heulandite at shallow levels or wairakite where temperatures are locally raised by subjacent hot igneous bodies. Prehnite and pumpellyite are by no means uncommon in the zeolite facies.

Prehnite-Pumpellyite Facies

At deepest levels is stratigraphically measured sections, laumontite is no longer present, and a highly characteristic assemblage prehnite-pumpellyite-quartz remains. This is also regionally developed in nonfoliated metagraywacke and metabasalts over wide areas in which its relation to depth cannot be demonstrated. The full metagraywacke assemblage diagnostic of the facies (Coombs, 1960, p. 341) is quartz-albite-"muscovite"-chlorite-prehnite-pumpellyite-sphene.

Pumpellyite-Actinolite Facies

Japanese and New Zealand geologists following Hashimoto (1966) recognize as a separate facies metagraywacke and metavolcanic assemblages in which pumpellyite is accompanied by actinolite while prehnite is lacking. This view is warranted (1) by the great areal extent of such rocks in a number of regions where a sharply defined isograd separates a prehnite-pumpellyite from a pumpellyite-actinolite-zone of higher grade (e.g., Bishop, 1972); and (2) by the consistent development of pumpellyite-actinolite, without preceding prehnite-pumpellyite assemblages, in the early stages of progressive metamorphism that culminates in the blueschist facies.

Lawsonite-Albite-Chlorite Facies

Only recently recognized as distinct from the blueschist facies—both mineralogically and with regard to field distribution—is a metasedimentary paragenesis with lawsonite and in many cases aragonite, but completely lacking both glaucophane and jadeitic pyroxene. It was based largely on a regional occurrence in New Zealand described by Coombs (1960); but the same facies has been reported also on a regional scale in northern California (Blake et al., 1967), New Caledonia (Brothers, 1970), and elsewhere.

Prior to his renunciation of the facies concept, Winkler (1965, p. 149)[*] designated this the lawsonite-albite facies. The slightly different name adopted here is that of Coombs and associates (e.g., Coombs et al., 1976a, pp. 571, 585). Characteristic mineral assemblages are

1. *Pelitic and metagraywacke:* Quartz-albite-lawsonite-chlorite-muscovite (± aragonite or calcite)
2. *Calcareous:* Aragonite (± calcite) or albite-pumpellyite-chlorite-sphene (-epidote)

Blueschist (Glaucophane-Schist) Facies

A striking facies mainly, but not exclusively, developed in young metamorphic belts located along the margins of the Pacific and in the Alpine-Tethyan orogenic zone of Europe and western Asia, is characterized by blue schists containing abundant glaucophane. With it, and also in associated rocks lacking glaucophane, are various combinations of phases demonstrably stable at high pressures and low temperatures (pp. 175–179) and diagnostic of the facies—lawsonite, aragonite, and jadeitic pyroxenes. The commonest assemblages also include one or more minerals that are almost ubiquitous in the greenschist facies—(see below): chlorite, phengitic muscovite, stilpnomelane, epidote, sphene, albite, quartz. Eskola, who first recognized the individuality of the facies, designated it the *glaucophane-schist facies*; and this term undoubtedly has priority in nomenclature (E. W. F. De Roever et al., 1976). Glaucophane also occurs, however, in rocks (here considered transitional to the greenschist facies) that lack any of the other diagnostic high-pressure phases. For this reason and to lend sharper definition to the facies, it was renamed the *glaucophane-lawsonite-schist facies* (Fyfe and Turner, 1966, p. 361; cf. Winkler, 1965, pp. 144–145). Meanwhile the term *blueschist facies* had been introduced (Bailey et al., 1964) as an exact synonym. It is an unfortunate name, even vaguer in its implications; for blue amphiboles other than glaucophane—riebeckite, crocidolite, sodic actinolites—occur in metamorphic rocks extraneous to the facies now under consideration. Yet the name blueschist facies, which at least has the advantage of conciseness, has gained wide acceptance, particularly in America, and has evidently come to stay. In any case it joins a list of standard facies names not notable for clarity or consistency in definition.

Here, therefore, to minimize confusion, the term "blueschist facies" is used as an alternative to Eskola's earlier and somewhat more exact term. It will be limited strictly to rock associations whose component mineral assemblages include glaucophane-lawsonite, glaucophane-omphacite, or glaucophane-jadeite-quartz.

---

[*]First edition of "Petrogenesis of Metamorphic Rocks" (cf. Winkler, 1974).

Highly characteristic of the blueschist facies (in contradistinction from the greenschist facies) is complete absence of biotite.

Parageneses with glaucophane or lawsonite as the sole high-pressure phase or with the pair lawsonite-aragonite are transitional toward but are not included in the blueschist facies.

Greenschist Facies

In most Paleozoic and some Mesozoic belts, early stages of complete recrystallization—in the zones of chlorite and biotite—yield a set of mineral assemblages that collectively constitute Eskola's greenschist facies. The facies thus covers the products of low- and low-medium-grade regional metamorphism as generally conceived prior to the middle of the century.[*] The diagnostic pair common to all common mineral assemblages in derivatives of shales, graywackes, and basic volcanics is albite-epidote (usually plus quartz). Other common and characteristic minerals include

1. In pelitic assemblages: phengitic muscovite, chlorites, sphene (chloritoid, stilpnomelane); biotite at higher grades
2. In basic assemblages: chlorites, actinolite, stilpnomelane, and calcite
3. In magnesian assemblages: antigorite, talc, and tremolite (diopside)

Notable absentees, in contrast to rocks of lower grades, are zeolites, prehnite, pumpellyite, lawsonite, glaucophane, and jadeitic pyroxenes.

Amphibolite Facies

In many facies series (e.g., Barrovian, Appalachian, and southern New Zealand), assemblages developed in rocks of medium to maximum grade from the zone of almandine onward fall in the amphibolite facies. The pair hornblende-plagioclase ($An_{>20}$) characteristic of amphibolites is diagnostic, too, of the facies. Typical assemblages are

1. Pelitic: quartz-muscovite-biotite-almandine; with or without staurolite and kyanite (sillimanite at maximum grade, andalusite in low-pressure series)
2. Basic: hornblende-plagioclase, with epidote, almandine, or diopside as possible additional phases
3. Calcareous: calcite-diopside-tremolite; calcite-grossularite-zoisite (clinozoisite)
4. Magnesian: tremolite-forsterite, with antigorite, talc, anthophyllite, or enstatite as an additional phase

Granulite Facies

This embraces mineral assemblages developed by extreme dehydration at maximum grades of regional metamorphism, almost exclusively in Precambrian provinces. White micas are absent, and biotites (typically phlogopitic) and hornblende may

---

[*]Until then the existence and regional extent of the zeolite and prehnite-pumpellyite and pumpellyite-actinolite facies had not been revealed, and the physical significance of the blueschist facies was not realized. The Barrovian series of Scotland was then accepted as the normal pattern of regional metamorphism.

be completely lacking and in any case are not nearly so prevalent as in the amphibolite facies. Some typical assemblages include

1. Pelitic: quartz-perthite-sillimanite-almandine (with cordierite, biotite, and kyanite as possible alternative or additional phases)
2. Basic: plagioclase-diopside-hypersthene (-garnet)
3. Calcareous: calcite-diopside-forsterite (-scapolite, corundum)
4. Mangesian: forsterite-enstatite-spinel

Eclogite Facies

Eclogites, rocks of basaltic composition and unique mineralogy (essentially omphacite plus garnet), are almost the sole representatives of a facies that stands apart from the rest. For the most part they appear as tectonically transported blocks enclosed in rocks of some other facies or in chaotic mélange zones that commonly occur in blueschist terranes. The diagnostic metabasaltic assemblage is omphacite-garnet (with rutile, quartz, and kyanite as possible additional phases). A unique isofacial assemblage in associated Hercynian rocks of granodioritic composition in the Italian Alps (Pennine domain) is quartz-jadeite-zoisite-phengite.

7

Facies Series, Tectonic Environment, and Time

PREAMBLE: DIVERSITY IN METAMORPHIC REGIMES

Any facies series is the tangible end product of one particular cycle of progressive metamorphism—the expression of a temperature-pressure gradient unique in place and in time. Until the 1930s, knowledge of mineralogical aspects of progressive regional metamorphism was based on narrowly limited data, mostly drawn from segments of the early- to mid-Paleozoic "Caledonian" fold systems of Scotland (e.g., Barrow, 1893, 1912; Tilley, 1925a) and Norway (Goldschmidt, 1915, 1921; Vogt, 1927[*]). For a long time, the picture that thus emerged was the generally accepted norm. It was embellished but not significantly changed by classic studies in the Appalachian province of New York (Barth, 1936) and New England (starting with Billings, 1937); for here, too, the age and pattern of metamorphism were much the same as in northwestern Europe. Significant departures began to appear in the earliest accounts of late Mesozoic metamorphism along the Pacific margin in Japan (e.g., Suzuki, 1930; Sugi, 1931, 1935) and in New Zealand (Turner, 1933, 1938; Hutton and Turner, 1936; Hutton, 1940). Following World War II, continued

---

[*]Vogt's extensive memoir on the Sulitelma region is a remarkable contribution that, in spite of its extensive English summary, has received scant attention in literature written in English.

investigation in these areas and numerous studies elsewhere (in the Alps especially) revealed still further variety, until Miyashiro (1961), in enunciating his valuable concept of facies series, set up what he considered distinct standard types correlated with different postulated pressure regimes. Diversity in pattern became underscored, too, by increasing knowledge of the granulite facies in Precambrian terranes and growing general realization of the great extent of low-grade metamorphic rocks in "greenstone belts" that comprise an important element of the most ancient parts of continental shields. Finally within the past dozen years low-grade metamorphism has been shown to be a widespread phenomenon in crustal rocks lying, probably at no great depth, below the sediments and lava flows that cover the ocean floors.

While all this variety in metamorphic pattern is generally recognized today, yet there is no question that petrologic concepts relating to mineralogy, geochemistry, and tectonic implications of metamorphism have long been biased—and to some degree remain so—by phenomena controlled by the continental geothermal regimes that prevailed during the last 600 million years. (The emphasis in Chap. 1 is on just such patterns.) The advent of radiometric geochronology, the stimulus of plate-tectonic theory, exploration of the ocean floor, the search for life in the earth's most ancient rocks, and mushrooming speculation in the field of terrestrial and continental evolution have now compelled a closer look at tangible metamorphic phenomena of all ages and situations. Fundamental questions have arisen, for the most part still inadequately answered, as to the possible roles of geographic situation, tectonics, and of time itself in the general metamorphic picture. Questions of this kind can be answered only by synthesis of data drawn from many sources—stratigraphy, tectonics, geophysics, and petrology. Their comprehensive treatment is far beyond the scope of this book. Yet one of the keys to their potential solution lies in the descriptive data of metamorphic facies series set in specific tectonic environments of various known ages.

That the thermal history of the earth must have followed an evolutionary course, with possible attendant changes in patterns of regional metamorphism, is a necessary consequence of the exponential rate of decay of radioactive (heat-generating) elements. Just how patterns have changed, and the extent to which the changes were discontinuous, can be inferred only from the evidence of the rocks themselves—metamorphic facies series seen against the background of time. That is why, in the treatment that follows, emphasis is placed upon chronologic aspects of regional metamorphism—particularly as it is now possible to assess these in quantitative terms based on radiometric data. Obvious differences are apparent, though not as striking as might have been expected, between the respective patterns of Phanerozoic ($<600 \times 10^6$ years) and Archaean ($>2500 \times 10^6$ years) time. Aspects of both overlap into the intervening Proterozoic.

As to tectonic regimes, we emphasize two pertinent criteria both readily assessed objectively in the field. First is the obvious one relating to location (especially with respect to major real crustal discontinuities) and dimensions of the metamorphic domain. The second concerns microscopically visible strain effects as seen in the outcrop and on smaller scales; for these reflect the style or mechanism of the metamorphic deformation process. In particular it is both significant and a simple matter to draw a distinction between domains of foliated (schistose) and those of nonschistose rocks—with allowance for the inevitable transitional types with poorly developed or localized schistosity. Foliation and associated minor pervasive structures (lineations, microfolds) attest to a strain regime of continuous flow. They comprise what Sander called the tectonite fabric. Its development is favored, among other factors, by high temperature. It is not surprising therefore to find that in nontectonite domains the prevailing grades of metamorphism are low.

It is impossible of course to arrange our material in any simple linear order. And there is no pretense at comprehensive or final treatment of what in fact is one complex facet of an even more complex picture that defies perception in totality. Nevertheless, an attempt will be made to marshall in synoptic form a tentative inventory of metamorphic data currently available for developing models of crustal and geothermal evolution on any desired scale. Indeed, those who are bold enough to speculate along such lines cannot afford (though some do) to ignore this particular, perhaps their most tangible, available asset.

PLAN OF TREATMENT

Topics are considered in the following order.

1. Facies of contact metamorphism
2. Regional facies series in nontectonite domains
   a. Currently active geothermal metamorphism
   b. Ocean-floor metamorphism
   c. Burial metamorphism
   d. Uniform regional low-grade metamorphism
   e. Spilites as metamorphic rocks
3. Regional facies series in tectonite domains (Phanerozoic, Proterozoic)
   a. Plan of treatment
   b. Continuous flow in rocks and its relation to metamorphic facies
   c. Blueschist facies series
   d. Greenschist facies series
   e. Amphibolite facies series
   f. Granulite facies series
   g. Eclogite facies
4. Aspects of Archaean metamorphism
   a. Regional high-grade facies in cratonic nuclei
   b. Facies in greenstone belts
   c. Notable absentees

FACIES SERIES OF CONTACT METAMORPHISM

Contact metamorphism in the sense employed in this book is a direct consequence of plutonic intrusion. Unlike regional metamorphism it has no direct connection with orogeny, even in the common case where posttectonic plutons and their contact aureoles are located in orogenic belts (e.g., the "Newer Granite" plutons of the Dalradian in Scotland and Ireland—cf. p. 25).

Highly characteristic of aureoles generated by granitic plutons are inward sequences (facies series):

Albite-epidote-hornfels → hornblende-hornfels

Less commonly, and more particularly in aureoles surrounding more basic plutons, the inward sequence is

Hornblende-hornfels → pyroxene-hornfels

The main interest of facies series of contact metamorphism lies in fields of pure mineralogy, ore geology, and igneous petrology.

REGIONAL FACIES SERIES IN NONTECTONITE DOMAINS

Facies of Currently Active Geothermal Metamorphism

Drilling for steam in geothermal areas has revealed patterns of low-grade metamorphism that can be directly related to measured variables, especially temperature and fluid composition, at shallow depths. Of particular interest are areas of high positive heat-flow anomaly situated along terrestrial extensions of ocean-ridge sites of current tectonic activity such as the Salton Sea geothermal field of southeastern California (Muffler and White, 1969) and the Reykjanes field of Iceland (Tómasson and Kristmannsdóttir, 1972).

In the Salton Sea field silty sediments with significant carbonates exhibit "diagenetic" changes—in which montmorillonite and dolomite give way to chlorite-"muscovite"-calcite assemblages—down to depths varying from 2 km to more than 4 km. Then, when temperatures exceed about 300°C, a greenschist assemblage, quartz-mica-chlorite-epidote-albite becomes fully developed. There are no zeolitic assemblages. Instead, at temperatures of ~200–250°C, we find a diagenetic mineral facies characterized by clay-carbonate assemblages conditioned it would seem by high levels of f_{CO_2} (cf. Zen, 1961, 1974).

In the Icelandic field the downward facies sequence in interlayered basaltic lavas, palagonites, and tuffs is

Zeolite → greenschist

Incoming of epidote marks a transition to the greenschist facies at temperatures between 200 and 250°C (depths 600–1200 m).

In two geothermal fields situated in broader provinces of recent andesite-dacite volcanism—Wairakei, New Zealand (e.g., Steiner, 1953; Coombs et al., 1959), and Katayama, Japan (Seki et al., 1969)—all newly developed mineral assemblages in volcanogenic rocks recovered from drills a few hundred meters deep belong to the zeolite facies. Laumontite gives way to wairakite at temperatures of 190–220°C in New Zealand, 80–180°C in Japan.

In every case transition from unmetamorphosed rock to mineral assemblages of the greenschist facies is accomplished without intermediate development of the prehnite-pumpellyite facies. The transition can take place via two alternative paths—one through the zeolite facies, the other through a clay-carbonate facies generally considered as diagenetic.

Facies of Ocean-Floor Metamorphism

Evidence of Dredged Samples

The surface of the ocean floor is covered with flows of basaltic lavas and a veneer of deep-sea sediments. Some of the surface lavas that have been in prolonged contact with ocean waters have been affected by submarine weathering. None show any sign of metamorphism. Even pillow lavas extruded at depths of 3–5 km (cf. Moore, 1965, 1970) remain remarkably fresh in spite of contact, while still hot, with sea water at pressures of several hundred bars.

By contrast there are now a good many records of metabasalts, metagabbros, and serpentinites in dredge hauls from stations on mid-oceanic ridges of the Atlantic and Indian Oceans (Melson and Van Andel, 1966; Cann, 1969; Myashiro et al., 1971; Miyashiro, 1972, pp. 153–155). It is reasonable to infer that basaltic and other igneous components of the suboceanic crust, at depths unknown below the water/rock interface, bear the imprint of widespread low-grade metamorphism, at least in the vicinity of oceanic ridges. Ocean-floor metamorphism is here envisioned as a special type of regional metamorphism.

Most of the metamorphic mineral assemblages so far recorded fall in the zeolite and greenschist facies.[*] Some rocks in the latter category are typical spilites as to both mineralogy and chemical composition (e.g., Cann, 1969). Prehnite-pumpellyite assemblages are notable absentees (in contrast with the facies series of later burial metamorphism as described below). Foliation is rarely displayed in rocks affected by ocean-floor metamorphism.

Only by inference can metamorphic grade be correlated, from the oceanic record alone, with vertical or lateral temperature gradients. Miyashiro and his coauthors advocate depth control of grade, and regard suboceanic metamorphism as a kind of burial metamorphism. This model receives some support from the relative depths at which rocks of the zeolite and the greenschist facies have been recovered at mutually adjacent stations on the eastern wall of the Median Valley of the Mid-Atlantic Ridge (Melson and Van Andel, 1966, p. 168). By analogy with well-documented geothermal patterns in Iceland and in the Red Sea, a more complex model has been proposed by Spooner and Fyfe (1973). They postulate the existence of numerous local intracrustal geothermal systems in the vicinity of ocean ridges; near these, as observed in terrestrial geothermal fields, temperatures would locally rise above some general background level, reaching values appropriate

---

[*]Some metagabbros display the amphibole-plagioclase pair that typifies the amphibolite facies; but in the absence of documented textural evidence the status of calcic plagioclase (metamorphic or relict) is somewhat dubious.

to the greenschist facies at relatively shallow depths below the water/rock interface. General absence of prehnite-pumpellyite assemblages in dredged samples supports the thesis of Spooner and Fyfe.

Significance of Ophiolites

Early in the century G. Steinmann[*] recognized a type of large-scale compound ultramafic-mafic rock association that he found to be widespread in the Alps of eastern Switzerland and in the Apennines of Italy. These associations he termed *ophiolites*; each consists of the following downward sequence of units beneath a capping of deep-sea sediments ("abyssites")—radiolarian cherts and foraminiferal limestones.

Pillow-basalts (mostly spilitic)
Gabbros
Peridotites (largely serpentinized)

Ophiolites are now recognized as prominent lithologic elements of deformed Phanerozoic geosynclinal belts the world over—e.g., in Newfoundland (Ordovician), southern New Zealand (Permian), the Coast Ranges of California (mid-Mesozoic), and throughout the Tethyan mountain systems (late Mesozoic) of the eastern Mediterranean and Asia Minor. They belong to the general category of ultramafic-mafic bodies that Benson (1926, p. 6) designated as "the Alpine type." Though it is unsafe to identify every "Alpine-type" serpentinite body as ophiolitic, all must have genetic implications in common. In today's usage basal ophiolite is the diagnostic criterion of the eugeosyncline.

Since W. P. de Roever (1957) first raised the question, more and more of us have come to regard ultramafic bodies of the Alpine type as tectonically emplaced fragments of upper-mantle rock. It is but one step further to interpret ophiolites as compound slices of oceanic crust and underlying mantle rocks, thrust as allochthonous sheets over somewhat younger rocks. And in keeping with current tectonic doctrine, it is easy to postulate distant ocean-ridge sources, the mode of transport being that of sea-floor spreading. Such a model has in fact come into recent vogue (e.g., see Moores, 1969; Moores and Vine, 1971; Page, 1972; papers collected in Ernst, 1975a, pp. 264–328; Smewing and Gass, 1975; Woodcock and Robertson, 1977).[†] If the basic assumptions be granted, we might look to some ophiolites for surviving patterns of ocean-floor metamorphism. Most ophiolitic masses are too disrupted or too much affected by metamorphism postdating emplacement to serve such a purpose. However, a few, located in the eastern

---

[*]For an accessible summary of his final concept, see Steinmann (1927). His name, if not his published work, is familiar to most of us through the phrase "Steinmann trinity," aptly coined by E. B. Bailey to emphasize the constancy of the association serpentine-spilite-chert in ophiolites.

[†]It is, however, only the newest of many models that have been proposed over the years (cf. Vuagnat, 1963). And radically different ideas have only recently been proposed although based on the same field data drawn from well-exposed Tethyan ophiolites—witness the vast submarine floods of ultramafic magma invoked by H. H. Wilson (1969) to explain the structural relations of the immense ultramafic sheet (partly ophiolitic) of Oman.

Mediterranean and Asia Minor, seem to meet the necessary requirements. Two specific instances will be cited:

(1) The much-investigated Troodos ophiolite of Cyprus is complete in every structural detail, including a vertically sheeted diabase-basalt zone at the base of the volcanic component. It is now thought to have been thrust over late Cretaceous marine sediments (Moores and Vine, 1971; Gass and Smewing, 1973); and an imprint of internal metamorphism has been found from fission-track data to be significantly older. (This model apparently supersedes others, radically different in nature, advocated but a few years before.) In a 2200-meter vertical section of pillow-basalts and underlying sheeted rocks, Gass and Smewing (1973) have traced, in the assemblage of secondary (metamorphic) minerals, a downward sequence from the zeolite to the greenschist facies. The transition occurs about 1500 m from the top.

(2) Parts of the great ultramafic sheet of Oman (H. H. Wilson, 1969) also display the full ophiolitic sequence, with 3000 m of upper pillow-basalts heavily sheeted toward the base with vertical dikes (B. Reinhardt in Amstutz, 1974, pp. 207–227). Here the metamorphic assemblages throughout the basaltic (spilitic) segment all typify the zeolite facies.

The metamorphic patterns recorded above, particularly absence of prehnite-pumpellyite[*] assemblages, duplicate those known in terrestrial areas of local geothermal metamorphism and are consistent with what we know of suboceanic metamorphic rocks. Herein possibly is mutual support between the Spooner-Fyfe model of ocean-floor metamorphism and the ocean-ridge model of ophiolitic sources—both tentatively adopted here, though either, judging from past experience, seems likely to be modified or superseded in the not too distant future.

Facies Series of Burial Metamorphism

The term *burial metamorphism* is here used in the strict sense as advocated in Chap. 1. [Note that Zen's (1974a) useful synopsis also covers metamorphic patterns of another kind, here treated in the next section.] With reference to large-scale deformation (open folding, tilting), the imprint is pretectonic.

In Phanerozoic Geosynclines

The term *geosyncline* is here used loosely (cf. Hsu, 1972), without its classical or any other tectonic implication, for any elongate thick stratigraphic sequence (sedimentary and/or volcanic) that has accumulated mainly under marine conditions close to a continental margin. Where the regional structure is simple and rocks have not been affected by penetrative deformation, it is commonly possible to trace the mineralogical imprint of metamorphism the grade of which increases with depth. This is burial metamorphism as first described in Triassic tuffaceous sandstones of southern New Zealand by Coombs (1954); and similar phenomena

---

[*]Fine-grained pumpellyite is notoriously difficult to recognize by optical means. In the low-grade fringes of the Haast Schist terrane of New Zealand, where it is almost ubiquitous, it was overlooked until its presence was demonstrated some forty years ago by C. O. Hutton (1937).

have since been recorded from many sites. Among these are Paleozoic graywackes and tuffs of the Lachlan and New England geosynclines in eastern Australia (Packham and Crook, 1960; R. E. Smith, 1968, 1969); late Mesozoic andesitic lavas, Andean geosyncline of Chile and Peru (Levi, 1969; Aguirre et al., 1978); upper Cretaceous tuffaceous sediments and lavas in Puerto Rico (Jolly, 1970).

Total stratigraphic thicknesses involved are of the order of 3000-10,000 meters. The gross downward facies series for this general lithology, though not completely represented in every case, is

Zeolite → prehnite-pumpellyite → pumpellyite-actinolite → greenschist

In the almost continuous lava pile of the Andean geosyncline, individual flows, 10–40 m thick, show internal departures from the overall pattern; and these are clearly related to texture (notably nonvesicular flow bases versus amygdaloidal tops). Mineralogical detail, it would seem, was to some degree controlled by rock permeability. In Chile and Peru independent successive episodes of burial metamorphism were terminated by periodic tectonic uplift. Thenceforward while a new metamorphic pattern was being imprinted above an unconformity, the volcanic pile beneath remained sealed against access of fluids necessary to promote further mineralogical transformations (cf. Aguirre et al., 1978).

In Proterozoic Basins and Troughs

Following a general stabilization of Archaean cratons about 2500 million years ago,* a changing pattern of tectonics and epicontinental sedimentation was initiated, moving gradually to what is generally considered as the typical geosynclinal pattern of the Phanerozoic. One feature of Archaean tectonics that was retained, especially in the earlier Proterozoic, was development of very extensive intracratonic basins and troughs. These were efficient traps for shallow-water sediments and volcanic flows. Individual basins may extend for 1000 km or more. The Labrador and Keweenawan troughs of the Canadian shield were even longer. Some though not all of these great Proterozoic depressions today retain much of their initial simple structure, scarcely disturbed by later tectonic or plutonic activity. Here recognizable effects of low-grade metamorphism (or deep diagenesis) can be safely correlated with *P-T* regimes controlled by burial. Three examples are noted below.

The *Hammersley Basin* (100,000 km^2 in area) of Western Australia (Fig. 7-1) illustrates a well-known type of early Proterozoic ($\sim$2000-2200 $\times$ 10^6 years) basin in which banded iron formation is a prominent and economically valuable lithologic type. The structure is remarkably simple: in a region where outcrop exposure is excellent, individual stratigraphic bands can be followed without interruption for 1000 km. Total depth is about 10 km. The Hammersley Group in which iron formation is extensively developed lies beneath a 4000-meter lava pile, and itself is 2400 m thick; so pressures of burial metamorphism were something less

---

*This important stage of continental evolution was reached at different times in different regions: perhaps at 3000 million years in Southern Africa; 2500 million years (Kenoran orogeny) in the Canadian shield.

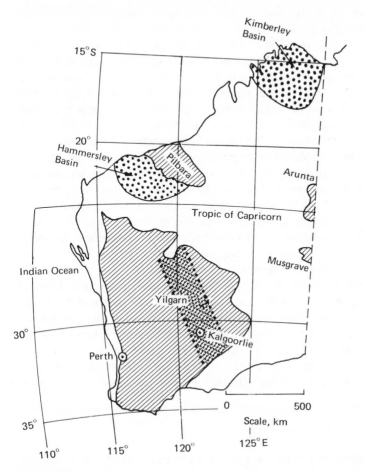

FIGURE 7-1

Two Proterozoic basins: Hammersley ($\sim$2200–2000 $\times$ 10^6 years) and Kimberley (1800–1400 $\times$ 10^6 years) in relation to Archaean granitic metamorphic complexes (shaded), Western Australia. Archaean "greenstones" of the Kalgoorlie belt are concentrated in lightly stippled area; blank areas denote Paleozoic, Mesozoic, and superficial desert cover. The whole area has been stable since the Archaean era (based on information compiled by E. A. Rudd).

than 2 kb. The iron formation here is a ferruginous chert consisting of quartz, iron oxide (martite after magnetite), and subordinate iron silicates (originally a mixture of greenalite and montmorillonite). The silicate fraction has been transformed by burial metamorphism to various combinations of stilpnomelane, minnesotaite, and riebeckite[*] (Grubb, 1971). These assemblages cannot be assigned with certainty to any of the low-grade facies, but the conditions of origin correspond to those generally thought to govern the zeolite and prehnite-pumpellyite facies. Situated about

[*]Here is a sharp reminder that abundant development of blue amphibole is no criterion of high metamorphic pressure, let alone of plate subduction!

1000 km northeast of the Hammersley is an even larger, younger basin of similar lithology—Kimberley Basin.

The late Proterozoic *Belt Series* of Montana and Idaho is a flat-lying sequence of mixed argillites, quartzites, and some carbonate strata that varies in thickness from 1000 m in the east to 10,000 m in western outcrops. Mineral assemblages, dominated everywhere by illite and quartz, show regular sequential changes that correlate generally with depth below the surface (Maxwell and Hower, 1967; Zen, 1974b, p. 446). The principal trend is increasing development of $2M$ polymorphs in the illite fraction. At the base of the thickest section, muscovite and even biotite appear, and recorded complete assemblages betoken the greenschist facies. Here, as pointed out by Zen (1974a), there is a gradual transition from sedimentary via metamorphic clay assemblages to the greenschist facies (cf. the Salton Sea geothermal pattern, pp. 214). The downward sequence of textural changes at first seems paradoxical: well-defined fissility (foliation) in the upper levels becomes largely obliterated by recrystallization toward the base of the section. The initial fissility is not, however, a strain structure. It represents a sedimentary fabric, enhanced perhaps by metamorphic elongation of illite crystals.

A pile of late Proterozoic (~ 1100–900×10^6 years) subaerially deposited flood basalts more than 5 km thick is exposed along the shores of *Keweenaw Peninsula*, Lake Superior (Jolly and Smith, 1972).[*] Volcanic textures are preserved with no hint of penetrative strain. Much as in Chile, amygdaloidal flow tops appear to have acted as channels for migrating fluids during regional burial metamorphism that produced an overall downward sequence of progressive mineralogical changes within the volcanic pile. This facies series, as recorded by Jolly and Smith, is

Zeolite → prehnite-pumpellyite

Appearance of epidote at the base of the exposed section, however, hints at transition toward the greenschist facies.

Uniform Regional Low-Grade Metamorphism

Regional Pumpellyite Metagraywackes

Metagraywackes of all ages in many parts of the world display over very large areas metamorphic assemblages prominent in which is pumpellyite. There is no general field correlation between degree and grade of metamorphism and stratigraphic level. In these rocks we see a very common pattern of regional metamorphism on the largest scale[†]; yet paradoxically until the present decade most such terranes were mapped—and some no doubt still are—as unmetamorphosed. From many recorded examples we cite the following.

1. Torlesse Group, occupying the greater part of the Carboniferous to early

---

[*]The Keweenaw Trough, of which this is one segment, is fault-bounded and thus is analogous more to a rift valley than to the typical down-warped early Proterozoic sedimentary basin. The maximum thickness prior to tilting is about 20 km.

[†]Examples will be found in contributions assembled in *Canadian Mineralogist*, Vol. 12, pp. 437–552, 1974.

Cretaceous New Zealand Geosyncline (Figs. 1-15 and 1-17). The complete facies series (e.g., Landis and Bishop, 1972, pp. 2274–2276), including rocks in the outer part of the Haast Schist into which the Torlesse Group merges southward with increasing metamorphism, is

Zeolite → prehnite-pumpellyite → pumpellyite-actinolite → greenschist

Transitions from the nontectonic fabric characteristic of the Torlesse (textural zone T1) to tectonite (schistose) fabric that typifies the Haast schists (zones T3 and T4) coincide more or less with the elimination of prehnite and development of the pumpellyite-actinolite facies toward the T2–T3 zonal boundary. The most widely developed facies throughout the Torlesse is prehnite-pumpellyite.

2. Early Tertiary Taveyanne Formation (flysch-type volcanic graywackes) Dauphiné-Helvetic domain (cf. Fig. 9-15), northwestern border of the French-Swiss Alps (Sawatzki and Vuagnat, 1971; Kubler et al., 1974; Coombs et al., 1976).

The facies series represented here is

Zeolite → prehnite-pumpellyite → pumpellyite-actinolite

Regional structural evidence suggests that metamorphic grade may be at least partly controlled by depth within and below the Helvetic nappe pile.

3. Early Paleozoic and late Proterozoic metavolcanics and metagraywackes exposed intermittently on the eastern edge of the Appalachian belt from Pennsylvania to Newfoundland (Zen, 1974). Both prehnite-pumpellyite and pumpellyite-actinolite facies are represented.

Facies in Shale Lithology

At the northern end of the Helvetic zone in Switzerland (Fig. 9-15), mid-Mesozoic shales and marls are conspicuous in the Glarus Alps. Here Frey (1970, 1978) has traced mineralogical and textural evolution accompanying the transition (anchimetamorphism) from diagenesis to complete metamorphism of clay-mineral assemblages. Crystallinity of illite increases, and micas (paragonite, phengite), pyrophyllite, and chlorite develop progressively at the expense of illite/montmorillonite and kaolinite. Neither zeolitic nor pumpellyite-bearing assemblages appear in this lithology. But the sequence of changes can be correlated by field distribution with the zeolite → prehnite-pumpellyite → pumpellyite-actinolite → greenschist facies series of metagraywacke lithology. Schistosity (cleavage) begins to develop earlier in metapelites than in metagraywackes (as commonly is the case in other provinces). Similar changes could well prove widespread among indurated shales elsewhere.

Regional Metagraywackes
with Blueschist Affinities

Along a 1000-km segment of the Pacific coast of California and Oregon, the lowest exposed broad rock unit is a thick mass of graywackes with subordinate shales, cherts, and pillow-basalts comprising the Franciscan Group (upper Jurassic and lower Cretaceous). Over most of this terrane, which exceeds 100 km in maximum width (Fig. 9-13), graywackes are nonfoliated or at most show incipient schistosity accompanied by microscopic granulation of quartz and feldspar. (These are structurally comparable with rocks of textural zones T1 and T2 as developed along the borders of the Haast Schist terrane of New Zealand (cf. p. 39). Such rocks were mapped until recently as unmetamorphosed, in contrast to the well-foliated blueschists that are conspicuous elsewhere in the Franciscan belt.

Following discoveries of widespread jadeitic pyroxene replacing clastic plagioclase in graywackes from several localities by M. Maddock and T. W. Bloxam (see Bloxam, 1956) it was quickly realized that much of the Franciscan graywacke terrane bears the partial mineralogical imprint of regional metamorphism (e.g., McKee, 1962; Bailey et al., 1964, pp. 89–92; 1970, pp. 70–81; Blake et al., 1967; Ernst et al., 1970; Ernst, 1971a, pp. 47–50). The generalized facies series representing the whole terrane is

Zeolite → pumpellyite-actinolite → lawsonite-albite-chlorite → blueschist

The most completely reconstituted metagraywackes, which nevertheless appear "to the casual observer . . . to be unmetamorphosed" (Ernst et al., 1970, p. 38), carry a full blueschist assemblage dominated by quartz plus jadeitic pyroxene. In northern California (Bailey et al., 1970), the lawsonite-albite-chlorite facies represents the highest grade reached in continuous surface outcrops.

Seki (1965, p. 39), in commenting on the absence of prehnite in pumpellyite metagraywackes of the Sanbagawa belt of Japan, noted also that this seems to be a general feature of rocks transitional to blueschists in other parts of the world.

Finally, there are yet other provinces of low-grade regional metamorphism where, although the blueschist facies is nowhere developed, metagraywacke assemblages of the prehnite-pumpellyite or the lawsonite-albite-chlorite facies convey a hint of approach toward blueschist metamorphism. Two examples will be cited: late Paleozoic prehnite-pumpellyite-metagraywackes and associated limestones of Orcas Island in western Washington, which carry widespread aragonite (Vance, 1968).[*] On the opposite side of the Pacific, one of the low-grade zones mapped by Kawachi (1974) in the Caples terrane, bordering the northwest corner of the Haast Schist province, southern New Zealand (Fig. 9-11), is marked by pumpellyite-bearing metagraywackes and metavolcanics, some of which also carry lawsonite (lawsonite-albite-chlorite facies of Coombs et al., 1976a, p. 569). These are non-schistose or incipiently schistose rocks (textural zones T1–T2) which pass laterally into a zone of foliated metagraywackes (T3) with pumpellyite and actinolite, but not lawsonite. The facies series, completed by continuation from the Caples into the Haast Schist Group immediately to the east, is

Prehnite-pumpellyite → lawsonite-albite-chlorite → pumpellyite-actinolite

→ greenschist

[*]In view of the location on the Pacific margin and consequent possibilities of high pressure conditioned by crustal subduction, Vance's original supposition that this aragonite crystallized metastably under low pressure consistent with observed thin stratigraphic cover is rendered unnecessary.

Spilites as Metamorphic Rocks

Spilites are nonfoliated basic and semibasic lavas, typical of but not confined to eugeosynclines; their principal coarse-grained constituents are augite and albite. They retain the porphyritic or ophitic textures of common basic lavas whose feldspar normally is labradorite. But the groundmass of spilites is typically a fine-grained mixture of minerals that are generally regarded as of secondary origin, among them chlorite, actinolite, epidote, and (only recently recognized) pumpelly-ite. Geosynclinal and ophiolitic spilitic basalts commonly show pillow structure (though by no means all pillow basalts are spilites).

From the outset spilites were of interest mainly to igneous petrologists; and during the first half of the century the concept of a spilitic suite of magmas, of unusually sodic composition was widely favored. Clear idiomorphic albite ophitically enclosed in almost equally clear augite seemed to some to be unequiv-ocal textural evidence of primary magmatic crystallization of both minerals. This view—until recently not completely relinquished by the present writer (cf. Turner and Verhoogen, 1960, pp. 272-273)—still has its adherents.[*] Gilluly (1935) cited varied evidence, since substantiated and amplified in many accounts of spilitic rocks, showing that some, possibly all albite of spilitic rocks has formed by postmagnetic replacement of labradorite. From this time onward the view that spilites are products of degradation of normal basalts, diabases, and ande-sites has grown in favor. A comprehensive reassessment of the problem by Vallance (1969) leads to just such a conclusion (see also Vallance, 1974). Finally, Coombs (1974) has so convincingly presented the case in the context of low-grade meta-morphism that the metamorphic status of the spilitic mineral assemblage (with the exception of augite, clearly a surviving igneous relic) can no longer be challenged.

To the present writer the "spilite problem" is a problem no longer: albite and coexisting combinations of chlorite, epidote, pumpellyite, prehnite, and actinolite in spilitic rocks comprise low-grade metamorphic assemblages isofacial with those in associated metagraywackes (as demonstrated by Coombs). We have already cited examples of spilitic metabasalts in a variety of geologic situations—in eugeosynclines, ophiolites, subaerially extruded volcanic piles, and even in rare dredge hauls from the ocean floor. That spilitization of basalts and diabases is effected by aqueous fluids at low metamorphic temperatures is abundantly clear from the nature of the resulting phase assemblage. It is clear too, that con-siderable changes in total chemical composition are involved in the process (e.g., Vallance, 1974). If and where oceanic water is the actual fluid agent, the pro-cess certainly does not occur at the rock-water interface on the sea floor itself; the testimony of dredge hauls is clear on that point. But spilitization could be one of the responses of ocean-floor basalts to geothermal systems involving sea water operating in the suboceanic crust. It should be noted, however, that changes induced by burial metamorphism of basalts in thick subaerial volcanic piles (e.g., the Keweenawan basalts) also fall precisely within the spilitization category. And

---

[*]See, for example, papers in the opening half of the recent volume edited by Amstutz (1974).

there are detailed records of spilitic degradation of basic lavas in environments that, if indeed marine, were at only shallow depth (Levi, 1969; Vallance, 1974, pp. 79, 80).

REGIONAL FACIES SERIES IN TECTONITE DOMAINS (PHANEROZOIC, PROTEROZOIC)

Plan of Treatment

The tectonite fabric is so commonly seen on a regional scale in metamorphic rocks of all ages that schistosity—its most obvious manifestation—until recently has been thought of loosely as an almost universal manifestation of regional metamorphism. Since the tectonic-metamorphic record is most clearly legible with respect to the last half of geologic time we draw in the first place from Phanerozoic and Proteozoic examples of facies series in regional tectonites. Many, though not all, have Archaean counterparts. But, since ancient tectonics are still the subject of sharp debate, Archaean metamorphism will be treated separately against the more sharply defined background provided by younger material.

In tectonite as in nontectonite domains facies series tend to conform to discernible pattern. With this in mind we shall review a number of generally recognizable, arbitrarily defined categories allowing for mutual gradation between some that share facies in common. Each category has here been designated by the name of some dominant or critical facies, not necessarily unique to that category.

Mineralogical reconstitution in tectonites was generally synchronous with, and in many cases outlasted, the deformation process that has shaped the rock fabric. So the metamorphic mineral assemblage and the tectonite fabric represent interrelated chemical and mechanical responses to the same physical conditions. Understandably there is a clear correlation between metamorphic grade (facies) and the first manifestations of schistosity. As a prelude, therefore, to considering the facies patterns displayed in tectonite domains, it is appropriate to digress briefly on the nature of the strain mechanism—continuous (ductile) flow—in relation to controlling physical variables.

Continuous Flow and Its Relation to Metamorphic Facies

A rock body, on any scale, within the crust is continually in a state of stress, one component of which is isotropic (hydrostatic stress, P of thermodynamics), its magnitude essentially determined by overlying rock load ($\sim$1 kb/3.5 km depth). An additional stress component in tectonically unstable domains is anisotropic (shear stress), a dynamic response to motions of crustal segments ("plates" in modern parlance) set up by thermal and density perturbations in the lower levels of the crust and in the underlying mantle. When shear stress exceeds some limiting value—the "fundamental strength"—the body yields continuously without loss of cohesion. Irreversible strain is then achieved by some process of continuous (ductile) flow, as contrasted with brittle fracture by which, under other conditions, a comparable body stressed above another threshold value ("breaking strength") yields irreversibly by separation into discrete internally unrestrained domains. Elastic flow, a necessary preliminary to both processes, gives rise to reversible strain of insignificant magnitude.

Metamorphic strain and its accompanying tectonite fabric is in fact the product of a much more complex process than the above simple statement might imply. Irreversible strains of great magnitude are seen as the result of continuous flow of long duration interrupted from time to time by brittle failure followed by rehealing (through recrystallization) of microfractures so formed. Several mechanisms may dominate or participate in the flow process—cataclasis involving small-scale fracturing and displacements without loss of cohesion in the strained body, crystallographically controlled plastic flow (gliding) in component crystals, and syntectonic recrystallization of strained crystals. Fine-grained crystalline aggregates resulting from this last process, though commonly reported as products of mechanical "granulation" are in fact analogous to products of annealing and recovery in metals—processes whereby a large strained crystal becomes converted to a mosaic of unstrained microdomains with simultaneous release of stored strain energy (diminution in free energy of the strained system).

In the metamorphic environment the whole flow regime—threshold stress, maintenance of continuity, participatory mechanisms—is a function of many physical variables, some of them interdependent.* Chief among them are strength properties inherent in the strained material, temperature, magnitude and duration of stress, strain rate, pressure, and the presence of aqueous or other pore fluids. Ductility is enhanced by high temperature, slow strain rate (prolonged duration of stress), high pressures, and (in the higher temperature range) permeation by water. (Plasticity of quartz, long an inexplicable but petrographically obvious phenomenon, was finally traced to an experimentally observed "water-weakening" effect at temperatures of a few hundred degrees.)

Jointing on all scales is an almost universal feature of metamorphic rocks, tectonites and nontectonites alike. In the former class it expresses the last phase of deformation—relaxation of elastic strain as breaking strength decreases with falling pressure during unloading. Joints in the nontectonites on the other hand tend to survive from the main period of metamorphism; for they are commonly filled with crystals of one or more phases typical of the metamorphic assemblage.

It was remarked in the opening chapter that the evolution of schistosity (i.e., of the tectonite fabric) is a progressive phenomenon whose course, usually parallel to progression in metamorphic grade, can be traced and mapped over great distances in the field. It is exemplified by textural zones (T1–T4; originally designated Chl 1–Chl 4) mapped in the common graywacke lithology, first in New Zealand and subsequently in California and elsewhere. At the one end of the textural series (zone T1) are nontectonites whose only record of strain lies in joints filled with newly generated minerals—zeolites, prehnite, albite, pumpellyite, and others. At the other end (zone T4) are coarse-grained, fully recrystallized, well-

---

*See H. C. Heard (in Griggs and Handin, 1960, pp. 193–226); E. C. Robertson, (ibid., pp. 227–244); Turner and Weiss (1963, pp. 285–320) and especially, for a critical, up-to-date review of experimental evidence, N. C. Carter (1976).

foliated schists. Between the two extremes one can trace the onset first of cataclastic flow, then of plastic strain and annealing to fine grain, leading finally to syn- and posttectonic crystallization in which earlier shear foliation becomes accentuated by metamorphic differentiation and overall coarsening of grain. Full development of the tectonite fabric (albeit still with reduced grain size) in metagraywackes marks the boundary between textural zones T2 and T3. Along the northeastern border of the Haast schist terrane in southern New Zealand (Fig. 9-3), this coincides more or less with a well-defined isograd separating the prehnite-pumpellyite from the pumpellyite-actinolite facies. Further north in the same general area, where the isograds tend to the northeast, the same textural stage is not reached until close to the biotite isograd, well within the greenschist facies. Again, in parts of California metagraywackes of the pumpellyite-actinolite and, in some areas, even of the full blueschist facies retain the nontectonite fabric in spite of extensive   development of new and diagnostic mineral assemblages. Postponement of ductile flow to advanced stages of metamorphism could be attributed equally to any of several possible conditions—not necessarily the same in every case: rapid loading, low pressure, influence of pore fluids at temperatures too low for "water-weakening" of quartz to be effective. Here is material to tantalize the architect of plate-tectonic models. But the possibilities are so diverse that speculation on the tectonic environment of the brittle regime in blueschist metamorphism seems idle. In keeping with the avowed purpose of this chapter we prefer merely to present the structural data.

Blueschist Facies Series

Limits of Distribution

The blueschist facies is at the same time mineralogically distinctive and sharply limited as to both chronologic and geologic distribution (cf. W. P. De Roever, 1956; Fyfe, 1967a; Ernst, 1972; 1975b, pp. 1-14). It is highly characteristic of the world's younger (late Mesozoic–early Tertiary) fold belts as developed along the margins of the Pacific Ocean and in the Alpine-Himalayan system. Ernst (1972, pp. 660-662) cites only two instances of blueschist metamorphism earlier than Ordovician, both probably latest Proterozoic, one being the well-known glaucophane schist of Anglesea, Wales (Greenly, 1919, pp. 115-118). It is not venturing too far into the realm of speculation to accept the widely held view that blueschist facies series express a distinctive type of metamorphism characteristic of and almost unique to a recently initiated pattern of tectonic activity localized along sutures between contiguous plates.

Mélange and Serpentinites (Ophiolites) in Blueschist Belts

The terms "mélange," "ophiolite," and "blueschist" appear together so frequently in today's burgeoning literature on plate tectonics that, collectively, they seem invested with a structural-petrologic entity almost as coherent as the Steinmann trinity itself. All three moreover are thought by some to have special significance with respect to fashionable concepts of subduction and obduction. Although such problematic aspects of tectonism are beyond the scope of present discussion it is appropriate to ask if mélange, ophiolites, and blueschists are indeed consistently related. If so, what is the manner of their interrelation? To answer such questions we turn to the two blueschist provinces—western California and New Caledonia—that are most fully documented by field and mineralogical observations.

The term "autoclastic mélange" was first applied to an extensive zone of chaotically mixed geosynclinal rocks in Anglesea, Wales (Greenly, 1919, p. 65). Here blocks of diverse lithologies, many of them unmetamorphosed, ranging from several kilometers in length to phacoidal fragments measured in centimeters, swim in a metamorphic matrix that swirls about them. The mineral assemblages of the matrix are in the greenschist facies. It is important to note that in Greenly's mélange, as in mélanges of other metamorphic facies figured on a smaller scale by Weiss (1972)—deformation and mineralogical metamorphism were essentially synchronous. The Anglesea mélange represents an interim stage in the development of greenschist with completely transposed internal structures from a sedimentary-volcanic assemblage (Greenly, 1919, p. 69). Metamorphic crystallization, to use Sander's terminology, was syntectonic. Nevertheless Greenly's definition of "mélange" does not stipulate any specific chronologic relation between metamorphic crystallization and disruptive deformation.

Chaotic structure and mixing of lithology has long been known to characterize areas of thousands of square kilometers in the Californian Franciscan (e.g., Taliaferro, 1943; Bailey et al., 1964; Ernst, 1965; Page, 1966, p. 260). Since Hsu (1968) in carefully defined terms urged use of the term "mélange" for extensive zones of highly disturbed structure in California, it has become part of the familiar vocabulary of Californian structural and metamorphic geology (e.g., Ernst, 1970, p. 887; Page, 1972, pp. 966, 1970). Where outcrops of glaucophane schist and related rocks of the blueschist facies are closely associated (as they commonly are) with Franciscan mélange, there is usually little in the way of schistose matrix apart from slivers of talcose serpentinite representing sheared ultramafic fragments that seem to have played a lubricating role. Franciscan blueschist metamorphism (by contrast with greenschist metamorphism in the Anglesea mélange) was clearly posttectonic with respect to the mixing event recorded in mélanges (cf. Bailey et al., 1964, pp. 93–105; Coleman and Lee, 1963, p. 269). Brought into jumbled juxtaposition are rocks of highly varied lithology and metamorphic facies: serpentinite, eclogite, coarse glaucophane schist, metachert, and metagraywacke. Whatever the tectonic mechanism of mélange development in the Franciscan, it certainly involved transport of ultramafic and high-grade metamorphic materials from great depth and mixture with lower grade and slightly metamorphosed rocks at significantly higher crustal levels (cf. Suppe, 1972).

Bodies of serpentinite are common in Franciscan mélanges. A few of the larger masses (Fig. 7-2) have been shown by careful mapping to be truly ophiolitic (e.g., Page, 1972); others possibly represent dismembered ophiolites. Again and again one finds large blocks ("knockers") of coarse glaucophane schist—some of them hundreds of meters long—and of eclogite, clustering round, overlying, or even embedded in extensive bodies of serpentinite (e.g., Brothers, 1954). So widespread indeed is this pattern of field association in the more disturbed parts of the Franciscan, that at one time ultramafic intrusion was thought to be directly responsible

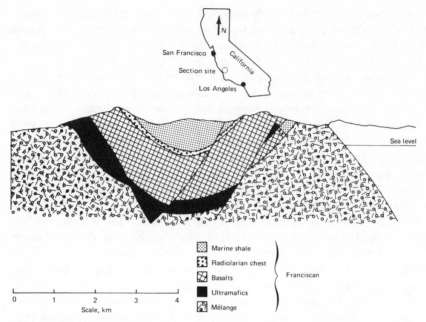

Marine shale

Radiolarian chest

Basalts

Ultramafics   Franciscan

Mélange

0   1   2   3   4
Scale, km

FIGURE 7-2
Major ophiolite fragment in Franciscan, Coast Ranges, San Luis Obispo, southern California,
mapped by B. M. Page (1972). Diagrammatic vertical section (after B. M. Page, 1972, p. 970).

for localized blueschist metamorphism. In northern California (cf. Fig. 9-10), a
facies series with blueschist affinities is developed more continuously and with
less structural interruption. Here the grade of metamorphism rises westward toward
an extensive serpentinite sheet (Fig. 7-3) that marks a tectonic contact between the
Franciscan and coeval sediments of the Great Valley sequence that occupies the
lowlands west of the Coast Ranges (e.g., Page, 1966, p. 267, Fig. 7; Bailey and
Jones, 1970; Ernst, 1970, 1971a, p. 48).

New Caledonia is an elongated continental fragment, 2000 km^2 in area,
separated by the Coral Sea from the Australian landmass 1500 km to the west
(for general setting see Lillie and Brothers, 1970, p. 146). Following on from
mapping by French geologists (P. Routhier, A. Arnould, J. J. Espirat, and others[*])
a series of recent structural, petrologic, and mineralogical studies by a New Zealand
group headed by A. R. Lillie (e.g., Lillie, 1970, 1975; Lillie and Brothers, 1970;
Brothers, 1970, 1974) have revealed the clearest and simplest picture of blueschist
metamorphism yet available. At the northwestern extremity of the island a belt of
rather simply folded Cretaceous and Eocene sediments and intercalated volcanic
rocks (170 X 25 km) shows the imprint of mid-Tertiary progressive metamorphism
in a blueschist facies series. The metamorphic grade increases northeastward,
transverse to the regional structural trend, and in the general direction of increasing stratigraphic depth (Fig. 9-12a). Isograds are generally parallel to stratigraphic
boundaries and to the regional structural trend.

[*]For specific references see Lillie and Brothers (1970).

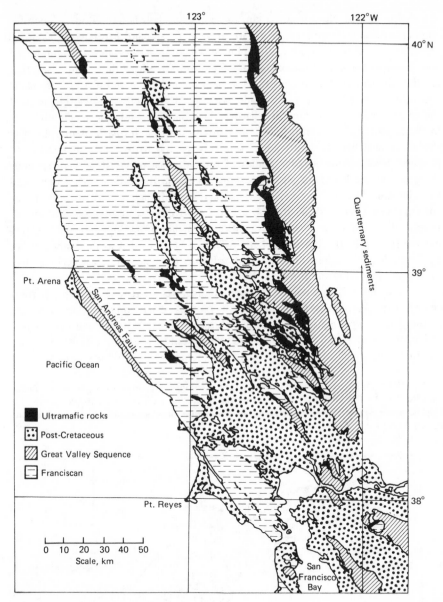

FIGURE 7-3
Simplified distribution of serpentinite bodies in Coast Ranges north of San Francisco (adapted by Carmichael et al., 1974, Fig. 12-13, from E. H. Bailey, W. P. Irwin, and D. L. Jones, 1964). Note continuous serpentinite (ophiolitic?) sheet at base of Great Valley Sequence between 39° and 40° north latitude. Structure south of 39° N tends to be chaotic and includes extensive mélange in Franciscan.

Along its southwestern margin, the blueschist belt is in continuous tectonic contact with a mélange zone 10 to 30 km wide (Black and Brothers, 1977). This consists of a stack of southwest-dipping lenses and slices of Mesozoic graywacke and Eocene chert-limestone, penetrated by slivers of serpentinite and basalt that are thought to represent fragments of a basal ophiolite. These ophiolitic remnants too have been affected by low-grade metamorphism, but this slightly predated the earliest phase recorded in the adjacent blueschist belt, and is decidedly different in facies pattern.[*] In contrast with the situation in California, metamorphism in the blueschist belt is posttectonic (possibly partly syntectonic) in relation to mélange development. Massive bodies of serpentinized peridotite are conspicuous along the whole length of New Caledonia. At the northwestern end of the island they lie southwest of the mélange zone, across an intervening right-lateral transcurrent fault (Fig. 7-4). There appears to be no direct causative connection between either emplacement of ultramafics or mélange development and regional metamorphism in the blueschist belt. All three are regarded as mutually distinct but broadly interrelated manifestations of a single comprehensive regional tectonic event (cf. Lillie and Brothers, 1970, p. 171).

From all this it would seem that no single consistent chronologic pattern characterizes tectonic events leading to the mutual association of ultramafic bodies of the Alpine type, mélange zones, and blueschist belts. Moreover neither regional mélanges nor ultramafic sheets (whether of ophiolitic or other affinities) are by any means confined to regions of blueschist metamorphism: witness the disrupted

---

[*]Metamorphic assemblages in the mélange ophiolites are closer to the lawsonite-albite-chlorite than to the blueschist facies. From the former they differ mainly in prevalence of a jadeitic acmite ($Jd_{\sim 30}$); from the latter in the nature of blue amphibole (riebeckite, not glaucophane).

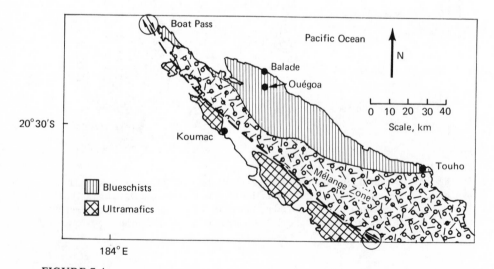

FIGURE 7-4

Regional mélange in relation to blueschist belt and ultramafic bodies, northern New Caledonia (after R. N. Brothers, 1974).

ophiolites of Cyprus and Oman (pp. 216-217) and the serpentinized peridotites and closely associated mélange zones of the Dun Mountain ophiolite belt and adjoining Haast Schists in southern New Zealand (Figs. 7-5 and 7-6).

Examples of Blueschist Facies Series

Japanese geologists based at Tokyo University have established the Sanbagawa belt of Honshu, Japan (Fig. 1-18) as the type example of regional blueschist metamorphism—in fact as the accepted illustration of Miyashiro's (1961) high-pressure (jadeite-glaucophane) type of facies series (see Seki, 1960a, 1961a; Miyashiro and Seki, 1958; Iwasaki, 1963; Banno, 1958, 1964a; Ernst et al., 1970, pp. 200-205). Nevertheless, the full blueschist facies with glaucophanic assemblages carrying lawsonite and/or jadeite, is only locally developed in but a few of the many mapped segments of the Sanbagawa belt. In most segments the complete metamorphic sequence lies within the greenschist facies, biotite, garnet, and hornblende being associated with albite at the high-grade end. In those with conspicuous glaucophane schists the general facies series is

Blueschist → transition facies → greenschist

with glaucophane prominent in the first two facies. Composite eclogite-dunite blocks occur here and there in the high-grade greenschist-facies zones of the Sanbagawa belt.

The "high-pressure schists" described by Brothers (1974) from the northwestern end of New Caledonia (Fig. 9-12) display a zonal sequence of assemblages characterized throughout by glaucophane. The whole facies series can be represented as

Lawsonite-albite-chlorite → blueschist → blueschist-greenschist transition

→ eclogitic transition facies

In the Franciscan terrane of California (Fig. 9-10), isograds mapped in the northern and structurally least disturbed segment clearly define a facies series

Zeolite → pumpellyite-actinolite → lawsonite-albite-chlorite

Further south, for instance, in the Diabolo Range, where the significance of "isograds" is somewhat obscured by the probability of structural control, progressive metamorphism is expressed in a sequence of blueschist subfacies (cf. Ernst et al., 1970, p. 56).

Lawsonite-albite-chlorite → blueschist

Highly tantalizing in the California picture is the problem of possible relations between blueschist and eclogite facies where these appear in closely juxtaposed blocks within zones of mélange. Eclogite specimens upon microscopic examination

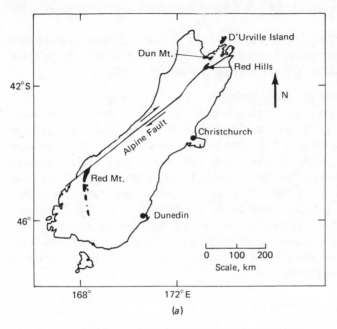

(a)

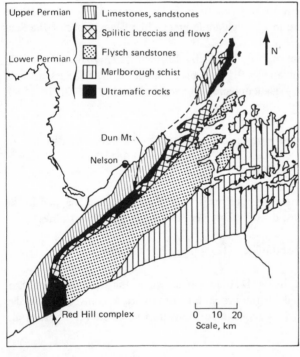

(b)

FIGURE 7-5

Dun Mt. ophiolite belt, South Island, New Zealand. (*a*) Distribution of ultramafic bodies (black) in northern and southern segments. (*b*) Simplified map of northern segment (adapted from R. I. Walcott, 1969). Ultramafic and spilitic units comprise the ophiolite belt; Marlborough Schist is roughly equivalent to Haast Schist of southern segment.

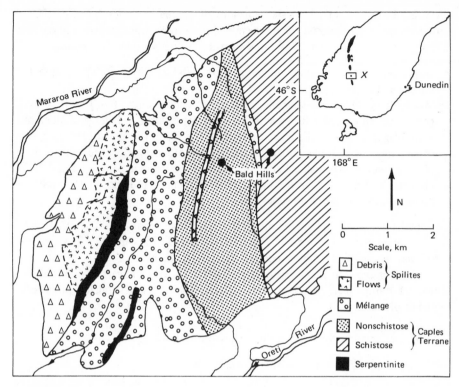

FIGURE 7-6
Detail of southern segment, Dun Mt. ophiolite belt, Maitai and Caples Terranes (adapted after
D. S. Coombs and coauthors, 1976).

more often than not show evidence of partial retrograde overprinting by blueschist
or greenschist assemblages (e.g., Borg, 1956, pp. 1576–1578). But what of a possible corresponding prograde change? There is a hint of such a transition in occurrences of omphacite and of garnet veins crosscutting specimens of glaucophane
schist (cf. Essene and Fyfe, 1967); but it must be admitted that, in spite of careful search, no indisputable evidence of a blueschist → eclogite transition has yet
materialized.

In the western and central European Alps, glaucophane-bearing rocks and
eclogites are prominent in the Pennine (inner) domain (Figs. 9-15 and 9-16).
From east to west across the Pennine and Helvetic domains in this segment of the
Alps, the gross metamorphic pattern changes regularly in a general northward and
westward sequence.

Eclogite and blueschist → greenschist → prehnite-pumpellyite and zeolite facies

But this is not strictly a facies series as the term is here used; for it crosses major
structure and metamorphic-chronologic boundaries. These complications are
clearly brought out in a recent illuminating summary of Alpine metamorphism

(Frey et al., 1974). At least three episodes of Alpine metamorphism, correlated with corresponding tectonic events, have been inferred from extensive radiometric dating (Frey et al., 1974, p. 277); but separation of the last two is uncertain.

1. Upper Cretaceous, Eoalpine metamorphism ($60-100 \times 10^6$ years): eclogite and blueschist facies
2. Mid-Tertiary, Oligocene-Miocene, Lepontine metamorphism ($\sim 40 \times 10^6$ years): greenschist-amphibolite facies series partially overprinting eclogite and blueschist assemblages in the southern sector and completely developed—to the exclusion of any trace of possible earlier metamorphism other than local eclogites (?Eoalpine or Hercynian)—in the Lepontine Alps of the Pennine zone (cf. Fig. 10-10).
3. Miocene (20×10^6 years) event, Helvetic domain (Glarus Alps): zeolite $\rightarrow$ prehnite-pumpellyite facies series.

The total picture of Alpine metamorphism raises the strong possibility that metamorphic gradients represented by mapped zonal sequences in other parts of the world may be complicated by concealed chronologic breaks.

Each of the four metamorphic provinces just reviewed bears an unmistakable individual stamp. Yet each conforms to some part of a generalized progressive sequence of facies:

Zeolite $\rightarrow$ pumpellyite-actinolite $\rightarrow$ lawsonite-albite-chlorite

$\rightarrow$ blueschist $\rightarrow$ greenschist(?) $\rightarrow$ eclogite

To categorize this as expressing a high-pressure type of progressive metamorphism, as Miyashiro (1961) has done, is clearly justified by the known stability relations of typical blueschist phases (and of eclogitic assemblages, if these indeed terminate the same general facies series). Equally significant are low-temperature implications of aragonite, lawsonite, and jadeitic pyroxenes.

Greenschist Facies Series

Haast Schist Terrane, Southern New Zealand

The Haast Schist terrane and the immediately adjacent southern fringe of the Torlesse terrane (Figs. 1-15 and 1-17, cf. Fig. 9-19), which grades into it, illustrate a type of facies series in which the greenschist facies continuously covers very large areas—in this case more than 3000 km^2. It is here designated the type example of what we shall call the greenschist facies series. Throughout almost the whole of this extent the Haast Schists are coarsely crystalline well-foliated metagraywackes with bedding now completely transposed and largely obliterated by multiple small-scale folding. Almost everywhere, the metamorphic assemblages typify the greenschist facies. There is a very extensive zone of chlorite and much more restricted zones of biotite[*] and almandine. Within the latter and on into the adjoining narrow zone of oligoclase where the Haast terrane is shorn off along its northwestern edge by the

---

[*]Extension of the biotite zone in some recent maps most likely is unwarranted; for much of the "biotite" recorded in the central part of the area proves to be oxidized chlorite.

Alpine Fault, the grade of metamorphism rises into the amphibolite facies. At the lowest end of the grade scale, there is rather rapid transition eastward from the Haast Schist Group through finer-grained but still well-foliated metagraywackes (textural zones T3–T2) of pumpellyite-actinolite facies into the Torlesse Group proper. Here the prehnite-pumpellyite assemblages prevail continuously in non-foliated incipiently metamorphosed rocks over an area as extensive as the Haast Schist terrane itself (cf. Fig. 9-3).

The complete facies series displayed in the Haast Schist tectonite domain is

Prehnite-pumpellyite → pumpellyite-actinolite → greenschist (→ amphibolite)

This simple statement, while setting up a general pattern for greenschist facies series, by no means conveys a complete picture of Cretaceous tectonism and metamorphism in the New Zealand geosyncline. The complexities of the total situation are brought out in a recent synthesis by Coombs et al. (1976) focused especially on the Dun Mountain ophiolite belt.[*] For present purposes, it is sufficient to note these facts: beyond the Haast Terrane to the southwest, and sharing the imprint of the same early-middle Cretaceous tectonic and metamorphic event (Rangitata orogeny) is a southwest succession of other tectonic-petrologic units, each with sediments of Permian age: Caples terrane (largely metavolcanic), Dun Mountain ophiolite belt and mélange (Figs. 7-5 and 7-6) southern segment, and Maitai Terrane; still further south is the Triassic-Jurassic Murihiku Terrane where Coombs (1954) first demonstrated the zeolite facies. In limited sections of the Caples, Dun Mountain, and Maitai blocks, metagraywackes with albite, pumpellyite, and muscovite also carry lawsonite and aragonite. These assemblages (lawsonite-albite-chlorite facies of Coombs and co-authors), and the local presence of somewhat sodic actinolites (not glaucophane; cf. E. H. Brown, 1974, p. 344) in greenschists of the Haast Terrane, suggest metamorphic pressures locally exceeding perhaps 5 kb. But this conclusion in no way warrants correlation with the blueschist pattern that some consider to be an essential feature of late Mesozoic and early Cenozoic circum-Pacific metamorphism. In fact there is no record of blueschist metamorphism in New Zealand.

Other Provinces

There seem to be few other carefully documented accounts of post-Archaean greenschist facies series (quite possibly this simply reflects lack of interest in monotonous development of "ordinary" rock types). Two unrelated east Australian provinces, known to this writer only through cursory examination, are the Proterozoic basement rocks of western Tasmania (A. H. Spry, in papers cited by Joplin, 1968, pp. 150–157), and the Brisbane Schist belt, extending for 150 km parallel to the coast across the Queensland–New South Wales border, south latitude ~28° (Denmead, 1928; Mathews, 1954; Bryan and Jones, 1954). The Brisbane

---

[*]This paper is recommended strongly to the student of plate tectonics. It illustrates the necessity for sustained field and laboratory work by a team of experts, each familiar from long experience with the local geology, to provide a basis for any comprehensive model that can win even tentative acceptance.

schists (later Paleozoic?) are metagraywackes and metavolcanics, everywhere in the greenschist facies. They are intensely deformed strongly foliated and lineated tectonites. Mineral assemblages are identical with those in the chlorite zone of other provinces, but with one exception: at one locality, interbedded with normal greenschists are two bands in which the metavolcanic assemblage is glaucophane-epidote-albite-quartz-sphene (cf. Joplin, 1968, p. 100).

Amphibolite Facies Series

This category is here proposed to cover the many recorded cases whose metamorphic grade increases via the greenschist to culmination and extensive areal development in the amphibolite facies. While not to be regarded as a general norm for regional metamorphism (cf. Miyashiro, 1961, p. 279) such series nevertheless do seem to be more widely distributed than any other type of facies series in Proterozoic and Phanerozoic metamorphic belts. A complete generalized sequence is

(Prehnite-pumpellyite) → greenschist → amphibolite

with the accent strongly on "amphibolite."

In individual series, greenschist subfacies can be defined by the index minerals biotite and almandine. There is some variety as to amphibolite subfacies depending partly on rock composition and partly, it would seem, upon metamorphic conditions (particularly pressure). A widely prevalent sequence of index minerals in pelitic assemblages is almandine, staurolite, Al_2SiO_5, K-feldspar plus sillimanite. The identity of the first Al_2SiO_5 polymorph to appear—kyanite versus andalusite—supplemented by the relative roles of almandine and cordierite in pelitic assemblages, serves as a basis for distinguishing broadly between series of high and of low pressure. The following examples, which include the classic and some other well-documented instances of progressive metamorphism, illustrate the twofold division. Mineralogical data will be detailed in Chap. 9 and possible dP/dT gradients are discussed in Chap. 11.

High-Pressure Series

The first Al_2SiO_5 polymorph in pelitic assemblages is kyanite; and this gives way with advancing grade to sillimanite. Cordierite is absent in metapelites of normal composition. Almandine and/or epidote are common in amphibolites with plagioclase An_{25}–An_{50}. Examples with metamorphic ages are:

1. Lepontine zone (Pennine domain), western Swiss Alps (E. Niggli, 1960; E. Wenk, 1962; Streckeisen and E. Wenk, 1974; Frey et al., 1974); mid-Tertiary (40×10^6 years) (Fig. 9-6)
2. New Hampshire–Vermont segment of New England metamorphic province (cf. pp. 32–34), mid-Devonian
3. Barrovian zones of southeastern Dalradian, Scotland (cf. pp. 26–28); early Ordovician
4. Parts of the Grenville province, Ontario (D. M. Carmichael, 1970; Lumbers,

1971; Chesworth, 1972; P. H. Thompson, 1973), and southwestern Quebec (Wynne-Edwards, 1969); late Proterozoic ($\sim$950 $\times$ 10^6 years) (Fig. 10-12)
5. Black Hills, South Dakota (Noble and Harder, 1948); mid-Proterozoic ($\sim$1200 $\times$ 10^6 years)
6. Northern Michigan (James, 1955); mid-Proterozoic

Low-Pressure Series

Mineral assemblages recall the hornblende-hornfels facies of contact metamorphism. Andalusite and/or cordierite are present in pelitic assemblages; wollastonite and grossularite in calcareous rocks. Almandine is absent, epidote rare in amphibolites. Classic examples are:

1. Ryoke metamorphic belt, Japan (Miyashiro, 1958; Suwa, 1961); Cretaceous, approximately synchronous with metamorphism in adjacent Sanbagawa belt (Chap. 1, p. 42)
2. Hercynian metamorphic belts, Pyrenees (Zwart, 1962, 1963) and northern Portugal (Brink, 1960); middle Paleozoic
3. Buchan zones, northeastern Dalradian, Scotland; early Paleozoic (Chap. 1, Figs. 1-11b, 1-12)
4. Orijärvi, southern Finland (Eskola, 1914, 1915); mid-Proterozoic (Fig. 10-4)
5. Yellowknife region, Slave craton, northwest Canada (Ramsay, 1973, 1974; Kamineni, 1975; Ramsay and Kamineni, 1977); Archaean

Regional development of low-pressure amphibolites facies series typically is associated with synchronous intrusion of granitic plutons toward whose contacts the grade of metamorphism tends to rise. Here is a distributional pattern of metamorphism that in many ways combines the respective characteristics of what we have distinguished as contact and regional categories. This applies, too, to diagnostic mineralogical characteristics mostly common to the hornblende-hornfels and the amphibolite facies.

Granulite Facies Series

In Proterozoic Mobile Belts

We shall find that the greatest development of the granulite facies is in the nuclei of Archaean cratons; but it is also widespread in Proterozoic belts bearing the imprint of high-grade metamorphism. In most of these belts, the amphibolite facies is comparably prominent over extensive areas, and where isograds have been mapped—as in the Grenville province of eastern Canada (Fig. 10-12), the northwest Adirondacks of New York State (Chap. 1, Figs. 1-20 and 1-21), and the Willyama complex of New South Wales, Australia (Fig. 10-14)—these may define wide zones of intervening transitional facies. One can therefore postulate a general type of Proterozoic facies series, albeit in most cases on a very large areal scale

$$\text{Amphibolite} \rightarrow \text{transition facies} \rightarrow \text{granulite}$$

Individual series that comply with this general specification can be designated *granulite facies series.* Partial imprints of corresponding retrograde changes can be traced locally in some provinces on the basis of textural evidence.

In typical Proterozoic basins and troughs the basement underlying the filling is composed of still earlier continental crust already bearing the imprints of previous plutonic and metamorphic cycles. So in the high-grade Proterozoic belts these questions always arise: How much of the metamorphic terrane represents reworked basement material? And where such remnants can be recognized, how much of their lithologic makeup and of the regional Proterozoic metamorphic pattern has been inherited from or influenced by earlier events? The complexities of this topic, to which we shall return in Chap. 10, are nicely brought out in Wynne-Edwards's (1969) synthesis of tectonic overprinting within an extensive segment of the Grenville province in southwestern Quebec. Clearly the physical gradients recorded in granulite facies series could be complex.

Finally it is noteworthy that in many middle Proterozoic granulite provinces—e.g., the Grenville of Canada, its southern offshoot in the Adirondacks (Fig. 7-7), and the Gothian belt of Southern Norway—there are massive plutons of andesine anorthosite, commonly accompanied by a suite of pyroxene granites (charnockites) and syenites (mangerites). Are all these plutonic rocks comagmatic (cf. Carmichael et al., 1974, pp. 600-601)? More germane to the present topic, is there any general relation, direct or indirect between anorthosite intrusion and granulite-facies metamorphism? This latter question can be partially answered in the light of radiometric chronologic data (cf. Wynne-Edwards, 1969; Windley, 1969, p. 912; 1977, p. 102): dates of anorthosite emphacement cluster round 1600×10^6 years ±200—the time of a worldwide "anorthosite event" proposed by Herz (1969); and in the Grenville province the date of granulite facies metamorphism—the partial imprint of which is visible in the anorthosites themselves—is $\sim 950 \times 10^6$ years.[*] If there is any relation between emplacement of anorthosite plutons and granulite metamorphism it must be a remote one (cf. DeWaard and Walton, 1967).

Early Paleozoic Granulites

So widespread is granulite metamorphism throughout the Precambrian that many of us have come to regard this pattern as exclusively Precambrian and mostly earlier than 900-1000 million years ago. Radiometric dating has nevertheless revealed isolated early Paleozoic granulite provinces, notably the Moldanubian block of eastern Austria (Arnold and Scharbert, 1973) and the Wilmington complexes of Delaware (Foland and Muessig, 1978). It may be significant that granulites in both terranes carry kyanite and lack cordierite—suggesting metamorphism at high pressure. The Wilmington complex is a restricted region displaying a facies series

Amphibolite → transition facies → granulite

along a 50-km section (Ward, 1969). Within it lies a small pluton of anorthosite

---

[*]The intervening time interval is greater than that which separated the Paleozoic intrusion of granite from the Pleistocene glaciation in the Cairngorms of Scotland.

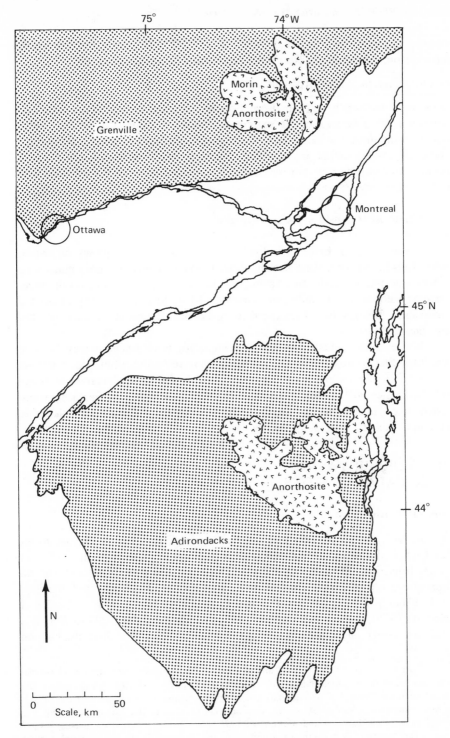

FIGURE 7-7
Geographic relation between Adirondack and southern Grenville metamorphic provinces with anorthosite massifs referred to in text (after J. Martignole and K. Schrijver, 1977).

5 km in diameter, yielding a radiometric data $\sim$500 $\times$ 10^6 years; but this hardly detracts from the validity of Herz's mid-Proterozoic "anorthositic event."

Eclogite Facies Metamorphism

The eclogite facies is highly tantalizing because its special interest as the petrologic expression of crystallization at extreme pressures is dampened by the elusive nature, stemming from field relations, of possible relations to other metamorphic facies. We cannot define any established crustal facies series with eclogite as a member, though one that can be tentatively inferred from all the available data is

Blueschist → transition facies → eclogite[*]

Some eclogites have undoubtedly formed by metamorphism of crustal rocks. Thus in the Swiss Alps, Bearth (1952, 1965) demonstrated direct conversion of Mesozoic pillow basalts to eclogite, and in the Sesia-Lanzo zone on the inner (eastern) side of the Pennine domain (Fig. 9-16), there are closely associated remarkable metagranites (quartz-jadeite-zoisite-phengite-garnet rocks) of the same facies.

Whatever the genetic and tectonic implications of eclogites may be, one established fact is outstanding. Though not quite so restricted as blueschists in time, they are virtually limited to the late Proterozoic (as in southwestern Norway) and the Phanerozoic. Unlike blueschists eclogites also appear as fragments transported from mantle depths in Phanerozoic (especially Cretaceous) diatremes (cf. Carmichael et al., 1974, pp. 642–644).

METAMORPHIC FACIES IN ARCHAEAN CRATONS

General Proposition

We start with the proposition that there are general, recognizable characteristics that tend to distinguish tectonic-plutonic-metamorphic patterns of the Archaean cratons from those of younger provinces. This has become amply obvious from an impressive array of recent studies[†] (e.g., Bridgewater, McGregor, and Windley, 1973; Windley, 1973; Bridgewater and Fyfe, 1974; Jolly, 1974; Holland and Lambert, 1975; Glikson and Lambert, 1976; Windley and Smith, 1976; Windley, 1977, pp. 1–64), and indeed is now a fundamental tenet of modern thinking on

[*]Not a few records of "eclogite" and of a loose "eclogite-blueschist (-ultramafic) association" are based on lithologic misidentifications and so must be rejected. An example is the Girvan-Ballantrae "complex" (of insignificant outcrop area) that figures prominently in models of early Paleozoic tectonics relating to the Grampian orogeny of the Scottish Highlands (for critical analysis see Lambert and McKerrow, 1976, pp. 276–277). Plate-tectonicians beware!

[†]The literature is voluminous, stimulating, and to some degree controversial. Only a few selected references are cited; and these include a comprehensive bibliography of earlier relevant material.

problems of continental evolution. To many of us it would seem equally apparent that individual cratons differ significantly among themselves. But here opinions are far from unanimous. Once again the student is confronted with the problem of recognizing and sifting out local variations upon some broader general theme.

In this section we are on surer ground in confining discussion to patterns of facies that characterize Archaean ($\sim$3800–2500 $\times$ 10^6 years) regional metamorphism (cf. also Sutton and Windley, 1974).

Archaean Lithology

Archaean cratons are made up principally of three types of rock association:

1. Most extensive in general are gneisses—henceforth termed "plutonic"—dominantly granodiorite in composition but including also significant basic elements (gabbroid, anorthositic, and ultramafic). Everywhere these carry the imprint of Archaean metamorphism; though this may have been widely obliterated in some areas by Proterozoic events (as in the Lewisian of northwestern Scotland). To many of us the truly igneous (plutonic) origin of these gneisses seems clearly established on compositional, textural, and in some cases field evidence. Yet there are some workers in the field of Archaean geology that regard these rocks as completely reworked, dominantly sedimentary piles. The gabbros, anorthosites, and peridotites (all now metamorphosed) are seen as remnants of disrupted, layered mafic intrusions (e.g., Windley, 1969, 1977, pp. 9, 10). The anorthosites, which are extensively developed in many Archaean terranes, are composed of labradorite-bytownite, and many carry layers of chromite—in sharp contrast with Proterozoic ilmenite-bearing andesine anorthosites (Windley, 1969, p. 912, 1975, p. 213).

2. As distinct from plutonic gneisses, there are widespread accumulations (or remnants of such) of what in today's fashion are termed "supracrustal" rocks—presumably implying deposition at a crust-water or crust-air interface. They include volcanics ranging from ultramafic (komatiite) to basaltic to rhyolitic; and a variety of metasediments—quartzites, graywackes, marbles, and iron formation. A wide total range of metamorphic grade is represented—from prehnite-pumpellyite to granulite facies.

3. Finally there are later, but still Archaean, plutons (granodioritic, gabbro-anorthosite) clearly intrusive into rocks of the first two categories.

Lithologic-Metamorphic Provinces

Windley (1977, p. 1) opens his discussion of Archaean geology thus:

> The Archaean [pre-2500 million years old] regions of the world contain two types of terrain: those whose rocks were metamorphosed largely to a high metamorphic grade, . . . and those that are well preserved in a low-grade state.

This generalization appears to hold very well throughout the world. Some regions such as the North Atlantic craton (Bridgewater, Watson, and Windley, 1973) consist almost entirely of rocks of the first category. In others, such as the Superior province of the Canadian shield, it is low-grade metamorphism that predominates (cf. Jolly, 1974). In still other cratons—southern Africa, western Australia, and the Karelian block of Finland—both types are well represented.

High-grade provinces, as exemplified in the North Atlantic craton (Fig. 7-8), consist of "plutonic" gneisses, strongly deformed and locally interleaved with remnants of early supracrustals. Low-grade terranes by contrast consist of supracrustal rocks, invaded in some instances by later granodioritic plutons. In older literature low-grade provinces were generally referred to (and the practice still continues) as "greenstone belts;" for in many of these are abundant and extensive flows of komatiite (ultramafic) and basalt—typically capped by siliceous volcanic debris. It is in such belts that iron formation is prominent. In the Canadian shield, however, "synclinal troughs of predominantly graywacke, conglomerate and arkosic sediments" (Jolly, 1974) also fit the general low-grade category. Here the term "greenstone belt" is scarcely appropriate.

Chronology

The breakthrough in distinguishing earlier from later tectonic-metamorphic episodes in the Archaean came in the first place from conventional geologic evidence based on field relations between intrusive basic dikes and metamorphically distinct terranes within the same general area: Scourian versus Laxfordian in the Lewisian of northwest Scotland (Sutton and Watson, 1951); Amîtsoq versus Nûk gneiss in western Greenland (McGregor, 1973).

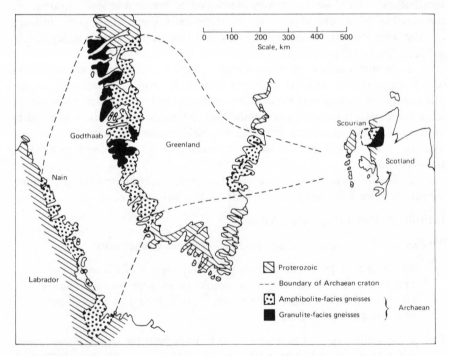

FIGURE 7-8
North Atlantic craton showing distribution of Archaean granulite-facies and amphibolite-facies gneiss (after D. Bridgewater, J. Watson, and B. F. Windley, 1973).

Radiometric dating has confirmed and quantified this distinction. In West Greenland Amîtsoq metamorphism ~3750-3700 × 10^6 years was followed by metamorphism of Nûk gneisses at ~2850 × 10^6 years. In Scotland, the two successive metamorphic events have now been dated: Scourian or Badcallian (~2700 × 10^6 years) followed by a mid-Proterozoic Laxfordian (or Invernian) episode (~2200 × 10^6 years). Parts of three provinces have been shown to retain imprints of metamorphism earlier than 3000 million years ago (cf. Windley, 1977, pp. 17, 24): a high-grade terrane (Godthaab region) in western Greenland (~3600 × 10^6 years), the comparable Uivak gneiss belt of Labrador; and the low-grade Barberton greenstone belt of South Africa (~3500 × 10^6 years). Elsewhere in both these cratons and in most other Archaean provinces round the world any history of possible early Archaean events has been obliterated by high-grade metamorphism in the range 3100-2800 million years ago.

Metamorphic Facies

In high-grade Archaean provinces metamorphic assemblages conform to either the granulite or high-grade subfacies of the amphibolite facies. Commonly, as in most of western Greenland and in the Scottish Lewisian, granulite metamorphism has been locally or regionally overprinted by later amphibolite-facies metamorphism—in spite of the very large quantity of externally supplied water required for the process (cf. Fyfe, 1973, p. 460). The corresponding prograde overprint (granulite upon amphibolite) is less common, an interesting sample being the Gothaab region of Greenland.

A general facies series of the greenstone belts (e.g., the Kalgoolie belt of the Yilgarn craton in Western Australia, Fig. 7-1) is

Greenschist → amphibolite

Facies of even lower grade are well known. One such is a regional development of the prehnite-pumpellyite facies, in an Archaean segment near Larder Lake, Ontario (Jolly, 1974); this has been locally overprinted by albite-epidote-actinolite and hornblende-hornfels assemblages in aureoles around intrusive granitic plutons.

Notable Absentees

Ultramafic bodies of the Alpine type and ophiolites, almost ubiquitous in Phanerozoic mobile belts, are conspicuously lacking in Archaean terranes. Notable absentees on the roster of facies are eclogitic and blueschist assemblages; and kyanite is a rarity in aluminous assemblages of the amphibolite facies. Such features point to a sustained feature of Archaean metamorphic regimes as expressed at crustal levels now exposed: throughout the first 1000 million years of recorded time, whatever the temperature range attained, metamorphic pressures were relatively low.

8

Mineralogy of Contact
Metamorphic Facies:
Illustrative Examples
and Physical Implications

PREAMBLE

It is now time to review the characteristic mineral assemblages of each facies in turn, starting with those of contact metamorphism as defined in Chap. 6. This will be done as far as possible through well-documented cases, not forgetting those on which the facies concept was founded and subsequently developed.

Most of the material of this chapter is drawn from contact aureoles developed by plutons emplaced at relatively high crustal levels: posttectonic "granitic" plutons cutting deformed geosynclinal fillings and Archaean "greenstone belts"; floors underlying massive Precambrian stratified mafic-ultramafic sheets injected into virtually undeformed basin sediments and volcanics. The general metamorphic regime consequently is one of low pressure (P commonly 2 kb, generally <3 kb) and temperatures for the most part consistent with Jaeger's models ($T \sim 300$–$750°C$). Facies therefore can be treated in simple sequence of increasing grade from the outside inward in zoned aureoles.

ALBITE–EPIDOTE–HORNFELS FACIES

General Chemographic Phase Relations

The albite-epidote-hornfels facies was proposed to cover mineral assemblages as they begin to form in the outermost fringes of contact aureoles. Because some rock types are more responsive to thermal influences than others, available petro-graphic accounts tend to treat limited ranges of lithology in which metamorphic effects are most clearly recognizable. It is possible too that some recorded assemblages were not in full equilibrium, and even that some phases (e.g., phyllosilicates in slaty rocks) may have been inherited from a condition predating the contact metamorphic episode. For these reasons a comprehensive general picture of chemographic relations between phases in the albite-epidote-hornfels facies must be based partly on inferred equivalence between assemblages recorded from different localities. Three examples—namely, talc, antigorite, and andalusite—may be cited.

Talc appears as the first silicate phase in metadolomites of some aureoles; and antigorite has been similarly recorded in aureoles in serpentinite (e.g., Tilley, 1951b; Trommsdorff and Evans, 1972). However, I know of no instance where antigorite- or talc-bearing assemblages have been found in close association with albite-epidote-hornfels.

Andalusite (porphyroblastic chiastolite) commonly seen in splotted slates far from visible plutonic contacts appears to be a stable phase in some pelitic assemblages of the albite-epidote-hornfels facies. The paragenesis recorded in the outermost zones of the Tôno aureole, Japan (Seki, 1957, pp. 320, 321, 353, Table 14) lends some support to this possibility (cf. p. 258). There are areas in the western contact zone of the Sierra Nevada batholith, California, where chiastolite phyllites are closely associated with quartz-albite-epidote-hornblende metavolcanics (Best, 1963, pp. 114–120). But more generally the status of andalusite with respect to this particular facies in specific areas may be equivocal. In one typical example—a perfectly exposed segment of a wide aureole bordering the Inyo granodioritic batholith at Birch Creek, southeastern California (cf. Verhoogen et al., 1970, pp. 550–553)—biotite begins to appear in metapelites at 3 km and andalusite at 2 km from the outcropping contact. The host rock still retains small-scale sedimentary structures. Not until 1 km from the contact are these obliterated, the completely recrystallized assemblage at this point being quartz-biotite-muscovite-andalusite, typical of the hornblende-hornfels facies. In such a situation to place the first appearance of andalusite in the albite-epidote-hornfels facies would be hardly better than a guess consistent with textural evidence and the dimensions of the aureole.

With such qualifications in mind chemographic phase relations in the albite-epidote-hornfels facies have been tentatively depicted in Figs. 8-1, 8-2, and 8-3. These combine data drawn from several specific instances (e.g., Kanisawa, 1964, pp. 185–189; Best, 1963; Black, 1972) one of which is elaborated below in slightly greater detail. Whether the data warrant recognition of a separate facies is of no great significance; they do, however, demonstrate the kind of mineral assemblages that lead up to development of the most important of contact metamorphic parageneses—the hornblende-hornfels facies.

Typical assemblages (numbered as in Figs. 8-1, 8-2, and 8-3) are

A. Pelitic assemblages:
   1. Quartz-muscovite-biotite (-chlorite)
   2. Quartz-muscovite-biotite-andalusite

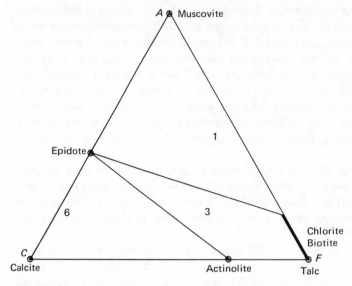

FIGURE 8-1
Albite-epidote-hornfels facies. ACF diagram for rocks with excess SiO_2 and K_2O. Quartz and albite are possible additional phases.

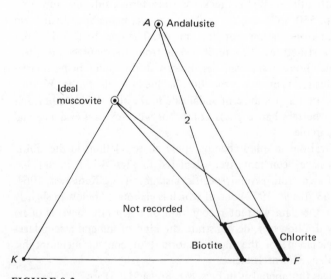

FIGURE 8-2
Albite-epidote-hornfels facies. AKF diagram for rocks with excess SiO_2 and Al_2O_3 (triangle 1 of Fig. 8-1). Quartz, epidote, and albite are possible additional phases.

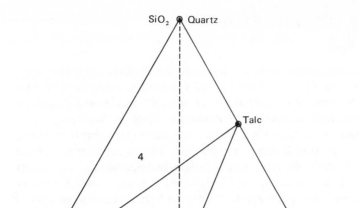

FIGURE 8-3
Albite-epidote-hornfels facies. Phase assemblages in derivatives of siliceous dolomitic limestones (compositions to left of broken line).

B. Basic assemblages:
   3. Albite-epidote-actinolite-chlorite (-quartz-biotite)
C. Calcareous assemblages:
   4. Calcite-talc (-quartz)
   5. Calcite-dolomite-talc
   6. Calcite-epidote

Paritu Pluton, Northern New Zealand

Near the village of Paritu, at the northern end of Caromandel Peninsula 50 km northeast of the city of Auckland, a Miocene tonalite-granodiorite pluton 5 km in diameter has developed an aureole 300–400 m wide in Jurassic psammopelitic sediments and mid-Miocene andesitic volcanics. The former show incipient effects of zeolite-facies regional metamorphism. The volcanics outside the aureole are unmetamorphosed. The cover at the time of intrusion was no more than 1000 m ($P \sim 250$ bars).

    The paragenesis in the outer zone, as recorded by Black (1972, p. 220) is as follows (numbers correspond to those of phase triangles in Fig. 8-1):

A. Psammophelitic assemblages:
   1. Quartz-albite-muscovite-biotite
  1a. Quartz-biotite
B. Metaandesite assemblage:
   3. Quartz-albite-epidote-actinolite-biotite

HORNBLENDE–HORNFELS FACIES

Mineralogical Limits

The greater part of the outcrop width of most contact aureoles is occupied by rocks of the hornblende-hornfels facies. Its outer limits (against the indefinitely defined fringe zone of incipient recrystallization) are marked by almost simultaneous appearance of andalusite in aluminous metapelites, of plagioclase ($An_{>20}$) and hornblende (in place of actinolite) in metavolcanics, and of tremolite in calcareous rocks. The hornblende-hornfels facies may continue right to the plutonic contact. Alternatively, as hornblende gives way to diopside-hypersthene, and quartz-muscovite to K-feldspar + sillimanite (or andalusite), it passes inward into a zone of pyroxene-hornfels-facies assemblages. Within the hornblende-hornfels zone of any individual aureole it is usually possible to recognize concentric subzones defined by mineral transformations that vary somewhat from one aureole to another. To illustrate the general mineralogical pattern, and local variations depending on general lithology and metasomatic modifications, we now turn to specific cases.

Metabasaltic Lithology

Coast Range Batholith, British Columbia

In Triassic basalts of Vancouver Island, British Columbia, the prevailing regional metamorphic mineral assemblage (albite-pumpellyite-prehnite-sphene, plus various accessories) is that of the prehnite-pumpellyite facies. This has been overprinted and obliterated in an aureole $3\frac{1}{2}$ km wide along the southwestern margin of the (Jurassic?) Coast Range tonalite batholith. As described by Kuniyoshi and Liou (1976), the aureole consists of two zones.[*]

1. Outer zone, 2600 m wide; albite-epidote-hornfels facies. Pumpellyite, prehnite, and zeolites have been eliminated. The metamorphic assemblage is actinolite-chlorite-epidote-albite.
2. Inner zone, 900 m wide; hornblende-hornfels facies, with hornblende-plagioclase ($An_{>20}$)-sphene; texture hornfelsic (schistose near the contact).

   Transition from the outer to the inner zone is marked by simultaneous abrupt changes in compositions of plagioclase and amphiboles: Plagioclase changes from nearly pure albite to more calcic varieties, An_{20} to An_{70}, while actinolite ($Al_2O_3 \sim$ 4%) gives way to hornblende (Al_2O_3 6-10%). Hornblende is significantly richer than actinolite in Na_2O (0.5-2.0%) and TiO_2 (0.5-2.5%). Contact metamorphism of basaltic flows was essentially isochemical (except for H_2O content).

Pelitic Lithology: The Classic Example

Barr-Andlau Aureole, Central Vosges

In the central part of the Vosges of Alsace, Paleozoic slates are cut by a granitic pluton along whose margin, within a kilometer or so of the contact, is a well-developed metamorphic aureole. This is classic ground; for here, between the towns

---

[*]Kuniyoshi and Liou (1976, pp. 92, 94), following Miyashiro's nomenclature, equate assemblages of the two zones with the greenschist and amphibolite facies, respectively.

of Barr and Andlau, Rosenbusch (1877) for the first time delineated on a map what he recognized as zones of progressive metamorphism. He described in detail both the textural evolution (from slate to hornfels) and mineralogical changes observed in traverses across the aureole (for more readily available bare details see Rosenbusch and Osann, 1923, pp. 605, 606; Harker, 1932, p. 24). The Barr-Andlau aureole became the type example for similar studies elsewhere.

Textural evidence was employed to define successive zones in pelitic rocks ("Steiger Schiefer") of the aureole:

1. Zone of *Knotentonschiefer* (knotted clay slates). Spots with concentrated dark carbonaceous pigment and indefinitely recrystallized chlorite, white mica, and quartz appear in an otherwise unchanged groundmass. Initial hematite is beginning to reduce (in the presence of carbon) to magnetite.
2. Zone of *Knotenglimmerschiefer* (knotted mica slates). The groundmass is now reconstituted, but spotting and schistosity are still obvious. Biotite develops at the expense of chlorite, and staurolite appears spasmodically. Graphite is crystallizing from the dark pigment of the groundmass. The metamorphic assemblage is quartz-biotite-muscovite-magnetite-graphite (-staurolite-chlorite).
3. Zone of *hornfelses*, with no trace of either spotting (except for porphyroblasts) or initial foliation; graphite has been eliminated. Andalusite and in some rocks cordierite develop porphyroblasts. The complete assemblage is quartz-biotite-andalusite-feldspars-magnetite (cordierite-muscovite).

Assemblages of Zone 3 (and probably in much of Zone 2) are those of the hornblende-hornfels facies.

The assemblage of Zone 3, not uncommonly with almandine as an additional phase, has been recorded from many other aureoles (e.g., that of Ardara, Donegal, pp. 12, 13). We shall meet it again, in some cases with staurolite instead of cordierite at a somewhat lower grade, or with sillimanite rather than andalusite in the innermost zone, in examples of mixed lithology to be considered below.

Dolomite-Limestone Lithology

Silica Saturation

In rocks that conform approximately to the "system" calcite-dolomite-quartz, the sequence of mineral assemblages that develops within the hornblende-hornfels facies depends upon whether the bulk composition lies above or below the calcite-tremolite tie. The former we shall call saturated, the latter deficient, in silica.

Silica-Saturated Paragenesis:
Granite Peak, Montana

The Granite Peak stock of Lewis and Clark County, Montana, is one of a series of late Cretaceous or early Tertiary granitic plutons intruded into initially unmetamorphosed, later Precambrian sediments. The Marysville stock, whose aureole was described in Chap. 1, belongs to the same group of intrusions. In composition the Granite Peak stock is essentially granitic. Its outcrop is about $2\frac{1}{2}$ km in diameter. Where it cuts the Helena dolomite formation, there is a contact aureole whose maximum width of outcrop is 1 km; but field evidence suggests a dipping contact, so that the true width may quite possibly be only 300 m. The aureole has been described by Melson (1966) from whose publication the above details and those relating to metamorphic paragenesis have been taken.

The Helena dolomite is banded on the scale of a hand specimen. Alternating beds, a centimeter or two in thickness, are of two main kinds: dolomite-calcite-quartz with minor "illite" and chlorite; and argillaceous assemblages containing abundant "illite," detrital micas, clay minerals, quartz, and some carbonates. Metamorphism was essentially isochemical. Reactions at the first stages, as represented today by assemblages on the fringe of the aureole, are thought to have been controlled by partial pressures of water and CO_2 that varied from bed to bed as dictated by the relative proportions of clay minerals and carbonates.

The carbonate-quartz beds in the aureole have been converted to three- and four-phase assemblages that are combinations of quartz, dolomite, calcite, tremolite, diopside, wollastonite. Minor sphene and clinozoisite are ubiquitous, K-feldspar and/or phlogopite less frequent. Various combinations of these phases with phologopite, K-feldspar, plagioclase, and (at highest grades) cordierite appear in the accompanying pelitic beds.

In the purer carbonate-quartz layers the silicate phases appear, as the contact is approached, in the order tremolite, diopside, and wollastonite. In the more argillaceous bands there are parallel reactions leading to the appearance of phlogopite in the outer aureole (by reactions involving illite and chlorite) and cordierite in the innermost zone. Corresponding phase diagrams are shown in Fig. 8-4. The approximate distances of the corresponding zonal boundaries from the outcrop of the contact (as plotted on the map) are as follows:

a. Transition zone, a few meters wide:
   1. Tremolite-calcite-quartz
b. Outer contact zone, 600–100 m:
   1. Tremolite-diopside-quartz
   2. Tremolite-calcite-quartz
   3. Diopside-calcite-quartz
c. Inner contact zone, 100–0 m:
   1. Tremolite-diopside-quartz
   2. Diopside-calcite-wollastonite
   3. Diopside-wollastonite-quartz

Melson (1966, p. 417) visualizes two parallel reaction sequences that respectively control the mineralogy of carbonate-quartz and marly beds:

Transition zones:
a. Dolomite-quartz-H_2O → tremolite-calcite-CO_2
b. Illite-calcite-quartz → tremolite-K-feldspar-clinozoisite-H_2O-CO_2
Outer zone (outer portion):
a. Tremolite-quartz-calcite → diopside-CO_2-H_2O
b. Dolomite-quartz → diopside-CO_2 (in initially anhydrous beds)
c. Illite-calcite-quartz → tremolite-phlogopite-clinozoisite-H_2O-CO_2

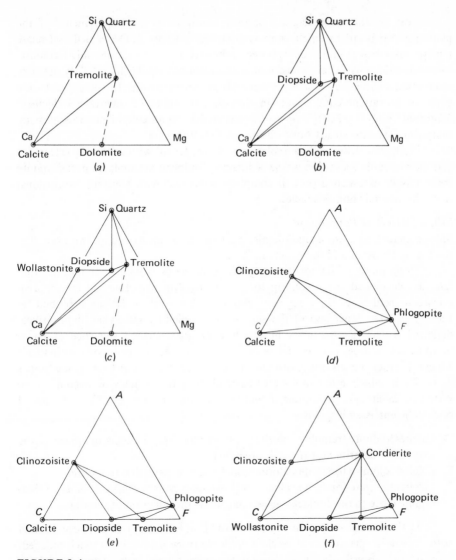

FIGURE 8-4

Hornblende-hornfels facies, Granite Peak aureole, Montana (after W. G. Melson). (*a*) to (*c*) Assemblages in the triangle calcite-dolomite-silica. (*d*) to (*f*) *ACF* diagrams for carbonate and agillaceous rocks with excess silica. Quartz and plagioclase are additional phases (K-feldspar in all but the tremolite assemblages of *f*). (*a*) transition zone; (*b*), (*d*), and (*e*) outer zone; (*c*) and (*f*) inner zone.

Outer zone (inner portion):

a. Tremolite-K-feldspar → diopside-phlogopite-quartz
b. Calcite-phlogopite-quartz → diopside-K-feldspar-H_2O-CO_2

Inner zone:

a. Calcite-quartz → wollastonite-CO_2
b. Clinozoisite-diopside-quartz → wollastonite-cordierite-H_2O

Most of the assemblages described conform to the requirements of the phase rule for bivariant equilibrium as discussed in Chap. 2. Occasional four-phase mineral assemblages in metamorphosed carbonate-quartz bands, notably tremolite-calcite-diopside-quartz, are consistent with univariant equilibrium.* They are here interpreted in this way; for local assemblages corresponding to some point on a curve of univariant equilibrium (in this case, tremolite + 2 quartz + 3 calcite $\rightleftharpoons$ 5 diopside + H_2O + $3CO_2$) are to be expected in an aureole of progressive metamorphism involving steady outward flow of CO_2 and water.

From comparison with aureoles (e.g., Tôno, Japan) with coexisting calcareous and metavolcanic rocks, the whole sequence of mineral assemblages in the Granite Peak aureole is assigned (not in complete agreement with Melson's conclusions) to the hornblende-hornfels facies.

Silica-Deficient Parageneses

Silica-deficient parageneses in dolomite marbles will be illustrated by two examples, the first in Montana and the second in Korea.

Along much of its northern edge the Cretaceous Boulder batholith of Montana has developed an aureole up to 2.5 km wide in Paleozoic and Precambrian calcareous sediments. In a segment about 10 km west of Helena described by Rice (1977) the inner part of the aureole is occupied by somewhat impure silica-deficient, Paleozoic dolomites in which a prograde inward sequence of metamorphic assemblages is listed below as D to F (lettered to correspond with Rice's zones). Further out are silica-saturated Precambrian marbles of lower grade—zones A to C—in which calcite-dolomite-quartz-phlogopite + K-feldspar becomes converted to calcite-quartz-diopside-tremolite + K-feldspar (zone C). The sequence of silica-deficient assemblages is

D. Calcite-dolomite-tremolite-chlorite ± phlogopite. Spinel begins to appear at the expense of chlorite near the D–E boundary.
E. Calcite-dolomite-forsterite-chlorite-spinel + minor pargasitic tremolite.
F. Calcite-dolomite-forsterite-spinel and calcite-forsterite-diopside-spinel. Clinohumite close to the contact suggests magmatic introduction of fluorine.

At the most sharply defined isograd (the D–E boundary), forsterite and spinel both appear in quantity, and calcic amphibole (now pargasitic) is much reduced. Two of the contributing reactions on the microscopic scale—demonstrated by reaction textures—are (in simplified form):

$$\text{Tremolite} + 11 \text{ dolomite} \rightleftharpoons 8 \text{ forsterite} + 13 \text{ calcite} + 9CO_2 + H_2O$$

and

$$\text{Chlorite} + 2 \text{ dolomite} \rightleftharpoons 4 \text{ forsterite} + 2 \text{ calcite} + 2CO_2 + 4H_2O$$

---

*Melson (1966, p. 413) treated the problem in an unnecessarily complicated way by assigning various degrees of mobility to participating components according to Korzhinski's approach, which was fashionable among some petrologists.

The resulting equilibrium assemblage E, with 7 phases (including fluid), in the six-component "system" $CaO-MgO-SiO_2-Al_2O_3-CO_2-H_2O$, must be univariant. Rice's chemographic treatment nicely illustrates the potential of Schreinemakers' approach to quantitative evaluation of low-variance equilibria. It also brings out deficiencies in currently available quantitative data, and the kinds of assumptions that are necessitated thereby. The outcome is a convincing model of reaction paths, with fluid composition internally buffered, leading to the "invariant" point (on an isobaric diagram) represented by the forsterite-spinel-bearing assemblage E. Temperatures computed from calcite-dolomite compositions in zones D–F are in the range 500–607°C. Using all available experimental data, eked out by accessory thermochemical values, Rice places the "invariant" point (zone E) at 540°C, $X_{CO_2}^{gas} \sim 0.82$, assuming $P_f = P = 1$ kb.

An interesting zoned paragenesis of contact metamorphism in the aureole of the Suian granodiorite, Korea, has been described by Watanabe (1943). The intrusive body is a stock 100 km² in area at the outcrop, cutting Proterozoic and Paleozoic sediments, mainly dolomites and limestones. The aureole in places is 1 km in width. The following sequence of assemblages, developed in siliceous and pure dolomites, marks a series of zones of progressive contact metamorphism.

1. From 1000 to 500 m from the contact: dolomite-tremolite-calcite
2. Between 500 and 200 m from the contact: dolomite-forsterite-calcite and diopside-forsterite
3. From 200 to 50 m from the contact, the assemblages of zone 2 have been affected by boron-fluorine metasomatism giving, in addition to dolomite and forsterite, such minerals as clinohumite, chondrodite, kotoite, and ludwigite
4. At distances of 50 m or less from the contact: calcite-brucite (pseudomorphous after periclase) and calcite-forsterite (clinohumite)-brucite

Associated pelitic rocks of zone 1 are spotted biotite phyllites. These pass into biotite hornfels (zone 2) and ultimately, in zone 4 into high-grade assemblages such as andalusite-cordierite-biotite-orthoclase-quartz and silica-deficient andalusite-corundum-spinel-orthoclase. Hornfelses derived from basic igneous rock consist of hornblende-plagioclase (-biotite) even in the zone of brucite-forsterite marble.

Skarn Paragenesis, Skye, Scotland

In the Broadford area of Skye, the Beinn an Dubhaich granite boss, several square kilometers in cross section, has developed a contact aureole in Cambrian dolomitic limestone and dolomite (Harker, 1904, pp. 141–151). In the outer part of the aureole, up to over 1 km from the contact, Tilley (1948) has recorded the successive development (with advancing grade) of the assemblages shown in Fig. 8-5a to c. The starting materials in every case were dolomite and silica, the latter in the form of chert nodules and sponge forms. Critical assemblages of the three early stages of metamorphism are

1. Talc-calcite-quartz
2. Tremolite-talc-calcite
3. Tremolite-calcite-dolomite

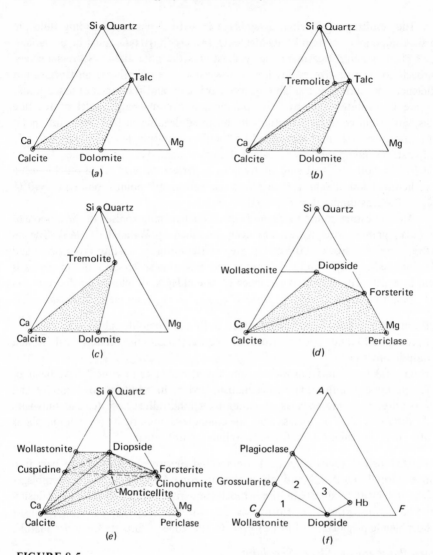

FIGURE 8-5

Hornblende-hornfels facies, granite aureole, Skye (data from C. E. Tilley, 1948, 1951a). (*a*) to (*c*) Successive stages in metamorphism of dolomite, outer zone of aureole. (*d*) High-grade dolomite assemblages, inner zone of aureole. (*e*) Skarn assemblages, inner aureole (phase assemblages in compositional triangle quartz-diopside-forsterite are not present). (*f*) Silica-saturated assemblages of skarns (1, 2) and associated metadiabase (3). Stippled areas in all diagrams are silica-deficient assemblages.

The high-grade assemblages in the inner aureole (Tilley, 1951a, pp. 623–624) are those of Fig. 8-5*d* (the silica-deficient assemblages much as in the Suian aureole, Korea). Although Tilley lists the order of appearance as talc, tremolite, forsterite, diopside, this writer can find no evidence in the literature as to whether elimination of tremolite was by reaction with dolomite to give calcite-forsterite, or by reaction with calcite to give diopside-dolomite. The first alternative is implied by Tilley's sequence of steps.

Close to the granite contacts, reaction between flint nodules and enclosing dolomite has been accompanied by outward diffusion of Si and inward diffusion of Mg and Ca. Each nodule, plus a peripheral envelope of dolomite, has thus been converted into a compositionally zoned aggregate. The assemblages are those on the quartz-dolomite join of Fig. 8-5*d*, from within outward:

1. Quartz-diopside
2. Diopside
3. Diopside-forsterite
4. Forsterite-calcite

At various points along the granite contact, zoned skarns have developed by outward diffusion of Si, Al, Fe from the granitic magma. This seems to have been effected by the continuous outward flow of an aqueous gas carrying fluorine and boron as additional components. The outward sequence (a few inches in total width) from the granite contact may be represented in its simplest form as follows (this neglects magnetite and a number of special fluorine- and boron-bearing phases locally introduced at a later stage):

1. Grossularite-wollastonite or hedenbergite-plagioclase
2. Dark clinopyroxene
3. Light clinopyroxene (poorer in Al and Fe)
4. Clinopyroxene-monticellite (-spinel)
5. Forsterite (-clinohumite-spinel)
6. Calcite-forsterite

The skarn paragenesis conforms in its simpler and principal aspects to that represented for silica-deficient assemblages in Fig. 8-5*e* (stippled) and for quartz-bearing assemblages (inner skarn zones) in Fig. 8-5*f*. The presence of the high-grade phases monticellite, periclase, and cuspidine—minerals commonly considered to represent very high metamorphic temperatures (sanidinite facies)—is strong evidence that $X_{H_2O}^{gas}$ was consistently maintained at a level high enough to reduce $X_{CO_2}^{gas}$ to low values.

Where primarily zoned chert replacements occur in the skarn zone, the sequence of assemblages has been modified by inward migration of Ca to such as the following two (again from within outward):

1. Quartz
   Quartz-wollastonite
   Wollastonite
   Cuspidine-diopside-calcite
   Diopside
   Forsterite (-clinohumite)

2. Diopside-cuspidine-clinohumite-magnetite
   Quartz-wollastonite
   Wollastonite
   Cuspidine-diopside
   Monticellite (calcite)

Metaserpentinite Lithology: Eastern Aureole, Bergell Pluton, Central Alps

Near the eastern end of the Swiss-Italian border, upper Pennine nappes of the central Alps are cut by a granodiorite-tonalite pluton, the Bergell "granite," some

250 km² in outcrop area. High-grade (amphibolite facies) metasediments and gneisses of the Lepontine zone of regional metamorphism extend to the western margin of the "granite" (H. R. Wenk et al., 1974). East of the Engadine Line (Fig. 8-6) and of the eastern plutonic contact, the grade of regional metamorphism in metapelites of the Pennine domain is lower—greenschist and low-grade amphibolite facies[*] (e.g., Trommsdorff and Evans, 1974, p. 339; Frey et al., 1974, pp. 261,

[*]To minimize confusion it should be noted that recent findings of Swiss workers and their colleagues, as cited above, are in major conflict with the facies pattern depicted at this point in Ernst's (1973, Fig. 2) regional map of the western Alps.

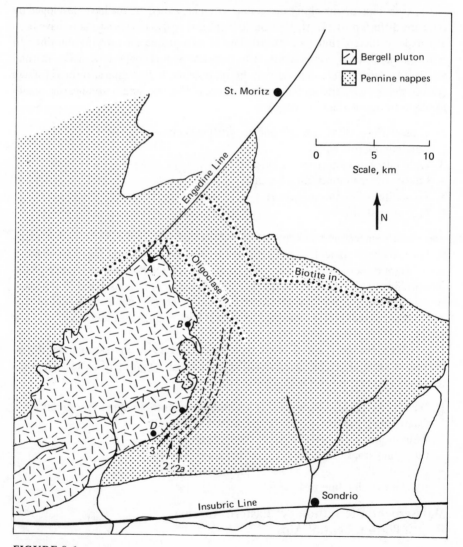

FIGURE 8-6
Eastern aureole of Bergell granite pluton, central Alps (simplified after Trommsdorff and Evans, 1972). Isograds: dotted (metapelites); dashed (metaserpentinites), numbered as in text.

262). Within this low-grade terrane a large ultramafic body, the Val Malenco serpentinite (170 km^2), is in direct or slightly interrupted contact with a segment of 10 km of the eastern boundary of the Bergell pluton.

The metamorphic-plutonic history of the Bergell area is complex and is still the subject of sharp debate (cf. Frey et al., 1974, p. 262; Ernst, 1977, p. 373). It certainly covers some part of the Alpine orogeny. Whether intrusion of the granite came late in the mid-Tertiary Lepontine phase of the orogeny or somewhat earlier during emplacement of the nappes, one fact seems clear from field and petrographic evidence: along its eastern contact the Bergell pluton has superposed a contact aureole a kilometer or so wide upon both pelitic and ultramafic rocks that already carried the imprint of an earlier phase of Alpine regional metamorphism. It is this contact effect upon the Val Malenco serpentinite that is our present topic.

Beyond the eastern limit of the aureole, the regional ultramafic metamorphic assemblage is antigorite-forsterite-diopside. Enclosing cofacial metapelites (Fig. 8-6) are mostly in the biotite zone, greenschist facies. Within the aureole, an inward sequence of metamorphic ultramafic assemblages, representing a series of reactions of progressive dehydration, has been recorded by Trommsdorff and Evans (1972). Successive reactions (numbered as in Chap. 4, Fig. 4-11) and resultant new assemblages (all in the hornblende-hornfels facies) are as follows.

(2a) $5Mg_3Si_2O_5(OH)_4 + 2CaMgSi_2O_6 \rightarrow 6Mg_2SiO_4 + Ca_2Mg_5Si_8O_{22}(OH)_2$
        antigorite   diopside   forsterite   tremolite

 $+ 9H_2O$

New assemblage: Antigorite-forsterite-tremolite

(2) $5Mg_3Si_2O_5(OH)_4 \rightarrow 6Mg_2SiO_4 + Mg_3Si_4O_{10}(OH)_2 + 9H_2O$
      antigorite   forsterite   talc

New assemblage: Forsterite-talc-tremolite

(3) $9Mg_3Si_4O_{10}(OH)_2 + 4Mg_2SiO_4 \rightarrow 5Mg_7Si_8O_{22}(OH)_2 + 4H_2O$
      talc   forsterite   anthophyllite

New assemblage: Forsterite-anthophyllite-tremolite

Between C and D (Fig. 8-6), the ultramafic body is separated from immediate contact with the Bergell tonalite by high-grade pelitic rocks with the general assemblage (H. R. Wenk et al., 1974) quartz-biotite-cordierite-sillimanite-plagioclase-K-feldspar (-muscovite). Elsewhere, e.g., in the Sierra Nevada of California, this assemblage characterizes the hornblende-hornfels $\rightarrow$ pyroxene-hornfels transition facies. Beyond the ultramafic-tonalite contact along the northeastern segment AB, the metapelite assemblage is similar but carries andalusite instead of sillimanite—betokening lower pressures of metamorphism consistent with significantly higher topographic and structural levels (H. R. Wenk et al., 1974, p. 510).

Mixed Lithology

Preliminary Statement

From the facies standpoint the most interesting aureoles are those of mixed lithology including metabasalts (basic assemblages). In these latter the pair hornblende-plagioclase ($An_{>25}$) with or without associated minerals—quartz, diopside, biotite, and garnet—defines the limits of the hornblende-hornfels facies and thus of cofacial associated assemblages of other lithology. Two examples of single aureoles that fulfill this requirement will be described.

Tôno Aureole, Japan

A Jurassic granodiorite pluton, 30 km in diameter, near Tôno in the northeastern part of the island of Honshu, has developed a zoned contact aureole in the surrounding Paleozoic sediments and associated basic volcanics. Mineralogical aspects of metamorphism have been described in detail by Seki (1957) and by Seki and Yamasaki (1957).

In the outermost zones of the aureole, pelitic assemblages include various combinations of quartz, muscovite, biotite, andalusite, and albite-oligoclase. Intercalated volcanics consist principally of chlorite, sodic plagioclase, epidote, and actinolite. Tremolite has developed in calcareous rocks. The mineral assemblages suggest the albite-epidote-hornfels rather than the typical hornblende-hornfels facies (cf. p. 245).

Rocks of distinctly higher metamorphic grade border the western margin of the pluton and extend from a few hundred meters to over 1 km from the exposed contact. The mineral assemblages are more complex than in the outer zone. With the exception of an unusually iron-rich aluminous ferroanthophyllite (Seki and Yamasaki, 1957), the constituent minerals have not been analyzed. But full data for refractive indices of coexisting biotites, cordierites, anthophyllites, and garnets make it possible to construct the essential features of AFM and $A'F'M'$ diagrams to illustrate the main features of the paragenesis. Pelitic rocks on the whole are unusually rich in iron and high in aluminum.

Throughout the inner aureole, basic hornfelses are always represented by the hornblende-plagioclase (An_{73} to An_{72}) assemblage, diagnostic of the hornblende-hornfels facies. But there are two concentric inner zones characterized by distinctive mineralogical criteria that stamp them as mutually distinct local subfacies:

First, a cordierite-almandine zone immediately follows the outermost zone of andalusite-mica hornfelses. Characteristic features of pelitic rocks are abundance of cordierite, andalusite, and anthophyllite. Calcareous rocks include the assemblages calcite-epidote-plagioclase-diopside and calcite-diopside-quartz.

Second, a sillimanite zone, developed within a few hundred meters of the plutonic contact and comprising the innermost portion of the aureole. Pelitic hornfelses contain sillimanite, not andalusite; anthophyllite is absent; microcline appears in some rocks. In calcareous assemblages of appropriate composition, wollastonite and grossularite are present.

Pelitic rocks in the cordierite-almandine zone include all possible combinations of quartz and plagioclase with three, four, or five of the six crystalline phases muscovite, biotite, andalusite, cordierite, anthophyllite, and almandine.

These are illustrated in *AFM* and *A′F′M′* plots (Figs. 8-7 and 8-8) based on the optical data of Seki (1957, p. 332) and of Yamasaki* for anthophyllite and associated minerals. It would seem that in any given assemblage Fe/(Fe + Mg) tends to decrease in the order almandine > anthophyllite > biotite ⩾ cordierite. Almandine, as usual, appears only in rocks whose FeO/MgO ratio is high (stippled area of Figs. 8-7 and 8-8). Typical assemblages consist of four or five phases, e.g., quartz-almandine-muscovite-biotite and quartz-almandine-andalusite-anthophyllite-cordierite. Six- and seven-phase assemblages with anthophyllite, garnet, and muscovite are shown by ties in the stippled area of Fig. 8-7). The corresponding assemblage without muscovite (quartz-almandine-andalusite-biotite-anthophyllite-cordierite) is represented in the stippled part of Fig. 8-8.

Mineral assemblages in rocks of fixed composition—each represented as unique points in Figs. 8-7 and 8-8—can be considered in terms of the phase rule. Take the common five-phase assemblage, quartz-muscovite-biotite-cordierite-gas (water). The minimum number of components $c = 6$ (SiO$_2$, Al$_2$O$_3$, FeO, MgO, K$_2$O, and H$_2$O), $\omega = (6 + 2 - 5) = 3$. So, if the rock system is in equilibrium at

*Values of γ refractive indices from which mineral compositions were inferred are shown for each (e.g., 1.54–1.57 for cordierite).

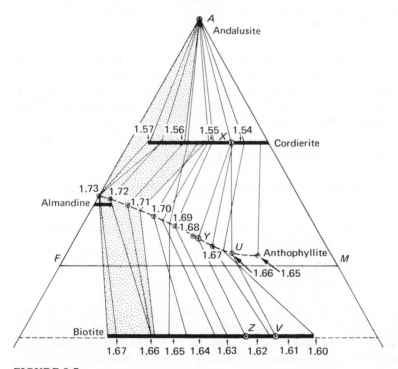

FIGURE 8-7

Hornblende-hornfels facies, Tôno aureole, Japan (cordierite-almandine zone). *AFM* diagram for pelitic hornfelses containing muscovite. Quartz and plagioclase are possible additional phases; garnet is present in all assemblages of stippled area. Mineral compositions are inferred from γ refractive index values as shown.

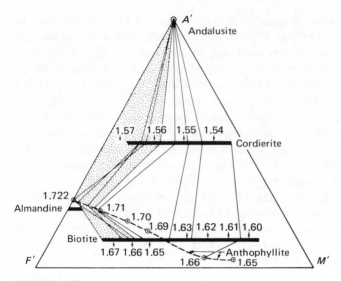

FIGURE 8-8

Hornblende-hornfels facies, Tôno aureole, Japan (cordierite-almandine zone). $A'F'M'$ diagram for pelitic hornfelses lacking muscovite. Quartz and plagioclase are possible additional phases; garnet is present in all assemblages of stippled area. Mineral compositions are inferred from γ refractive index values as shown (aluminum content of magnesian anthophyllites is uncertain).

some constant P and T, one other variable X_{Mg}^{cord} or X_{Mg}^{bi} remains free. Crossing tie lines in Fig. 8-7, provided all intersect in the point representing the composition of the system, would still be consistent with equilibrium.* Additional phases correspondingly reduce the degree of freedom. Take the seven-phase assemblage, quartz-muscovite-biotite-andalusite-anthophyllite-cordierite-gas (water). The value of c is still 6, $\omega = (6 + 2 - 7) = 1$. It is still possible that the system is in equilibrium at some P and T on a univariant curve for the reaction

$$(1) \quad 6KAl_2(AlSi_3O_{10})(OH)_2 + 2(Mg,Fe)_{6\,1/2}Al_{1/2}(Al_{1/2}Si_{7\,1/2}O_{22})(OH)_2$$
$$\text{muscovite} \qquad\qquad\qquad \text{anthophyllite}$$

$$+ (Mg,Fe)_2Al_4Si_5O_{18} \rightleftharpoons 6K(Mg,Fe)_{2\,1/2}Al_{1/2}(Al_{1\,1/2}Si_{2\,1/2}O_{10})(OH)_2$$
$$\text{cordierite} \qquad\qquad\qquad\qquad \text{biotite}$$

$$+ 6Al_2SiO_5 + 17SiO_2 + 2H_2O$$
$$\text{andalusite} \quad \text{quartz}$$

If so, all compositional variables must be constant for the system: each of the zigzag lines connecting andalusite-cordierite-anthophyllite-biotite in Fig. 8-7 represents a unique rock composition, and crossing ties are here prohibited for univariant equilibrium. Fig. 8-7 thus suggests either departure from equilibrium or a significant range in temperature within the cordierite-almandine zone.

---

*Addition of plagioclase to the assemblage would not affect this conclusion. (c and φ would each be increased by 1.)

Other pelitic assemblages in the cordierite-almandine zone do show unmistakable signs of internal disequilibrium. Such are spinel-corundum-biotite-muscovite-quartz and assemblages containing spinel, corundum, cordierite, and quartz. Not only is the phase assemblage itself inconsistent with equilibrium, but there is textural evidence of reaction between the constituent phases (Seki, 1957, pp. 329, 330).

In the sillimanite zone of the Tôno aureole, the pelitic assemblages are much simpler. The Al_2SiO_5 polymorph is sillimanite. There are the usual three- and four-phase combinations of quartz, biotite, muscovite, sillimanite, and cordierite (and in iron-rich rocks, almandine) shown in Fig. 8-9. Anthophyllite is completely lacking,[*] and in rocks relatively rich in FeO and MgO, cordierite (and/or almandine) is associated with both biotite and muscovite. Microcline appears in sillimanite-, cordierite-, or almandine-bearing assemblages, with one or both micas. In the *AKF* diagram (Fig. 8-9), there are many crossing ties. Again there is strong indication of either disequilibrium or possible univariant equilibrium expressed by equations such as

$$(2) \quad 4KMg_{2\,1/2}Al_{1/2}(Al_{1\,1/2}Si_{2\,1/2}O_{10})(OH)_2 + KAl_2(AlSi_3O_{10})(OH)_2$$
$$\text{biotite} \qquad\qquad\qquad\qquad\qquad\qquad \text{muscovite}$$

$$+\ 7Al_2SiO_5 + 20SiO_2 \rightleftharpoons 5KAlSi_3O_8 + 5Mg_2Al_4Si_5O_{18} + 5H_2O$$
$$\text{sillimanite} \quad\ \text{quartz} \qquad \text{microcline} \qquad\ \text{cordierite}$$

[*]The reaction leading to elimination of anthophyllite is perhaps that expressed in equation (1) above.

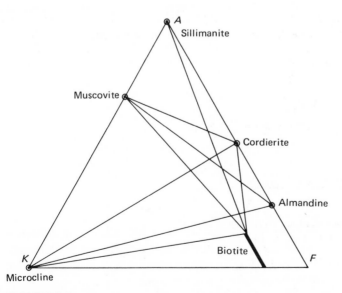

FIGURE 8-9
Hornblende-hornfels facies, Tôno aureole, Japan (sillimanite zone). *AKF* diagram for pelitic quartz-bearing assemblages. Quartz and plagioclase are possible additional phases.

Figure 8-10 is an *AFM* plot showing the compositions (inferred from the γ refractive index) of coexisting biotites, cordierites, and (in the stippled area) almandines in muscovite-bearing rocks of the sillimanite zone.

Santa Rosa Aureoles, Nevada

In the Santa Rosa range, northern Nevada, late Triassic low-grade metasediments—largely pelitic—were invaded in late Cretaceous times by several cross-cutting steep-sided granodiorite and tonalite plutons. One of these is the Santa Rosa stock whose elliptical outcrop covers 90 km^2 (Fig. 8-25). Rocks of the Triassic envelope, already affected by low-grade regional metamorphism (greenschist facies), have been completely reconstituted under the thermal influence of the Santa Rosa stock within 1 to 2 km of the plutonic contacts. The effects of contact metamorphism adjacent to the Santa Rosa plutons have been documented in unusual detail by Compton (1960). He estimates cover at the time of metamorphism as between 3 and 8 km thick, with 3 km ($P_l = 1$ kb) as the most probable value.

The mineral paragenesis in the outer and intermediate zones of the aureole is mostly normal for the hornblende-hornfels facies (Fig. 8-11). The ubiquitous basic mineral assemblage is hornblende-plagioclase. In the purer calcareous rocks, calcite-quartz is stable. Pelitic rocks show a prolific development of aluminum silicates reflecting a generally high content of Al_2O_3. They consist of the following combinations:

1. Cordierite-biotite
2. Cordierite-andalusite-biotite $\Big\}$ plus quartz-muscovite-plagioclase
3. Staurolite-andalusite-biotite
4. Andalusite-biotite

Cordierite and staurolite are mutually exclusive. The many chemical analyses that are available reveal no obvious correlation between the occurrence of these phases

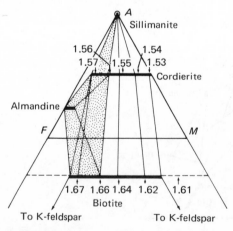

FIGURE 8-10
Hornblende-hornfels facies, Tôno aureole, Japan (sillimanite zone). *AFM* diagram (schematic) for pelitic assemblages. Muscovite, quartz, and plagioclase are possible additional phases; garnet may be present in assemblages of the stippled area. Numbers refer to γ refractive indices.

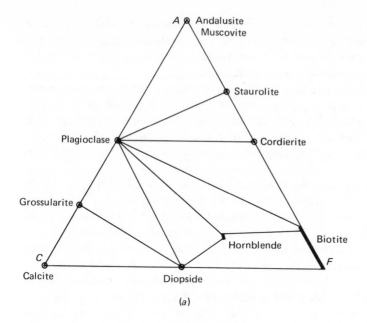

(a)

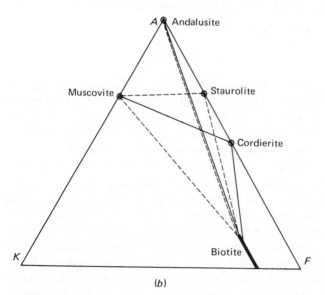

(b)

FIGURE 8-11

Hornblende-hornfels facies, Santa Rosa stocks, Nevada (intermediate zone of aureole). (a) *ACF* diagram for rocks with excess SiO_2 and deficient in K_2O. Quartz is a possible additional phase. (b) *AKF* diagram for rocks with excess SiO_2 and Al_2O_3. Quartz and plagioclase are possible additional phases. Broken lines show staurolite-bearing assemblages.

and the chemical composition of the total rock. The absence of andalusite in assemblage 1 has been shown by Compton to be due to relatively high CaO and low Al_2O_3 compared with assemblage 2. Consequently, plagioclase has crystallized in greater quantity, and andalusite has been suppressed.

Close to the contacts, staurolite no longer appears. At the same time muscovite, and to a lesser extent biotite, begin to break down toward the ideal high-temperature assemblage, quartz-plagioclase-microcline-cordierite-sillimanite. In this inner zone, wollastonite appears in place of calcite-quartz in calcareous rocks relatively low in alumina. The paragenesis approximates that of Fig. 8-13a (Sierra Nevada).

Significant changes in the oxidation ratio $(2Fe_2O_3 \times 100)/(2Fe_2O_3 + FeO)$ accompany progressive metamorphism in the Santa Rosa aureoles.[*] The mean value in the regional schists beyond the aureole is 17.6 (these rocks contain graphite as well as ores). It rises to 24 (and simultaneously graphite is eliminated) in the outer zone of the aureole and then falls in the inner zone to 12. Possibly high values favor crystallization of staurolite; for this mineral is not found in the inner aureole, and the value for staurolite-andalusite assemblages is somewhat higher than that for cordierite-andalusite assemblages (24 versus 16 as computed from Compton's Table 4). Analyses of staurolite listed by Deer, Howie, and Zussman (1962, pp. 154–155) consistently show a high oxidation ratio (17–35).

Contact Imprint of a Major Batholith, Sierra Nevada, California

Geologic Setting

The Sierra Nevada batholith of California (Fig. 8-12), continuously exposed over an elongate area roughly 500×100 km, consists of perhaps 200 separately emplaced plutons, some several hundred km^2 in extent, the majority a good deal smaller. The whole episode of intrusion, as deduced from radiometric data occupied more than 100 million years: the great bulk of the batholith—the axial portion—gives middle Cretaceous dates ($90–80 \times 10^6$ years); dates determined for the flanking plutons on either side are close to the Jurassic-Cretaceous boundary ($140–130 \times 10^6$ years), and in some sectors as far back as early Jurassic ($\sim 210 \times 10^6$ years). Considering the prolonged nature of the plutonic event, and the fact that, since it closed only 80 million years ago, the whole region has been uplifted and stripped of its cover, the general pattern of contact metamorphism, in aureole segments and roof remnants, is remarkably consistent. Everywhere, except in the outermost fringes of the flanking aureole, contact mineral assemblages—with only one recorded exception—are those of the hornblende-hornfels facies.

The invaded rocks along the western border of the batholith are Paleozoic and Mesozoic metasediments and metavolcanics bearing the imprint of low-grade regional metamorphism. Remnant masses of similar rocks, commonly several kilometers long, occur as roof pendants and as masses separating individual plutons, scattered along the axis of the batholith. These are enclosed in or separate the

---

[*]Values calculated from Compton (1960, p. 1403, Table 3).

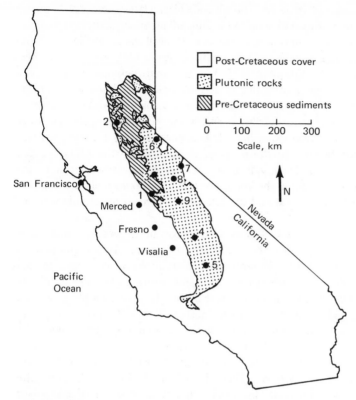

FIGURE 8-12
Sierra Nevada batholith, California (after G. H. Curtis). Localities referred to in text: western contact at Indian Gulch (1), Bidwell Bar (2), near Sonora (Standard) (3); pendants and roof remnants near Visalia (4), Issabella (5), Ebbett Pass (Hope Valley) (6), Tioga Pass (7), May Lake (8), and Twin Lakes (9).

younger plutonic bodies. Opinion differs as to the depth of cover at the time of intrusion at the presently exposed level. The maximum stratigraphic thicknesses of sections of Paleozoic and Mesozoic metasediments preserved in roof pendants are each about 10 km (Bateman et al., 1963, pp. 5, 6). From the chemical composition of the more siliceous plutonic rocks, Bateman et al. have inferred water pressures of around 5 kb, such as might develop under a cover upward of 15 km in thickness. Loomis (1966, p. 243) estimates the thickness of cover as about 8 km.

Contact Metamorphism at the Western Margin

Contact effects of the older intrusions along the western border of the batholith are illustrated by the observations of Best (1963, pp. 114–120) in the Indian Gulch quadrangle (1 in Fig. 8-12). Here there is an outer zone in which basic metavolcanics have recrystallized to the assemblage quartz-albite-epidote-hornblende. Associated pelites are graphitic muscovite-biotite phyllites with large andalusite porphyroblasts. This is the albite-epidote-hornfels facies of contact metamorphism. Nearer the contact the grade of metamorphism rises and the assemblages are those of the hornblende-hornfels facies: hornblende-plagioclase-sphene, and quartz-plagioclase-biotite-muscovite with andalusite, almandine, or cordierite.

At the contact with an outlying pluton at Bidwell Bar (2 in Fig. 8-12), the development of the hornblende-plagioclase assemblage in basic volcanics has been studied in more detail by Compton (1958). The parent rock outside the aureole is metabasalt ("greenstone") consisting of actinolite-albite-epidote-chlorite. In the outer part of the aureole this gives way to the first contact assemblage: hornblende-oligoclase (An_{26}), with minor epidote. Nearer the contact, epidote disappears completely; the final assemblage is hornblende-andesine (An_{38}), sometimes with minor diopside-hedenbergite. At the onset of metamorphism the Al_2O_3 content of the amphibole changes abruptly from $4\frac{1}{2}$ percent in the greenstone actinolite, to between 10 and 11 percent in the hornblendes of the two hornfels assemblages.[*] At the same time Fe_2O_3 increases from less than 1 percent in actinolites to 5–7 percent in hornblendes.

The most detailed account of phase assemblages in the western contact zone is due to Kerrick (1970) who refers specifically to an area 10 km southeast of Sonora (locality 3, Fig. 8-12). The aureole here is about a kilometer wide and includes marbles interbedded with pelitic schists and hornfels, all in the hornblende-hornfels facies. The dominant pelitic assemblage is quartz-biotite-muscovite-plagioclase (An_{30-40}), in some cases with K-feldspar. Within 200 m of the contact this gives way to coarse sillimanite hornfels with the assemblage quartz-sillimanite-muscovite-biotite-plagioclase-K-feldspar (-minor garnet). This suggests transition toward the pyroxene-hornfels facies, but locally associated amphibolites have the usual hornblende-plagioclase pair. Tectonic inclusions of marble in metapelites of the inner aureole are concentrically zoned, the inward sequence of assemblages being

1. Actinolite-clinozoisite (-quartz)
2. Actinolite-diopside-clinozoisite (-quartz)
3. Calcite-dolomite (-clinohumite)

Two samples from the sillimanite zone consist of calcite-quartz-wollastonite.

Contact Metamorphism in Roof Remnants

Enclosed roof pendants of country rock and larger remnants interspersed between the upper portions of individual plutons are widely distributed along the axis of the batholith. Many are between 1 km and 3 km in length. In all of them calcite- or dolomite-marble is a prominent, in many the dominant lithological component. The prevailing paragenesis which is remarkably constant is illustrated below by specific examples.

Northeast of Visalia (4 in Fig. 8-12) is an enclosed strip of metasediments and metavolcanics 50 km by 2 to 8 km, the mineralogy of which was recorded by Durrell (1940). The principal assemblages (cf. Fig. 8-13) are as follows:

---

[*]This important change can be detected optically. In actinolite outside the aureole, $\gamma = 1.645$, $2V_\alpha = 77–80°$; in hornblendes within the aureole, $\gamma = 1.670$ to 1.680, $2V_\alpha = 64–69°$.

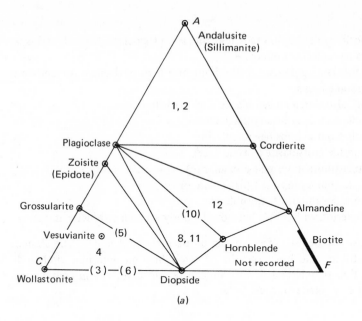

(a)

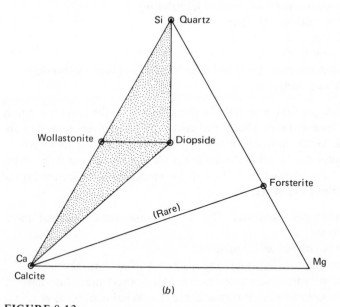

(b)

FIGURE 8-13
Hornblende-hornfels facies near Visalia, western Sierra Nevada, California. (a) *ACF* diagram.
Quartz is a possible additional phase; K-feldspar (sometimes with muscovite) may occur in
pelitic assemblages (triangles 1 and 2). (b) Simple assemblages (stippled triangles and ties) in
marbles.

A. Pelitic:
1. Quartz-biotite-andalusite-muscovite-orthoclase-plagioclase. Potash feldspar appears to be replacing muscovite.
2. Quartz-orthoclase-cordierite-biotite-sillimanite (or andalusite). Almandine is present in some rocks.
B. Calcareous (cf. also simpler assemblages, Fig. 8-13b):
3. Calcite-wollastonite-diopside (-plagioclase)
4. Calcite-wollastonite-diopside-grossularite
5. Calcite-diopside-grossularite (-plagioclase)
6. Quartz-wollastonite-diopside (-grossularite)
7. Quartz-wollastonite-diopside (-plagioclase or zoisite)
8. Quartz-diopside-labradorite-hornblende
9. Calcite-forsterite, with minor but not obviously secondary brucite and talc

Vesuvianite and/or clinozoisite may appear in assemblages 4 and 7. The absence of tremolite is striking and bears out the relatively high metamorphic grade indicated by association of microcline with andalusite and cordierite in pelitic horn-felses just as in the pyroxene-hornfels facies.

C. Basic:
10. Hornblende-plagioclase (-andesine or labradorite)
11. Hornblende-plagioclase-diopside
12. Hornblende-bytownite-almandine
D. Magnesian; deficient in silica:
13. Enstatite-forsterite-chlorite*-spinel. This is metamorphosed serpentinite.
14. Hornblende-hypersthene-spinel

In an extensive pendant near Isabella (5 in Fig. 8-12), the rocks are mainly pelitic. There are some associated basic and calcareous assemblages typical of the hornblende-hornfels facies. Best and Weiss (1964) have recognized four zones of progressive metamorphism of pelitic rocks, the grade increasing from deep within the pendant toward the exposed contacts with the enclosing granodiorite. Typical assemblages in order of increasing grade, are:

1. Quartz-muscovite-chlorite-hematite. This is the preintrusive regional meta-morphic assemblage.
2. Quartz-muscovite-biotite-andalusite-ilmenite.[†]
3. Quartz-biotite-andalusite (sillimanite)-oligoclase-microcline-ilmenite.
4. Quartz-biotite-sillimanite-cordierite-plagioclase (An_{20}–An_{37})-microcline-ilmenite. Almandine may also be present or may occur to the exclusion of cordierite.

Increase in metamorphic grade is accompanied by decreasing oxidation of iron. In assemblage 2, ilmenite appears in place of hematite and remains the sole iron-oxide phase to the highest grade of metamorphism. In biotites, the oxidation ratio (molecular)

---

*Approximately $Mg_{5 1/2} Al_{1/2} (Al_{1/2} Si_{3 1/2} O_{10})(OH)_8$.
†Composition of accompanying feldspars not recorded for assemblages 1 and 2.

$$\frac{2FeO_3 \times 100}{2Fe_2O_3 + FeO}$$

decreases from 17.8 in assemblage 2 to 11.0 in assemblage 3 to between 1.9 and 4.2 in assemblages 4. Figure 8-14 is an $A'F'M'$ plot of coexisting analyzed biotites, cordierites, and garnets in three high-grade quartz-ilmenite-bearing assemblages of type 4 above:

Biotite-sillimanite-almandine-perthite-plagioclase (An_{25}) (stippled triangle *a*)
Biotite-sillimanite-cordierite-perthite-plagioclase (An_{21}–An_{37}) (stippled triangle *b*)
Biotite-andalusite-cordierite-almandine-plagioclase (An_{24}–An_{30}) (quadrilateral *c* bounded by broken lines)

Some 8–10 km southeast of the foothills town of Sonora (locality 3, Fig. 8-12; Standard area of Kerrick, 1970) rocks of the outer aureole are pelitic schists (quartz-muscovite-biotite-plagioclase) and dolomitic marbles. Within 500 m of the granodiorite contact (Kerrick's sillimanite zone) the general pelitic assemblage is quartz-sillimanite-biotite-muscovite-plagioclase-K-feldspar with or without garnet. Metavolcanic (amphibolite) lenses consist of hornblende-plagioclase (-biotite-garnet-muscovite). Calcareous tectonic inclusions in the metapelites are concentrically zoned: from the outside inward (in one mass ~2 m in diameter).

Actinolite-clinozoisite-quartz
Actinolite-diopside-clinozoisite-quartz
Calcite-dolomite-clinohumite

Also recorded is the assemblage (in textural equilibrium) quartz-wollastonite-calcite.

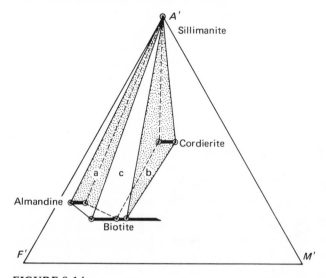

FIGURE 8-14
Hornblende-hornfels facies, Isabella pendant, Sierra Nevada, California. $A'F'M'$ diagram for high-grade pelitic assemblages. Quartz, ilmenite, microcline, and plagioclase are possible additional phases.

Calcitic and dolomitic marbles and related calcsilicate hornfelses and skarns are the main components of a group of roof pendants, typically 1–3 km long, strung out along the axis of the Sierra at elevations of 2000–3000 m. Examples referred to below are numbered as follows in Fig. 8-12: 6, Ebbett Pass (Hope Valley) area (Parker, 1961; Kerrick et al., 1973); 7, Tioga Pass (Kerrick, 1970); 8, May Lake (Rose, 1958); and 9, Twin Lakes (Chesterman, 1942; Kerrick et al., 1973).

Calcareous assemblages in pendants of the Ebbett Pass (Hope Valley) area are derivatives of essentially nondolomitic limestones with Al-Si impurities. They include most five- and six-phase combinations of calcite, wollastonite, diopside, grossularite,* plagioclase, scapolite, clinozoisite, and quartz, some with vesuvianite as an additional phase (plagioclase-calcite-diopside triangle of Fig. 8-15). Kerrick et al. (1973) have explored the possible implications of variation in $X^{gas}_{H_2O}$ and $X^{gas}_{CO_2}$ in the development of this paragenesis. At Tioga Pass calcareous assemblages are simpler (lacking vesuvianite and scapolite). Here the general calcsilicate-hornfels assemblage is epidote-actinolite-diopside-grossularite (cf. Fig. 8-16f). That of marbles (in which calcite is the only carbonate) is calcite-grossularite-wollastonite-diopside.

Assemblages in dolomitic marbles are well displayed in the Twin Lakes and May Lake pendants. The paragenesis in the former locality (Fig. 8-16), where silicates and oxides occur as knots in a carbonate base, includes simple combinations such as

*As elsewhere in the Sierran province, Ebbett Pass grossularite carries a significant concentration (mostly 10–20 percent) of andradite.

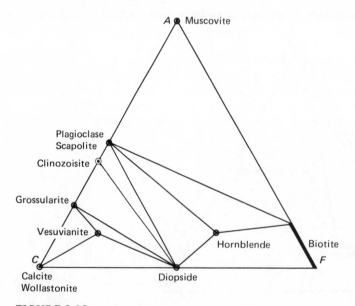

FIGURE 8-15
Hornblende-hornfels facies, Ebbett Pass (Hope Valley) pendants, Sierra Nevada, California. Assemblages in rocks with excess SiO_2 and K_2O. Quartz and (less often) microcline are possible additional phases.

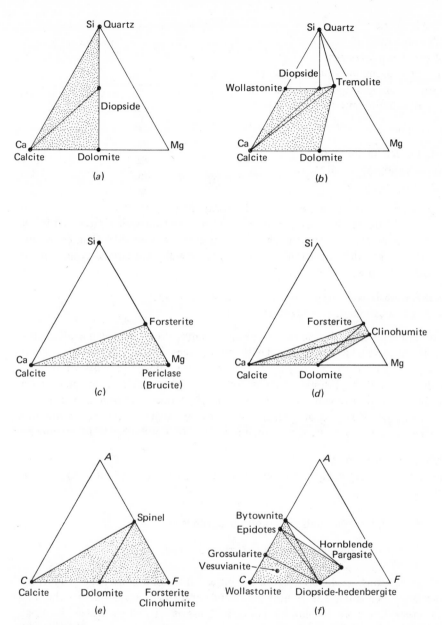

FIGURE 8-16

Paragenesis at individual localities, Twin Lakes, Sierra Nevada, California. (*a*) to (*e*) Dolomitic marbles; calcsilicate (skarn assemblages with quartz and phlogopite are also possible); (*f*) stippled areas and ties, observed assemblages; in (*d*) and (*e*), four phases commonly coexist.

Diopside-calcite
Wollastonite-calcite
Wollastonite-quartz-calcite
Forsterite-clinohumite-spinel-dolomite
Forsterite-clinohumite-dolomite-calcite
Forsterite-clinohumite-spinel-calcite

Less common are

Tremolite-calcite-dolomite
Tremolite-diopside-calcite
Forsterite-periclase*-calcite

Pargasite and phlogopite are common additional phases.

Coexisting pelitic and metavolcanic assemblages are well represented in the Ebbett Pass pendants where the paragenesis is chemically broader than elsewhere. Here (Fig. 8-15) they conform to the pattern generally considered typical of the hornblende-hornfels facies:

Quartz-plagioclase-biotite-muscovite-microcline
Quartz-plagioclase-hornblende (-microcline)

At other localities, with a single exception (Loomis, 1966), hornblende-plagioclase is a ubiquitous metavolcanic pair. Pelitic assemblages, on the other hand, while in some places similar to that of Ebbett Pass, more typically (especially within a few hundred meters of plutonic contacts) reflect a higher metamorphic grade more typical of the pyroxene-hornfels facies. Typical of this condition, found at May Lake and Tioga Pass, is quartz-andalusite-biotite-muscovite-microcline (-cordierite). Also recorded at Tioga Pass is corundum-andalusite-biotite-plagioclase-microcline.

General Facies Series

The Sierran contact paragenesis conforms with remarkable consistency to a general facies series

Albite-epidote-hornfels → hornblende-hornfels

→ transition facies (toward pyroxene-hornfels)

The first facies is developed only on the outer fringes of aureoles and deep within some larger pendants. The typical hornblende-hornfels facies dominates the total paragenesis; but close to plutonic contacts it passes (as first recognized by Rose, 1958) into a well-defined facies transitional toward pyroxene-hornfels. In this the metavolcanic hornblende-plagioclase assemblage still persists, but it is now associated with high-grade pelitic assemblages carrying cordierite, andalusite (sillimanite), and microcline, with wollastonite-bearing marbles, and with magnesian marbles carrying forsterite, clinohumite, and rarely periclase (subsequently hydrated to brucite). All these overlap into the pyroxene-hornfels facies.

---

*Completely pseudomorphed by brucite.

PYROXENE–HORNFELS FACIES

Field Occurrence

Rocks of this facies occur in the inner zones of contact aureoles. Favorable conditions are shallow depth of cover and high temperature (as inferred from proximity to plutonic contacts, particularly where the intrusive rock is basic or semibasic in composition). Mineralogically similar rocks in areas of regional metamorphism have distinctive features that place them in a low-pressure division of the granulite facies rather than in the pyroxene-hornfels facies proper.

Oslo Region, Norway

Goldschmidt's (1911a) account of contact metamorphism in the Oslo district is one of the classics of petrology. The aureoles are developed round small plutons of essexite, sodic syenites, and granites where these cut Paleozoic pelitic, arenaceous, and calcareous sediments. In most aureoles the assemblages of the pyroxene-hornfels facies are confined to an inner zone that is flanked on the outside by rocks of the hornblende-hornfels facies. From stratigraphic evidence Goldschmidt computed the load pressure at the time of metamorphism as between 400 and 1000 bars. The Oslo paragenesis is of special interest in that it is the type of Eskola's original hornfels facies (now the pyroxene-hornfels facies). Goldschmidt recognized 10 principal assemblages (cf. Fig. 8-17a) any of which may contain both quartz and K-feldspar.

A. Pelitic and quartzo-feldspathic:
    1. Quartz-orthoclase-andalusite-cordierite (-biotite)
    2. Quartz-orthoclase-plagioclase-andalusite-cordierite (-biotite)
    3. Quartz-orthoclase-plagioclase-cordierite (-biotite)
    4. Quartz-orthoclase-plagioclase-cordierite-hypersthene
B. Calcareous:
    8. Plagioclase-diopside-grossularite
    9. Diopside-grossularite (-vesuvianite)
    10. Diopside-grossularite-wollastonite (-vesuvianite)

It has been generally assumed, following Goldschmidt (1911a), that grossularite-quartz is stable in the pyroxene-hornfels facies. This combination is common enough in calcareous assemblages of the hornblende-hornfels facies. Moreover, such assemblages as grossularite-diopside-wollastonite and grossularite-diopside-plagioclase have been recorded in association with high-grade marbles (calcite-forsterite-diopside, calcite-forsterite-periclase) in the inner zones of some aureoles (e.g., Osborne, 1932). But most such rocks contain calcite and lack quartz. And although the grade of contact metamorphism is high, these grossularite-bearing assemblages are rarely, if ever, found in close association with the diagnostic basic assemblage plagioclase-diopside-hypersthene. Further ambiguity arises from the variable andradite content of metamorphic grossularite and the albite content of even the more calcic plagioclases. Anorthite-wollastonite, the chemically equivalent assemblage to grossularite-quartz, has long been considered characteristic of the

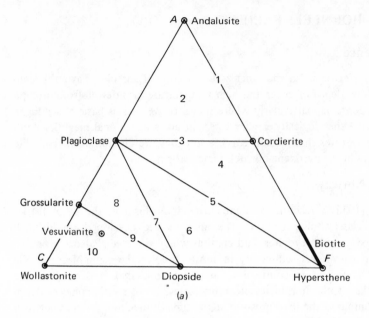

(a)

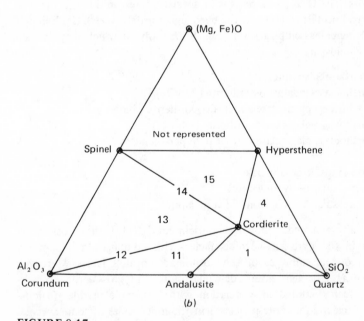

(b)

FIGURE 8-17
Pyroxene-hornfels facies. (a) Oslo, Norway: ACF diagram for assemblages with excess SiO_2 and K_2O: quartz and potash feldspar are possible additional phases. (b) Comrie, Scotland: three-phase assemblages in aluminous rocks; orthoclase, biotite, and plagioclase are possible additional phases.

sanidinite facies. Experimental reversal of the equilibrium

Grossularite + quartz ⇌ anorthite + wollastonite

by Newton (1966) at $T = 600°C$, $P = 2$ kb supports the possibility that in the pyroxene-hornfels facies, the stable assemblage of *pure phases* is anorthite-wollastonite, not grossularite-quartz. Andesine-wollastonite-diopside has been recorded in association with grossularite-plagioclase assemblages in high-grade hornfelses of uncertain facies (Osborne, 1932, pp. 223–224; Harker, 1932, p. 94; Kerrick et al., 1973, pp. 321, 322).

C. Basic:
    5. Plagioclase-hypersthene (-quartz)
    6. Plagioclase-diopside-hypersthene (-quartz)
    7. Plagioclase-diopside (-quartz)

Comrie Aureole, Scotland

Near Comrie (Perthshire, Scotland), the Carn Chois diorite pluton has imposed a zoned contact aureole on the adjacent low-grade phyllites and slates of the Dalradian series as described in Chap. 1. Tilley's (1924a) account of the mineralogy and chemistry of the resulting hornfelses in the innermost zone of the aureole is still one of the clearest discussions of high-grade contact metamorphism.

The dominant mineral assemblages are pelitic and semipelitic types carrying quartz and feldspar. They duplicate precisely corresponding assemblages in the Oslo aureoles (1 to 5 and 7 in Fig. 8-17a). Again, the polymorph of Al_2SiO_5 is andalusite, and again muscovite has been eliminated in favor of andalusite-orthoclase. Basic igneous assemblages in the outer zone consist of hornblende-plagioclase-biotite (hornblende-hornfels facies). Within about 150–200 m of the contact, this assemblage gives way to that typical of the pyroxene-hornfels facies—diopside-hypersthene-plagioclase.

There is also an interesting series of aluminous silica-deficient hornfelses in which corundum and spinel appear in place of, or associated with, andalusite and cordierite. These rocks generally contain orthoclase, plagioclase, biotite, and magnetite as well. Recorded assemblages (cf. Fig. 8-17b) include

11. Andalusite-cordierite-corundum
12. Corundum-cordierite
13. Corundum-cordierite-spinel (the commonest assemblage)
14. Cordierite-spinel
15. Cordierite-spinel-hypersthene

The high-temperature paragenesis of the Comrie aureole represents temperatures and pressures outside the stability fields not only of muscovite-quartz but of muscovite alone. Tilley finds clear evidence that biotite too is beginning to break down to assemblages with cordierite, cordierite-hypersthene, or spinel-magnetite-cordierite. The recorded products (hercynite-spinel and magnetite) agree with experimental findings that ferrous biotites, approaching annite, are likely to decompose at rather high metamorphic temperatures to give sanidine, magnetite, and simple ferrous silicates (fayalite under experimental conditions; hypersthene and cordierite in the Comrie assemblages). Since oxidation of Fe^{2+} to Fe^{3+} is involved in most such reactions, they must be sensitive not only to temperature and P_{H_2O} but also to f_{O_2}. Presumably assemblages containing hercynite-magnetite-ilmenite in addition to biotite, cordierite, and orthoclase must have been internally buffered to some constant f_{O_2} at any given temperature. Simplified possible versions of the complex breakdown reactions involving dehydration of biotite at temperatures outside the stability field of muscovite are

(1) $K_2 Fe_6^{2+}(Al_2 Si_6 O_{20})(OH)_4 + O_2 \rightarrow 2KAlSi_3 O_8 + 2Fe_3 O_4 + 2H_2 O$
   biotite (annite)   orthoclase   magnetite

(2) $K_2 Mg_2 Fe_3^{2+}Al(Al_3 Si_5 O_{20})(OH)_4 + 6Al_2 SiO_5 \rightarrow 2KAlSi_3 O_8$
   biotite   andalusite   orthoclase

   $+ Al_3 Mg_2 (Si_5 AlO_{18}) + 2Al_2 O_3 + 3FeAl_2 O_4 + 2H_2 O$
   cordierite   corundum   hercynite

Lochnagar Aureole, Scotland

In the Oslo and Comrie aureoles almandine is a notable absentee, and at one time it was thought that absence of garnets of this composition is characteristic of the pyroxene-hornfels facies. More recently it has come to be recognized that almandine is not uncommon in high-grade contact metamorphic assemblages, but that it is restricted to rocks with a relatively high FeO/MgO ratio (Turner and Verhoogen, 1960, p. 522). The role of almandine in relation to the more widespread cordierite-biotite pair in pelitic assemblages of the pyroxene-hornfels facies has been clearly documented by Chinner's (1962) account of the Lochnagar aureole in the Highlands of Scotland. The Lochnagar pluton is essentially dioritic. It is one of many posttectonic, late Caledonian intrusions, and it has developed an aureole, up to 3 km in width, in Dalradian metasediments that had previously reached an advanced grade of regional metamorphism. The initial pelitic assemblage thus was quartz-oligoclase-biotite-almandine-sillimanite (-magnetite-hematite), with a high oxidation ratio (probably >40). In places, it has been obliterated by migmatitization (Ashworth and Chinner, 1978, p. 382).

   In the innermost part of the aureole, amphibolites have recrystallized to the typical pyroxene-hornfels assemblage plagioclase-diopside-hypersthene. Siliceous marbles are represented by calcite-wollastonite assemblages. Pelitic rocks duplicate the quartz-bearing and silica-deficient assemblages of the Comrie aureole, except that the $Al_2 SiO_5$ polymorph is sillimanite; they invariably contain biotite, cordierite, and K-feldspar in association with any of the two- and three-phase associations shown in Fig. 8-18a Iron-oxide phases other than spinel (hercynite) have been eliminated during metamorphism. The oxidation ratio in the completely recrystallized hornfels is invariably low (<2), showing that metamorphism involved reactions of reduction. Silica-deficient assemblages include combinations of K-feldspar, corundum, and spinel.

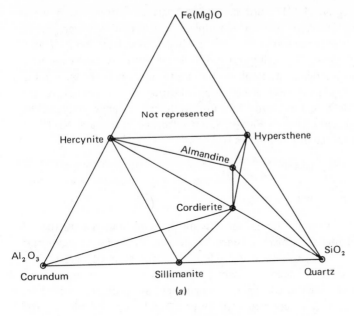

(a)

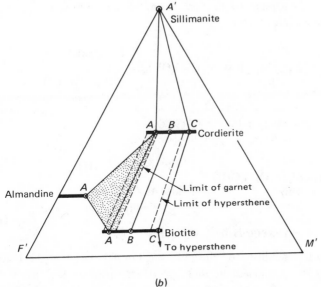

(b)

FIGURE 8-18

Pyroxene-hornfels facies, Lochnagar aureole, Scotland. (*a*) Coexisting phases in pelitic horn-felses; orthoclase and biotite can be present in all assemblages. (*b*) $A'F'M'$ diagram for phase assemblages coexisting with orthoclase (and other minerals). Circled points are analyzed min-erals. Broken ties show compositions of phases estimated from refractive indices. Stippled area shows limits of composition field for garnetiferous assemblages.

Figure 8-18*b* is an $A'F'M'$ plot coexisting analyzed cordierites, biotites, and garnet (Chinner, 1962, p. 323). The stippled field is that in which garnet, cordierite, and biotite (composition *A*) are mutually associated with quartz, orthoclase, and plagioclase. Cordierite and biotite *C* are mutually associated with hypersthene in a silica-deficient assemblage. Refractive index data (broken ties in Fig. 8-18*b*) show that in all assemblages, quartz-bearing or silica-deficient, the respective ratios of MgO/FeO in biotite vary uniformly in the manner indicated by the ties between analyzed phases in Fig. 8-18. With decrease in the ratio MgO/FeO the compositional sequence of assemblages is

Biotite-cordierite-hypersthene-spinel
Biotite-cordierite-quartz
Biotite-cordierite-quartz-garnet

The composition field of garnetiferous rocks is much more limited than that of the garnet-bearing high-grade schists outside the aureole. Rocks in the outer part of the aureole whose MgO/FeO ratio exceeds that of the stippled field of Fig. 8-18*b* show clear textural evidence of reaction between garnet and surrounding minerals. Garnet may be seen in all stages of replacement by cordierite, orthoclase, and biotite, wherever it is in contact with biotite, quartz, and sillimanite. The kind of reaction that is suggested by Chinner is one of dehydration and reduction. It might perhaps be expressed thus:

$$4K_2(Mg_{2\,1/2}Fe^{2+}_{2\,1/2}Fe^{3+}_{1/2}Al_{1/2})(Al_3Si_5O_{20})(OH)_4 + \begin{cases} 8Fe_3Al_2Si_3O_{12} \\ 2Mg_3Al_2Si_3O_{12} \end{cases}$$

biotite   garnet

$$+ 27Al_2SiO_5 + 47SiO_2 + H_2 \rightarrow 4KAlSi_3O_8$$

sillimanite   quartz   orthoclase

$$+ 2K_2MgFe^{2+}_5(Al_2Si_6O_{20})(OH)_4 + \begin{cases} 13Fe_2Al_3(AlSi_5O_{18}) \\ 7Mg_2Al_3(AlSi_5O_{18}) \end{cases} + 5H_2O$$

biotite   cordierite

Basic Assemblages of Pyroxene-Hornfels Facies

A characteristic mineral assemblage of the pyroxene-hornfels facies in the Oslo and Comrie aureoles is plagioclase-diopside-hypersthene (-quartz). This and silica-deficient assemblages of rather similar composition have been described in detail from other aureoles and from xenolithic blocks that have been subjected to unusually high temperature by total immersion in granitic magmas.

The aureole of the Tertiary Cuillin gabbro on the Scottish island of Skye illustrates the effects of contact metamorphism on a series of alkali basaltic lavas including some picritic types. Within 200 to 400 m of the gabbro contact these have been converted—probably with slight addition of silica—to three types of hornfels (Almond, 1964):

Plagioclase-clinopyroxene-olivine
Plagioclase-clinopyroxene-hypersthene
Plagioclase-hypersthene

Opaque ores are present in all three assemblages. Plagioclase is An_{50} to An_{65}.

The above is one of many examples of the formation of two-pyroxene hornfelses from basaltic lavas in aureoles generated by gabbro intrusions in the Hebridean Tertiary igneous province. According to MacGregor (1931) the usual assemblage is clinopyroxene-labradorite-olivine-magnetite; biotite and/or hypersthene may also be present. MacGregor recorded the composition of the olivine phase as being near to fayalite in many rocks. Basic assemblages very deficient in silica recorded by Thomas (1930, pp. 237, 308, 316) from the Ardnamurchan aureoles, include

Spinel-anorthite-hypersthene-olivine
Spinel-anorthite-diopside-olivine
Anorthite-hypersthene-diopside-olivine

Compositions of coexisting pyroxenes and olivines in several basic assemblages of the pyroxene-hornfels facies from the Hebridean province have been recorded by Muir and Tilley (1958). These are shown as tie lines in Fig. 8-19. The tie CC (Muir and Tilley, 1958, pp. 404, 405, OO') represents the pair diopside-hypersthene in a basic hornfels from the Oslo area. In the two olivine-bearing hornfelses from Scotland (A, B, Fig. 8-19), the orthopyroxene is more magnesian than the associated olivine. As pointed out by Almond (1964, p. 425) this relation is that predicted on experimental grounds by Bowen and Schairer (1935, p. 213) for equilibrium at low pressures.

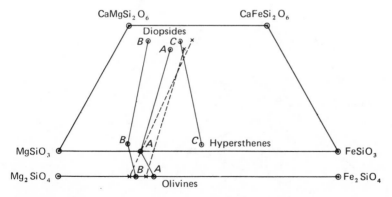

FIGURE 8-19

Pyroxene-hornfels facies. Coexisting pyroxenes and olivines in basic hornfelses: A, B: Hebridean province, Scotland; C: Oslo. Broken lines show coexisting pyroxene and olivine in basic lavas from which was derived hornfels A (data from I. D. Muir and C. F. Tilley [B, C] and from D. C. Almond [A]).

Silica-Deficient Calcareous Assemblages in Pyroxene-Hornfels Facies

Among the many accounts of contact metamorphism of slightly impure calcite and dolomite marbles, few record unequivocally the simultaneous appearance of plagioclase-diopside-hypersthene in associated basic rocks. So we are frequently in doubt as to whether the familiar silica-deficient assemblages in marbles should be assigned to the pyroxene-hornfels or to the hornblende-hornfels facies. The assemblages shown in Fig. 8-20 are those most widely developed in the innermost zones of relatively shallow aureoles, especially in the vicinity of dioritic rather than granitic plutons. With K_2O and Al_2O_3 as additional components, there appear such primary assemblages as the following (recorded by Joplin, 1935, from a contact between dolomitic limestones and a dioritic pluton at Ben Bullen, Australia).

1. Calcite-periclase-forsterite-spinel
2a. Calcite-forsterite-spinel
2b. Calcite-forsterite-spinel-phlogopite
3. Calcite-forsterite-diopside-phlogopite

As is usual in high-grade magnesian assemblages, periclase has been partially or completely replaced by pseudomorphs of brucite; in some rocks forsterite is partly replaced by antigorite-brucite. These changes are an expectable consequence of reaction with gas ($X_{H_2O}^{gas}$ high compared with $X_{CO_2}^{gas}$) during postmetamorphic cooling. The brucite pseudomorphs in the Ben Bullen marbles, as has also been observed elsewhere (Turner, 1965, p. 396), are rimmed with clear dolomite. The reaction sequence with falling temperature has been

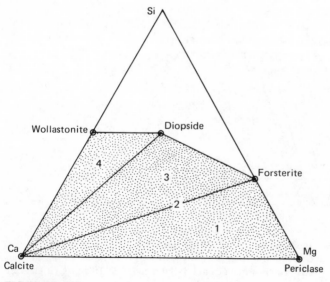

FIGURE 8-20

Pyroxene-hornfels facies. Simple silica-deficient assemblages (stippled) in the triangle calcite-dolomite-silica.

(1) $MgO + H_2O \rightarrow Mg(OH)_2$
        periclase   brucite

(2) $Mg(OH)_2 + CaCO_3 + CO_2 \rightarrow CaMg(CO_3)_2 + H_2O$
        brucite   calcite   dolomite

At the high temperatures reasonably assumed for the pyroxene-hornfels facies, there is no reason why minerals such as monticellite, and even melilite and spurrite, should not appear in slightly siliceous dolomites and marbles. Thermochemical and experimental data show that these extreme steps in Bowen's reaction sequence are likely to occur at temperatures on either side of that of the periclase reaction (cf. Fig. 4-7). The necessary condition (as also for formation of periclase) is that the partial pressure of CO_2 be maintained continuously at a low level (perhaps no more than 50 bars) by free influx of water from the cooling pluton. In the innermost zone of the contact aureole of the Cuillin gabbro, Skye, plagioclase-hypersthene-diopside (-olivine) hornfelses derived from basic lavas are locally associated with marbles containing rankinite and spurrite. There is no reason to assign these assemblages to the sanidinite rather than to the pyroxene-hornfels facies. The significant inference is that metamorphism took place at high temperature (perhaps no more than $700°C$) and under conditions such that, whatever the total fluid pressure may have been, P_{CO_2} never exceeded a few tens of bars. To what facies the assemblage is assigned is immaterial.

Metasomatic Calc-Magnesian Assemblages, Crestmore, California

One of the clearest available accounts of high-grade metamorphism and metasomatism of slightly impure dolomites and limestones is Burnham's (1959) discussion of the complex paragenesis at Crestmore, California. Here there were two episodes of metamorphism. First, masses of limestone around 100 m thick were engulfed in a quartz-diorite pluton and converted to nearly pure calcite marble and to periclase (brucite) marble. The mineral assemblages where silica was locally available conform to those of Fig. 8-20. Subsequently the marbles so formed were invaded by a pipe of quartz-monzonite porphyry. Aqueous fluids from the porphyry magma introduced silica, alumina, magnesia, and iron into what is now a zoned silicated aureole 15 m in width. The influx of water was sufficiently rapid to maintain f_{CO_2} at a low level. In consequence high-grade minerals such as monticellite, merwinite, and spurrite, as well as a number of hydrous silicates (clinohumite, xanthophyllite) appear in various combinations in the aureole. The latter is roughly zoned, the sequence away from the contact being

1. Grossularite-wollastonite-diopside
2. Vesuvianite
3. Monticellite with various combinations of clinohumite, forsterite, melilite, spurrite, tilleyite, spinel, etc.
4. Marble and brucite-marble

The zones of the aureole express a metasomatically imposed composition gradient rather than a gradient in temperature or pressure conditions. Each zone

has developed at the expense of the assemblage now represented in the zone immediately outside it. The principal assemblages along a traverse from the marble
into and across the monticellite zone approximate the following sequence, which
can be represented in terms of the $CaO-MgO-SiO_2 \cdot Al_2O_3$ tetrahedron. These
are shown in Fig. 8-21, on the $CaO-MgO-SiO_2$ triangle, omitting the coexisting
aluminous phases (italicized below)

1. Calcite-periclase (brucite)-clinohumite-*spinel*
2. Calcite-clinohumite-forsterite-*spinel*
3. Calcite-forsterite-*spinel* (*-xanthophyllite*)
4. Calcite-forsterite-monticellite (*-xanthophyllite*)
5. Calcite-monticellite-*melilite* (*xanthophyllite*)
6. Calcite-monticellite-spurrite (or tilleyite)-*melilite*
7. Monticellite-spurite-merwinite-*melilite*

This sequence, starting from brucite marble *P*, is represented in Fig. 8-21 by
analyzed rocks lying along the line *PM*. The same sequence of assemblages has
developed where the starting material is pure calcite marble.

  With full attainment of assemblage 7, carbonate phases have been eliminated.
Further metasomatism in the vesuvianite and grossularite zones approximates the
sequence

7a. *Vesuvianite*-monticellite-spurrite-merwinite-*melilite*
 8. *Vesuvianite*-monticellite-diopside-wollastonite (*grossularite*)
 9. *Grossularite*-diopside-wollastonite

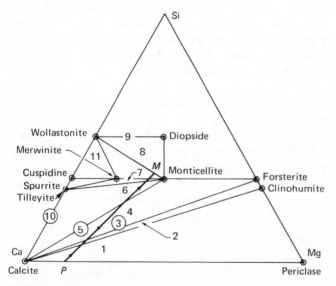

FIGURE 8-21

Pyroxene-hornfels facies, Crestmore, California. Silica-deficient assemblages in the triangle
calcite-dolomite-silica. *PM* represents the path of metasomatism from brucite-calcite marble
into and through the monticellite zone (after C. W. Burnham—simplified).

Assemblage 10, calcite-spurrite, is found in the outer part of the aureole in contact with pure calcite marble. This and the assemblages approximating 11, spurrite-merwinite (cuspidine-wollastonite), represent the rare case where silicon is the only metasomatically introduced element. The usual case is that in which early introduction of magnesium as well as silicon diverts the compositional trend into triangle 6 of Fig. 8-21.

Burnham's study has demonstrated that the mineral assemblages—contrary to a view once generally held (Harker, 1932, p. 95; Turner and Verhoogen, 1951, p. 377)—closely approximate bivariant equilibrium* attained by irreversible reactions in systems open to many components, for example,

$$\underset{\text{forsterite}}{Mg_2SiO_4} + \underset{\text{calcite}}{2CaCO_3} + \underset{\text{(in solution)}}{SiO_2} \rightarrow \underset{\text{monticellite}}{2CaMgSiO_4} + 2CO_2$$

SANIDINITE FACIES

General Characteristics

The sanidinite facies was erected by Eskola to cover mineral assemblages whose mineralogical composition and geologic occurrence show that they have formed at maximum temperatures and minimum pressures of metamorphism (cf. Eskola, 1939, p. 347). They are represented by xenoliths in basic lavas (or near-surface intrusions), by fragments in tuffs, and by the rocks of narrow contact zones bordering shallow basic pipes and necks. In this latter situation, unusually high temperatures have been maintained by continuous flow of magma along the contact.

The geologic occurrence of the sanidinite facies is insignificant compared with that of the other facies of contact metamorphism. But it shows some interesting and unusual features of mineral paragenesis. Some of the characteristic phases are analogous with products of crystallization from melts at atmospheric pressure: tridymite, mullite, monticellite, forsterite, larnite, and so on. The characteristic alkaline phase is sanidine, commonly a variety rich in Na. Cordierite, wollastonite (usually containing excess Mg or Fe^{2+}), and anorthite are all typical of siliceous assemblages. Micas, amphiboles, and garnets are absent. The only carbonate mineral is calcite. Some of the principal phase assemblages of the sanidinite facies, as recorded by Eskola (1939, pp. 347–349) are shown graphically in Figs. 8-22 and 8-23.

Quartzo-feldspathic and pelitic rocks in the sanidinite facies in most cases have been brought to the point of partial fusion. These are buchites: rocks in which minerals such as cordierite, corundum, mullite, or tridymite are enclosed in glass. When the crystalline phases are minerals not normally found in common igneous rocks, it is customary to consider the assemblage as metamorphic, in the sanidinite facies. But quartzo-feldspathic rocks at only slightly higher pressures may become

---

*There are expectable departures. For example, two intergrown phases may be seen in process of replacing a third. Again, an anhydrous equilibrium assemblage may have been partially converted to hydrous phases during postmetamorphic cooling (e.g., forsterite → serpentine + brucite).

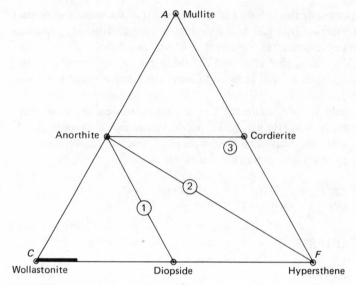

FIGURE 8-22
Sanidinite facies. ACF diagram for rocks with excess SiO_2 and K_2O (after P. Eskola).

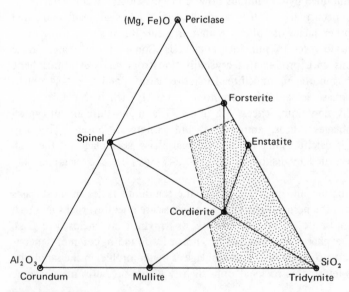

FIGURE 8-23
Sanidinite facies. Assemblages in the triangle $MgO-Al_2O_3-SiO_2$ (after P. Eskola). Field of pelitic rocks stippled.

converted to what can only be considered igneous products, namely granophyres. Even at near-surface pressures metamorphic merge into igneous rocks via the sanidinite facies.

Pelitic and Quartzo-Feldspathic Assemblages

Classic examples of the sanidinite facies paragenesis are the suites of pelitic xenoliths in trachyte tuffs of the Laacher See region, German Eifel (Brauns, 1911), and in minor tholeiitic intrusions on the Scottish island of Mull (Thomas, 1922). The Laacher See rocks have been modified by the pneumatolytic introduction of sodium, and include various combinations of sanidine, cordierite, spinel, hypersthene, and sillimanite. Many of the rocks have not reached equilibrium at low pressure and contain unstable relics—garnet and staurolite—inherited from an earlier facies. In the Mull xenoliths, representative assemblages are corundum-spinel-anorthite, cordierite-spinel-mullite, cordierite-glass, and mullite-glass. In quartzo-feldspathic xenoliths in the Mull suite, tridymite has crystallized around nuclei of unfused quartz enclosed in glass.

Generally similar assemblages have been described and excellently illustrated by Searle (1962) from the quasi-Recent basaltic province of Auckland, New Zealand. The agent of metamorphism is alkaline olivine basalt. The metamorphic rocks are xenoliths in lava flows and pyroclastic deposits and baked silts (porcellanites) intercalated between or underlying surface flows. So this is a clearly demonstrated case of metamorphism at near-atmospheric pressure. As is usually the case in the sanidinite facies, reciprocal diffusion has modified both the metamorphic rock and the immediately adjacent basalt magma. The result is relative enrichment of the metamorphic rock in Ca, Mg, and Fe, with complementary loss of Si and Al. The principal metamorphic assemblages are mullite-glass, cordierite-mullite-glass, cordierite-mullite, cordierite-quartz, cordierite-plagioclase(calcic)-sanidine-clinopyroxene, sanidine-clinopyroxene-hematite-glass. The sanidine is the high-temperature polymorph. Quartz in many assemblages (e.g., in the sanidinites) appears to have inverted from tridymite that had crystallized in the first place from glass.

Basic Assemblages

There are many records of basic hornfelses formed by recrystallization of basalt on the walls of conduits or in shallow basalt magma chambers. Xenoliths of such material in the Auckland basalts (Searle, 1962) consist essentially of calcic plagioclase and hypersthene. Ejected bocks from the walls of the Kilauea crater vent in Hawaii (Muir and Tilley, 1958) consist of plagioclase(An_{62})-augite-hypersthene, with minor pseudobrookite and tridymite. Relict phenocrysts of olivine are in process of conversion to hypersthene-magnetite by a reaction involving oxidation of iron.

Agrell and Langley (1958) have recorded a suite of unusual mineral assemblages resulting from low-pressure metamorphism of basalt and its associated weathering products, adjacent to and within a Tertiary plug of olivine diabase in Antrim, Ireland:

1. Olivine-clinopyroxene-plagioclase-magnetite-ilmenite
2. Hypersthene-plagioclase-magnetite-ilmenite-pseudobrookite
3. Cordierite-plagioclase-magnetite-hematite-pseudobrookite-tridymite (or cristo-balite)-mullite

The sequence 1 to 3 (numbered as in Fig. 8-22) represents premetamorphic compositional changes from olivine basalt to a montmorillonitic weathering product (bole). A second suite of assemblages, very rich in Al and Fe and deficient in Si, has formed by marginal metamorphism of an engulfed block of porcellanite. This represents an initial lateritic weathering product of basalt

4a. Corundum-hematite)
 b. Corundum-mullite-hematite } + pseudobrookite
 c. Mullite-hematite-cristobalite (or tridymite)) + magnetite
5a. Corundum-hercynite-ilmenite-magnetite
 b. Corundum-mullite-hercynite-ilmenite-magnetite
 c. Mullite-hercynite-cristobalite (or tridymite)
 d. Mullite-hercynite-cordierite-cristobalite (or tridymite)
 e. Mullite-cordierite-cristobalite (or tridymite)

Assemblages in 4 are highly oxidized; both corundum and mullite carry significant Fe^{3+}. Assemblages in 5, which occur closer to the contact, have been reduced to a comparatively low oxidation ratio; corundum and mullite are normal. Cordierite appears in assemblages with appreciable MgO (cf. Fig. 8-23).

Calcareous Assemblages

According to Eskola (1939, p. 348) the characteristic silica-saturated assemblages in calcareous rocks are combinations of wollastonite, anorthite, and diopside. Grossularite, which is so common in hornfelses of other facies, is a notable absentee. In its place appears the pair anorthite-wollastonite. This assemblage, once thought to be critical of the sanidinite facies, has now been recorded, with associated quartz, in situations that indicate pressures certainly much higher than those of the sanidinite facies. It has been observed in some granite aureoles in the Californian Coast Ranges (e.g., near Inverness, north of San Francisco), and is widely developed adjacent to granite plutons on Nanga Parbat, in the Himalayas (Misch, 1964).* Anorthite-wollastonite may also prove to be characteristic of the pyroxene-hornfels facies (cf. p. 275).

Silica-deficient marbles and dolomitic marbles in the sanidinite facies display mineral assemblages unique in metamorphic paragenesis. At Scawt Hill in northern Ireland, chalk with enclosed nodules of flint has been metamorphosed at the contact with an intrusion of diabase. The assemblages developed by reaction between flint and calcite have been recorded in detail by Tilley (e.g., 1929, 1942). They correspond to the products of the later steps in Bowen's (1940) sequence of progressive reactions, with rankinite, $Ca_3Si_2O_5$, as an additional phase. Since

---

*Whether or not Misch is correct in interpreting this granitic massif as a product of granitization representing the culmination of deep regional metamorphism of the Barrovian type, pressures must have been much higher than those of the near-surface sanidinite facies.

reaction has involved the outward diffusion of Si from the chert nodule and the inward diffusion of Ca and Mg from the chalk, each metamorphosed nodule is now concentrically zoned as to composition and mineral paragenesis. The full inward sequence follows the three-phase triangles 1 to 4 in Fig. 8-24. Magnesian variants include merwinite, melilite or monticellite, as shown in Fig. 8-24. Where aluminum and iron are present, they are represented by melilite and/or pleonaste. While melilite, spurrite, and monticellite rarely appear in the pyroxene-hornfels facies (presumably where $X_{CO_2}^{gas}$ values have been kept at a low level), larnite and rankinite have not yet been recorded outside the sanidinite facies.

A remarkable paragenesis occurs in blocks of limestone engulfed in flows of leucite tephrite near Mayen in the Laacher See region (Jasmund and Hentschel, 1964). These rocks have a very high ratio Ca/Mg (mostly 20–50) and contain 10–20 percent SiO_2 and a few percent each of Fe_2O_3 and Al_2O_3. Neglecting late hydrated phases such as afwillite and portlandite, there are two groups of assemblages.

1. Wollastonite-melilite-magnetite (or spinel)
2a. Calcite-brownmillerite (± mayenite)
 b. Calcite-larnite-brownmillerite-mayenite
 c. Larnite-brownmillerite-mayenite

The minerals brownmillerite, $Ca_2(Al,Fe)_2O_5$, and mayenite, $Ca_{12}Al_{14}O_{33}$, are unique in that they are otherwise recorded only as constituents of cement clinker. Their appearance is attributed to gas pressures even lower than those normally developed in shallow contact zones as exemplified by Scawt Hill (Jasmund and Hentschel, 1964, p. 311).

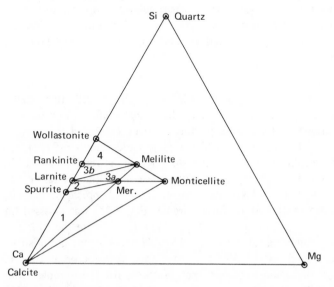

FIGURE 8-24
Sanidinite facies. Mineral assemblages formed by reaction between flint nodules and enclosing calcite (chalk), Scawt Hill, Ireland (after C. E. Tilley, 1942).

PHYSICAL GRADIENTS
IN CONTACT AUREOLES

The General Problem

A facies series mapped radially across an aureole expresses a gradient in physical conditions—P, T, f_{CO_2}, f_{O_2}, and so on—with reference to distance X from the contact. The problem is to construct such gradients from observed sequences of critical natural phase assemblages, supplemented by classic stratigraphic-geomorphic data, and to relate appropriate variables, notably P and T, to facies boundaries.

Basic Postulates

For a contact aureole as contrasted with a province of regional metamorphism, some simplifying postulates place limits upon pressure and temperature gradients and on possible influences of time. Briefly these are as follows:

Role of Time

In Chap. 1, the time span covered by rise and fall of temperature at points in an aureole was considered as a function of X and of the size of the generating pluton (Fig. 1-6). It was shown, from Jaeger's cooling models, that for plutons a few kilometers in diameter, temperatures stay near their maximum values for periods between about 10^4-10^5 years in the innermost zone and perhaps 1-3 $\times$ 10^6 years further out in the aureole. So we can assume that on the time scale of tectonic and geomorphic processes metamorphic temperatures peaked almost synchronously—though with minor outward lag—along any traverse normal to the contact. For the whole of an extensive province such as the Sierra Nevada batholith this assumption is not valid. In this particular case the western component plutons have been dated as early Jurassic, the axial plutons as late-middle Cretaceous; and the intervening time span exceeds that in which the youngest plutons have been unroofed.

Uniformity of Pressure

Except in regions of very high topographic relief—(e.g., the Bergell Alps)—metamorphic pressure along any radial traverse must be almost uniform. For aureoles generated by posttectonic plutons pressure limits can be estimated from stratigraphic and geomorphic data based on field mapping. Goldschmidt (1911a), for example, placed metamorphic pressure in the Oslo aureoles between 0.4 and 1 kb; estimates of the thickness of eroded cover along the axis of the Sierra Nevada batholith give pressures about 2-3 kb (Bateman et al., 1963, pp. 5, 6; Loomis, 1966, p. 243); pressure in the Santa Rosa aureole (Fig. 8-25) was assessed on similar grounds as 1-$2\frac{1}{2}$ kb (Compton, 1960, p. 1411). Even where the structure is simple, such estimates may be subject to considerable uncertainty; and in structurally complex regions such as the Alps they may vary by a factor of 2 more. Nevertheless this kind of argument shows that pressures for the aureoles considered in this and earlier chapters cannot have exceeded about $3\frac{1}{2}$ kb and in many instances must have been much lower.

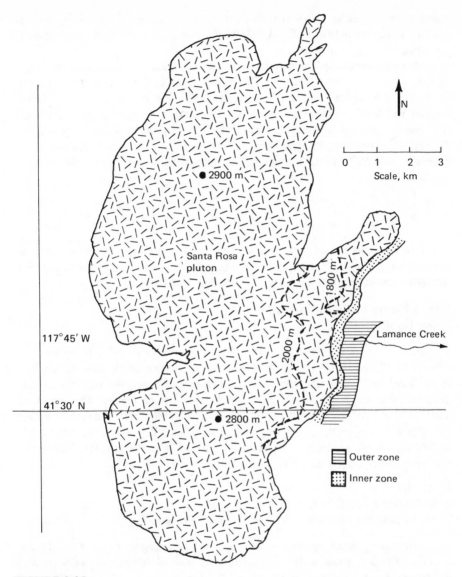

FIGURE 8-25
Simplified map of Santa Rosa pluton and an eastern segment of its contact aureole, Nevada
(after R. Compton).

Temperature Limits

Thermal models of the kind developed by Jaeger place broad limits on maximum
temperatures attained at plutonic contacts—anywhere perhaps between 100 and
250° below the temperature of magma instantaneously emplaced in initially cool
rocks (below 200°C). Thus at contacts with granodioritic plutons temperatures
might reach between 500 and 700°C. Assuming that biotite may appear on the

fringe of an aureole at 350–400°C, the total temperature span covered by a radial gradient could be between 100 and 350°. Obviously a wide range of gradients is permitted by Jaeger's models.

Another useful approximation concerns estimated slopes dT_m/dX of curves showing maximum temperature T_m as a function of X, distance from the contact. From Fig. 1-8, again based on Jaeger's data, dT_m/dX is almost constant across the full width of the aureole (to 350°C) for plutons 5 km or more in diameter. (For smaller plutons it increases perceptibly close to the contact.) Temperatures T_x and T_y, estimated by geothermometry for any two mapped isograds X, Y, distant X_x and X_y from the contact, define the radial gradient

$$\frac{T_x - T_y}{X_y - X_x} = dT/dX$$

Any three isograds should yield temperatures on a smooth nearby rectilineal curve [underlying assumptions are (1) a constant gradient measured normal to the contact; (2) a vertical contact or one with a constant radial dip].

Use of Numerically Calibrated Phase Equilibria

The total temperature-pressure field to be explored is completely covered by 0.5–4.0 kb, 350–750°C. The greatest uncertainty centers on pressure values. Few of the many equilibria that have been calibrated experimentally or from thermodynamic data are adequate for direct application to the present problem. Most must be qualified or excluded on the grounds that they are influenced by fluid variables (P_f, X_{H_2O}, X_{CO_2}, f_{O_2}) as well as by P and T. So modern attempts at calibrating aureole gradients still focus, in spite of inherent imperfections in the data, on three equilibria in natural pelitic systems.

1. Al_2SiO_5 polymorphs
2. Muscovite + quartz $\rightleftharpoons Al_2SiO_5$ + K-feldspar + H_2O
3. Mg-Fe partition between coexisting cordierite and garnet

While the general topology of the Al_2SiO_5 phase diagram (Figs. 4-2 and 8-26) is well established, there is still wide latitude as to absolute calibration (location of the triple point). The first appearance of K-feldspar with an Al_2SiO_5 polymorph has also been satisfactorily established by Evans's curve based on data for a natural muscovite (Fig. 4-3). But until uncertainty as to numerical values for Mg-Fe partition in terms of P and T is cleared up the cordierite-garnet pair can be employed only qualitatively as a geobarometer; $Mg/(Mg + Fe^{2+})$ increasing in a general way with P (cf. Fig. 4-5).

Staurolite, a mineral by no means as rare as was once supposed in pelitic contact assemblages, provides a potential check on temperature (Figs. 4-4 and 8-26) estimated from other equilibria. It has a limited stability field, the low-temperature limit being about 500°C, and at temperatures up to 620°C (increasing in the pressure range $1\frac{1}{2}$–5 kb) it gives place to iron-rich cordierite.

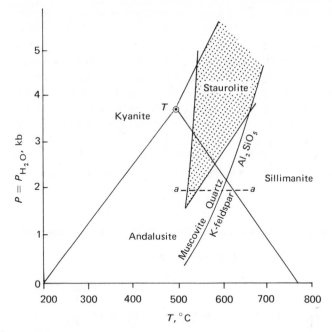

FIGURE 8-26
Stability fields of critical minerals in pelitic assemblages of Santa Rosa aureole (cf. Figs. 4-1 to
4-3). Section *aa* (2 kb) shows temperature limits from curves *a* and *a'* in Fig. 8-27.

Assessment of the General *P-T* Regime

The accumulated numerical data of contact metamorphism, accruing from
stratigraphic-geomorphic considerations, the general pattern of theoretical thermal
models such as those of Jaeger, mutual field relations of isograds and plutonic contacts, and the experimental and thermodynamic data of phase equilibria should
yield a comprehensive general picture of metamorphic facies in relation to the
broad *P-T* regime of contact metamorphism. The total picture that emerges is in
fact internally consistent in a general way. Critical minerals appear and disappear
along any inward radial traverse in the order prescribed by experiment and thermodynamics for increasing temperature at constant pressure. Distribution coefficients
for partitioning of elements in mineral pairs correlate broadly with experimental
data backed by solid-solution theory. Phases known to be stable at low pressures
are typical of aureoles that can be assigned on geologic grounds to shallow depths.
Aureole dimensions conform to the very broad limits imposed by thermal models.

General consistency of the total picture outlined above convincingly suggests a regional approximation to mineralogical equilibrium in contact aureoles;
and this generalization is here accepted as a tenet of metamorphic petrology and
the basis of the ensuing discussion. Nevertheless, this in no way implies universal
prevalence of precise equilibrium. Nor does it preclude the likelihood of significant
"overstepping" of equilibrium curves in systems (such as Al_2SiO_5) characterized
by low values of ΔS_r and correspondingly slow reaction rates. Such situations

undoubtedly detract from a sense of precision conveyed by individual gradients expressed by numbers.

With such reservations regarding particular cases in mind, we can still perceive a regular general pattern in the distribution of certain common key minerals in contact aureoles. More especially the Al_2SiO_5 polymorphs and their associates muscovite, staurolite, and cordierite, consistently develop in three types of prograde sequences that correlate in a general way with pressure [absolute pressure values given below, on which there will be some divergence of opinion, are drawn from data of Figs. 4-2, 4-3, 4-4, and 4-5 (cf. Fig. 8-26)] .[*]

(1) Andalusite-muscovite-quartz → andalusite-K-feldspar (-quartz-muscovite)

$P < {\sim}\, 2$ kb

(2) Andalusite-muscovite quartz → sillimanite-K-feldspar (-quartz-muscovite)

Staurolite-andalusite → cordierite-andalusite

$P \approx 2$ kb

(3) Andalusite-muscovite-quartz → sillimanite-muscovite-quartz

→ sillimanite-K-feldspar (-muscovite-quartz)

Staurolite-andalusite → staurolite-sillimanite → cordierite-sillimanite[†]

$P \approx 2\text{-}3\frac{1}{2}$ kb

Very rarely, e.g., in the innermost zone of the aureole of the Main Donegal Granite (Fig. 1-3), coexisting kyanite and staurolite suggest even higher pressures (perhaps >4 kb).

Assessment of Individual Gradients

The general pressure-temperature picture set out above is provisionally considered as satisfactory. What then can be said as to validity of temperature gradients and models proposed for individual cases? A single well-documented example brings out the difficulties and inherent ambiguity attending individual calibrations.

The Santa Rosa Aureole, Northern Nevada

The aureole generated by the Santa Rosa stock in a pelitic envelope has been chosen for the precision and breadth of field and petrographic data presented in Compton's (1960) exceptionally detailed study in an area of high topographic relief (1500 m) and good outcrop exposure (Fig. 8-25). The Santa Rosa pluton, 15 × 6 km, is the largest of several in the area mapped by Compton. Its composition is granodioritic, and it was forcefully emplaced in an almost completely liquid state. Internal temperatures close to the borders of the pluton on completion of

---

[*]Cf. D. M. Carmichael's (1978) bathograd concept as discussed in Chap. 11 (Fig. 11-9).
[†]In a restricted but not uncommon range of rock composition.

intrusion may have been 700–800°C, possibly as high as 900°C; and depth of cover has been estimated as 3–8 km—corresponding pressures between 1 and 2.5 kb (Compton, 1960, p. 1411). Contacts everywhere are steep, and over stretches of several kilometers map as almost vertical.

Attention will be confined to pelitic rocks whose chemical composition permits abundant development of staurolite in the outer zone of the aureole. With increasing grade staurolite is eliminated from such rocks in favor of cordierite. The two minerals are mutually exclusive, cordierite being ubiquitous in the middle and inner zones of the aureole. The data in Table 8-1 are taken from a radial traverse across the eastern aureole north of Lamance Creek (Fig. 8-25) as recorded by Compton (1960, pp. 1405, 1406).

All assemblages include quartz, biotite, muscovite, and andalusite. Nearly simultaneous breakdown of muscovite-quartz (to K-feldspar plus sillimanite) and appearance of sillimanite (in some instances visibly at the expense of andalusite) place metamorphic pressure close to 2 kb (cf. Fig. 8-26). Presence of staurolite in the outer zone betokens pressures no lower than $1\frac{1}{2}$ kb; and, at $2-2\frac{1}{2}$ kb, its field of stability cannot much exceed 500–600°C (even allowing for influences of f_{O_2} and Mg-Fe^{2+} partitioning between staurolite and cordierite).

Curves a and a' in Fig. 8-27 are radial thermal gradients consistent with field data and assumptions just stated (cf. line aa, Fig. 8-26). Curve b has been constructed on Jaeger's specifications (cf. Fig. 1-8) for the envelope of a vertical sheet (6 km thick) of granodioritic magma instantaneously emplaced at 800°C in pelitic rocks initially at 200°C. By postulating magmatic or country-rock temperatures 50° lower or by slight juggling of the assumed thermal properties of rocks concerned it would be a simple matter to bring curve b into perfect coincidence with either a or a' (or with comparable curves based on different but still plausible stability limits of critical mineral phases). Even so, anomalies still remain unexplained: at the perimeter (X_0), biotite appears virtually at the same point as staurolite (T not less than 500°C). Elsewhere in much smaller aureoles, biotite first crystallizes at temperatures considered no greater than 400°C. What is the reason for this discrepancy? How can high contact temperatures (~630–650°C) implied by sillimanite and K-feldspar on curves a, a', and computed on a Jaegar model (curve b) be reconciled with temperatures of ~525°C given by oxygen-isotope

TABLE 8-1

Description of the Santa Rosa Aureole, Nevada (radial width = 1400 m)

Radial distance from contact (meters)	Index minerals	Reference points
1400–1100	Staurolite-andalusite	$X_0 - X_1$
1100–800	Obscured by metasomatism	$X_1 - X_1'$
800–0	Cordierite-andalusite	$X_1' - X_C$
300–0	Sillimanite-K-feldspar (forming from muscovite and andalusite)	$X_2 - X_C$

Source: Compton (1960, pp. 1405, 1406).

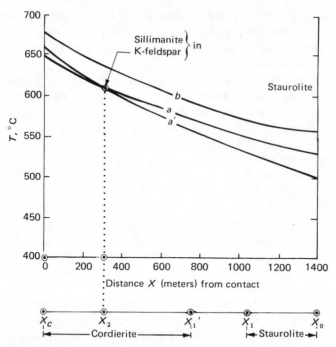

FIGURE 8-27
Possible temperature gradients in Santa Rosa aureole north of Lamance Creek (Fig. 8-25).
Curves a and a' based on key minerals in pelitic assemblages (see text). Curve b, thermal cooling
curve based on models of J. Jaeger (see text for numerical data). X_0 perimeter (staurolite-
andalusite); X_1-X_1' cordierite comes in in place of staurolite; X_2 sillimanite and K-feldspar
come in; X_c = plutonic contact.

geothermometry (Shieh and Taylor, 1969, p. 353a)? One way would be to lower
the magmatic temperature to 700°C to reduce metamorphic pressure to a kilobar
or so and to assign the lowest possible pressure limit (2.7 kb) to the Al_2SiO_5
triple point. This was actually done in a previous attempt at general calibration
of the Santa Rosa aureole (in Verhoogen et al., 1970, p. 590),[*] which ignored
the limitations imposed by stability of staurolite.

There are indeed cases where independently estimated aureole gradients
seem to be in somewhat closer agreement. But such apparent agreement may
well be illusory. In the well-documented case of the Cretaceous Birch Creek pluton
in southeastern California,[†] there is only one point calibrated from phase equilibria: at 300 m from the contact simultaneous elimination of muscovite and
appearance of sillimanite in place of andalusite again indicate $T \sim 600°C$ at $P =
P_{H_2O} \approx 2$ kb. If the first appearance of biotite at 3 km from the contact is placed
$\sim 400°C$, contact temperatures should be around 620°C—still 80° higher than the
oxygen-isotope estimate (540°C) of Shieh and Taylor (1969a, pp. 328, 353).

---

[*] Here rejected in favor of curves a and a' Fig. 8-27.
[†] See Verhoogen et al. (1970, pp. 550–553) for a summary of field and petrographic
details taken from a study by D. B. Nash.

Possibly in the light of earlier discussion (pp. 142-144) oxygen-isotope temperatures should be disregarded as unreliable; but who is to say whether it is the estimate based on mineralogical evidence that is at fault?

I have come reluctantly to a conclusion that now seems inescapable: in the light of present knowledge construction of thermal aureole gradients with uncertainty less than ±50° (involving estimates of pressure closer than ±1 kb) is little more than an exercise in manipulation of numbers. In such exercises, provided inherent uncertainties are kept in mind, there is still some merit. They demonstrate the complexities of the problem as it applies to specific aureoles. They permit comparison of different aureoles (and facies series) in relative terms; e.g., specific cases discussed in this chapter can be placed tentatively in a general order of increasing pressure.[*]

Low, $P < 1$ kb: Paritu, New Zealand; Comrie, Scotland
Medium, $P \sim 1\frac{1}{2}$-$2\frac{1}{2}$ kb: Sierra Nevada pendants and Birch Creek aureole, California; Santa Rosa aureole, Nevada
High, $P \sim 2\frac{1}{2}$-$3\frac{1}{2}$ kb: Tôno, Japan; Lochnagar, Scotland; Main Donegal Granite, Ireland

Finally, when metamorphic paragenesis is viewed on a broader scale numerical estimates have a more lasting value in setting up provisional limits (still far from precise) on mutual relations and boundaries of standard facies in terms of temperature and pressure. Whatever their relative order in terms of pressure, the whole or the greater part of each of the facies series represented in the aureoles listed above falls within the hornblende-hornfels facies.

TEMPERATURE-PRESSURE FIELDS OF INDIVIDUAL FACIES

Greater optimism seems justified in attempting to evaluate numerically the *P-T* fields of individual contact facies. The same kind of data are again employed. But calibration points in this case are much more widely spaced than along an aureole gradient, and a lesser degree of refinement is needed to yield meaningful results of geologic significance.

The lower temperature limit of the albite-epidote-hornfels facies is but vaguely defined. In the field it normally coincides with the aureole perimeter, where reaction kinetics rather than some univariant equilibrium temperature determines the point at which metamorphic response of an initially unstable mineral assemblage first becomes obvious. Since biotite first appears somewhat in advance of andalusite, the lower facies boundary (1 in Fig. 8-28) is arbitrarily assigned to temperatures a little below those of the pyrophyllite dehydration curve (*a* in Fig. 8-28) where andalusite first becomes stable, and a little above the stability field of wairakite—a mineral widespread at shallow depth in hydrothermally altered

---

[*]Note that earlier estimates in the 1968 edition (p. 258) differ in generally lower pressure values and to some degree in relative order with increasing pressure—a further illustration of the ephemeral nature of conclusions based on exercises in numbers.

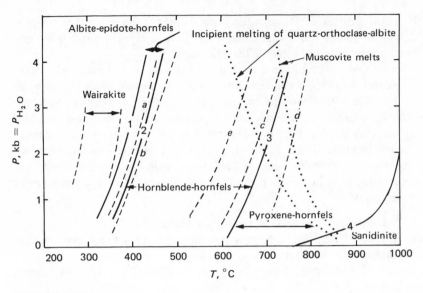

FIGURE 8-28

Temperature-pressure fields of facies of contact metamorphism (see text). Experimentally calibrated curves: (*a*) Pyrophyllite → andalusite + quartz (see Fig. 4-1); (*b*) clinozoisite + kyanite → anorthite + quartz (after A. L. Boettcher, 1970, p. 352); (*c*) Muscovite → corundum + K-feldspar (after B. W. Evans, 1965); (*d*) Anthophyllite → enstatite + quartz (see Fig. 4-11); (*e*) Muscovite + quartz → Al_2SiO_s + K-feldspar (see Fig. 4-3); (4) Calcite + diopside → akermanite (after L. S. Walter, 1963; H. S. Yoder, 1973); stability limits of wairakite from Liou (1971, p. 399).

volcanic rocks, but foreign to the albite-epidote-hornfels facies. The high-temperature limit is sharply defined mineralogically by simultaneous elimination of epidote, sharp rise in the anorthite content of plagioclase (from An_0 to $An_{>20}$), and transition from actinolite to aluminous hornblende. Precise calibration of such a complicated transformation can scarcely be expected; but isograd temperatures must be below those of the clinozoisite-kyanite ⇌ anorthite-quartz-H_2O equilibrium (located with some uncertainty as curve *b*). With this restriction in mind the upper limit of the facies (curve 2) has been located about 50° higher than the lower limit—the narrow temperature span being in keeping with the restricted width of the corresponding zone in most aureoles.

A similar line of reasoning predicts that the hornblende-hornfels facies must embrace a much greater range of temperature. It certainly extends to and probably somewhat beyond the equilibrium curve (*c*) for muscovite ⇌ K-feldspar-corundum-H_2O. On the other hand, ferrohypersthene (a phase typical of the pyroxene-hornfels facies) becomes stable on the dehydration curves of ferrous noncalcic amphiboles (cummingtonite, anthophyllite); and these in turn are offset (to a degree unknown) to temperatures below those experimentally determined for dehydration of pure magnesium anthophyllite (curve *d*). The upper limit of the hornblende-hornfels facies accordingly has been arbitrarily located (curve 3) between curves *c* and *d* of Fig. 8-28. It will not be a sharply drawn line, but rather a family of closely spaced curves for dehydration of metamorphic hornblendes under conditions of low f_{O_2} implied by low oxidation ratios in the inner aureoles of Comrie and Lochnagar.[*] The common appearance of forsterite- and wollastonite-bearing assemblages (and much rarer development of periclase) in the upper-temperature sector of the hornblende-hornfels facies (cf. Fig. 4-6) implies that $X_{CO_2}^{gas}$ in carbonate systems commonly is maintained at rather low levels, probably as a consequence of thermally controlled systems of water circulation within the aureole.

The high-temperature limit of the pyroxene-hornfels facies at pressures above a few hundred kilobars could extend into the field of incipient fusion of common rocks. On Jaeger's model of cooling it should lie significantly below the temperature range of largely molten granodioritic and tonalitic magmas, which might well be not much greater than $800°C$ at $P_{H_2O} = 2000$ bars. At very low pressures there is a pyroxene-hornfels → sanidinite boundary. A convenient datum might be the experimentally established curve 4 for the diopside-calcite ⇌ aker-manite equilibrium. The field of the sanidinite facies certainly overlaps far into that of fusion of pelitic and quartzo-feldspathic sediments. Aramaki (1961) experimentally investigated the beginning of fusion in pelitic and calcareous assemblages of the sanidinite facies occurring as bombs ejected during eruption (from the Asama volcano) of a lava whose temperature was directly measured as $1000°C$. He placed the *P-T* range of the metamorphic assemblages between 945 and $1005°C$ at $P_1 = 200-800$ bars.

[*]Corresponding temperatures presumably are much higher than those recorded by Tilley and Yoder (1962) for laboratory breakdown of hornblende under extreme oxidizing conditions.

9

Facies of Low-Grade Regional Metamorphism: Illustrative Examples

PRELIMINARY POSTULATE: CRITERIA OF FACIES STATUS

There is widespread agreement among geologists today as to what constitutes a metamorphic facies: Eskola's original concept remains unchallenged (cf. Chap. 2). Just how many facies should be recognized, however, is a matter in which opinions differ depending partly on the breadth of individual treatment. Here, where we attempt to review the complete gamut of metamorphic paragenesis, the scale of classificatory division and subdivision must be correspondingly broad. What are legitimately recognized by students of local or more restricted paragenesis as separate facies will here be grouped together as one or treated as transitional facies.

As a preliminary to reviewing the complete spectrum of regional metamorphism, two essential conditions are postulated for valid facies status.

1. There must be well-defined mineralogical criteria that distinguish each facies from all others except immediately related transitions.
2. To justify full status in a general treatment such as this, a facies must have significant areal extent in several independent metamorphic provinces.

In the interests of clarity, where "facies" recognized by other writers are relegated here to transitional or subfacies status, the fact will be duly noted; so, too, where subfacies of other writers, found to fulfill criterion 2 above are now accorded the status of facies.

LOW–GRADE REGIONAL METAMORPHISM

Incipient Metamorphism and Diagenesis

By burial alone, water-saturated geosynclinal sediments and associated volcanic rocks eventually reach an environment of temperature and pressure conducive to mutual reaction between associated mineral phases. It is customary to treat as diagenesis the first incomplete responses to conditions of increasing load. The initial assemblages may have approximated equilibrium in the sedimentary environment: e.g., montmorillonitic and illite-bearing shales and many calcareous sediments. Or, as in volcanic sands consisting of high-temperature phases (glass, pyroxenes, hornblendes, etc.), they may, from the moment of deposition, have been significantly out of equilibrium. Factors such as these, and especially environmental temperature and strain induced by nonhydrostatic stress, bring the activation energy of potential chemical reactions to the point where these become effective.

There must be a transition, with increasing depth of burial, from diagenesis to regional metamorphism. Many of the changes involved (e.g., reconstitution of clays, crystallization of quartz and alkali feldspars, destruction of high-temperature minerals, and precipitation of carbonates) are common to both. Where the bulk of the rock, including even coarse sand particles, is substantially affected, and particularly where schistosity (foliation) bears witness to simultaneous yielding of the solid rock by stress-induced continuous flow, the processes concerned are by general agreement termed *metamorphic.* The same applies to incompletely developed "diagenetic" or "anchimetamorphic" mineral assemblages (with zeolites, chlorites, 2-M micas and hydrated Ca-Al silicates) that elsewhere are the principal constituents of what on textural grounds are generally recognized as metamorphic rocks (slates, semischists, and so on). Knowledge of their mineralogical character and of depths at which they have been found to develop to maturity comes from research in many fields: metamorphism (e.g., Coombs, 1954, 1975; Frey, 1970; Kubler et al., 1974; Coombs et al., 1976); stratigraphy and sedimentology (e.g., Packham and Crook, 1960; Hay, 1966); coal petrology (e.g., Kisch, 1966, 1969, 1974).

Low-Grade Metamorphism Arbitrarily Defined

The prograde sense of progressive metamorphism was equated in Chap. 2 with corresponding reactions in the sense of increasing entropy. However, the terms "low," "medium," and "high," which are so widely applied to metamorphic grade, cannot be defined in such rigorous terms. Their usage is necessarily subjective and depends on the experience and field of special interest of those concerned (e.g., in the North Atlantic craton versus the circum-Pacific mobile belts). For present convenience we shall arbitrarily limit "low-grade" regional metamorphism to facies and facies series of the greenschist, blueschist, and lower grades. Low down in the prograde sequence are mineral assemblages—commonly imperfectly crystallized—in rocks lacking or just beginning to develop a schistose (foliated) texture. Rocks of the greenschist and blueschist facies, on the other hand, typically are conspicuously schistose and contain few or no mineral relics surviving from the premetamorphic assemblage. Such general relationships, all subject to exception, are shown in purely schematic form in Table 9-1.

Within the frame of reference thus bounded (Table 9-1, left-hand side) the mineralogical character of individual low-grade facies will now be reviewed, in general prograde order.

ZEOLITE FACIES

Parageneses Related to Depth

Taringatura Hills, New Zealand

The zeolite facies was proposed (Fyfe et al., 1958, p. 216) to cover zeolitic assemblages recorded by Coombs (1954) in Triassic volcanogenic marine sediments in southernmost New Zealand. The type area, Taringatura Hills, is situated in what is now termed the Murihiku Terrane of the New Zealand Geosyncline, some 25 km beyond the southwestern border of the Otago Schist belt (Fig. 9-1; cf. Fig. 1-17). Between lie Permian metavolcanics and metasediments (prehnite-pumpellyite and lawsonite-albite-chlorite facies) of the southeastern end of the Dun Mountain ophiolite belt.

Coombs described mineralogical changes that he observed in an uninterrupted stratigraphic section 10 km thick. There is some correlation throughout this section between metamorphic paragenesis and depth; and it was on this basis that Coombs first proposed the term *burial metamorphism*. A similar correlation, though as we shall shortly see not ubiquitous, characterizes the zeolitic facies at other points in the New Zealand Geosyncline (Coombs, 1960; Coombs et al., 1959). Typical assemblages in partially metamorphosed graywacke and volcanic sands are as follows:

TABLE 9-1

Schematic Representation of General Relations between Facies, Facies Series (along arrows), Metamorphic Grade (increasing along arrows), and Textural Evolution

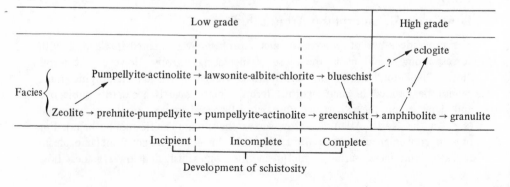

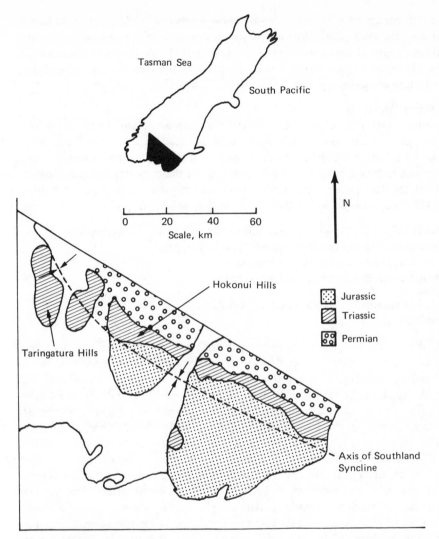

FIGURE 9-1

Type localities for zeolite facies, Triassic of Murihiku Terrane, southern end of New Zealand Geosyncline. Axis of South Island Syncline is shown dashed (after J. R. Boles and D. S. Coombs, 1975).

1. Heulandite-analcite-quartz with montmorillonite, celadonite, and sphene as possible additional phases
2. Laumontite-albite-quartz (-chlorite)
3. Quartz-albite-adularia (metasomatic)

The first assemblage is formed in the upper half of the stratigraphic section, the second and third only in the lower half. Allowing for 3-5 km as the maximum possible thickness of post-Triassic overburden at the time of metamorphism (Coombs et al., 1959, p. 59), the heulandite-analcite-quartz assemblage of New

Zealand is correlated with depths whose upper limits are 1–5 km and lower limits 5–10 km. The laumontite-albite-quartz assemblage is formed in a lower zone, the maximum depth of which may have been as great as 15 km, and was not less than 9 km. Throughout the laumontite zone, especially in the deeper levels, pumpellyite and prehnite are beginning to appear in place of laumontite.

Southern Puerto Rico

In south-central Puerto Rico late Cretaceous marine andesite lavas and debris (graywackes) display low-grade mineralogical changes that correlate closely with depth over a section about 4 km thick. In spite of shallower burial the metamorphic paragenesis follows a pattern that proceeds beyond the stage reached at the lowest levels of the Taringatura section. The downward zonal sequence as described by Jolly (1970) is from the zeolite to the prehnite-pumpellyite facies:

1. Sericite-albite-quartz-analcite-laumontite-celadonite; analcite decreasing, laumontite first appearing toward the base of the zone
2. Laumontite-albite-prehnite-pumpellyite
3. Albite-pumpellyite-prehnite-epidote-quartz

Zeolitic Paragenesis in Relation to Solution Chemistry and Time

Both the zeolite and the prehnite-pumpellyite facies express partial or local responses of unstable initial materials—typically volcanogenic—to some limited range of P and T, by mutual reaction through the medium of aqueous pore fluids that have the capacity to move freely through the permeable reacting system. Just how effective the role of the fluid phase can be is seen where zeolitic and similar assemblages tend to develop preferentially in vesicular domains and along flow tops in volcanic piles (e.g., Levi, 1969; Jolly and Smith, 1972; Aguirre et al., 1978). Participation of the fluid phase can markedly affect the ultimate nature of the low-grade assemblage in several interrelated ways. Well known to sedimentologists (as set forth in an extensive review by Hay, 1966) is a kinetic effect. With passage of time (as well as with progressive burial) complex zeolitic assemblages in Cenozoic rocks tend to give place in older rocks to simpler more mature assemblages with laumontite, analcite, albite, and K-feldspar (cf. Hay, 1966, p. 72). The nature of the initial material can have a marked kinetically related influence: unstable volcanic glass is particularly prone to complete replacement by more stable phase assemblages. Even more significant can be externally controlled fluid compositional variables—μ_{H_2O}, μ_{CO_2}, and activities of ionic species dissolved in a freely diffusing fluid phase. Such influences have been discussed by Helgeson (1967), Coombs (1971), Surdam (1973), and others. Their cumulative effects in disturbing depth-related sequences of low-grade facies have been made clear in several recent contributions (among them Eugster, 1970; Surdam, 1973). Here we note a single example, again from the Murihiku Terrane, Southern New Zealand.

Hokonui Hills, New Zealand

Boles and Coombs (1975) have described a zeolitic paragenesis in a second section of marine Triassic sediments in the Murihiku Terrane—the Hokonui Hills, located some 50 km east of the Taringatura Hills site on the opposite limb of a major syncline (Fig. 9-1). The following prograde reaction sequence, again in volcanogenic (andesitic, rhyolitic) sediments, has been established in a stratigraphic section between 5–8 km thick:

Glass → heulandite-chlorite-celadonite

Heulandite → laumontite (or prehnite, calcite, analcite, or albite)

Here there is no general correlation between phase assemblages and depth. Nor, in contrast with other localities throughout the New Zealand Geosyncline, are other zeolites ultimately eliminated in favor of laumontite. Boles and Coombs (1975, p. 172) see the varied paragenesis as a set of local equilibria reflecting the combined influence of initial rock composition and externally buffered circulating stratal waters, together overshadowing the direct control by P and T as determined by relative depth.

Scope of Zeolite Facies Reassessed

From the above accounts it should be clear that no single mineral assemblage is diagnostic of the zeolite facies, and that within the facies there is rather wide mineralogical variety, partly because the ultimate phase assemblage is so sensitive to externally influenced compositional variables, especially μ_{H_2O} and μ_{CO_2}. But from the voluminous literature now available some generalizations have emerged that warrant—for those who favor classificatory refinements—establishment of subfacies. In general order of increasing grade, whether controlled by depth or by decrease in the ratio μ_{H_2O}/μ_{CO_2}, are quartz-bearing paragenesis (Fig. 9-2) with heulandite, heulandite-prehnite, laumontite-prehnite, and finally, laumontite-prehnite-pumpellyite (cf. Coombs, 1971). Analcite is common in quartz-bearing assemblages at the heulandite stage of evolution.

Rather than attempting general facies refinements on such a basis we accept Coombs' recent loose definition (Coombs, 1971, p. 325) which scarcely differs from the original definition of 1958: the zeolite facies "includes all mineral assemblages characterized in rocks of appropriate composition by zeolites other than analcite of silica-deficient environments" (the latter can persist almost to magmatic temperatures). Some typical parageneses as developed at different levels and in different parts of the Murihiku Terrane, New Zealand, are shown in Fig. 9-2 (grade increasing from *a* to *d*).

Coal Rank in Zeolite and Related Facies
of Burial Metamorphism

The chemical character of Phanerozoic coals evolves in a regular manner with increasing depths of burial and passage of time. To specialists in the field this process, which involves progressive decrease in content of volatile matter, is known as *coalification*. A measure of *coal rank*—the degree of coalification—is the percentage of volatile matter (V.M.), or less sensitively, the total carbon, in the vitrinite component of the coal. In the rank range semibituminous to anthracite, the V.M.

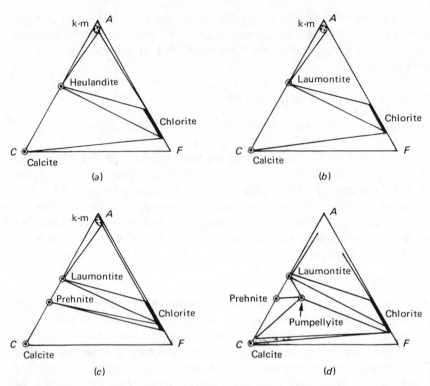

FIGURE 9-2
Zeolite facies: chemographic relations of some combinations of phases, with quartz as an additional phase (after D. S. Coombs, 1971, p. 321). Kaolin and montmorillonite shown as k-m.

index decreases from ~40 to 4; coals of highest rank with V.M. <4 are termed metaanthracite.

The principal controls of coal rank are thought to be temperature (depending on depth and geothermal gradient) and time—the influence of the latter falling off logarithmically in coals as old as Paleozoic. There is something in common, then, between coal rank and the zeolite facies of burial metamorphism; but genesis of the latter is further complicated by influence of fluid-compositional variables, μ_{H_2O}, μ_{CO_2}, and so on, and the time required to reach a nearly stationary state of "maturity" seems to be less for zeolitic parageneses than for coals. In the extensive and specialized literature on coal rank, many items deal with depth controls but only a few with relations between rank and mineral facies of burial metamorphism (diagenesis) in associated sediments (e.g., Quinn and Glass, 1958; Kisch, 1966; Frey and Niggli, 1971). Yet the topic has considerable interest to metamorphic petrologists as providing a potential means for correlating mineral assemblages of different lithology (especially metapelitic and metavolcanic) on the facies scale, and perhaps for assessing relative temperatures of low-grade facies of burial metamorphism. This general topic has been critically reviewed in the light of comprehensive data from many and varied sources by Kisch (1969, 1974). Most of this section is based on Kisch's contributions, and some of his conclusions will now be summarized:

1. In every coalfield there is a correlation between downward increase in coal rank (decrease in V.M.) and in grade recorded in associated mineral facies of burial metamorphism (diagenesis). However, there is no absolute correlation of this kind from one coalfield to another.

2. The transition from the upper analcite-heulandite-quartz zone to the lower laumontite-albite zone of the zeolite facies occurs at ranks that appear to increase significantly with age: V.M. ~39 in Cretaceous coals of Yakutia, Siberia; V.M. 36-77 in Upper Permian coals of Sydney Basin, eastern Australia; and V.M. 31 in Upper Carboniferous coals of Tamworth Trough 150 km north of Sydney (cf. Fig. 9-5).

3. The general span of the zeolite facies in Paleozoic and Mesozoic coalfields corresponds to a range of rank from semibituminous to semianthracitic, V.M. about 50-15. Coals in rocks of the two pumpellyite facies are essentially anthracite— V.M. 10-4.

4. In pelitic sediments bearing the imprint of burial metamorphism, the development of illite at the expense of kaolin becomes noticeable where coal approaches semianthracitic rank ("lean coal," V.M. = 17-16-17). Elimination of kaolin and appearance of pyrophyllite—which we have taken to mark the beginning of the greenschist facies—is correlated with anthracite rank of coal (V.M. ~7-4). Carbonaceous matter from schists of the greenschist facies typically is well-ordered graphite.

Finally, it may be noted that standard rank-depth correlations accepted and used among coal petrologists (reproduced as Fig. 1 in Kisch, 1969) suggest that the total span of the zeolite facies (V.M. ~45-15 in associated coals) in Paleozoic sections may correspond to a relative depth span ΔD of about 2000 m ($\Delta P \sim \frac{1}{2}$ kb; $\Delta T \sim 70$-$80°C$).

REGIONAL FACIES WITH PUMPELLYITE

Role of Pumpellyite in Low-Grade Facies Series

Since its recognition forty years ago (Hutton, 1937) as a widespread constituent of semischists and metagraywacke in southern New Zealand, pumpellyite has become known as the diagnostic index of two of the principal facies of low-grade metamorphism, and also as a common mineral in metavolcanic assemblages of the blueschist facies. In both the facies after which it is named pumpellyite is characteristic of eugeosynclinal metagraywackes and metavolcanics. What lends pumpellyite additional interest in the present context is its different roles in several distinct types of facies series.

Pumpellyite is absent or rare in products of ocean-floor metamorphism, whose typical pattern involves direct transition from the zeolite to the greenschist facies.

The general downward sequence developed in facies of burial metamorphism in continental troughs, basins, and geosynclines is

Zeolite → prehnite-pumpellyite (→ greenschist)

The final stage is reached only in the lowest levels of some burial sequences, e.g., in parts of the Tasman Geosyncline of eastern Australia (R. E. Smith, 1969).

The typical prograde sequence in greenschist facies series of mobile belts such as the eastern Appalachians and the New Zealand Geosyncline is

Zeolite → prehnite-pumpellyite → pumpellyite-actinolite → greenschist

The prehnite-pumpellyite facies is dominant in nontectonic domains, the greenschist facies in tectonic domains of strongly schistose rocks.

By contrast the prehnite-pumpellyite facies is not found in some blueschist series (e.g., in Japan and California), but the pumpellyite-actinolite facies is extensively developed. The typical blueschist facies series is

Zeolite → pumpellyite-actinolite → blueschist

Within the blueschist facies itself pumpellyite remains a stable phase, prominent in metavolcanic assemblages containing glaucophane and lawsonite.

So from purely geologic and petrographic evidence there appear to be radical differences between P-T paths traversed in the earliest stages by the several low-grade types of facies series. And the key mineral concerned is pumpellyite. The respective paths of burial and greenschist facies series cross the stability fields of both prehnite and pumpellyite; that of some, but not all, blueschist series bypasses the field of prehnite but remains until the end in that of pumpellyite; the path of ocean-floor metamorphism bypasses both fields.

Prehnite-Pumpellyite Facies

Torlesse Group, New Zealand Geosyncline

The most important lithofacial element in the New Zealand Geosyncline is the Torlesse Group (Upper Carboniferous-Triassic), extending from the northern and eastern edges of the Haast Schist belt (into which it merges) for more than 1000 km northward along the length of the two principal islands (cf. Figs. 1-15 and 9-3). Everywhere the dominant lithologic type is indurated (incipiently metamorphosed) nonschistose graywacke, commonly with a high content of volcanogenic debris of sand grade. The pattern of metamorphic facies likewise is monotonous—zeolitic assemblages in some places but more generally a paragenesis in which pumpellyite and prehnite are prominent and zeolites are lacking. To cover this paragenesis, as first recorded by Brothers (1956) in the North and by Coombs and others (1959) in the South Island, Coombs (1960, p. 341) proposed a prehnite-pumpellyite-metagraywacke facies.* Later, this was subdivided by Hashimoto (1966) into two independent facies respectively named after the critical index pairs prehnite-pumpellyite and pumpellyite-actinolite (see also Coombs et al., 1970).

Characteristic assemblages of the prehnite-pumpellyite facies as displayed

---

*The same suggestion was made independently on the basis of studies in New South Wales by Packham and Crook (1960, p. 403).

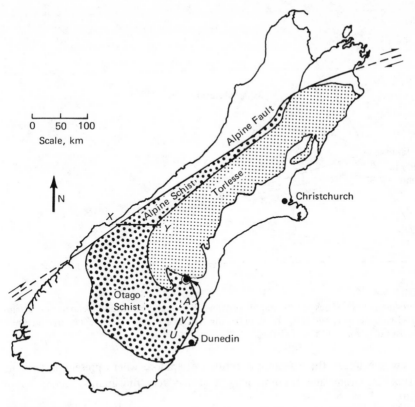

FIGURE 9-3
Torlesse Group (mainly prehnite-pumpellyite facies) in relation to Alpine and Otago schists
(Haast Schist belt), east of Alpine Fault, South Island, New Zealand (simplified).

in the Torlesse Group were recorded by Coombs (1960, 1961; Coombs et al.,
1969, pp. 65–68) as follows (Fig. 9-4):

1. Quartz-albite-pumpellyite-chlorite-muscovite-sphene (-stilpnomelane) is the typi-
    cal recrystallized component of metagraywackes of textural zones T1 and T2[*]
    (cf. pp. 38–39).
2. Quartz-prehnite (-calcite-pumpellyite); in segregation veinlets in metagraywackes.
3. Albite-pumpellyite-chlorite-sphene-epidote-quartz; in spilitic lavas.
4. Prehnite-calcite (-albite-quartz-chlorite); in slightly recrystallized limestones.

In detailed accounts of progressive metamorphism across a segment of the
Torlesse–Haast Schist transition zone (*A* in Fig. 9-3), Bishop (1972, 1974) has
provided additional mineralogical details of metagraywackes in both the pumpellyite facies as well as an unusually complete regional structural picture. He
noted that pumpellyite in the present facies typically is pleochroic as contrasted
with a colorless variety that is typical of the pumpellyite-actinolite facies; in a

---

[*]Originally designated Chl 1, Chl 2, and so on, of the chlorite zone.

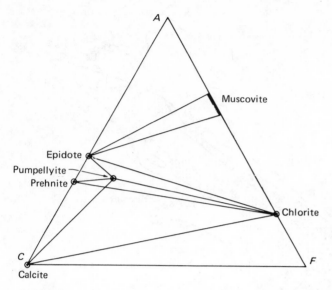

FIGURE 9-4

Prehnite-pumpellyite facies: chemographic relations in metagraywacke and metavolcanic assemblages with excess SiO_2 and K_2O, Torlesse Group, New Zealand Geosyncline. Quartz and albite are almost ubiquitous additional phases.

very few specimens there is minor actinolite; epidote where present is an iron-rich type; stilpnomelane is common, but always very fine-grained and in minor quantity.

Tasman Geosyncline, New South Wales

Eastern Australia, across an east-west width of 1000 km in the latitude of Sydney, is a tract of folded Paleozoic geosynclinal sediments and intercalated volcanics (mainly tuffaceous) known as the Tasman Geosyncline.* It is a compound structure (Fig. 9-5) consisting of several major longitudinal (north-south) tectonic units. Two of these in particular, the Molong Geanticline (Ordovician-Silurian rocks) and the Tamworth Trough (Devonian-Carboniferous) have been sites of mineralogical studies of burial metamorphism encompassing the prehnite-pumpellyite facies.

In the Tamworth Trough (Packham and Crook, 1960; R. E. Smith, 1969; pp. 160–161), the downward sequence of facies in a stratigraphic section whose estimated total depth is over 13 km is from zeolite to prehnite-pumpellyite facies to greenschist facies. The transition between the first two occurs at about the 7-km level. Mineral assemblages in volcanogenic metasediments parallel those of the same facies in the Torlesse Group of New Zealand (which, it will be remembered, cannot be directly related to depth).

In the Molong Geanticline (R. E. Smith, 1968, 1969), the mineralogical pattern, although it includes the prehnite-pumpellyite facies, is not exactly the same. The downward zonal sequence, again in volcanogenic materials, is

*Not to be confused with the Paleozoic Tasman Geosyncline of New Zealand.

1. Quartz-albite-chlorite-epidote-carbonate
2. Quartz-albite-chlorite-epidote-*prehnite*-carbonate
3. Quartz-albite-chlorite-epidote-*prehnite-pumpellyite*-carbonate
4. Quartz-albite-chlorite-epidote-*actinolite*-carbonate
5. Similar to 4, but with biotite in addition

This is a general paragenesis in which zeolites fail to appear but carbonate is present throughout. The prehnite-pumpellyite facies however is true to type; and again

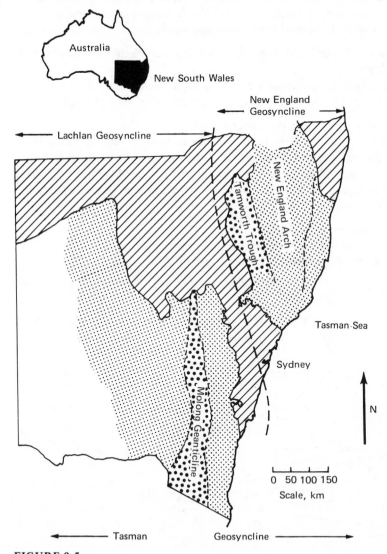

FIGURE 9-5
Some structural elements in Paleozoic Tasman Geosyncline (stippled), New South Wales, Australia. Sites of burial metamorphism referred to in text, heavy stipple; post-Devonian cover, cross-hatched (after R. E. Smith, 1969).

pumpellyite is eliminated as actinolite first comes in, marking a direct transition to the greenschist facies.

In the Molong sequence basic lavas of the prehnite-pumpellyite zone have developed remarkable mineralogical and compositional heterogeneity (on the scale of perhaps 10–20 cm) as a result of metamorphic differentiation during burial metamorphism (R. E. Smith, 1968). The processes involved are not well understood, but in this case fluid diffusion certainly has been active. The result is a patchwork of rock domains of different color, frequently cross-cutting structural features such as flow boundaries, in which contrasted simple mineral assemblages (all consistent, however, with the present facies) have developed:

1. Gray domains of spilitic lithology: albitized plagioclase, chlorite, quartz, and relict pyroxene
2. Green and yellow-green domains of Ca-Al-silicate concentration, the former consisting essentially of pumpellyite-quartz, the second of epidote-quartz.

Orcas Island, Northwestern Washington

In the San Juan Islands just off the northwestern corner of the state of Washington, metamorphic assemblages developed in late Paleozoic and early Mesozoic metagraywackes and metavolcanics are typical of the prehnite-pumpellyite facies. Vance (1968) described the following paragenesis, based on an intensive study on Orcas Island (Fig. 9-6).

1. Metaandesite: chlorite-albite-prehnite
2. Metabasalt: chlorite-albite (±pumpellyite and/or prehnite)
3. Metagraywacke and metapelite: albite-quartz-chlorite-prehnite

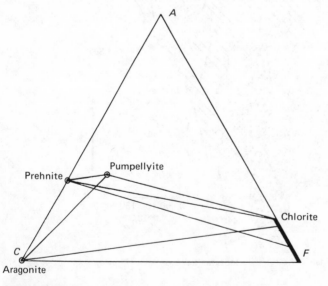

FIGURE 9-6
Prehnite-pumpellyite facies: chemographic relations in metagraywacke-metavolcanic paragenesis with aragonite, Orcas Island, northwestern Washington State. Quartz and albite are common additional phases (data from J. A. Vance, 1968).

The paragenesis is peculiar in two respects: prehnite is much more abundant and widespread than pumpellyite; more significantly aragonite is widespread as re-crystallized masses in limestones and in cross-cutting veinlets in rocks of varied lithology.

Vance has proposed on combined evidence of shallow stratigraphic depth and the regional metamorphic paragenesis that aragonite has crystallized as a metastable phase well below the pressure-range of true stability. This I find dif-ficult to accept; for aragonite is seen in many cases to replace calcite (some of it admittedly showing microscopic evidence of strain), and according to current thinking stratigraphic depth is no certain criterion of maximum pressures attained in rocks along the Pacific margin. If one accepts (as I tentatively do) the alterna-tive possibility that the Orcas Island aragonite crystallized as a stable phase, an interesting corollary arises: under some conditions the P-T stability fields of prehnite and aragonite must overlap. Such a condition could be relatively low X_{H_2O} in the fluid phase—which is likely enough in a system with abundant carbon-ate (much of it in veins).

Pumpellyite-Actinolite Facies

Definition and Status

Following Tsuboi's (1936) discovery of pumpellyite veining metavolcanics in the Sanbagawa blueschist terrane of Japan, pumpellyite was soon recognized as a common constituent of glaucophane schists and equivalent rocks of lower grade. In W. P. De Roever's account of regional metamorphism in Celebes, there is a dis-cussion of pumpellyite in glaucophanic and in nonglaucophanic parageneses (De Roever, 1947, pp. 150-152, 162). Noting that pumpellyite is by no means always associated with glaucophane, De Roever (1947, p. 162) was

> inclined to assume that the pumpellyite in eastern Central Celebes
> belongs to a separate metamorphic facies, containing among others
> colorless amphibole, albite, quartz, and carbonate as other typical
> minerals, and which is a kind of precursor of the lawsonite-
> glaucophanite subfacies.

Assemblages of this kind were included for some time in Coombs' (1960) prehnite-pumpellyite-metagraywacke facies. Later, Hashimoto (1966[*]) proposed a division into two separate facies respectively characterized by prehnite-pumpellyite and by pumpellyite-actinolite—a procedure followed since by Japanese and New Zealand geologists (e.g., Coombs et al., 1970) and here adopted for these reasons: the two facies as already pointed out are independent members of different kinds of low-grade facies series of regional metamorphism. The prehnite-pumpellyite facies, for example, dominates one pattern of very low-grade metamorphism and is an integral member of other types of series; the pumpellyite-actinolite facies is the only one of the two to appear in blueschist series, and in these it typically has great areal extent (e.g., in the Franciscan of California, the Sanbagawa belt of Japan).

[*]Cited from Bishop (1972, p. 3182); I have not seen Hashimoto's paper.

Torlesse–Otago Schist Transition, New Zealand Geosyncline

The prograde metamorphic transition from the Torlesse metagraywacke terrane into the chlorite zone of the Otago Schist block (greenschist facies) has been mapped and petrographically studied in great detail by Bishop (1972) in the vicinity of Dansey's Pass on the northeastern edge of the schist block (*A*, Fig. 9-3). Textural and mineralogical isograds in metagraywacke lithology have both been mapped with unusual sharpness. Except where disturbed by postmetamorphic faulting the two have the same general trend, though they nowhere precisely coincide.

The lowest grade is that of the prehnite-pumpellyite facies regionally typical of the whole Torlesse Group starting from this paragenesis to the north. Isograds are based on successive elimination, in prograde order, of prehnite and pumpellyite. In the three zones thus defined characteristic minerals in metagraywacke assemblages (with quartz and albite in all cases) are as listed in prograde order below (minor or sporadic constituents in parentheses; textural zones indicated T1, T2, T3):

1. Prehnite-pumpellyite facies (T1): prehnite-pumpellyite-chlorite-white mica-stilpnomelane (rare actinolite).
2. Pumpellyite-actinolite facies (mainly T2): pumpellyite-actinolite-clinozoisite-chlorite-white mica-stilpnomelane (prehnite very rare indeed). Actinolite and clinozoisite are present, respectively, in 20 and 10 percent of the many specimens examined (as compared with 45 and 98 percent of specimens in the greenschist zone).
3. Greenschist facies (T3): clinozoisite-actinolite-chlorite-white mica-stilpnomelane (with minor pumpellyite still present in 30 percent of the specimens).

Extrapolating these findings to other parts of the New Zealand Geosyncline with which he is familiar, Bishop (1972, p. 3194) considers it likely that most of the rocks in the extensive Chl 2 (T2) zone as shown on the geological map of New Zealand belong to the pumpellyite-actinolite facies.

Taveyanne Formation, Swiss Alps

The Eocene Taveyanne formation of the Dauphiné-Helvetic domain in the Swiss-French Alps (cf. Fig. 9-15) carries a regional imprint of low-grade metamorphism in a prograde zeolite-prehnite-pumpellyite → pumpellyite-actinolite sequence (cf. pp. 337–338). The phase chemistry of the prehnite-pumpellyite facies, as it appears in a limited area of volcanogenic metagraywackes in Valais, has been studied in detail by Coombs et al. (1976), whose report brings out the complexities introduced into an otherwise simple metamorphic paragenesis by fluctuations in f_{O_2} and in $X_{CO_2}^{fl}$ in a dominantly aqueous fluid phase. The principal recorded metamorphic assemblages (Fig. 9-7) are

A. Metagraywacke:
1. Quartz-albite-pumpellyite-chlorite-actinolite-white mica-sphene (-epidote-calcite); this is the typical assemblage of the newly crystallized matrix
2. Albite-chlorite-sericite-calcite-anatase; represented by a single specimen

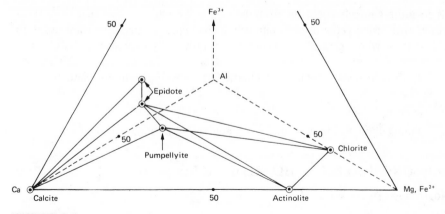

FIGURE 9-7

Pumpellyite-actinolite facies: chemographic relations in metagraywacke assemblages, Taveyanne formation, Valais, Switzerland. Quartz and albite are ubiquitous additional phases (simplified after D. S. Coombs and co-authors, 1968).

B. Veinlets in metagraywacke:
   3. Calcite-albite (-white mica-chlorite)
   4. Albite-clinozoisite-calcite-actinolite
C. Pelitic:
   5. White mica-chlorite-clinozoisite-actinolite-quartz-albite-sphene

     Pumpellyite is uniformly colorless, with a low Fe^{3+}/Al ratio, comparable with that of higher-grade parts of the pumpellyite-actinolite zones on both borders of the Otago–Haast Schist block in New Zealand (Bishop, 1972; Kawachi, 1974). In this respect it closely approaches pumpellyites of Californian blueschists as recorded by Ernst et al. (1970)[*] and contrasts with pumpellyite in assemblages of lower grade elsewhere. White micas, just as in the same facies (and the green-schist facies) in southern New Zealand are phengitic, the Si content being partly a function of rock composition. Actinolites consistently have a Mg/Fe ratio (atomic) about 1.5 and are very low in Al. Absence of stilpnomelane is attributed, not to physical constraints, but to relatively low FeO/MgO ratio in the metagray-wacke system.

     At relatively low temperatures and pressures appropriate to the facies calcium silicates cannot survive the presence of fluids containing appreciable concentra-tions of CO_2. Presence of sphene—the most vulnerable of these silicates—in all but one specimen implies very low $X_{CO_2}^{fl}$ values, estimated at no greater than 0.02. Values of f_{O_2} likewise must have been low—estimated at $<10^{-27}$ for a single specimen containing coexisting pyrrhotite and pyrite (but no magnetite).

     Partly because of the variable compositions of principal phases involved and for lack of textural evidence, critical reactions leading to development of actinolite and to ultimate elimination of pumpellyite are a matter of conjecture. Coombs and

---

[*]Some Californian pumpellyites (porphyroblasts in glaucophane schist) nevertheless are strongly colored.

his co-authors merely conclude, from the now well-established fact that Fe^{3+}/Al decreases with rising grade in both pumpellyite and epidote, that important reactions include those whose general forms (not stoichiometrically treated) may be

$$Fe^{3+}\text{-pumpellyite} + \text{chlorite} + \text{quartz} + H_2 \rightarrow Al\text{-pumpellyite} \pm \text{actinolite}$$

and

$$\text{Pumpellyite} + \text{chlorite} + \text{quartz} \rightarrow \text{``epidote''} + \text{actinolite} + H_2O$$

LAWSONITE–ALBITE–CHLORITE FACIES

Northwestern New Caledonia

Throughout the 150-km extent of a metamorphic belt in northwestern New Caledonia (cf. Fig. 9-12a), metapelitic and metavolcanic assemblages conform for the most part to the blueschist facies (if one includes a subfacies of high grade with decided eclogitic affinities). Most of the rocks themselves are thoroughly schistose and (in metapelites especially) completely recrystallized glaucophane is ubiquitous. The grade diminishes southwestward. Very locally in a narrow coastal strip at the northwestern extremity of the island (Brothers, 1970, Fig. 1, p. 191) it falls off into the lawsonite-albite-chlorite facies. Here, in subzone 1 of the regional lawsonite zone (Fig. 9-8) glaucophane amphiboles are absent even in rocks of metavolcanic lithology. Typical mineral assemblages (cf. Fig. 9-9) are:

1. Metapelitic: quartz-albite-micas (phengite, paragonite)-lawsonite-aragonite (-stilpnomelane-chlorite-sphene-calcite)
2. Metavolcanic: pumpellyite-chlorite (-quartz-albite-phengite-stilpnomelane-sphene-calcite)

Northern California

The structure of the Franciscan terrane in an inland portion of the northern segment of the Californian Coast Ranges is much less disturbed than further south, where in a region centered round San Francisco, numerous major dislocations and mélange zones render it chaotic. So in the north of the state it has been possible to map zones of progressive metamorphism on a regional scale and even to relate these in a general fashion to relative stratigraphic depth (Blake et al., 1967). Isograds trend subparallel to the NW–SE regional structure. Metamorphic grade rises eastward (stratigraphically upward) toward a major NW–SE dislocation that brings the Franciscan into tectonic contact, along its eastern margin, with the Great Valley Sequence of comparable age (Fig. 9-10).

Textural zones have been mapped in rocks of metagraywacke lithology (Ghent, 1965; Blake et al., 1967) along lines similar to those in general use in New Zealand. Microstructures develop progressively from almost purely clastic (zone T1), through semischistose (T2) to recrystallized fully schistose (T3).[*] Two

---

[*]Following usage adopted in this book. Ghent used correspondingly numbered symbols Mgw 1, Mgw 2; Blake and co-authors designate the same zones simply as 1, 2, 3.

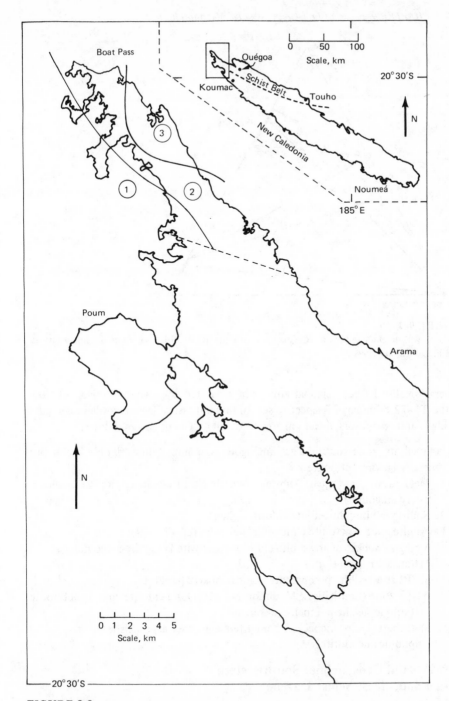

FIGURE 9-8

Northwestern tip of New Caledonia showing subzones 1–3 of the regional lawsonite zone (as defined for the whole blueschist belt) (see Fig. 9-12) (after R. N. Brothers, 1970, Fig. 1). Lawsonite-albite-chlorite facies is confined to subzone 1; subzones 2 and 3 are blueschist facies. Broken line is the approximate northern limit of mélange zone.

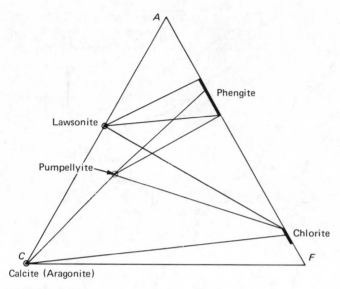

FIGURE 9-9
Lawsonite-albite-chlorite facies: *ACF* diagram for mineral assemblages with quartz and albite as possible additional phases.

mineralogically defined regional zones are separated by a lawsonite isograd close to the T1–T2 boundary. Respective sets of mineral assemblages recorded regionally by Blake and co-authors, locally in greater detail by Ghent, are as follows:

A. Pumpellyite zone: assemblages analogous to pumpellyite-actinolite facies but generally lacking actinolite:
  1. Metagraywacke: quartz-albite-muscovite-chlorite-pumpellyite (± calcite, rarely aragonite)
  2. Spilitic: albite-pumpellyite-chlorite-sphene
B. Lawsonite zone: lawsonite-albite-chlorite facies (cf. Fig. 9-9):
  1. Metagraywacke: quartz-albite-chlorite-muscovite-lawsonite-aragonite
  2. Metabasaltic (spilitic):
    a. T2 zone: albite-pumpellyite-chlorite-quartz (-epidote)
    b. T3 zone (South Fork Mountain Schist): albite-chlorite-epidote-actinolite (stilpnomelane-pumpellyite-sphene)[*]
  3. Metachert: quartz-riebeckite-hematite-magnetite (-aegirine-spessartite-stilpnomelane-biotite)

New Zealand Geosyncline: Southwestern Borderland, Haast Schist Terrane

Toward the southern end of the New Zealand Geosyncline, the grade of metamorphism in the Haast Schist terrane falls off on both the northeastern and the

[*]Ghent records local crossite developing from relict augite—a textural situation that I am inclined to ascribe to metastable crystallization according to Ostwald's principle.

southwestern flanks. But the history and the pattern of metamorphism in the opposite borderlands are decidedly asymmetric (cf. Coombs et al., 1976a). By contrast with the relatively simple pattern recorded along the northeastern flank in the Torlesse–Haast transition just described, that in the southwestern borderlands involves a greater range of stratigraphic-lithologic units; and fragments of the record of metamorphic-tectonic episodes extend further back in time—certainly to the beginning of the Cretaceous (130×10^6 years), and locally perhaps even into the Permian (cf. Coombs et al., pp. 587, 588). Here, in several lithologic-tectonic units, rocks of Permian age show a regional metamorphic pattern that includes the lawsonite-albite-chlorite facies.

Both in this southwestern borderland, and in a precisely matching northern segment of the New Zealand Geosyncline (offset some 400 km along the Alpine

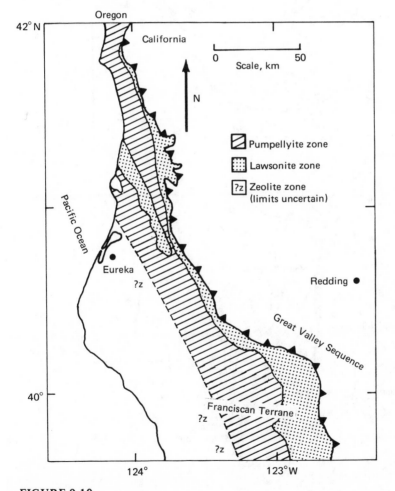

FIGURE 9-10
Low-grade metamorphic zones, Franciscan terrane of northern California (after M. C. Blake, W. P. Irwin, and R. G. Coleman, 1967).

Fault),[*] there is an outward (westward) sequence of stratigraphic-lithologic-tectonic units ("terranes" of Coombs and co-authors) separated by regional vertical dislocations. All of them bear to some degree—even in the outermost Murihiku Terrane (type area of the zeolite facies)—the imprint of Cretaceous (Rangitatan) metamorphism that culminated within the Haast Schist Terrane itself. In sharp tectonic contrast with the latter along the West Wakatipu Fault (Fig. 9-11) is a block of less

[*]Where Coombs (1960) first recorded widespread existence of lawsonite metagraywackes.

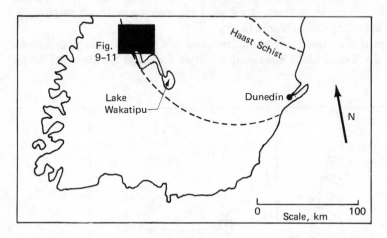

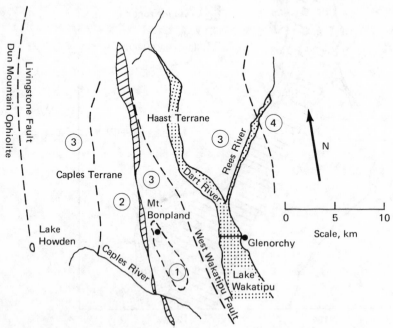

FIGURE 9-11
Metamorphic zones in portion of the Haast-Caples borderland northwest of Lake Wakatipu, southwestern New Zealand (after Y. Kawachi, 1974). (1) Zeolite, (2) lawsonite, and (3) pumpellyite-actinolite.

strongly metamorphosed rocks designated the Caples Terrane. It is generally thought that the western part of the Haast Schist Group includes more strongly metamorphosed equivalents of Caples metavolcanics, tectonically integrated with schists that, 100 km to the east, merge into metagraywackes of the Torlesse Group. The western margin of the Caples Terrane is an abrupt tectonic contact—along the Livingstone Fault—with the southern segment of a mélange-ridden ophiolite belt (Dun Mountain belt), also of Permian age.

It is within the Caples Terrane that the progressive series that includes the lawsonite-albite-chlorite facies is most clearly displayed. We turn particularly to an account by Kawachi (1974), who has mapped an area of some 900 km^2 in a region of high topographic relief (~2000 m) northwest of Lake Wakatipu (Fig. 9-11). Here the Caples Terrane is about 15 km wide, and within it the prograde facies series is

Prehnite-pumpellyite → lawsonite-albite-chlorite → pumpellyite-actinolite

But beyond the West Wakatipu Fault in the adjacent Haast Terrane, the series is extended one stage further into the greenschist facies.

The prograde zonal mineralogical sequence mapped by Kawachi in metagraywackes and metavolcanics of the Caples, with corresponding stages of textural development T1 → T4 is as follows:

1. Prehnite zone: prehnite-pumpellyite facies; textural zone T1. Zeolites are absent.
2. Lawsonite zone: lawsonite-albite-chlorite facies; textural zones T1–T2.
3. Pumpellyite-actinolite zone: pumpellyite-actinolite facies; textural zones T2–T3.
4. Greenschist-facies zone of Haast Schists; textural zone T4; pumpellyite absent.

In the lawsonite zone the diagnostic assemblage is quartz-albite-pumpellyite-lawsonite-muscovite-chlorite-sphene. Lawsonite is widespread, but in only 20 percent of specimens having this general lithology. Aragonite, though carefully sought, has not been found.

Lawsonite metagraywackes of an identical kind were first discovered by Coombs (1960) in same tectonic-stratigraphic situation but in the northern segment of the corresponding terrane (Pelorus group) where it is offset some 400 km northeast along the Alpine Fault (Fig. 7-5a).

Synthesis: Relation to Blueschist Facies

The lawsonite-albite-chlorite and the blueschist facies have unique characteristics in common. They are the only two facies characterized by lawsonite and/or aragonite, both of them dense phases known from experiment to be stable (even at low temperatures) only at pressures above $3\frac{1}{2}$–5 kb. And, not unexpectedly in view of their common association in the field, the lawsonite-albite-chlorite, like the blueschist facies, is virtually unknown in rocks more than 300 million years old. Yet the two facies are neither identical nor inseparable. The three examples described were selected to bring out the reality and yet the looseness of the mutual relation between the two:

In New Caledonia there is direct prograde transition (albeit in a limited area) from the lawsonite-albite-chlorite into the blueschist facies.

In northern California a sequence otherwise like that of typical blueschist facies series reaches its maximum grade—along a major dislocation zone—in the lawsonite-albite-chlorite facies. Yet in the same region masses of coarse blueschist lithology, mostly small, but some as much as 1000 m long, have been tectonically transported onto the regional low-grade Franciscan Terrane (e.g., Ernst et al., 1970, Pl. 1, p. 34). Further south in the Franciscan belt field in the Diabolo Range (Fig. 9-13) transitions have been mapped between the two facies (Ernst et al., 1970, p. 56).

In southern New Zealand the lawsonite-albite-chlorite facies is a member of a facies series of a distinctly different type. In this series the prehnite-pumpellyite facies is widely represented in low-grade rocks, and metamorphism culminates in the greenschist facies. The blueschist facies as here defined, in spite of careful search, seems to be absent. Implications as to a possible unusual pressure-temperature regime, complicated perhaps by chronological breaks, will be taken up in the final chapter.

BLUESCHIST FACIES

Scope and Limits

Eskola's glaucophane-schist facies, notwithstanding earlier views to the contrary (e.g., Turner, 1948, p. 100) has long come to be recognized as having valid status (e.g., Brouwer and Egeler, 1952, pp. 56, 57). In fact in its typical development, with assemblages containing lawsonite and/or jadeitic pyroxene as well as glaucophane, it is one of the most satisfactorily defined facies generally recognized today. There has been a good deal of confusion during the past four decades as to nomenclature and mineralogical limits of the facies and regarding the status (component subfacies, transitional or independent facies) of certain parageneses that have obvious field and mineralogical affiliations with the typical glaucophane-lawsonite (-jadeite) paragenesis.[*] Much of this confusion is now resolved. But the reader of classic accounts of glaucophane-schist metamorphism should be aware of the changing context in which they were written; and opinions still differ on some aspects of nomenclature and interpretation.

To clarify the present discussion these points in terminology are stressed at the outset:

1. For reasons stated in Chap. 7, Bailey's term "blueschist facies" has been adopted in place of "glaucophane-schist" and "glaucophane-lawsonite-schist" as previously used for the same paragenesis.

2. The blueschist facies is limited here to parageneses with mineral assemblages that include a true glaucophanic amphibole (as distinct from the blue amphiboles of the riebeckite and actinolite series), along with at least one of the characteristic high-pressure phases—aragonite, lawsonite, jadeitic pyroxene.

---

[*]Witness changes in treatment by the present writer since 1948.

3. Parageneses with lawsonite and/or aragonite but lacking glaucophane are now placed in the separate lawsonite-albite-chlorite facies.

4. Parageneses with widespread glaucophane (or crossite) but lacking any of the other diagnostic phases (aragonite, lawsonite, or jadeitic pyroxene) are treated as transitional toward the greenschist facies. If a sharp line of demarcation must be drawn between the two, the appropriate point is where glaucophane (or crossite) plus epidote gives way to actinolite-albite-magnetite (E. H. Brown, 1974, p. 342).

Choice of Illustrative Examples

The mineral paragenesis and tectonic settings of the blueschist facies will be illustrated by four examples, all located in young (Cretaceous to mid-Tertiary) metamorphic belts. In northwestern New Caledonia various stages of prograde metamorphism within the blueschist facies are fully and continuously displayed. In the Franciscan Terrane of the California Coast Ranges there is a somewhat similar (though not identical) prograde pattern; but the structure, and thus the facies series itself, is highly disturbed over large areas. In the Pennine domain of the western Alps, early eclogitic and blueschist metamorphism has been partially obliterated by a greenschist-amphibolite imprint later in the same major orogeny. And finally the extensive Sanbagawa belt of Japan illustrates a greenschist facies pattern that locally develops characteristics of blueschist metamorphism.

Blueschist Belt, New Caledonia

We have already referred to a small area at the northwestern tip of New Caledonia, where the metamorphic paragenesis is that of the lawsonite-albite-chlorite facies (Fig. 9-8). This is marginal to a much more extensive belt, 170 km long, in which a thick mass of Cretaceous and Eocene sediments and volcanics was metamorphosed in the blueschist facies in late Eocene to early Oligocene times, $\sim 38 \times 10^6$ years (Blake et al., 1977).[*] The belt has been mapped in detail and extensively studied—following regional mapping by French geologists—by a New Zealand team headed by A. R. Lillie (stratigraphy and structure, Lillie, 1970, 1975, Lillie and Brothers, 1970; metamorphic geology, Brothers, 1970, 1974; mineralogy and geochemistry, Black, 1969, 1973a, 1973b, 1974a, 1974b, 1978).

The gross regional structure, especially along the southwestern longitudinal sector is rather simple. Bedding and schistosity folded about regional horizontal axes dip vertically or southwestward toward the adjoining (structurally higher) mélange of Jurassic and Triassic sediments (cf. Fig. 7-6). But on a generally smaller scale—extending down to penetrative mesoscopic structures—a second generation of folds and accompanying lineations plunges steeply down. This second phase of folding was essentially synchronous with culmination of metamorphism (Lillie, 1970, p. 169; 1975, p. 237). On the eastern side of the belt where metamorphic grade attains its maximum, the structure is much more complex.

---

[*]Blueschist assemblages with glaucophane and lawsonite appear locally in Mesozoic metagraywackes extending southeast of the mélange zone of Fig. 9-12a and affected by regional metamorphism of lower grade (pumpellyite assemblages). This is an earlier and independent phase of blueschist metamorphism dated as late Jurassic.

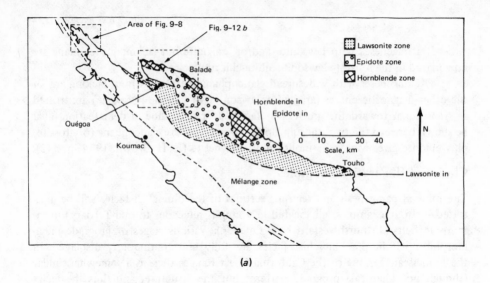

(a)

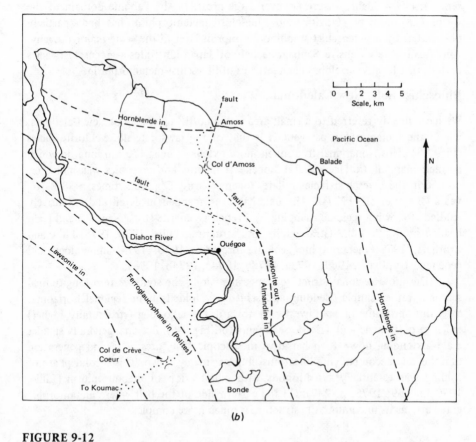

(b)

FIGURE 9-12

(a) Metamorphic zones in blueschist belt, northwestern New Caledonia (after R. N. Brothers, 1974). (b) Detail of rectangular area in (a) (after P. M. Black, 1977); Koumac-Amoss Road, dotted.

Isograd Pattern

Isograds everywhere run parallel to the regional (mainly NW–SE) structural trend; where the latter swings sharply to the south at the great bend in the Diahot River near Ouégoa, the isograds do precisely likewise as shown in Fig. 9-12*b* (cf. maps of Lillie, 1970, Fig. 2, and Black, 1978, Fig. 1).* In the regional picture the grade of metamorphism increases northeastward, i.e., in a general way stratigraphically downward, and in the sense of increasing structural complexity. These relations can be seen in an almost continuous section east of Col de Crève Couer on the Koumac-Ouégoa-Amoss road (Fig. 9-12).

Brothers mapped three principal zones of prograde metamorphism trending NW–SE parallel to the blueschist belt and to the axis of the island. Successive mineral indices in completely recrystallized metapelites are lawsonite, epidote-almandine, and blue-green (barroisitic) hornblende. A glaucophanic amphibole is prominent, at least in metabasalts, at all grades (except at the extreme northwestern tip of the island, Fig. 9-8); so the regional paragenesis represents an unusually complete and well-documented blueschist facies series. The three corresponding isograds in metabasalts approximately coincide with those based on metapelitic lithology. But intermediate isograds (e.g., Na-amphibole in and omphacite in) in metabasalts are offset in the downgrade sense with respect to counterparts in metapelites.

Finally Black (1977) has combined results of her own field and mineralogical studies in the Ouégoa district with Brothers's regional work to map, across a transverse strip 25 km wide, a sequence of no fewer than nine isograds in the two combined lithologies. The result, based on thousands of field observations and examination of several thousand thin sections by both workers, is the most refined picture of progressive blueschist metamorphism known to this writer. The summary that follows refers to the three principal zones mapped in metapelites by Brothers and elaborated by Black with special emphasis on the Ouégoa district (Fig. 9-12*b*). Assessment of facies, which differs somewhat from views expressed by Brothers (1974, p. 119) and by Black (1977, p. 106), represents the opinion of the present author.

Lawsonite Zone

At the southwestern edge of the blueschist belt (along the adjacent mélange boundary), lawsonite is already widespread in metapelites and metabasalts alike. So the lawsonite isograd coincides with the northeastern edge of the mélange zone. A ferroglaucophane isograd, 4 km beyond that for lawsonite, marks the first appearance of sodic amphibole in metapelites and consequent full development of typical lawsonite-zone assemblages.

1. Metapelitic: quartz-albite-phengite-paragonite-lawsonite-ferroglaucophane-chlorite-sphene (-spessartite-calcite)†
2. Metabasaltic: albite-lawsonite-pumpellyite-glaucophane-actinolite-chlorite-stilpnomelane-sphene

---

*This major flexure is ascribed by Lillie (1970, p. 102) to a third (postmetamorphic) phase of deformation.

†Aragonite, the typical carbonate at the lowest grade represented at the northwestern tip of the island (zone 1, Fig. 9-8), is found nowhere else in the blueschist belt.

Pelitic assemblages in the subzone of minimal metamorphism just before the law-sonite isograd lack both ferroglaucophane and spessartite.

Epidote Zone

The epidote isograd is drawn where epidote first appears in both lithologies at the expense of lawsonite. This occurs within a narrow transition zone 3 or 4 km wide where a prograde sequence of changes, each expressed as an isograd, is clustered: omphacite first appears sparingly (rimming relict augite) in metabasalt; graphite in metapelites becomes fully ordered; epidote appears at the expense of lawsonite, and pumpellyite cuts out; almandine comes in, and lawsonite is finally eliminated. Beyond this transition area, in the epidote zone proper, the general paragenesis can be represented thus:

1. Metapelitic assemblages: quartz-albite-phengite-paragonite-epidote-glaucophane-chlorite-graphite-sphene (-calcite)
2. Metabasaltic assemblages: albite-epidote-glaucophane-actinolite (aluminous)-chlorite-phengite-omphacite (Jd_{40-50})-almandine-sphene (±rutile)

Hornblende Zone

At the hornblende isograd a calcic amphibole, blue-green barroisitic hornblende, appears for the first time in metapelites; and simultaneously actinolite of meta-basalts, which has become increasingly aluminous across the epidote zone, assumes the same composition. These changes signify the maximum grade reached in the blueschist belt. Coexisting with hornblende, glaucophane remains a characteristic mineral. Rutile now takes the place of sphene in both lithologies; omphacite now becomes widespread in metapelites, and paragonite in metabasalts.

Isograd Reactions

Black (1977, p. 98) suggests the following general reactions at the principal isograds.
   At the *epidote* and closely adjacent *almandine* isograds:

A. In metapelites:
   1. Lawsonite + Fe-chlorite + ferroglaucophane → epidote + almandine + Mg-chlorite + glaucophane
   2. Lawsonite + Fe-chlorite + albite → epidote + Mg-chlorite + paragonite
B. In metabasalts:
   3. Pumpellyite + chlorite → epidote + actinolite
   4. Lawsonite + Fe-chlorite + crossite → epidote + almandine + Mg-chlorite + glaucophane
   At the *hornblende* isograd:
   5. Albite + epidote + glaucophane → omphacite + almandine + paragonite + hornblende

Prograde Changes in Solid-Solution Series

Prograde changes in solid solution series, some of them interdependent (especially with regard to Mg-Fe partitioning) are as follows:

1. The ratio $Mg/(Mg + Fe^{2+})$ in chlorite rises sharply at the epidote isograd (cf. reactions 1, 2, and 4 above).

2. At the same point ferroglaucophane of metapelites gives way to typical magnesian glaucophane-crossite (which from the first was the ubiquitous sodic amphibole of metabasalts).
3. In metabasalts calcic amphibole gradually changes, with increasing Na and Al, to aluminous actinolite and then to barroisitic hornblende (cf. reaction 5).
4. Fe^{2+} of phengites drops significantly at the epidote isograd.
5. Garnet (Black, 1973a) occurs in zoned crystals mostly between 0.2-1.0 mm in diameter. Except for spessartites of low-grade metapelites they are almandines with 15-25 percent grossularite. With increasing metamorphic grade, and in individual grains from core to rim, spessartite diminishes and pyrope shows a tendency to increase. Even in the hornblende zone the rim garnet remains essentially a grossularite-bearing almandine. The average composition of five high-grade garnets tabulated by Black (1973a, Table 2, 9938 to 9674 listed consecutively, p. 229) is: core, $Al_{38} Sp_{36} Pyr_7 Gr_{19}$; rim, $Al_{57} Sp_{12} Pyr_{13} Gr_{18}$.
6. Albite shows a slight but significant increase in anorthite content (An_0 to An_7).

Metamorphic Facies

The lawsonite-zone paragenesis (except at the extreme northwestern tip of the island) is typical, by any definition, of the blueschist facies. It covers about half the total area of the blueschist belt. In the epidote zone absence of lawsonite represents a significant departure, but glaucophane is ubiquitous and omphacite is a common minor phase. The total picture suggests a high-grade variant (local subfacies) of the blueschist facies. A still higher grade is reached in the hornblende zone, where rutile, omphacite, and paragonite convey a strong hint of eclogitic affinities. Moreover rim compositions in garnet fall neatly into the field characteristic of eclogites of "Group C" as defined by Coleman and co-authors (1965). These are eclogites that occur as tectonically emplaced blocks in Californian and other blueschist terranes—including a block located on the beach close to Amoss, New Caledonia (Coleman et al., 1965, p. 490). The hornblende-zone paragenesis nevertheless is far removed from that of typical eclogites, even those of Group C; for albite, amphiboles, and epidote far outweigh garnet, omphacite, and rutile in metabasaltic assemblages. It represents a high-grade variant (local subfacies) of the blueschist facies, trending in the direction of eclogite.

Franciscan Blueschists, California Coast Ranges

Synopsis of Franciscan Metamorphism

Throughout the northern half of the California Coast Ranges the oldest exposed rocks are geosynclinal sediments (mainly graywackes) and subordinate but widespread basic volcanics, collectively comprising the Franciscan Group, of Jurassic and early Cretaceous age. As mentioned in Chap. 7, regional mélange is widespread and "Alpine-type" serpentinite bodies, some of them demonstrably ophiolitic, abound. Along its eastern margin, the Franciscan Terrane is in tectonic contact with roughly contemporaneous marine sediments of a different lithofacies, the Great Valley Sequence, at the base of which (i.e., along the contact itself) is a more or less continuous ophiolitic sheet.

From the metamorphic standpoint Franciscan rocks in different domains fall into three categories.

1. Most extensive are domains of apparently unmetamorphosed rocks indurated by diagenesis but totally lacking schistosity (textural type T1). Even here, however, microscopic scrutiny of metagraywackes reveals signs of incipient recrystallization in a thin discontinuous matrix of quartz, albite, and phyllosilicates—in some cases, pumpellyite or laumontite as well—separating clasts of quartz, plagioclase and mica, shale chips, and other lithic fragments. Associated pillow basalts commonly are spilitic. Such domains have in the past been mapped as "unmetamorphosed." And so for the purpose of present discussion—without prejudice as to semantic niceties—we may continue to call them.

2. Domains of the first type pass gradually into or are faulted against a second type in which signs of regional metamorphism everywhere are obvious on both the microscopic and the mesoscopic scale. Graywackes (more properly metagraywackes) are now distinctly schistose, but lack segregation banding; and microscopically the fine-grained newly crystallized matrix is conspicuous (textural type T2) and ultimately comes completely to dominate the microstructure (T3). Such rocks are metamorphic by any standard. Conspicuous among the metamorphic phases are lawsonite, aragonite, and in the higher grades of metamorphism, impure jadeite and glaucophane. Only since Bloxam (1956) discovered the widespread development of Franciscan jadeite metagraywackes* has the metamorphic status of such domains been generally recognized. Now we realize that metagraywackes once mapped as "unmetamorphosed" represent the only continuous and truly regional development of the blueschist and lawsonite-albite-chlorite facies in the Franciscan Terrane.

3. Much more spectacular mineralogically, and intermittently widespread, are clusters of isolated blocks, individually seldom more than a few meters across ("knockers") and numerous interspersed smaller fragments of coarsely crystalline glaucophane schist, "greenstone," and subordinate but still widely distributed amphibolite and eclogite.† Almost invariably they are littered over outcropping surfaces of metagraywacke and serpentinite. There is in fact a pronounced tendency for field association with serpentinite; and there are specific records of blocks of blueschist, amphibolite, and related rocks partially enclosed in serpentinite bodies (e.g., Coleman, 1961; Ernst et al., 1970, p. 59). Underscoring this tendency is the common presence of superficial rinds of actinolite, chlorite, and talc, sometimes bright green with dispersed chrome mica, coating blueschist or amphibolite blocks and testifying to former prolonged reaction of these with enclosing serpentinite. It is now generally agreed that metamorphic rocks of this third category are fragments tectonically transported from some deeper source to their present sites; and in some cases at least serpentinite seems to have been an aid to or even the actual vehicle of transport. In a few localities, much larger

---

*W. P. De Roever (1955) had already identified quartz-jadeite metagraywackes in Celebes and drawn attention to their possible significance in blueschist metamorphism.

†Classic accounts of Californian blueschists and eclogites are based exclusively on materials of this kind (e.g., Ransome, 1894, 1895; J. P. Smith, 1907; Taliaferro, 1943).

coarse blueschist slabs, hundreds of meters long, have clearly been transported long distances from unknown sources. Some of these carry the familiar external chrome-mica or actinolite-talc rind.

No direct transition has been observed in the field between rocks of categories 2 and 3. There is greater mineralogical variety among rocks of the latter class and some rather striking mineralogical differences between the two groups. Collectively, however, the "tectonic blocks"—as we shall now call them—conform to Franciscan protolithology, with emphasis on basaltic rather than graywacke parentage. Together, all three categories could be said to represent a Franciscan metamorphic pattern (facies series), partially disrupted in space, perhaps discontinuous even in time, and with the nature—the existence even—of the final link questionable. It could perhaps be represented as

Zeolite → pumpellyite-actinolite → lawsonite-albite-chlorite

→ blueschist- — ? → eclogite

It is now proposed to consider the blueschist paragenesis as it is developed in a central sector of the Coast Ranges within about 200 km north and south of the city of San Francisco—a region of highly disturbed structure and abundant serpentinite intrusions. Regionally developed assemblages will be treated separately from those displayed in tectonically transported blocks. The eclogite end of the series will be considered more appropriately once more, along with other eclogites, late in the next chapter.

Regional Blueschist Metamorphism, Central Coast Ranges

Blueschist metamorphism on a regional scale will be illustrated by data from two widely separated well-documented occurrences (Fig. 9-13): the Diablo Range, 130 X 25 km, southeast of San Francisco (Ernst, 1965, 1971b; Seki et al., 1969, pp. 14-30; Ernst et al., 1970, pp. 37-56, 113-172), and a 300-m continuous section along Ward Creek, near Cazadero 100 km to the northwest (Coleman and Lee, 1963; Coleman et al., 1965, pp. 491-492). Both in the Diablo Range and in the general region mapped by E. H. Bailey (Coleman and Lee, 1963, p. 263) within a radius of a kilometer or two of the Ward Creek section, domains of different metamorphic grade are mutually interspersed, the maximum grade being that of the blueschist facies. Domain boundaries seem in some cases to be transitional (a true isograd), as between lawsonite-albite-chlorite and blueschist domains in the Diablo Range and between domains of "unmetamorphosed" rocks and of partially developed blueschist facies in the Cazadero region (type I → type II in the terminology of Coleman and Lee). More commonly boundaries are tectonically defined or at most of a problematic nature; for this central sector of the Coast Ranges is a region of maximum structural disturbance within a strongly deformed mobile belt.

In parts of the Diablo Range a jadeite "isograd" has been mapped separating blueschist domains covering more than 500 km^2 from even larger domains of lawsonite-albite-chlorite grade (McKee, 1962). It represents sharp diminution and

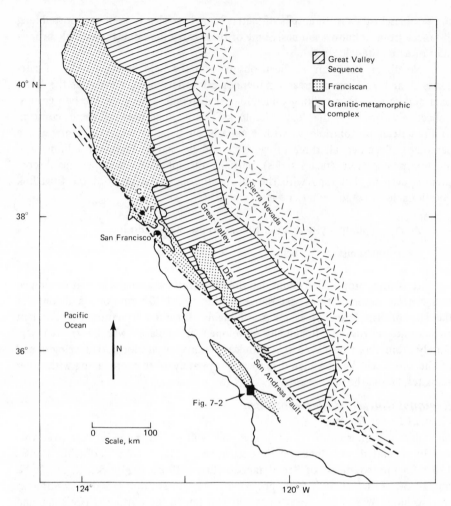

FIGURE 9-13
Franciscan terrane east of the San Andreas Fault, central Coast Ranges, California (simplified after B. M. Page, 1966) showing localities of regional blueschist metamorphism referred to in text (DR, Diablo Range; C, Cazadero; VF, Valley Ford). Also shown is the location of the mélange zone, Fig. 2.

final elimination of albite, and appearance of jadeitic pyroxene in the regionally dominant metagraywacke lithology; but the significance of such "isograds"—transitional or faulted—remains in doubt (Ernst, 1971b, p. 434).

The blueschist paragenesis in the Diablo Range, as displayed especially in the Pacheco Pass area (Ernst et al., 1971b), can be summarized thus:

A. Metagraywacke:
   1. Quartz-jadeite (Jd_{75-90})-muscovite-chlorite-lawsonite (-glaucophane), always with accessory sphene

B. Metabasalt:
   2. Lawsonite-chlorite-jadeite (Jd_{70}–Jd_{80})-glaucophane-sphene
   3. Glaucophane-lawsonite-sphene

Possible minor constituents in both cases are quartz, stilpnomelane, aragonite (or calcite). Absence of pumpellyite and epidote is characteristic.

    Sodic pyroxenes of Pacheco Pass metabasalts have been identified on the basis of a dozen measurements of d_{310} spacings (Seki et al., 1969, Table 20; compare with Table 8) as omphacite similar to that of eclogite in tectonic blocks (Ernst et al., 1970, p. 153). However the d_{310} values cluster strongly between 2.85 and 2.855, which, according to the chart of Ernst and co-authors (1971, p. 154), correspond to Jd_{65}–Jd_{70}. A single recorded chemical analysis (X-24, *ibid.*, p. 150[*]) calculates to $Di_{19}Jd_{75}Ac_6$. One can only conclude that the pyroxenes in these metabasalts are impure jadeites, appreciably but not greatly more diopsidic than those of associated metagraywackes.

    Here and there in the Diablo Range Franciscan metasediments include small bands and lenses of conglomerate with pebbles of granitic rocks, porphyritic volcanics, chert, and other materials. In a few cases these have been completely replaced by assemblages isofacial with enclosing metagraywackes. The products tend to be simple combinations of lawsonite, glaucophane, jadeite, chlorite, quartz, and aragonite (Fyfe and Zardini, 1967; Platt et al., 1976).

    Turning now to the Cazadero locality, the section continuously exposed for 300 m along Ward Creek (Coleman and Lee, 1963) is thought to represent a local domain of regional metamorphism within the larger region of E. H. Bailey's map. Coleman and co-authors recognize two mutually gradational lithologic suites— type II partially, type III fully, recrystallized.[†] Both types conform to the blueschist facies. Recorded mineral assemblages include

A. Pelitic:
   1. Quartz-muscovite-crossite-epidote-garnet (-ilmenohematite)
B. Metachert:
   2. Quartz-stilpnomelane-garnet (manganiferous)-pyrite-orthoamphibole?
C. Metacarbonate:
   3. Aragonite plus minor silicates
D. Metabasalt (the dominant lithology in the Ward Creek section):
   4. Glaucophane-pumpellyite-omphacite-muscovite-chlorite-lawsonite (-sphene-pyrite-quartz) in rocks of type III
   5. Lawsonite-omphacite-glaucophane-chlorite (-aragonite-muscovite-sphene-quartz) in rocks of type II

The protolithology differs from that in the Diablo Range in that metagraywacke is not represented and metabasalts predominate. The respective metabasaltic assemblages of the two regions are similar in complete absence of epidote; but they

[*]Pyroxene from an analyzed spilitic metabasalt, *ibid.*, p. 53, Table 8.
[†]In the same general region, type I comprises virtually "unmetamorphosed" rocks, type IV the coarsely crystalline rocks of exotic tectonic blocks.

differ in two important respects: presence of pumpellyite at Ward Creek and significant difference as to composition of sodic pyroxene. In Ward Creek metabasalts this is omphacite, $Jd_{40}Di_{50}Ac_{10}$ (similar to the pyroxene of California eclogites) or in one case chloromelanite, $Jd_{40}Di_{30}Ac_{30}$ (Coleman et al., 1965, analyses 6 and 7); in metabasalts of the Diabolo Range it is impure jadeite, $Jd_{\geqslant 70}$, suggesting perhaps a somewhat lower grade of metamorphism than at Cazadero.

Blueschist Paragenesis of Tectonic Blocks

Much of the literature on blueschist metamorphism in the Franciscan concerns the mineralogy and petrography of tectonically emplaced blocks. For, in spite of their insignificant total volume, these are conspicuous in outcrop and spectacular mineralogically. A few selected references illustrate the nature and variety of paragenesis collectively represented by this type of occurrence (category 3, earlier in this section) and some of the problems they pose regarding facies pattern and possible mutual relationships: J. P. Smith (1907); Brothers (1954); Borg (1956); Bloxam (1959); Bailey et al. (1962); Coleman and Lee (1963): Coleman et al. (1965); Agrell et al. (1965); Ernst et al. (1971, pp. 57–82); Hermes (1973).

From the facies standpoint, it is convenient to consider tectonic blocks in several lithological categories.

A. Jadeite metagraywackes and massive "greenstones" that duplicate blueschist lithology as developed elsewhere in the Franciscan on a regional scale (Bloxam, 1959). Such occurrences have received little attention and present no special problem.

B. Coarse-grained well-foliated glaucophane schists, commonly showing segregation banding and cut here and there by cross veinlets of pumpellyite, lawsonite, or some other cofacial single mineral. This is the commonest type of tectonic block. Most blocks are metabasalts but some are metagraywackes. On the scale of a thin section the mineralogical composition tends to be rather simple— some combination of two to five principal phases plus accessories. Glaucophane is almost ubiquitous, lawsonite very common, pumpellyite and omphacite ($Jd_{\sim 40}$) less so but each prominent in some rocks. Widespread less abundant associates are chlorite, phengite, actinolite, and stilpnomelane. A few rocks contain albite and/or quartz. Sphene is a universal and in some rocks prominent accessory, apatite almost equally common. Carbonate where present may be aragonite or calcite.

What distinguishes the general paragenesis from blueschists of regional domains in the Franciscan—apart from coarse grain and segregation banding—is the common appearance of porphyroblastic almandine and in some rocks conspicuous green epidote. As in New Caledonia, almandines invariably carry significant amounts (30–35 mol%) of grossularite but are low in pyrope and spessartite (cf. Pabst, 1931; Lee et al., 1963; Ernst et al., 1971, pp. 164–168).

C. Metacherts. Large blocks of ferruginous chert from several localities yield the same general type of mineral assemblage—greatly predominent quartz plus combinations of stilpnomelane, spessartite, crossite, and, less commonly, green epidote or aegirine. A large mass of metachert near Laytonville, 250 km northwest of San Francisco, is remarkable for the presence of three additional otherwise rare minerals—deerite, howieite, and zussmanite.

D. Jadeite rock. This is a rare type of tectonic block, but of interest from a mineralogical standpoint and for its pressure-temperature implications. The best-known occurrence—Clear Creek in San Benito County, 230 km southeast of San Francisco—takes the form of blocks a meter or two across completely enclosed in a large body of serpentinite (Yoder and Chesterman, 1951; Coleman, 1961). Their principal mineral constituent is almost pure jadeite (Jd_{95}) with which may be associated albite, never quartz. The parent rock is metakeratophyre, in some cases perhaps albitite, which appears to have attained present compositions by loss of silica to enclosing serpentinite. Such an origin is rendered plausible by the general presence of microscopically dispersed brucite in Franciscan serpentinites elsewhere; for this, if also a component of San Benito serpentinite, could provide the necessary "silica-sink" for the kind of desilication reaction necessary to produce jadeite from albite. Pure jadeites of this kind are quite distinct from impure jadeites characteristic of Franciscan quartz-jadeite metagraywackes.

E. Eclogite. Eclogite is one of the more spectacular lithologic types widely represented among tectonic blocks. Its petrogenic significance is considered further, along with that of other types of eclogite, in Chap. 10. Here it is enough to note that Californian eclogites conform to type in that they are of basaltic composition and consist of omphacite, almandine-rich garnet and minor but ubiquitous rutile. In almost every occurrence there are indications of retrograde alterations to minerals of the blueschist facies—among them pumpellyite, lawsonite, glaucophane, aragonite, chlorite, and white mica. On the other hand there are also blueschists in which abundance of garnet and veining with omphacite suggest a possible prograde transition in progress (Essene and Fyfe, 1967); for in such rocks both garnet and omphacite are identical chemically with corresponding phases in eclogite. Most intriguing, and seemingly impossible to explain by any simple physical model, is a gneissic block of blueschist from the Ward Creek locality. In a single thin section taken from this block, Coleman and co-authors (1965, p. 493, Fig. 7) found a sharply defined eclogite band (omphacite and euhedral garnet) sandwiched between bands consisting individually of glaucophane-epidote-muscovite-garnet, epidote-garnet, and garnet-glaucophane-omphacite.

The sum of recorded mineralogical and textural evidence strongly suggests that in the Franciscan terrane there is some kind of a genetic relation between the blueschist and the eclogite facies as they are presently displayed in isolated tectonic blocks.

F. Amphibolite. A common rock type where serpentinite is abundant consists largely of blue-green or olive-green hornblende. Although plagioclase is usually lacking—or if present is albite—such rocks have generally been called amphibolite. Some contain ragged remnants of omphacite, partially destroyed garnets and sphene-coated grains of rutile. These clearly are retrograde derivatives of eclogite—a status that is emphasized by a tendency for cross-veining with glaucophane, actinolite, chlorite, or pumpellyite. But there is another category of "amphibolite," for which there is no reason to suppose such an origin: associated here with hornblende may be almandine, epidote, aluminous diopside, or glaucophane. The paragenesis corresponds strictly neither to the blueschist nor to the amphibolite facies. Yet the field association suggests some kind of vague relation to the blue-schist and possibly to the eclogite facies.

Two unusually large tectonic blocks of pyroxene-garnet amphibolite en-closed in metagraywacke (lawsonite-albite-chlorite facies) near Panoche Pass in the Diablo Range show pervasive retrograde changes to an assemblage of albite-lawsonite-pumpellyite-phengite-sphene with sodic pyroxene and second-generation amphiboles (Hermes, 1973). The latter include actinolite and crossite-riebeckite; the pyroxene is acmitic in cross-cutting veinlets, but omphacite where it fringes first-generation calcic pyroxene. Textural relations suggest (to the present writer) that both omphacite and blue amphibole could have crystallized metastably accord-ing to Ostwald's step principle.

Chronology of Franciscan Sedimentation and Metamorphism

Paleontological evidence places the total span of Franciscan sedimentation as late Jurassic to late Cretaceous. Radiometric dates for metamorphic micas are rather scanty, but they cover a closely comparable time span—latest Jurassic (150×10^6 years) to mid-Cretaceous (100×10^6 years). It is possible, but by no means estab-lished, that they represent successive distinct episodes, separated in time by as much as 50 million years (cf. Ernst et al., 1970, p. 36). More data are required. Since maximum metamorphic temperatures in all cases must have been low, radio-metric data may represent true "metamorphic" rather than "cooling" dates.

Blueschist-Greenschist Transition, Sanbagawa Belt, Japan

Location and General Character

The Sanbagawa metamorphic belt—consisting largely of Permian sediments and volcanic rocks metamorphosed in mid-Cretaceous or possibly earlier times (Ueda et al., 1977)—extends longitudinally for more than 1000 km along the main islands of Japan. Its width, exclusive of the zeolite zone, averages 35 km. Its northwestern margin is a profound vertical axial dislocation, the Median Tectonic Line (Fig. 9-14); from this the grade everywhere drops off southward and eastward toward the Pacific Ocean. This is the site of many studies of regional metamorphism in which glaucophane schists are conspicuous (e.g., Suzuki, 1930; Miyashiro and Banno, 1958; Miyashiro and Seki, 1958; Banno, 1958, 1959, 1964; Seki, 1961; Iwasaki, 1963). It was here that Miyashiro (1961) drew attention to the importance of glaucophane schists in regional metamorphism around the Pacific margins. He designated the Sanbagawa belt as a type for regional metamorphism with high-pressure implications; and its spectacular juxtaposition with the Ryoke low-pressure belt across the Median Tectonic Line was the basis of his generalized concept of "paired metamorphic belts."

Glaucophanic amphibole (mainly crossite) is widespread, at least as a scat-tered minor mineral, throughout the Sanbagawa belt. But the overall metamorphic pattern only impinges on the blueschist facies proper; for this is limited to a few small patches of jadeite- and lawsonite-bearing rocks within an extensive green-schist (chlorite) zone in the Kanto Mountains and the Sibukawa district of central

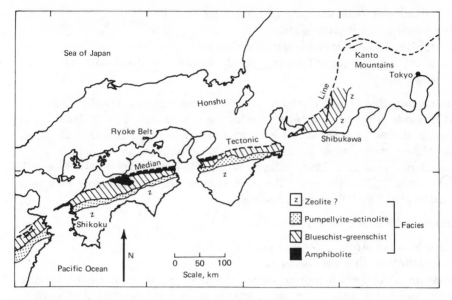

FIGURE 9-14
Metamorphic zones, Sanbagawa belt, Shikoku and Honshu, Japan (largely after G. Ernst,
1971a, based on Japanese data).

Honshu (Seki, 1960). It is in fact the pumpellyite-actinolite and the greenschist
facies that dominate Sanbagawa metamorphism; and in one zone there are interleaved greenschists and glaucophane schists (without lawsonite, aragonite, or
jadeite) that represent a blueschist-greenschist transition facies. The difference
between this paragenesis and the lawsonite-albite-chlorite → blueschist facies series
of the Californian Franciscan is brought out in the comprehensive comparative
survey of the two regions by Ernst, Seki, and co-authors (1970).

Metamorphic Zones, Paragenesis, and Facies
Isograds trend roughly parallel to the axis of the metamorphic belt and the regional structure (Fig. 9-14), but there is no regular relation between metamorphic
grade and depths of burial. A prograde generalized zonal sequence, allowing for
local variation in different segments of the belt, has been established especially
on the basis of metavolcanic assemblages (cf. Ernst et al., 1970, pp. 200–203)
along lines set out below. (Minor constituents common to all zones—quartz, white
mica, and calcite—are not listed; facies appraisal is that of the present writer.)

1. Incipiently developed zeolitic assemblages   } Zeolite facies
2. Pumpellyite-albite-chlorite-sphene (±crossite
   ±lawsonite ±stilpnomelane)
3. Pumpellyite-actinolite-albite-chlorite-sphene   Pumpellyite-actinolite
   (±crossite ±stilpnomelane)   facies
4. Epidote-albite-actinolite-chlorite-sphene. Crossite   Greenschist-blueschist
   is plentiful in some units   transition facies

5. Epidote-albite-actinolite (aluminous)-chlorite-
    sphene (±garnet ±rutile ±crossite) $\Big\}$ Greenschist facies

6. Hornblende-diopside-plagioclase (sodic)-garnet-
    rutile (±biotite ±epidote), enclosing local eclogitic
    lenses $\Bigg\}$ Amphibolite facies

An unmistakable hint at blueschist affinities is conveyed by sporadic appearance of lawsonite in zone 2 (somewhat as along the western fringes of the Haast Schist terrane of New Zealand) and at least scattered presence of crossite at all except the highest metamorphic grades. Appearance of rutile instead of sphene in the amphibolite zone and actual presence of eclogite lenses point to affinities with the eclogite facies at this end of the series. Implications of high pressure, as emphasized by Miyashiro (1961), are inescapable.

Blueschist Facies, Western and Central Alps

Digression on Alpine Metamorphism in Relation to Regional Structure

Nowhere in the world is regional metamorphism in relation to a complex tectonic cycle displayed on such a spectacular scale as in the European Alps. And nowhere has so much sustained varied skill and effort been so effectively devoted to unraveling the course of metamorphism during such a complex and protracted tectonic event as the Alpine orogeny. Readers in English are likely to be unfamiliar with some of the classic and much of the voluminous modern literature pertinent to this topic. Here we can only remind ourselves that Austria and Switzerland were the birthplace and cradle of much of the technique and some of the basic concepts that constitute the foundations of modern metamorphic-structural petrography and petrology. Names such as these inevitably come to mind: F. Becke (1903, 1913), U. Grubenmann (1904), P. Niggli (1912, 1924), E. Argand (1911), B. Sander (1911, 1930). Among recent contributions one that is especially valuable for present purposes is a synoptic review of Alpine metamorphism in English—concise, lucid, and readily available—by an international group of collaborators, all experienced and currently active in Alpine metamorphic petrology (Frey et al., 1974).* My own indebtedness to this work will be obvious in what now follows and in treatment of various aspects of Alpine metamorphism in the ensuing chapters. Regarding the immediate topic of the blueschist facies, readers with a taste for tectonic speculation will also find useful Ernst's (1971a) comparative essay on this type of metamorphism as variously manifested in California and Japan as well as in the Alps.

The European Alps cover an arc 1000 km long and 150–200 km wide, stretching across Austria, northern Italy, and Switzerland into southeastern France. Their geologic history is one of prolonged episodic deformation and synchronous metamorphism (and accompanying and subsequent erosion) of an extensive mass of late Paleozoic and Mesozoic marine sediments and locally prominent interlayered ophiolites, together with massive fragments (massifs) torn from the underlying

---

*Schweiz. Mineral. Petrogr. Mitteil., vol. 54, 1974. Included is a comprehensive selected bibliography and separately specific references to each of the topics treated.

crystalline basement. The whole 100-million-year tectonic cycle, the earliest phases of which have been dated as at least middle Cretaceous, is called the Alpine orogeny. Statigraphic evidence suggests that it proceeded in discontinuous pulses (cf. Trümpy, 1973); but radiometric data combined with precise leveling (e.g., Schaer and Jeanrichard, 1974; Schaer et al., 1975; Wagner et al., 1977) show that throughout the Alps over the past 20 million years uplift at rates between 0.2 mm and 1.3 mm per annum has proceeded continuously without detectable breaks. Rates vary from one province to another, slowly falling off in some, gradually accelerating in others. The Alpine Orogeny indeed seems still to be in progress.

The lithologic-structural-metamorphic pattern throughout the Alpine Terrane is markedly heterogeneous. Major arcuate domains, each covering tens of thousands of square kilometers, have moved and internally responded as independent units, while at the same time conforming to a coherent general pattern of overthrusting westward and northward. They are in mutual contact along regional sutures that have been mapped with great precision—thrust faults and an east-west vertical transcurrent fault system that includes the Insubric Line of the central and eastern Alps. Within each major domain are structurally delineated subdomains—windows, nappes, and protruding massifs of pre-Alpine crystalline basement rocks.

Below are listed the principal Alpine domains (Fig. 9-15) from structurally higher units on the inner (southern and southeastern) side of the arc to successively lower units on the northwestern convex side facing the European foreland (Frey et al., 1974; cf. also Ernst, 1973a, pp. 2054–2055).

In the eastern geographic division, we find the Southern Alpine domain, east and south of the Insubric Line and its eastward extensions, and the Austroalpine domain north of the Insubric Line and east of a major zigzag north-south tectonic break not far from the Swiss-Austrian border. This break, the Alpine Suture of Ernst (1973a), is the outcrop of a low-angle southeast-dipping thrust that carries the Austroalpine sheet over the Pennine domain (which is locally exposed far to the east in the Engadine and Tauern windows).

The eastern Alps consist of a pre-Carboniferous crystalline basement, preserving the imprint of regional early or mid-Paleozoic metamorphism and plutonism, and a late Paleozoic-Mesozoic cover, prominent in which are limestones of the Calcareous Alps in the Austroalpine and the Dolomites in the Southern Alpine domain. All have been folded during the Alpine orogeny but effects of accompanying metamorphism are lacking or minimal.

In the central and western Alps, we find the Pennine and Dauphiné-Helvetic domains. The Pennine domain is bounded on the east by the Alpine Suture and on the southeast by the Insubric Line. It is now a pile of nappes consisting of folded Mesozoic covering strata (including ophiolite sheets) and massifs of crystalline basement rocks (paraschists, granitic gneisses, and basic-ultramafic units) typical of which are those of the Lepontine Alps, Monte Rosa, and Gran Paradiso. These were affected in turn by Hercynian, Permian, and finally the Alpine metamorphism. Included in the Pennine domain on its eastern border is an outlying nappe of Austroalpine rocks between the Alpine Suture and the Insubric Line. This is the Sesia-Lanzo zone, a region of great interest regarding eclogitic metamorphism.

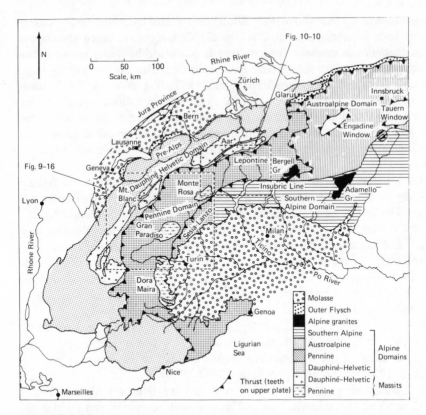

FIGURE 9-15
Tectonic-lithologic zones, western and central sectors of the European Alps (simplified after
M. Frey, J. C. Hunziker, W. Frank, J. Bocquet, G. V. Dal Piaz, E. Jäger, and E. Niggli, 1974).
Rectangular areas enlarged in Figs. 9-16 and 10-10.

It is in the Pennine domain that the pattern and variety of Alpine metamorphism
are most powerfully and fully displayed, overprinting and over wide areas obliterating—except for radiometrically perceptible memories—the effects of Paleozoic
metamorphism in the crystalline massifs. Subsequent discussion of Alpine metamorphism focuses largely on the Pennine domain.

The Dauphiné-Helvetic domain embraces the full sweep of the outermost
Swiss-French Alps. Within it, successive nappes of Triassic to Eocene sediments
have slipped outward leaving the crystalline basement exposed intermittently
(e.g., in the Aar and Mt. Blanc massifs) along its inner border. The Pre-Alps, above
Geneva and Lausanne, are a subdomain that comprises Eocene and older flysch
sediments that themselves have been overridden by mostly unmetamorphosed Pennine nappes.

Alpine metamorphism occurred in several episodes.

The first, upper Cretaceous Eoalpine phase (100–60×10^6 years) expressed
in an eclogite-blueschist imprint, is still preserved in most of the southern half of
the Pennine domain.

The second, a mid-Tertiary phase is responsible for the greenschist → amphibolite regional pattern seen in the Lepontine Alps (northern sector of the Pennine domain) and partially overprints the effects of Eoalpine metamorphism in the southern sector. The metamorphic grade rises inward across the Pennine domain, and falls off outward into greenschist and lower-grade facies in the Dauphiné-Helvetic domain.

The third, a very mild Oligocene-Miocene phase ($\sim 25 \times 10^6$ years) whose effects are seen in zeolite- and prehnite-pumpellyite facies parageneses in the outermost Alps, e.g., in the Glarus, southeast of Zürich.

The Alpine orogeny was accompanied by only scattered insignificant granite plutonism within the central and western Alps. Its main products, on the inner border of the Alps close to the Insubric Line, are the Bergell and Adamello plutons.

Eoalpine Blueschist-Eclogite Metamorphism, Pennine Domain

The principal manifestation of Eoalpine metamorphism is a regional blueschist zone in the southern half of the Pennine domain from the Simplon southward to Genoa. Here as elsewhere in the western and central Alps, the grade of metamorphism rises regularly from west to east across the whole width of the Alpine Terrane. But this pattern as seen on the map is misleadingly simple. At least two episodes (Eoalpine and Lepontine) are involved. Low-grade metamorphism in the Helvetic nappes is assigned to the second (Lepontine) phase, and its effects are seen across most of the Pennine domain as well—partially overprinting but not obliterating the earlier blueschist-eclogite metamorphism in the southern region. Most of the Pennine blueschist zone as shown in Fig. 9-16 carries this imprint. The boundary against the greenschist zone in the western Pennine nappes thus has implications of time as well as of metamorphic conditions.

Another problem of crucial interest concerns the relation of blueschist to eclogitic metamorphism. Both facies are well represented, eclogite appearing not as a continuous zone but as scattered outcrops concentrated near the eastern (inner) border of the blueschist belt—including the Sesia-Lanzo zone of which there will be more to say in a later section concerning eclogite paragenesis (Chap. 10). The mineralogy of the most widespread blueschist assemblages hints at prograde blueschist → eclogite transition—much as we have seen in higher-grade subfacies in New Caledonia and California: along with ubiquitous alkaline amphiboles, garnet, omphacite, and rutile are all common, lawsonite and pumpellyite much more restricted. A reverse retrograde relation is more clearly established by partial overprinting of blueschist on eclogite assemblages wherever eclogite is found. Frey and co-authors (1974, p. 255) speak of two successive stages of Eoalpine high-pressure metamorphism in genesis of eclogites: "the first with garnet, jadeite and/or omphacite, rutile; the second with glaucophane, phengite and/or paragonite, associated with the first distinctive Alpine schistosity."

A further complication concerns the equivocal chronologic significance of the amphiboles. These are not infallible criteria of the Eoalpine phase; for near the southwestern border of the Pennine zone some have been dated at 50–40 million years ago (J. Bocquet, cited by Frey et al., 1974, p. 272).

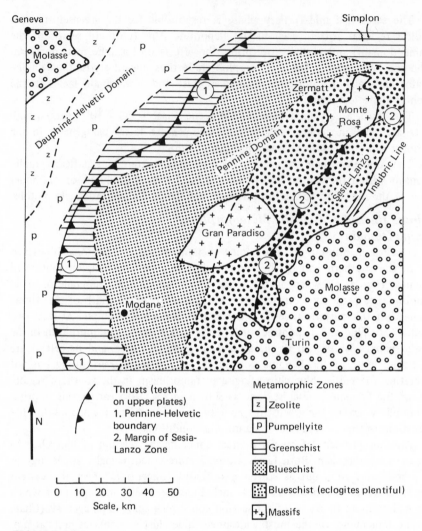

FIGURE 9-16
Metamorphic zones in a portion of the Pennine and Dauphiné-Helvetic domains, central Alps
(diagrammatic, after M. Frey and co-authors, 1974).

Special Mineralogical Features

Alpine blueschist metamorphism is marked by several features that, if not unique,
are still characteristic of the Pennine domain.

Lawsonite assemblages seem to be limited to their extent—restricted perhaps
to an outer southwest zone stretching 100 km south of Modane (Bearth, 1962,
1966). Here assemblages with jadeite and quartz also occur.

Throughout the rest of the blueschist belt garnet, chloritoid, phengite, and
paragonite are common components of pelitic glaucophane schists both in the
Mesozoic cover and in the reworked pre-Triassic crystalline basement. Some of
these rocks also contain kyanite. Especially characteristic of these higher-grade

blueschists, according to Bearth, is the pair chloritoid-glaucophane; while kyanite-chloritoid, a more sparsely distributed pair, is indeed remarkable in a regional blueschist paragenesis.

No sharp line of demarcation can be drawn between the two parageneses just described. But they seem to represent respectively local lower- and higher-grade subfacies of the blueschist facies.

Blueschist Mineralogy: Some Broad Generalizations

The mineral parageneses of the four provinces considered above collectively suggest common mineralogical characteristics that seem to apply to the facies as a whole.

Sodic Amphiboles and Pyroxenes

The sodic amphiboles can be treated in terms of four end components (cf. Borg, 1967):

Glaucophane $Na_2 Mg_3 Al_2 Si_8 O_{22} (OH)_2$
Riebeckite $Na_2 Fe_3^{2+} Fe_2^{3+} Si_8 O_{22} (OH)_2$
Magnesioriebeckite $Na_2 Mg_3 Fe_2^{3+} Si_8 O_{22} (OH)_2$
Ferroglaucophane $Na_2 Fe_3^{2+} Al_2 Si_8 O_{22} (OH)_2$

Blue amphiboles that are common in and diagnostic of the blueschist facies mostly belong to a glaucophane-crossite series (crossite being a term long in use to cover optically distinctive members of the glaucophane-riebeckite solid-solution series with subequal amounts of the two end members). Ferroglaucophane is also known (e.g., in New Caledonia), and has possibly been overlooked elsewhere because of its optical resemblance to glaucophane.

Highly characteristic also are sodic pyroxenes of the diopside-jadeite series, notably omphacites ($Jd_{\sim 40-50}$) and impure jadeites ($Jd_{> 80}$). Lack of intermediate members suggests a miscibility break whose exact limits are uncertain. The pair jadeite-quartz is especially significant as an index of high pressure. Chemographic relations between pyroxene-amphibole pairs (Fig. 9-17) vary from one province to another depending at least in part on relative metamorphic grade (E. H. Brown, 1978).

Pyroxenes and amphiboles rich in ferric iron, i.e., acmites and riebeckites appear commonly in metachert assemblages both in the blueschist and in other low-grade facies.

Almandine Garnet

Garnets rich in almandine are characteristic of the higher-grade blueschist assemblages. Typically they contain 20–30 percent of the grossularite molecule and 10 percent or so of pyrope. High manganese depends on rock composition and has no implications regarding grade or facies; for spessartites are common in metacherts of several metamorphic facies, the blueschist included.

Phyllosilicates

As in the chlorite zone of the greenschist facies, white micas and chlorites are almost ubiquitous in blueschist assemblages, biotite invariably absent, stilpno-

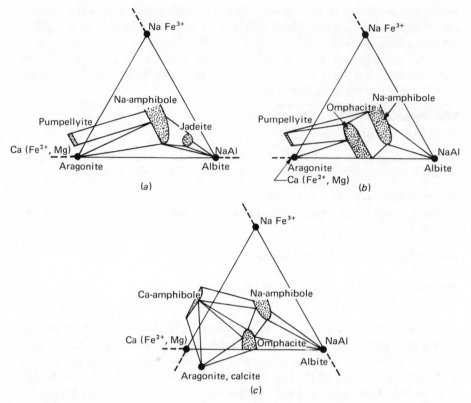

FIGURE 9-17
Chemographic relations, principal phases of various blueschist parageneses, Franciscan, California (modified after E. H. Brown, 1978). Greenwood-Thompson projections from chlorite-lawsonite-quartz-fluid (*a*) and (*b*), and from garnet-epidote quartz fluid (*c*): (*a*) Diabolo Range; (*b*) Ward Creek section, Cazadero; (*c*) high-grade tectonic blocks.

melane common. White micas, again as in greenschists, include phengitic muscovite and paragonite, frequently coexistent.

Calcium-Aluminum Silicates

Lawsonite and pumpellyite—the latter especially in metavolcanic assemblages—are widespread and highly characteristic. In subfacies transitional toward the eclogite or the greenschist facies, epidote tends to take the place of lawsonite. At the same time Ca and Al may be accommodated in a second amphibole phase coexisting with glaucophane—aluminous actinolite or blue hornblende (barroisite).

Carbonates

The sole carbonates are calcite and aragonite, both of them common, aragonite when present usually showing signs of inversion to calcite. Neither can be used as an index of relative grade; for survival of aragonite depends entirely on reaction kinetics during unloading.

Magnesian Silicates

Serpentinite members of ophiolite complexes are for the most part recrystallized to the stable serpentine polymorph, antigorite. With it may be associated talc and/or tremolite.

Minor Constituents

Sphene is almost universal and in some glaucophane schists unusually abundant. Albite appears in some rocks (e.g., quartz-jadeite-albite metagraywackes) but is typically absent. Since their discovery a dozen years ago deerite, howieite, or zussmanite have been recorded in metacherts of several provinces (e.g., the western Alps and New Caledonia). Though rare, where they do appear they are phases diagnostic of the blueschist facies.

Monomineralic Veinlets

A characteristic feature of blueschist fabrics is the presence of late cross-cutting monomineralic veinlets carrying one or other of the diagnostic phases—pumpellyite, omphacite, jadeite, lawsonite, aragonite, and even garnet. Veining of associated eclogite blocks with such minerals with glaucophane, rutile, chlorite, and muscovite-apatite-sphene as additional possibilities is also common. All this seems to point to continuous late circulation of pore fluids, facilitated perhaps by a strain regime of brittle fracture, itself conditioned by low temperature and high pressure.

GREENSCHIST FACIES

Scope and Limits

There are two general patterns of regional metamorphism in pervasively schistose rocks. One leads through or culminates in the blueschist facies. In the other, the first full development of schistosity and segregation banding (textural zones T3–T4) is accompanied by complete recrystallization of mineral assemblages of the greenschist facies. In a prograde facies sequence, the low-grade limit of the greenschist facies is marked by elimination of pumpellyite in favor of epidote (where preceded by a pumpellyite facies), or much less commonly (where the antecedent is the blueschist facies) by disappearance of glaucophane and entry of actinolite (plus albite and epidote). The upper limit is more sharply defined by sudden incoming of oligoclase ($An_{>20}$) accompanying or replacing nearly pure albite, which is ubiquitous in greenschist assemblages.

On zonal maps at least one biotite isograd distinguishes higher from lower-grade greenschist paragenesis. And in some but not all regions the greenschist facies continues beyond the biotite zone into the zone of almandine as defined for metapelites. We shall return later in this chapter to difficult questions regarding the mineralogical nature and physical significance of biotite isograds. These have been found to represent any of a whole series of reactions, and so differ from one province to another and even (within a single domain) according to the nature of the lithology and thus of the particular biotite-generating reaction selected to define the isograd.

Chlorite-zone assemblages vary of course according to lithology. But for any given kind of rock at the low-grade level they are essentially uniform the world over thus exemplifying the very essence of the facies concept. Below we consider their nature in three regions collectively covering a broad range of familiar lithology.

Chlorite Zone, Haast Schist Terrane, New Zealand

Areal Extent and Local Variations in Grade

The chlorite zone occupies the greater part of the Haast Schist terrane (Figs. 1-15 and 1-17) covering an area of about 250 × 100 km across almost the whole width of the South Island of New Zealand in the province of Otago and continuing in a narrow strip that projects northeastward along the southern Alps. For the most part the rocks are completely recrystallized, well foliated and lineated schists (textural zone T4)—the products of repeated penetrative deformation that was outlasted by crystallization of the greenschist-facies assemblages. Its low-grade limit (somewhere in zone T3) is marked by elimination of pumpellyite from a preceding pumpellyite-actinolite paragenesis (cf. E. H. Brown, 1967; Bishop, 1972; Kawachi, 1974). The high-grade limit as it appears on New Zealand geological survey maps is the biotite isograd mapped for metapelites in the far west, along the Haast River (Figs. 1-17 and 9-19). These are the limits here adopted for present discussion of chlorite-zone parageneses. The vexing but secondary problem of defining biotite isograds (E. H. Brown, 1975) will be postponed to a later section.

The Otago Schist belt for the most part is the fully metamorphosed equivalent of the Torlesse Group that borders it along its northeastern margin. The regionally prevailing lithology is metagraywacke; but in the northwestern sector where rocks of the Caples Group merge eastward with increasing metamorphism into the schist terrane (cf. Fig. 9-11), there are metavolcanics (mainly of basaltic origin) and some intercalated bands of manganiferous metachert.

Dominant Low-Grade Paragenesis

Common assemblages over the whole extent of the chlorite zones (Hutton, 1940; E. H. Brown, 1967, 1971, 1974) are as follows (Figs. 9-18 and 9-19):

A. Metagraywacke:
    1. Quartz-albite-epidote-muscovite-chlorite-sphene (-graphite)
    2. Quartz-albite-epidote-muscovite-chlorite-stilpnomelane-sphene
    3. Quartz-albite-epidote-muscovite-chlorite-actinolite-sphene[*]
B. Metabasalts:
    4. Albite-chlorite-stilpnomelane-actinolite-muscovite-epidote-sphene (±quartz ±calcite)
    5. Albite-stilpnomelane-actinolite-calcite (-epidote-sphene-pyrite); rare
C. Metacherts and ironstones:
    6. Quartz-spessartite-graphite-muscovite
    7. Quartz-piedmontite-spessartite-muscovite (with minor tourmaline, apatite, and barite)
    8. Quartz-spessartite-stilpnomelane

---

[*]Minor calcite takes the place of epidote in some rocks.

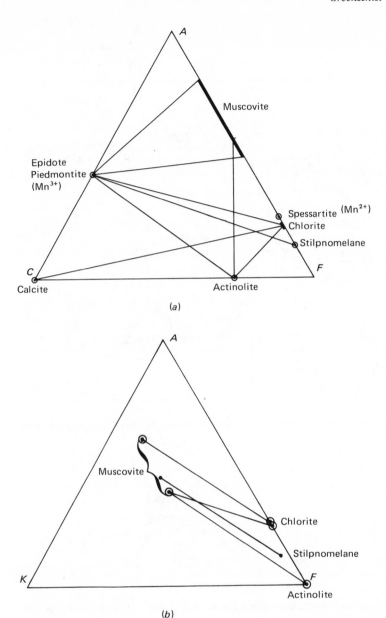

FIGURE 9-18
Greenschist facies, chlorite zone, eastern sector, Haast Schist, New Zealand (data from E. H. Brown, 1967). All Fe shown as FeO. (*a*) *ACF* diagram; quartz, albite, and graphite are possible additional phases. (*b*) *AKF* diagram; quartz, albite, and epidote are possible additional phases.

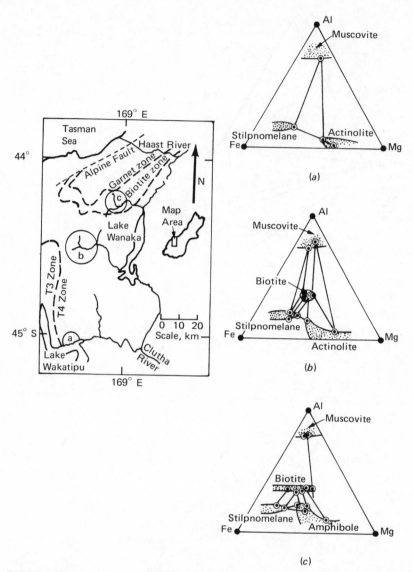

FIGURE 9-19

Greenschist facies, western sector, Haast Schist terrane, New Zealand: some chemographic relations in metabasaltic assemblages, prograde sequence $(a) \rightarrow (b) \rightarrow (c)$ as located on map (after E. H. Brown, 1976). Analyzed coexisting phases (circled points) connected by ties. (a) Chlorite zone close to T3–T4 textural boundary. (b) Higher grade (= Brown's "lower biotite zone") within chlorite zone as here defined. (c) Biotite zone.

9. Spessartite-stilpnomelane-calcite
10. Chlorite-stilpnomelane-actinolite-magnetite-epidote (-quartz)

As in chlorite-zone assemblages the world over albite (the low-temperature polymorph) is virtually devoid of anorthite ($An_{<1}$). Muscovites are phengitic (E. H. Brown, 1967), e.g.,

$$K_2 Mg_{0.6} Fe^{2+}_{0.2} Fe^{3+}_{0.3} Al_{2.9}(Al_{1.2} Si_{6.8} O_{20})(OH)_4$$

Chlorites are high in Al and Fe, for example,

$$Mg_{4.5} Fe^{2+}_5 Al_{2.3} Fe^{3+}_{0.2}(Al_{2.5} Si_{5.5} O_{20})(OH)_{16}$$

Actinolites have lower $Fe/(Fe + Mg)$ and epidotes lower $Fe/(Fe + Al)$ than corresponding phases in the antecedent pumpellyite-actinolite facies have: typical for epidote would be

$$Ca_2 Al_{2.4} Fe^{3+}_{0.6} Si_3 O_{12}(OH)$$

Stilpnomelane is a highly oxidized variety. But this condition is generally attributed (e.g., E. H. Brown, 1971, p. 280) to postmetamorphic oxidation. A well-established analogous effect is late oxidation of metamorphic chlorites to a brown pleochroic mineral (vermiculite?) that is easily confused with biotite or stilpnomelane.[*] The sole recorded carbonate, common as a minor phase in the metavolcanics especially is calcite (never aragonite). Sphene and apatite are ubiquitous, and tourmaline and graphitic carbon common minor accessories in semipelitic schists.

The composition and stability relations of actinolite deserve further comment. In metabasalts in the northwestern portion of the chlorite zone east of Lake Wakatipu, actinolite is microscopically conspicuous by virtue of strong pleochroism from green to deep blue. This blue color is the essential basis of the "blueschist" belt with attendant implications of deep subduction once proposed by some writers. This area may indeed have been the site of Mesozoic subduction (cf. Coombs et al., 1976), but in no sense of the term is it a blueschist belt. As recognized long ago by Hutton (1940, pp. 12-15), these strongly colored amphiboles are essentially actinolites, albeit with significant Na, Al, and Fe^{3+}. A typical composition is

$$(Ca_{1.5} Na_{0.5})(Mg_{2.5} Fe^{2+}_{1.7} Fe^{3+}_{0.5} Al_{0.3})(Si_{7.7} Al_{0.3} O_{22})(OH)_2$$

This has been confirmed in comprehensive studies by E. H. Brown (1977a), who identifies the blue-green amphiboles of northwest Otago as actinolite with crossite

---

[*]Some early erroneous reports of direct derivation of stilpnomelane from an earlier generation of chlorite (e.g., Turner, 1934, p. 165, Pl. 23) are due to this kind of mistaken identity. So too, I suspect, may be much of the continuous NW–SE axial "biotite" zone that appears in some maps of the Otago Schist belt.

(~15–35 percent) in solid solution; and considers the crossite content an important index of relatively high pressure. A second point of interest is the common occurrence of significant calcite and minor quartz in actinolitic greenschists of the same region. It follows that here actinolite-calcite is stable in relation to the equivalent pair ankerite-quartz as illustrated simply by

$$5 \text{ ankerite} + 8 \text{ quartz} + H_2O \rightleftharpoons \text{actinolite} + 3 \text{ calcite} + 7CO_2$$

Stability of the right-hand assemblage in New Zealand suggests low f_{CO_2} in the fluid phase—a likely enough condition in a region where calcareous rocks are generally lacking.

Local Higher-Grade Parageneses

Over limited areas within the chlorite zone, a grade significantly higher than normal is indicated by appearance of biotite, almandine, or hornblende in certain regionally prevalent assemblages. There are two particular areas where such departures—each with its unique features—have been explored in detail by E. H. Brown (1967, 1971) who would place them together in what he designates a "lower" biotite zone, distinct from the biotite zone as here recognized which he designates "upper" (referring to relative grade).

At the eastern end of the Otago schist belt just west of Dunedin, Brown has mapped, for a short distance within our chlorite zone, a biotite isograd *UV*, Figs. 1-15 and 9-3, based on the metagraywacke lithology. At this point small amounts of brown biotite and of porphyroblastic almandine (with significant Ca and Mn)—neither phase exceeding 5 percent of the total rock composition—enter into the common assemblages 1 and 2 listed above. These become

1*a*. Quartz-albite-muscovite (phengitic)-chlorite-biotite-epidote-almandine-sphene
2*a*. Quartz-albite-muscovite (phengitic)-chlorite-stilpnomelane-biotite-epidote-sphene

But assemblage 1 lacking either biotite or garnet remains equally common in the "biotite zone" beyond the local isograd. Stilpnomelane diminishes in quantity but is by no means eliminated in the biotite-generating process. Its presence in textural equilibrium with biotite in assemblage 2a is unusual elsewhere but has been recorded (e.g., E. Niggli, 1956; Miyakawa, 1964).

About 200 km to the west, in the upper Matukituki Valley west of Lake Wanaka (Fig. 9-19), E. H. Brown (1971) has recorded a second local higher-grade paragenesis within the regional chlorite zone and still 20 km distant from the generally accepted isograd.[*] Biotite and muscovite are constituents of many of the rocks examined. All combinations of biotite, stilpnomelane, actinolite, and chlorite have been recorded. The paragenesis differs from that beyond the biotite isograd in that the amphibole is a somewhat aluminous actinolite, not hornblende; and muscovite is compatible with both actinolite and stilpnomelane (as in assemblages

---

[*]Rugged topography, heavy forest cover up to 1500 m elevation, exceptionally high rainfall and difficulty of access combine to hinder mapping in the intervening area along the southern Alps.

of the "normal" lower grade). This last property is a consequence of the narrow compositional range of biotite. All these aspects of the three parageneses as developed in northwest Otago are illustrated in Fig. 9-19. The "transition" there depicted is one based on comparative mineralogy, not field observation. There is no mapped isograd or transition zone that can be traced in the field between the higher-grade chlorite-zone paragenesis (that of Brown's "lower biotite zone") and that of the biotite zone proper.

Chlorite Zone, Castleton, Vermont

An unusually complete picture of greenschist metasedimentary paragenesis is presented by Zen's (1960) account of metamorphism in the Castleton area, Vermont, in a portion of the chlorite zone on the western side of the Appalachian belt. The recorded assemblages are mostly pelitic (some highly aluminous) and calcareous. Collectively they complement the metagraywacke-metavolcanic paragenesis of the Haast Schist terrane. Phase compositions were estimated mostly from X-ray data and refractive-index measurements, supplemented by a few check analyses; in stilpnomelane ($Fe^{2+} + Fe^{3+}$) is calculated as FeO. Muscovite and paragonite, in the absence of complete chemical data, have been plotted in chemographic diagrams (Figs. 9-20, 9-21, and 9-22) as ideal pure end members, except where (in Fig. 9-20*b*) an analyzed muscovite from the biotite zone of western Vermont (Crawford, 1966, p. 278, #19) has been substituted. Typical assemblages include the following:

A. Pelitic:
1. Muscovite-chlorite-quartz-rutile-carbonate. This is the commonest assemblage. Less widespread are variants with albite, microcline, or both; magnetite or hematite.
2. Muscovite-chlorite-paragonite-quartz (-rutile)
3. Muscovite-chlorite-chloritoid-paragonite-quartz (-rutile)
4. Muscovite-chlorite-chloritoid-quartz (-rutile) ±hematite
5. Muscovite-chlorite-chloritoid-epidote-magnetite-hematite-quartz (-rutile)
6. Muscovite-stilpnomelane-chlorite-albite-quartz (-rutile)
7. Muscovite-chlorite-stilpnomelane-albite-microcline-quartz-hematite (-rutile)

Stilpnomelane is limited to rocks relatively low in Al. Both paragonite and chloritoid appear in highly aluminous assemblages, the former favored by high Al(Na + K), the latter by high Fe/Mg (Fig. 9-21*b*). Albite is compatible with both.

B. Calcareous (marbles):
8. Calcite; with combinations (in minor amounts) of quartz, albite, microcline, muscovite, and chlorite
9. Calcite-dolomite-zoisite
10. Calcite-dolomite-chlorite-muscovite

Dolomite-calcite-quartz remains stable in massive marbles as it does up to the garnet zone throughout most of Vermont. This could reflect low permeability, hindering the infiltration of water (cf. White and Billings, 1951, p. 691). Actinolite appears

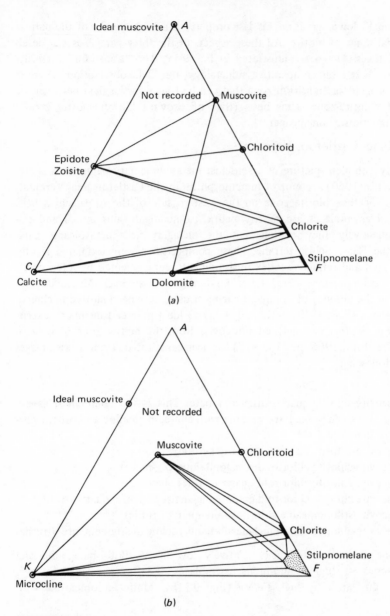

FIGURE 9-20

Greenschist facies, chlorite zone, Castleton area, Vermont. Chemographic relations in assemblages with excess SiO_2 and Al_2O_3, lacking paragonite. Quartz and albite are possible additional phases. (*a*) *ACF* projection; (*b*) *AKF* projection (modified after E-an Zen, 1960).

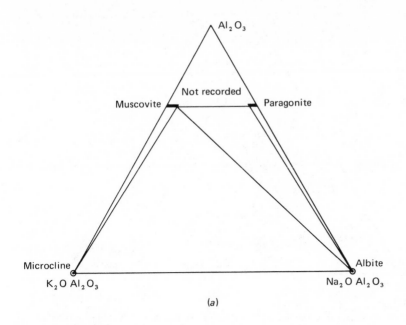

(a)

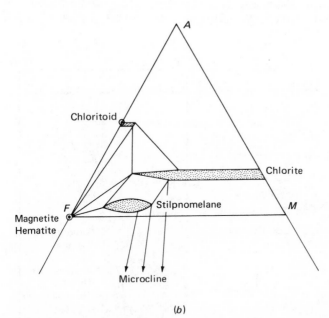

(b)

FIGURE 9-21

Greenschist facies, chlorite zone, Castleton area, Vermont. Chemographic relations in pelitic assemblages with quartz (after E-an Zen, 1960). (a) Al_2O_3-Na_2O-K_2O projection. (b) *AFM* diagram for assemblages containing muscovite and quartz.

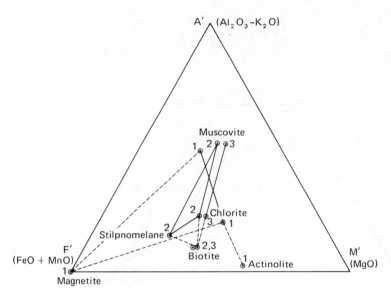

FIGURE 9-22
Greenschist facies, chlorite zone (higher grade sector = E. H. Brown's "lower biotite zone"), eastern end Haast Schist terrane, New Zealand (after data of E. H. Brown, 1967). Chemographic relations on $(Al_2O_3-K_2O)$-$(FeO + MnO)$-MgO projection; total Fe^{2+} and Fe^{3+} shown as FeO. Circled points analyzed coexisting phases.

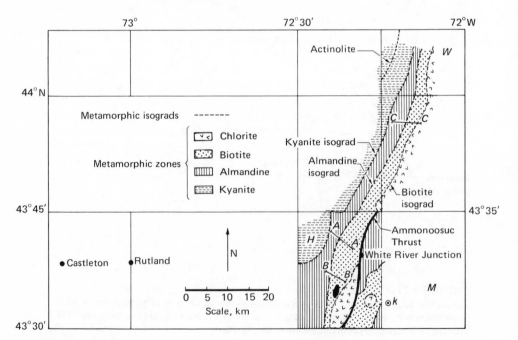

FIGURE 9-23
Portion of mid-Vermont and New Hampshire (see also Fig. 1-13): *H*, Hanover; *M*, Mascoma, *W*, Woodville Quadrangle. *AA*, *BB*, and *CC* traverses studied by M. L. Crawford (1966).

in Vermont marbles only at higher grades and has then been used to map an actinolite isograd (Fig. 9-23).

Biotite Zones: Typical Parageneses and Biotite Isograds

Haast Schist Terrane, New Zealand

A biotite isograd was located in the section along the Haast River (at the western
end of the Haast Schist block) over forty years ago and has subsequently been
mapped in reconnaissance fashion for a distance of over 50 km (Figs. 1-16 and
9-19). The corresponding biotite zone (E. H. Brown's "upper biotite zone"), about
5 km wide, is limited upgrade by an almandine isograd. Eighty percent of the
constituent rocks contain biotite, chlorite is ubiquitous, and phengitic muscovite
is widespread except in metabasalts. Typical assemblages (cf. Brown, 1971, p. 288)
are

A. Metagraywacke:
   1. Quartz-albite-biotite-muscovite-chlorite-epidote-sphene
   2. Quartz-albite-biotite-chlorite-epidote-sphene
B. Metabasalt:
   3. Albite-chlorite-biotite
   4. Albite-chlorite-actinolite-biotite
   5. Albite-chlorite-hornblende-biotite   } All with sphene, epidote, and possible quartz and/or calcite
   6. Albite-chlorite-stilpnomelane-biotite-hornblende
   7. Albite-chlorite-stilpnomelane-biotite

Stilpnomelane is reduced in quantity in metabasalts (compared with chlorite-zone
parageneses) and is absent from metagraywackes. Muscovite is incompatible with
both stilpnomelane and actinolite (cf. Fig. 9-19c). The common calcic amphibole
is now hornblende. In all these respects the paragenesis differs from that recorded
25 km to the south within the chlorite zone (E. H. Brown's "lower biotite zone").

Western Vermont and New Hampshire

In the biotite zone of Hanover quadrangle, 50 km east of Zen's Castleton area, the
paragenesis (Lyons, 1955) is as follows (cf. Fig. 9-24):

A. Pelitic and semipelitic:
   1. Quartz-albite-muscovite-biotite-chlorite-clinozoisite (-sphene-magnetite), with
     widespread ankerite or calcite
B. Calcareous:
   2. Calcite-quartz
   3. Dolomite-calcite-quartz
C. Metabasalt:
   4. Albite-chlorite-biotite-clinozoisite (-quartz)
   5. Chlorite-muscovite-calcite-clinozoisite-quartz
   6. Hornblende-oligoclase-biotite-quartz

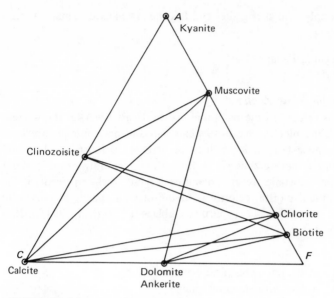

FIGURE 9-24

Greenschist facies, biotite zone, Vermont and New Hampshire. Chemographic relations (*ACF* projection) in assemblages with carbonates and albite as additional phases (K-feldspar rarely present) (data from J. B. Lyons, 1955).

Figure 9-25 shows chemographic relations as recorded by Crawford (1966) in metapelites of the biotite zone in the same area. Muscovites remain phengitic but appreciably less so than in pelitic schists of Zen's chlorite zone. Stilpnomelane and chloritoid are absent. Reactions at the biotite isograd apparently involved elimination of both these phases, simultaneous change in composition of musco- vite, and probably participation of chlorite as well. Some distance upgrade from the isograd but still well within the zone of biotite a second plagioclase appears— oligoclase coexisting with albite—and this signals transition toward the amphibolite facies.

Brown's (1971, pp. 278, 289) observations in the biotite zone of Vermont 50–60 km west and northwest of the Hanover quadrangle (Fig. 1-14, left-hand margin) suggest that biotite becomes plentiful only within about 5 km of the garnet isograd; and even in this area of higher grade, it is lacking in half the rocks collected by him. He records stilpnomelane in a few specimens nearer the biotite isograd.

Southern Dalradian, Scotland

The Dalradian biotite isograd as generally recognized today is that mapped by Tilley (1925a; also Elles and Tilley, 1930) to connect "points of first entry of brown biotite in pelitic and psammopelitic sediments." The upgrade limit of the biotite zone is the almandine isograd based on the same lithology (cf. Figs. 1-11*a* and 1-12).

According to Atherton (1964), the dominant pelitic assemblage is still the same as in the preceding chlorite zone—quartz-muscovite-chlorite (-albite). Much

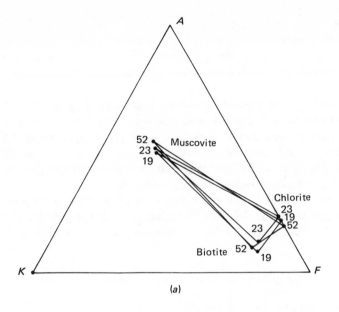

(a)

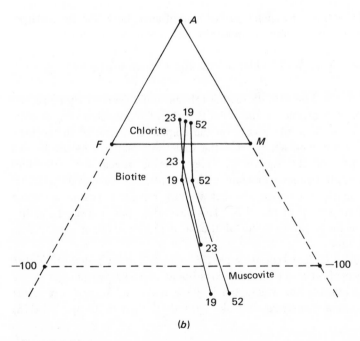

(b)

FIGURE 9-25
Greenschist facies, biotite zone, Hanover quadrangle, Vermont. Chemographic projections—
(a) *AKF*, (b) *AFM*—for analyzed coexisting phases in the prevailing assemblage quartz-albite-
muscovite-biotite-chlorite-ankerite (plus oligoclase in 52). Total Fe plotted as FeO. Data and
specimen numbers from M. L. Crawford (1966). Ankerite compositions from associated
specimens.

less common is the index assemblage quartz-muscovite-biotite (-chlorite-albite), which throughout the biotite zone is more typical of quartzo-feldspathic (psammo-pelitic) schists with plentiful albite. Basic metavolcanics, also as in the chlorite zone, display the assemblage chlorite-albite-epidote-sphene ± biotite ± actinolite ± calcite.

In a detailed study of a segment of the chlorite zone 20 km long east of Loch Lomond, Mather (1970) mapped another biotite isograd some 5 km downgrade from the limit of Tilley's classic biotite zone, and based on metagraywacke not pelitic lithology. The resultant assemblage—well within the chlorite zone, it will be noted—is quartz-albite-muscovite-biotite-microcline. It is derived from a parental lower-grade assemblage quartz-albite-muscovite-microcline-chlorite.

Muscovites in all the above pelitic and metagraywacke assemblages are phengitic types—the phengite content decreasing significantly with rising grade. This property is the key to two successive biotite-generating reactions envisaged by Mather:

(1) Microcline + chlorite + muscovite (phengitic) → biotite

+ muscovite (less phengitic) + quartz

At this point, even though the chemographic field of phengite + chlorite is sharply reduced it still encompasses pelitic compositions which remain unchanged.

(2) Muscovite (phengitic) + chlorite → biotite + muscovite (less phengitic)

This second reaction depends on decreasing tolerance of celadonite by muscovite with rising grade. In consequence the stability field of biotite-chlorite-muscovite in Fig. 9-26 grows until it encroaches on the composition field of metapelites, in which rocks biotite then appears for the first time. Mather's biotite isograd for metagraywackes reflects reaction 1. Tilley's classic isograd for metapelites expresses reaction 2. Relevant chemographic phase relations as envisaged by Mather (neglecting stilpnomelane on grounds that it may represent postmetamorphic recrystallization) are shown in Fig. 9-26. This also brings out continued stability of the muscovite-chlorite pair (without biotite) in the more aluminous metapelites of Tilley's biotite zone.

In yet another lithology (volcanogenic "green beds") in the Dalradian, biotite has long been recognized as an essential constituent of some assemblages in the chlorite zone. Carbonates are widespread in these rocks and suggest a probable influence of f_{CO_2} as a controlling variable. Typical (Mather, 1970, pp. 272–273) are

Quartz-albite-chlorite-biotite-actinolite-epidote
Quartz-albite-chlorite-phengite-biotite-epidote-calcite

Clearly from the situation described by Mather and from Brown's observations in New Zealand there must be a number of possible biotite-generating reactions within the greenschist facies; and to this topic we now turn.

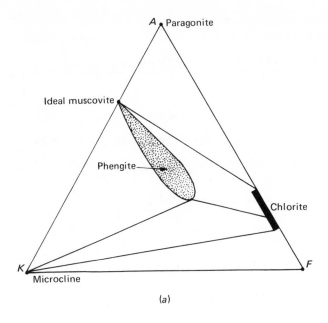

(a)

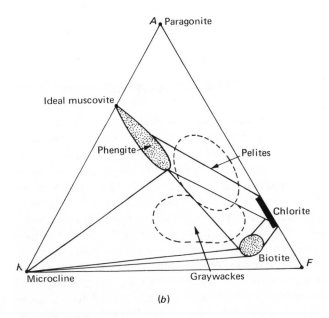

(b)

FIGURE 9-26

Greenschist facies, Dalradian, east of Loch Lomond, Scotland. Chemographic relations in meta-pelites and metagraywackes; approximate composition fields—dashed ellipses in (b). Quartz and albite are additional phases. (a) Chlorite zone (minimal grade); (b) Tilley's biotite zone (slightly modified after J. D. Mather, 1970).

Biotite-Generating Reactions and General Significance of Biotite Isograds

From combined field and petrochemical data a number of reactions may lead to generation of biotite within the greenschist facies (Mather, 1970; E. H. Brown, 1971; De Béthune, 1976):

In metavolcanics:

(1) Muscovite + stilpnomelane + actinolite → biotite + chlorite + epidote

(2) Muscovite + actinolite + chlorite → biotite (Mg-rich) + epidote

In metaarkose and some metagraywackes:

Microcline + chlorite → biotite + muscovite

In metapelites and metagraywackes:

(1) Chlorite + phengite → biotite + muscovite

(2) Muscovite + stilpnomelane → biotite (Fe-rich) + epidote

In calcschists and impure marbles, various decarbonation reactions such as:

(1) Dolomite + microcline → biotite + calcite

(2) Calcite + muscovite + chlorite → biotite + anorthite (or zoisite)

The above list is by no means exhaustive. It does not include possible reactions involving chloritoid among the reactants or almandine among the products.

Inevitably the general situation described in the preceding pages permits wide freedom of choice from among possible alternative isograds designated by the same index—in this case biotite—but in different lithologies. Which is the "best" choice—the first to be established, or the more recent to be recognized? The one that can be most sharply defined in chemical terms (a "discontinuous" reaction) or the one most readily recognized and mapped in the field? And then some geologists with a predilection for orderly arrangement of natural phenomena, and certain geochemists, will ask: is it possible to recognize a type of biotite isograd equally applicable to every greenschist province and capable of being translated in quantitative physical terms onto a petrogenic grid? These and related questions are being asked today (cf. Mather, 1970; Brown, 1971) and will be asked tomorrow—still with no chance of unanimous response.

Questions of the above kind, though important, are largely irrelevant to present discussion, which is focused on descriptive mineralogical-chemical data presented in the framework of field and tectonic environment. Any well-mapped isograd could serve as a datum separating assemblages of higher from those of lower grade within the greenschist facies as displayed in a given region. The preference of this writer is for well-established isograds based on a prevalent regional lithology and mapped over large areas. Tilley's biotite isograd in the Dalradian and the standard biotite isograd of New Zealand Geological Survey maps serve our purpose better than any others—even though the two cannot possibly be precisely equivalent in terms of *P–T* calibration.

Finally the great diversity among likely and proved biotite-generating reactions illustrates the futility of any quest for a universal biotite isograd having identical physical significance in all greenschist provinces and capable of being transferred in numerical terms to a petrogenic grid or to a pigeon-hole classification of metamorphic phase assemblages.

Carbonate-Silicate Parageneses

Rocks in which carbonates and silicates are mutually associated are common in the greenschist facies. Progressive metamorphism tends to reduce the content of carbonate in favor of silicate phases, CO_2 being expelled in the process. Another effect is to simplify the primary carbonate assemblage, the surviving phases at higher grades being calcite and (in initially magnesian marbles) dolomite.

It has already been shown that in the greenschist facies a common minor phase in many assemblages is calcite. Aragonite, if indeed it ever crystallizes, fails to survive postmetamorphic decompression and cooling (cf. W. H. Brown et al., 1962). In siliceous magnesian marbles, the trio calcite-dolomite-quartz generally remains unchanged, and tremolite appears only in the amphibolite facies.

Banded ironstones in the greenschist facies (and these are widespread in Precambrian terranes of low-grade metamorphism) become converted to interlayered metacherts and silicate-carbonate bands. In the former newly generated iron silicates, notably stilpnomelane and riebeckite are associated with recrystallized quartz and iron oxides. The carbonate paragenesis is illustrated by Huronian iron formation of northern Michigan (James, 1955, pp. 1462, 1475):

1. Stilpnomelane-minnesotaite-siderite-quartz-magnetite
2. Chlorite-stilpnomelane-quartz-siderite-magnetite
3. Hematite-quartz-calcite

In Archaean ironstones of slightly different composition in the Lead district, South Dakota, widely prevalent assemblages in the biotite zone of metapelites are

4. Ankerite-muscovite-quartz-phlogopite
5. Sideroplesite [$(Fe,Mg)CO_3$]-quartz-biotite-chlorite

In neither area does an amphibole (grunerite or cummingtonite) appear until beyond the garnet isograd.

Many serpentinite bodies show local or large-scale effects of carbon-dioxide metasomatism, the extreme end-product of which is talc-magnesite or even quartz-magnesite rock (e.g., Wellman, 1942; Turner, 1948, pp. 135, 136). Ophicalcites and some commercial deposits of magnesite have originated thus under greenschist facies conditions. Clearly the metasomatic process, like the transformation of peridotite to serpentinite, has involved free diffusion of aqueous fluids with concomitant removal of MgO, FeO, and, for an equal-volume replacement, SiO_2. For carbonates to develop along with or in preference to hydrous silicates, high values of f_{CO_2} must be prerequisite.

Some of the common resultant assemblages, presumably in equilibrium under conditions of the greenschist facies are:

1. Antigorite
2. Antigorite-talc-tremolite
3. Antigorite-talc-magnesite
4. Talc-magnesite
5. Quartz-magnesite

In more calcic rocks calcite or dolomite may take the place of magnesite in assemblages consisting mainly of antigorite, talc, and tremolite.

10

Facies of High-Grade Regional Metamorphism: Illustrative Examples

SCOPE AND PLAN OF TREATMENT

The division between low- and high-grade metamorphism has been arbitrarily fixed at a sharply defined mineralogical datum: complete elimination of the pair albite ($An_{<8}$)-epidote that is so widespread in facies of low grades. This step marks the transition from greenschist to amphibolite facies. In the latter the plagioclase that coexists with epidote is significantly calcic, $An_{>20}$. A completely different transformation eliminates albite-epidote at extreme pressures: plagioclase itself becomes unstable and its components enter omphacite and garnet typifying the eclogite facies.

In the following treatment individual facies will be reviewed in the order amphibolite, granulite, eclogite—which of course is not a simple linear prograde sequence. Both the amphibolite and the eclogite facies are preceded by transitional facies linking low- to high-grade parageneses. The blueschist-eclogite transition, so far as it has been verified, has already been reviewed. Illustrations will now be presented of the much more firmly documented transition that leads from the greenschist into the amphibolite facies, and so to what we designate "high-grade" regional metamorphism.

GREENSCHIST–AMPHIBOLITE FACIES TRANSITION

Nature of the Oligoclase Isograd

When oligoclase (An_{25}–An_{30}) was first proposed as the index for an isograd that can be mapped on quartzo-feldspathic sediments (Vogt, 1927; Turner, 1933) it was thought that with advancing grade the composition of plagioclase coexisting with clinozoisitic epidotes takes a sudden jump from nearly pure albite ($An_{<5}$) to calcic oligoclase. And this step is readily perceptible under the microscope. An observation by De Waard (1959)[*] that in Timor the oligoclase isograd in pelitic rocks does not precisely coincide with that based on metabasalts, showed that other phases than plagioclase and epidote were involved—almandine in the former, hornblende in the latter lithology. Then Evans (1964) found that for several kilometers upgrade from the almandine isograd in the Haast River section of southwestern New Zealand (Fig. 1-16) *two* plagioclases coexist—oligoclase and nearly pure albite. It was the disappearance of albite—readily perceptible under the microscope—not the first appearance of oligoclase that had been used earlier to mark the oligoclase isograd. Evans' observations were confirmed and amplified by Crawford (1966) who also found a zone of coexisting albite and oligoclase in Vermont—in this case, however, *preceding* the almandine isograd. It seems probable from later observations in other areas that coexistence of albite and oligoclase is a general phenomenon that immediately precedes the full development of the amphibolite facies.

It is easy to distinguish unequivocally between the greenschist and the amphibolite facies where each has a single plagioclase phase—albite in the former, oligoclase or a more calcic type in the latter. However, intervening two-plagioclase parageneses tend to differ from one province to another in a rather subtle manner, especially in terms of location with respect to broadly comparable isograds. Contrary to Cooper's (1972, pp. 480–481) recommendation to revive for such parageneses Eskola's term *epidote-amphibolite-facies*,[†] nomenclatural clarity would seem better served by recognizing a transitional facies (probably encompassing a narrow temperature span) to accommodate assemblages with coexisting albite and oligoclase.

Two other mineralogical changes slightly precede or closely follow the first appearance of oligoclase (still associated with albite). Aluminous hornblende takes the place of actinolite—the typical amphibole of the greenschist facies. And in pelitic rocks and in some amphibolites almandine, characteristically low in Mg and Mn, for the first time appears in profusion thus making it possible to map an almandine isograd. These changes too are reflected in local variants of the greenschist-amphibolite transition.

Four illustrative examples will now be reviewed briefly in order of what on independent evidence is thought to be increasing pressure of metamorphism (cf. Chap. 1).

---

[*]For further discussion see Rutland (1961, 1962) and Christie (1962).

[†]This term must always remain ambiguous since epidote-andesine is a widespread pair in the amphibolite facies.

Biotite Zone, Vermont

In a part of the Vermont biotite zone examined by Crawford (1966) (Fig. 9-23) two plagioclases—An_{3-7} and An_{20-26}—coexist in semipelitic assemblages for a distance of 1–2 km downgrade from the almandine isograd. The typical assemblage is quartz-oligoclase-albite-muscovite-biotite-chlorite-ankerite (or calcite). Close to the almandine isograd there are two comparable alternative assemblages, one with oligoclase and ankerite, the other with oligoclase and albite. At this point the pair albite-ankerite is no longer stable.

Beyond the almandine isograd, the assemblage in hornblende schists (Lyons, 1955, p. 110, Table 1, no. 5) is quartz-plagioclase(An_{27})-hornblende-biotite-chlorite (-ankerite-calcite).

Almandine Zone, Southern Dalradian, Scotland

In the Barrow-Tilley zonal sequence of the Dalradian, transition from the greenschist to the amphibolite facies begins at the almandine isograd and becomes complete at a somewhat higher grade, still, however, within the almandine zone. At the almandine isograd, almandine first appears and biotite first becomes a constituent of most pelitic schists (Atherton, 1964). At the same time, the amphibole of metabasaltic lithology ("Highland epidiorites" of classic literature) becomes sufficiently aluminous to be classed as hornblende (Wiseman, 1934, p. 379). Albite, however, remains conspicuous across most of the almandine zone, so that in standard accounts of Dalradian metamorphism the changeover to oligoclase has been placed at or close to the staurolite isograd (cf. Chinner, 1967, p. 276). However, E. H. Brown (1969, p. 1666) has reported coexisting albite and oligoclase in a single specimen of quartzofeldspathic schist (metagraywacke) just beyond the almandine isograd. It would seem likely that both phases coexist up to the staurolite isograd, oligoclase (because of its microscopically inconspicuous character in quartz-plagioclase aggregates) simply having been overlooked—as until recently it was in similar situations elsewhere.

Characteristic assemblages in the Dalradian almandine zone, most of them illustrated by Harker (1932, pp. 222–224, 253–257) include the following (Fig. 10-1):

A. Pelitic and psammopelitic (Williamson, 1953; Atherton, 1964; Brown, 1969):
   1. Quartz-muscovite-biotite-almandine-albite (+oligoclase?) (-epidote-chlorite)
   2. Quartz-muscovite-biotite-chloritoid-chlorite-almandine: confined to the east coastal region where its presence is favored by local compositional factors, notably, high Al (e.g., Williamson, 1953; Chinner, 1967).
B. Metabasaltic (Wiseman, 1934, p. 379):
   3. Hornblende-albite-clinozoisite-biotite (-almandine)
   4. Hornblende-albite-epidote-chlorite-biotite
   5. Hornblende-andesine- (-epidote-almandine-biotite)

The typical amphibolite-facies assemblage 5 develops only at maximum grade close to the staurolite isograd. It is possible (though it has not yet been reported) that oligoclase may be present as well as albite in assemblages 1 and 2; almandine at this early stage has a significant content of grossularite (~25 percent).

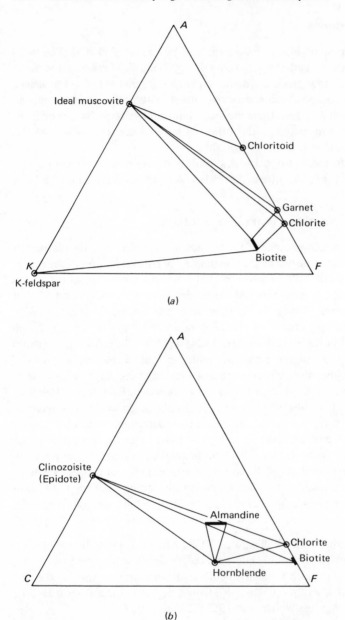

(a)

(b)

FIGURE 10-1

Greenschist-amphibolite transitional facies, almandine zone, Dalradian, southeast Highlands, Scotland. (a) *AKF* diagram for rocks with excess SiO_2 and Al_2O_3; quartz and albite (+oligoclase?) are possible additional phases. (b) *ACF* diagram for metabasalts (epidiorites) (data after J. D. H. Wiseman, 1934).

Almandine Zone, Western Haast Schist Terrane, New Zealand

In the extreme western part of the Haast Schist terrane postmetamorphic uplift along the Alpine Fault has locally exposed rocks of the amphibolite facies. Isograds dip steeply here and a prograde westward sequence through the greenschist and amphibolite facies is exposed in a 30-km section in the lower part of the Haast River (Fig. 1-16). The lithology is dominantly quartzo-feldspathic (metagraywacke), but there are some metabasaltic bands and lenses in which effects of progressive metamorphism have recently been studied by Cooper (1972). His data and those of Mason (1962), Grindley (1963), and Crawford (1966) have been combined below to supplement earlier less detailed work by the present writer and others.

Isograds have been mapped in metagraywacke lithology for the successive indices biotite, almandine, and oligoclase, and a complementary sequence of mineralogical changes has been traced by Cooper (1972) in metabasalts. The almandine isograd, though in all respects valid, is rather elusive since the low aluminum content of the dominant metagraywackes inhibits profuse crystallization of garnet. The oligoclase isograd can be defined more sharply, but it requires microscopic confirmation. As first mapped—and still retained in the current scheme of mapping—it expresses final elimination of albite, a stage easily identified under the microscope.

Three significant changes in mineralogy occur simultaneously at the almandine isograd: scattered crystals of almandine appear in quartzo-feldspathic schists of sufficiently aluminous composition; oligoclase comes in, coexisting with the more conspicuous phase albite; and actinolite of metabasaltic assemblages gives way to hornblende.

Principal assemblages of the almandine zone, which covers the greenschist-amphibolite transition in this region, are as follows:

A. Metagraywacke:
   1. Quartz-albite $(An_{<5})$-oligoclase $(An_{>24})$-biotite-muscovite (-almandine-epidote-sphene)
B. Metabasalt (Cooper, 1972):
   2. Hornblende-albite-oligoclase-epidote-chlorite-sphene
C. Metachert (Cooper, 1971):
   3. Quartz-spessartite
   4. Quartz-albite-muscovite-phlogopite-piedmontite-spessartite (-hematite-apatite-tourmaline)

Presence of phlogopite distinguishes the almandine-zone piedmontite schists from those of the chlorite zone in western Otago. Also distinctive of higher grade, though rare, is cummingtonite (Cooper, 1972, p. 459).

D. Marble:
   5. Calcite-quartz-albite-epidote-tremolite

Within the greenschist-amphibolite transition facies along the Haast River section, chlorite and epidote diminish with increasing grade and both typically are absent from amphibolites in the oligoclase zone. Chlorites and biotites both have much the same composition as in the preceding biotite zone (greenschist facies) (Crawford, 1966, p. 279). The compositional change from actinolite to hornblende in metabasalts at or near the almandine isograd is abrupt and probably expresses an immiscibility gap (Cooper, 1972, pp. 470–472). Analyzed coexisting amphiboles from one specimen approximate

Actinolite: $(Na_{0.2}Ca_{1.7}Mg_{3.1}Fe_{2.15}Al_{0.1})(Si_{7.6}Al_{0.4}O_{22})(OH)_2$
Hornblende: $(Na_{0.5}Ca_{1.85}Mg_{1.8}Fe_{2.9}Al_{0.6})(Si_{6.5}Al_{1.5}O_{22})(OH)_2$

Garnets (except in cherts) are zoned almandines with significant Gr and Sp, both these components being consistently high in the cores. Two analyzed garnets from quartzo-feldspathic schists are

$$Al_{55 \to 69}Gr_{24 \to 12}Sp_{18 \to 15}Py_{3 \to 5}$$

and

$$Al_{44 \to 55}Gr_{28 \to 24.5}Sp_{26.5 \to 20}Py_{1.5 \to 2.5}$$

Arrows indicate core → rim.[*]

At the oligoclase isograd albite is completely eliminated as also are chlorite and epidote in most metabasalts, which now have the simple composition hornblende-andesine-sphene (±almandine). Here transition from the greenschist to the amphibolite facies is now complete—although because of prevailingly low aluminum, other characteristic amphibolite-facies minerals—kyanite, staurolite—have been recorded only rarely (e.g., Wallace, 1975).

Epidote-Amphibolite Zone, Sanbagawa Belt, Japan

In the Sanbagawa belt of Japan as described by Iwasaki (1963) and Banno (1964), the generalized facies series, not fully developed in all segments of the belt, may be represented (cf. pp. 333–334) as

Pumpellyite-actinolite → blueschist-greenschist transition → greenschist

→ amphibolite

A zone of epidote-amphibolite encompasses the highest grades. Much of it represents the greenschist-amphibolite transition with the assemblages

---

[*]Cooper explains the zoned condition so commonly found in metamorphic almandines in terms of a model of crystal growth, ionic diffusion, and fractionation within a limited range of diffusion in the enclosing rock (cf. Atherton, 1968, 1976). This latter thereby becomes progressively depleted in Mn^{2+} for which the distribution coefficient $K^{gar/rock}$ is high. The manganese content of the growing crystal consequently falls off from core to rim. Implicit in the postmetamorphic survival of zonary structure in garnets is an internal velocity of ionic diffusion that must be close to zero within the garnet lattice.

1. Pelitic: quartz-muscovite-chlorite-almandine
2. Metabasaltic: hornblende-epidote-albite-chlorite-almandine

The paragenesis differs from that of any of the other examples just described by absence of biotite—a mineral ubiquitous in other provinces even in the preceding greenschist facies.

There is, however, a further subzone of maximum grade in which biotite comes in in metapelites and oligoclase (recorded as An_{15}) in amphibolites. This is the full amphibolite facies with quartz-muscovite-biotite-almandine in metapelites, hornblende-epidote-oligoclase (+almandine or diopside) in metabasalts, and calcite-quartz-diopside-grossularite in calcareous bands.

Order of Appearance of Key Minerals

Key minerals in the transition from low to high grades of regional metamorphism are biotite and almandine in metapelites; oligoclase and hornblende in metagraywackes and amphibolites. The relative order of their appearance in a prograde sequence is not precisely the same in any two of the four examples that have just been reviewed. Currently available records indicate the following sequences:

Vermont: Biotite → oligoclase (+albite) → $\begin{cases} \text{almandine} \\ \text{oligoclase-andesine} \\ \text{hornblende} \end{cases}$

Dalradian: Biotite → almandine → oligoclase (+ albite) → $\begin{cases} \text{hornblende} \\ \text{oligoclase-andesine} \\ \text{staurolite} \end{cases}$

Western Haast terrane: Biotite → $\begin{cases} \text{almandine} \\ \text{oligoclase (+ albite)} \\ \text{hornblende} \end{cases}$ → oligoclase-andesine

Sanbagawa belt: $\begin{rcases} \text{Almandine} \\ \text{hornblende} \end{rcases}$ → $\begin{cases} \text{biotite} \\ \text{oligoclase} \\ \text{diopside} \end{cases}$

The variability so displayed in the greenschist-amphibolite transition probably reflects, at least in part, the influence of chemical factors. Carbonates for example are minor but widespread ingredients of antecedent greenschist assemblages in Vermont and in parts of the Dalradian (e.g., McNamara, 1965); and these are likely participants in the oligoclase-generating reactions. In the Haast Terrane on the other hand epidote seems to play the corresponding role (Crawford, 1966; Cooper, 1972). One must also ask however if differences in physical conditions of metamorphism may be partly responsible for observed variations on the general theme of transition. The Sanbagawa facies series, with obvious blueschist affinities at middle grades, undoubtedly reflects a combination of high pressure with relatively low temperature. This pressure factor would seem the most likely control underlying postponement of biotite to the culminating grade (amphibolite facies) represented in this province.

AMPHIBOLITE FACIES

General Characteristics

The amphibolite facies can be defined rather sharply by assemblages in metabasalt lithology. In these the key mineral pair is hornblende-plagioclase ($An_{>25}$), which may be accompanied, according to variation in rock composition, by combinations of epidote, almandine, diopside, and biotite. In pelitic rocks almandine, staurolite, and one of the $Al_2 SiO_5$ polymorphs, alone or in combination, accompany the ubiquitous biotite and muscovite. A wide variety of CaMg and CaAl silicates is represented—tremolite, diopside, grossularite, clinozoisite, and calcic plagioclase. Sphene remains a characteristic minor constituent, but because titanium becomes increasingly accommodated in other places (hornblende, biotite) sphene is less plentiful than in the greenschist facies.

Pressure Indices

Pressure considerations loom large in modern tectonic models that place an emphasis on the evidence of metamorphic paragenesis. However, in the amphibolite and the granulite facies, which together cover virtually the whole field of high-grade regional metamorphism, mineralogical pressure indices are less sharply defined than in facies of lower grade. The problem has been taken up by D. M. Carmichael (1978) who has set up a generalized sequence of "bathozones," each covering some finite range of pressure, based on medium- and high-grade metapelitic assemblages. This will be considered further in Chap. 11.

In the meantime, to illustrate the mineralogical character and environmental setting of the amphibolite facies, selected examples have been grouped arbitrarily in two categories: that of low and that of medium to high pressure (at high grades extreme pressures are represented by the eclogite facies). In spite of all the other mineral equilibria that have been tested quantitatively and of inherent uncertainties as to stability limits and the possible role of reaction kinetics, the $Al_2 SiO_5$ polymorphs still remain the most reliable general indices of pressure that are widely available in rocks of high metamorphic grade. The line between our two pressure categories is arbitrarily drawn therefore between the two alternative prograde sequences andalusite → sillimanite and kyanite → sillimanite in adjacent sub-·facies of the amphibolite facies. A second general index of low pressure is cordierite (with or without almandine), as opposed to almandine alone at higher pressures. Tentative numerical appraisal of pressure limits appropriate to individual examples is postponed to Chap. 11. It should be obvious, however, from earlier discussion (pp. 150-151) that an arbitrary dividing line has been drawn at between 3 and 4 kb.

Parageneses of Relatively Low Pressure

Orijärvi District, Southern Finland:
Springboard for the Facies Concept

The eastern segment of the Svecofennian block in the Fennoscandian shield covers southern and central Finland (latitude ~60-64°N; longitude ~20-30°E). It is a region of high-grade metamorphic rocks interspersed between very extensive granitic plutons (cf. Sederholm, 1932, general map; Hietanen, 1975, pp. 637–639), once mapped as Archaean but recently found to bear the all-pervasive imprint of a tectonic-plutonic-metamorphic event dated as mid-Proterozoic (1700–1800×10^6 years). Of particular interest in the present context is a region centered at the copper-mining district of Orijärvi, some 60 km northwest of Helsinki (Fig. 10-2); for this is the site of Eskola's (1914, 1915) classic study of metamorphic paragenesis in the vicinity of a syntectonic oligoclase-granite pluton, from which emerged his concept of metamorphic facies.

Here the metamorphic envelope consists of metagraywackes (leptites of Swedish and Finnish writers), amphibolites, and minor calcareous lenses, all in the amphibolite facies of regional metamorphism. As at many places elsewhere in the Svecofennian block, patchy magnesium-iron metasomatism is widespread (cf. Simonen, 1948; Tuominen and Mikkola, 1950; Eskola, 1951; Härme and Pertunen, 1971). Its nature and cause, the subject of some controversy, are immaterial to present discussions; but, because metasomatic effects are especially conspicuous at points close to the Orijärvi oligoclase-granite contacts, Eskola originally described the whole metamorphic facies as one of contact metamorphism. It was treated thus within the hornblende-hornfels facies in the earlier edition of this book; but now, in accordance with the scheme of facies series outlined in Chap. 7, the Orijärvi metamorphic paragenesis, including mineral assemblages that reflect synchronous metasomatism, will be considered simply as the local expression of the regional amphibolite facies in southern Finland, much in the same way as Miyashiro has treated

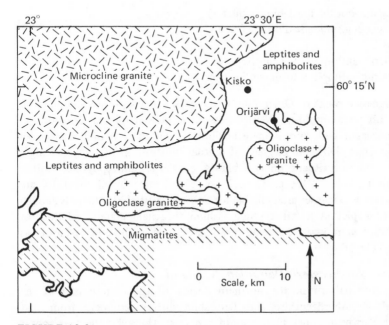

FIGURE 10-2
Distribution of granitic plutons, migmatites, and metamorphic rocks, Orijärvi district, Finland (after P. Eskola, 1914).

metamorphic facies adjacent to syntectonic granitic plutons in the Ryoke-Abukuma belt of Japan.

Because of its historic importance and detailed documentation by Eskola when modern metamorphic petrology was in its very infancy, the Orijärvi paragenesis as originally described is reviewed below and illustrated in Figs. 10-3 and 10-4. It was the contrast between this and the contact metamorphic paragenesis of Oslo as recorded shortly before by Goldschmidt that led Eskola to the concept of metamorphic facies. (The Orijärvi pattern he designated the amphibolite, that of the Oslo aureoles the hornfels facies.)

Principal mineral assemblages in the Orijärvi district, numbered as in Fig. 10-3, are as follows:

A. Pelitic:
   1. Quartz-muscovite-biotite (-plagioclase-microcline)
   2. Quartz-muscovite-cordierite-andalusite (-plagioclase)
   3. Quartz-muscovite-biotite-cordierite (-plagioclase)
   4. Quartz-biotite-cordierite-andalusite
   5. Quartz-muscovite-biotite-andalusite
B. Quartzo-feldspathic:
   1. Quartz-plagioclase-microcline-muscovite-biotite
   7. Quartz-plagioclase-microcline-biotite-hornblende
C. Calcareous:
   9. Diopside-grossularite (-quartz-plagioclase)
   10. Grossularite-diopside-calcite-quartz or grossularite-diopside-wollastonite
D. Basic:
   7. Plagioclase-hornblende (-biotite-quartz)
   8. Plagioclase-hornblende-diopside (-quartz)
E. Magnesian:
   6a. Cordierite-anthophyllite (-biotite)
    b. Cordierite-anthophyllite-almandine (-biotite)

The magnesian rocks of Orijärvi are products of magnesia-iron metasomatism concurrent with metamorphism. Nevertheless their present mineral composition is broadly consistent with approximate equilibrium within each of the principal mineral assemblages. Different degrees of mutual substitution of Fe^{2+} and Mg^{2+} are shown by the constituent mineral phases: cordierite, anthophyllite, biotite, and almandine (Eskola, 1915, p. 122). Eskola's data on mineral chemistry are imperfect; in fact no analyses are available for Orijärvi biotites. Still there is enough information to depict in a rather crude fashion the chemographic relations of coexisting phases in muscovite-bearing assemblages and in those with biotite as the only mica (Fig. 10-4).

Buchan Type, Northeastern Dalradian, Scotland

The metamorphic pattern in the northern corner of the eastern part of the Dalradian belt—in Aberdeenshire and Banffshire—differs strikingly from that of the classic Barrovian zones to the south and west. However, the two appear to be mutually gradational west of Portsoy and south and west of Aberdeen

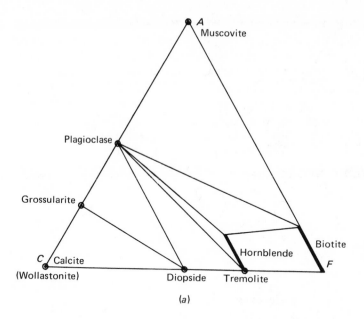

(a)

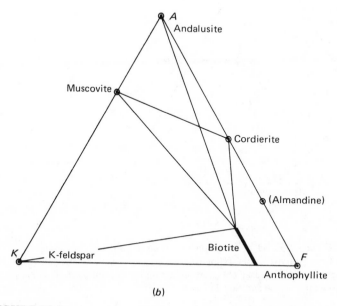

(b)

FIGURE 10-3

Amphibolite facies, Orijärvi, Finland: chemographic relations in assemblages with excess SiO_2 and K_2O. (a) *ACF* diagram; quartz and microcline are possible additional phases. (b) *AKF* diagram—muscovite-plagioclase-biotite triangle of (a); quartz and plagioclase are possible additional phases.

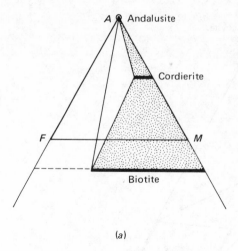

(a)

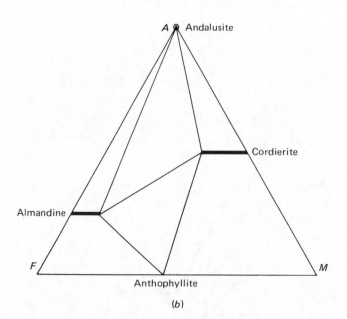

(b)

FIGURE 10-4
Amphibolite facies, Orijärvi, Finland, chemographic relations in magnesian assemblages.
(*a*) *AFM* projection from muscovite point (stippled areas are two-phase assemblages; quartz and muscovite are possible additional phases. (*b*) *AFM* projection for assemblages lacking muscovite; quartz and biotite are possible additional phases.

(Fig. 1-11*b*).* Harker (1932, pp. 230–235) clearly set out the distinctive features of rocks in the Aberdeenshire-Banffshire domain; texturally they show little sign of penetrative strain and in fact are akin more to hornfelses than to typical schists; mineralogically they are distinguished by widespread occurrence of the "anti-stress minerals" andalusite and cordierite in pelitic members.

Paucity of inland outcrop hinders zonal mapping. But a beginning was made by H. H. Read (1952) in an area of 400 km^2 centered 25 km north-northwest of Aberdeen. This was later expanded into a regional map (Chinner, 1966) covering the whole domain, some 2500 km^2 in all (Fig. 1-11*b*).

The west-to-east prograde sequence in the western part of the domain is much as described by Read (1952).

1. Quartz-sericite-chlorite-biotite
2. Quartz-sericite-chlorite-biotite-andalusite-cordierite
3. Quartz-muscovite-biotite-cordierite-andalusite-staurolite-plagioclase (sodic)
4. Quartz-muscovite-biotite-cordierite-andalusite-sillimanite
5. Quartz-muscovite-biotite-sillimanite-almandine-K-feldspar-oligoclase

Chinner's map shows successive zones for

a. Hydrous silicates (assemblage 1)
b. Andalusite (assemblages 2 and 3)
c. Andalusite + sillimanite (assemblages 4 and 5)

The third of these zones is associated in the field with migmatite complexes, and Chinner attributes development of sillimanite to overprinting in a late-metamorphic episode that left its stamp also on the contiguous part of Barrow's kyanite zone to the southeast.

All except the first of the metapelitic assemblages fall within the amphibolite-facies as presently defined. Read (1952, pp. 265, 278), in emphasizing the distinctive mineralogical pattern of the whole paragenesis, designated it the *Buchan type* of regional metamorphism and migmatitization as contrasted with what he termed the *Barrovian type* displayed to the south and west in Barrow's zones. These terms were quickly adopted into general usage to signify contrasted general patterns of regional metamorphism. They figure as standards in early attempts to assess field gradients quantitatively in terms of pressure and temperature (e.g., Fyfe et al., 1958, Figs. 107, 108).

Ryoke Belt, Japan

North and west of the Median Tectonic Line of Japan, which brings it into continuous vertical contact with the Sanbagawa belt (Fig. 10-5; cf. Fig. 9-14) is the Ryoke belt, 1000 km long and 50 km wide. The age of metamorphism (mid-Cretaceous) is about the same as in the Sanbagawa belt, but the pattern is utterly different. The dominant facies is amphibolite and the characteristic indices of low pressure—andalusite and cordierite—though not plentiful are widely distributed

---

*The nature of the transition (Chinner, 1966; Porteous, 1973; Atherton, 1977) though of interest with respect to the regional *P–T* picture does not concern present discussion.

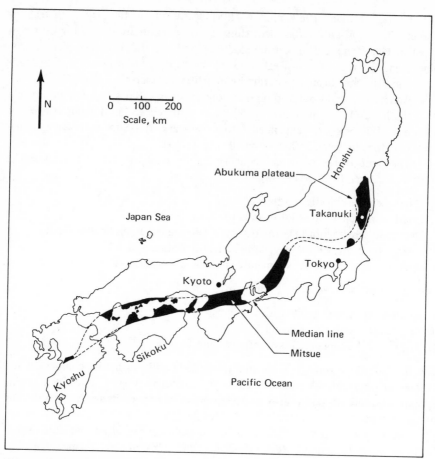

FIGURE 10-5
Ryoke metamorphic belt, Japan, showing location of areas studied intensively by K. Sugi and A. Miyashiro (Abukuma) and K. Suwa (Mitsue).

in pelitic members. There are numerous granodioritic plutons, many of them synmetamorphic. The field distribution of the latter correlates broadly but not in precise detail with the higher grades of regional metamorphism.

In a remarkable early contribution K. Sugi (1935) presented the first coherent picture of what has since become known as regional metamorphism of the Abukuma-Ryoke type and he contrasted it with the well-known pattern in Barrows' zones in the Grampian Highlands (Sugi, 1935, pp. 142, 150). A prograde sequence of zones was defined by successive pelitic indices—chlorite-sericite, biotite, oligoclase, and garnet—and culminated in migmatitic gneisses with orthoclase and sillimanite as minor constituents (Sugi, 1935, p. 149).

Subsequent work by Miyashiro (1958) in the Abukuma plateau and by Suwa (1961) at Mitsue about 300 km southwest of Tokyo has greatly amplified the picture presented two decades earlier by Sugi. The general zonal paragenesis based on this later work is summarized in a generalized fashion in Table 10-1.

TABLE 10-1
Mineral Assemblages of Ryoke Metamorphic Belt, Japan. Grade Increasing, Zone 1 → Zone 4

	Zone			
	1	2	3	4
Pelitic assemblages	Quartz-albite-biotite-chlorite; rare muscovite, spessartite-almandine (Mn/Fe = 1)	Quartz-andesine-biotite (-muscovite); rare K-feldspar, andalusite, almandine (Mn/Fe = 0.8 − 0.5)	Quartz-andesine-biotite (-muscovite-almandine-K-feldspar); rare andalusite, cordierite (Mn/Fe in garnet = 0.2)	Quartz-andesine-K-feldspar-biotite (-sillimanite-almandine); rare cordierite
Basic assemblages	Albite-chlorite-actinolite-epidote (-calcite); rare quartz, biotite	Andesine-hornblende (-epidote-sphene-chlorite); rare diopside, biotite, quartz	Labradorite-hornblende (-diopside); rare cummingtonite, biotite, quartz	Bytownite-hornblende-diopside (-cummingtonite); rare quartz
Calcareous assemblages	Calcite-actinolite-quartz; rare K-feldspar, epidote	Diopside-epidote (-calcite-quartz-hornblende-sphene); same assemblage with grossularite instead of epidote; rare K-feldspar	Diopside-grossularite (-calcite-hornblende-sphene); rare quartz, K-feldspar	Diopside-grossularite-wollastonite (-hornblende-sphene); rare calcite, K-feldspar

After A. Myashiro and K. Suwa.

Amphibolite (metabasaltic) assemblages provide the basis of metamorphic zoning. Except in zone 1 all are typical of the amphibolite facies. The rare occurrences of hypersthene-bearing amphibolite, bytownite-hornblende (brown)-cummingtonite (-diopside-hypersthene-olivine-spinel), in zone 4 perhaps suggests the beginning of a transition to the pyroxene-hornfels facies.

Miyashiro (1958, pp. 243, 246, 267) records some significant mineralogical indications of *P–T* conditions in the fourth zone.

1. At maximum grades muscovite is beginning to break down to sillimanite and K-feldspar.
2. Common occurrence of the assemblage calcite-wollastonite-diopside-grossularite in marble beds 1–10 m thick enclosed in semipelitic gneiss could be an index of externally buffered low f_{CO_2} in the pore fluids. This possibility is strengthened by the presence, in relatively rare dolomitic layers, of calcite-dolomite-tremolite-diopside-forsterite-phlogopite-graphite.
3. The oxidation ratio both in biotites and in hornblendes drops markedly with increasing metamorphic grade.

In the Mitsue region of the Ryoke belt (Suwa, 1961), metamorphism occurs mainly in the third and fourth zones. The andalusite → sillimanite transition takes place in the lower-grade part of zone 4. Small amounts of muscovite persist throughout. The appearance of cordierite and K-feldspar in abundance is thought by both writers to be due to reaction between muscovite, biotite, and quartz; evidently at temperatures lower than those of the muscovite-quartz ⇌ sillimanite-orthoclase equilibrium.

Hercynian Metamorphism, Pyrenees

The amphibolite facies is widely developed in Paleozoic sediments affected by regional Hercynian (mid-Paleozoic) metamorphism in the central Pyrenees (Zwart, 1962, 1963, 1965). Here the mineralogical pattern is reminiscent of the Buchan zones in Scotland. The zonal distribution in the Pyrenees is closely related to thermal highs, the sites of gneissic granitic plutons and migmatite complexes from which the metamorphic grade falls off radially outward. Around two such foci mapped by Zwart—Bosost and Aston-Hospitalet (the one 5–10 km, the other 30 km, in diameter)—concentric zones in quartz-muscovite-bearing metapelites show this prograde sequence:

1. Biotite
2. Biotite-staurolite-andalusite-cordierite (less often, garnet)
3. Biotite-cordierite-sillimanite

From a detailed textural analysis Zwart has put forward a model of polymetamorphic history encompassed in a single major metamorphic-tectonic event. As well as the "stable" minerals that characterize individual zones (as listed above) rock specimens may show "unstable" relict phases surviving from the preceding stage as a micaceous matrix or as rotated and partly destroyed porphyroblasts.

Zwart interpreted the granitic migmatites and gneissic plutons as products of "granitization"—a concept at that time still fashionable. Whatever the granitization process may have been, it obviously involved partial melting and probably intrusive emplacement of magma as well.

Concluding Notes: Role and Implications of Granite Plutonism

That regional metamorphism in the amphibolite facies has occurred repeatedly throughout geological time and the world over under a regime of relatively low pressure has now been thoroughly established. It is obvious, too, that an inseparable feature of this general pattern is widespread emplacement of synmetamorphic granitic plutons and generation of migmatites that are broadly related, at least in a general manner, to foci of high-grade amphibolite-facies metamorphism. This raises a question as to the relative roles of plutonism and metamorphism in low-pressure belts—a topic to which we shall return in Chap. 11.

Not unrelated to the question just raised is the tedious but to many geologists urgent one of nomenclature: is there a real difference between the hornblende-hornfels facies and the amphibolite facies in the low-temperature environment? It should be apparent that there are no distinctive mineralogical criteria that unequivocally separate the two categories. And mineralogical criteria are by definition the very basis of facies. If rock specimens or chemical equilibria were the subject of this book, both classes of rocks could be placed in a single facies (as indeed they were treated in my earlier work). What justifies, even compels, separate treatment according to the plan here adopted is the completely different tectonic environments and scales of development of the hornblende-hornfels and the low-pressure amphibolite facies.

Finally there is a question concerning standardization of facies and facies series in relation to various postulated levels of pressure. As far as it applies to the amphibolite facies this approach seems to me to be artificial and undesirable except on the simplest scale—a twofold but completely gradational division into low- and high-pressure variants. For those who wish to adopt geographic names for standard types so designated—a principle long since abandoned in igneous petrology—Read's original terms *Buchan* and *Barrovian types* are adequate and have priority. But the *facies series* correspondingly named are each unique; both are located in specified domains of the Scottish Dalradian.

Parageneses of Moderate and High Pressures

General Characteristics

Metamorphic pressures in the higher bracket (3–6 kb?) can reasonably be assigned to amphibolite facies parageneses on two general grounds: (1) widespread occurrence of certain phases, notably almandine and kyanite, and absence of others, andalusite and cordierite; and (2) preceding low-grade facies (in the same facies series) with other high-pressure indices—lawsonite, aragonite, and glaucophane.

Synmetamorphic granodioritic plutons and centers of migmatitization are common though not ubiquitous. They are perhaps less conspicuous than in low-pressure terranes and their localization is possibly less specifically related to distribution of high-temperature isograds.

Staurolite-Kyanite Zone,
New Hampshire–Vermont

The only obvious change in paragenesis with passage from the almandine zone to that of staurolite and kyanite is in the more aluminous pelitic assemblages. Chloritoid and chlorite are no longer present; staurolite and/or kyanite may appear in rocks deficient in K_2O (that is, in assemblages lacking K-feldspar). Some of the recorded assemblages are as follows (Lyons, 1955, pp. 110, 115, 118, 140–142).

A. Pelitic (cf. Fig. 10-6):
    1. Quartz-andesine-muscovite-biotite-almandine-kyanite (-staurolite)[*]
    2. Quartz-oligoclase-muscovite-biotite-almandine-staurolite
B. Metabasaltic:
    3. Quartz-andesine-hornblende-biotite (-clinozoisite-almandine)
C. Calcareous:
    4. Quartz-clinozoisite (-hornblende-garnet)
    5. Calcite-actinolite (-hornblende)
    6. Calcite-quartz
D. Magnesian:
    7. Chlorite-anthophyllite-talc (-magnetite-ankerite)

Sillimanite-Muscovite Zone, New Hampshire

Over much of western New Hampshire (cf. Fig. 1-13) some 50 km southeast of the Hanover quadrangle described by Lyons, the pelitic paragenesis is characterized

[*]This assemblage (with magnetite plus graphite) marks the kyanite isograd in the Barrovian sequence in Scotland (Chinner, 1966, p. 163).

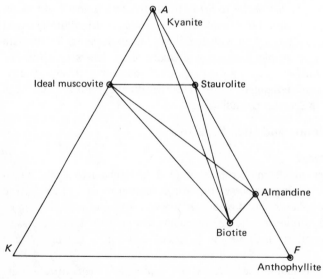

FIGURE 10-6
Amphibolite facies, staurolite-kyanite zone, Hanover Quadrangle, New Hampshire–Vermont. *AKF* diagram for rocks with excess SiO_2 and Al_2O_3. Quartz and plagioclase are additional phases.

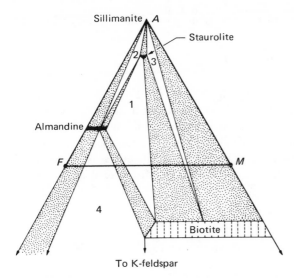

FIGURE 10-7

Amphibolite facies, sillimanite-muscovite zone, west central New Hampshire. *AFM* diagram for pelitic assemblages containing quartz and muscovite (after J. B. Thompson). Three-phase fields number as in text; two phase fields stippled.

by sillimanite in association with muscovite. Otherwise it resembles that depicted in Fig. 10-6. These are the rocks of the sillimanite-muscovite-zone, as distinguished from assemblages of even higher grade in which sillimanite is associated with K-feldspar while muscovite and staurolite are lacking.

J. B. Thompson (1957) has illustrated the pelitic paragenesis in detail by means of his *AFM* projection, here reproduced as Fig. 10-7.

1. Quartz-muscovite-biotite-almandine-staurolite
2. Quartz-muscovite-almandine-staurolite-sillimanite
3. Quartz-muscovite-biotite-staurolite-sillimanite
4. Quartz-muscovite-biotite-almandine-orthoclase

In the same zone of New Hampshire, Heald (1950, pp. 48–50) recorded the paragenesis of pelitic schists similar to the above, but containing oligoclase (An_{28}) and no staurolite.

6. Quartz-oligoclase-biotite-muscovite-almandine
7. Quartz-oligoclase-biotite-muscovite-sillimanite-almandine
8. Quartz-oligoclase-biotite-microcline

With these are associated thinly bedded alternating calc-magnesian and calc-pelitic schists with the assemblages

9. Microcline-anorthite-diopside (-quartz)
10. Diopside-actinolite-microcline-bytownite (-quartz)
11. Actinolite-anorthite-microcline (-garnet-quartz)
12. Anorthite-biotite-microcline (-microcline-quartz-biotite)

The complete paragenesis of the New Hampshire sillimanite-muscovite zone is shown in Fig. 10-8.

Sillimanite Zones of the Scottish Highlands and New Hampshire

The respective parageneses representing the highest grade of metamorphism attained in these two regions have much in common. Pelitic assemblages contain sillimanite, not kyanite. In New Hampshire this is associated with orthoclase and biotite, but not with muscovite. In Scotland, all four phases are commonly present, and textures suggest that in many rocks the pair muscovite-quartz is in process of breaking down to sillimanite-orthoclase. Ideal muscovite-free assemblages (Harker, 1932, pp. 227–229, 255, 263, 283; Wiseman, 1934, pp. 394, 395; Heald, 1950, pp. 50–55) are

A. Pelitic and quartzo-feldspathic:
  1. Quartz-plagioclase (An_{30})-biotite-almandine-sillimanite-orthoclase (-muscovite)
  2. Quartz-plagioclase (An_{30})-biotite-almandine-sillimanite
  3. Quartz-plagioclase (An_{30})-biotite-sillimanite
B. Basic ("epidiorite"):
  4. Hornblende-andesine-almandine (-quartz); epidote and biotite, common at lower grades, absent
C. Calcareous (cf. W. Q. Kennedy, 1949, pp. 49, 53):
  5. Grossularite-anorthite-diopside-hornblende

Geochemical studies in pelitic assemblages in the higher grades of regional metamorphism in Scotland and eastern United States have brought out several interesting details:

In the Scottish Dalradian, the boundary (sillimanite isograd) between the zones of kyanite and sillimanite is by no means sharply defined. The two aluminum silicates commonly coexist. Chinner (1960) records the influence of different degrees of oxidation, reflected by the respective occurrences of ilmenite-magnetite, ilmenite-magnetite-hematite, and magnetite-hematite in pelitic gneisses in which the principal silicate phases are quartz-oligoclase-muscovite-biotite-almandine-kyanite-sillimanite. These rocks occur on the outer fringe of the sillimanite zone in Glen Clova in the classic region of Barrow's zones. Chinner finds that in each sedimentary unit, the degree of oxidation, reflecting the fugacity of oxygen during metamorphism, remained constant. The range of oxidation ratio is from 6 (in ilmenite-magnetite assemblages) to 75 (in magnetite-hematite assemblages). With increasing oxidation, the amounts of biotite and garnet decrease, and there is a complementary increment in the amounts of muscovite and iron oxides. At the same time there is a marked rise in Mg/Fe in biotite and in Mn/Fe in associated garnet (Fig. 10-9).

The gradual breakdown of muscovite-quartz to sillimanite-orthoclase has been traced by Evans and Guidotti (1966) along a traverse across the orthoclase isograd between the zones of sillimanite-muscovite and sillimanite-orthoclase

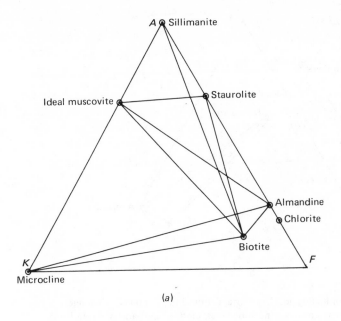

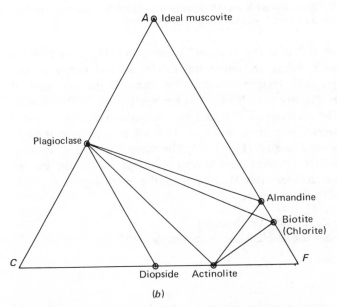

FIGURE 10-8

Amphibolite facies, sillimanite-muscovite zone, New Hampshire. (*a*) *AKF* diagram for pelitic and psammopelitic assemblages with quartz, muscovite, and plagioclase (typically An$_{\sim 30}$). (*b*) *ACF* diagram for rocks with excess K_2O and SiO_2. Microcline and quartz are almost ubiquitous additional phases.

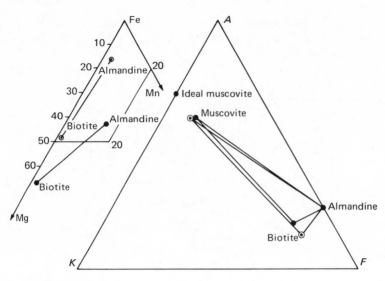

FIGURE 10-9

Amphibolite facies, sillimanite isograd, Glen Clova, Scotland (data from G. A. Chinner). Chemographic relations between coexisting muscovites, biotites, and garnets, on AKF and $MgFe^{2+}Mn$ projections. Circled points are low-oxidation assemblages (with magnetite-ilmenite); solid circles are high-oxidation assemblages (with magnetite-hematite).

in Maine, eastern United States. The "isograd" is not a line, but a zone 10 km wide throughout which sillimanite, muscovite, K-feldspar, and quartz coexist, while muscovite is gradually eliminated with rising grade. At the same time, ilmenite diminishes in quantity and there is a corresponding rise in the titanium content of biotite. The composition of muscovites throughout the whole region is very uniform. Analyses plotted in terms of AKF fall very close to those of the Glen Clova sillimanite isograd (Fig. 10-9). The paragonite content is about Pa_8 except in muscovites in assemblages lacking K-feldspar below the isograd. Here the composition approximates $Ms_{85}Pa_{15}$. All the assemblages are pelitic. Below the sillimanite-orthoclase isograd

1. Quartz-biotite-oligoclase (-garnet-orthoclase)
2. Quartz-biotite-muscovite-oligoclase-sillimanite (-garnet)

Above the isograd

3. The same as 2
4. Quartz-biotite-oligoclase-muscovite-sillimanite-orthoclase (-garnet)

Albee (1965) found that as metamorphic grade increases from the staurolite through the kyanite to the sillimanite zone, there is a very marked rise in the distribution coefficient (Mg/Fe in garnet)/(Mg/Fe in biotite). At any given metamorphic grade, the coefficient is reduced below its average value if the garnet carries significant manganese.

These and similar studies have clarified the nature of the usually complex (i.e., "continuous") interphase reactions that mark the various classic isograds. They also tend to support, in considerable detail, our general hypothesis that the common phase assemblages in metamorphic rocks closely approximate equilibrium.

Lepontine Province, Central Alps, Switzerland

Along the southern slopes of the Alps below the Simplon-Gotthard crest (cf. Figs. 9-15 and 10-10), rocks of the Pennine nappes in the Lepontine region show mainly the imprint of the mid-Tertiary phase of Alpine metamorphism. Local eclogites could equally well be relics of either Eoalpine or Hercynian metamorphism. Isograds and regional structure are unrelated. Isogradic surfaces, moreover, have been proved to dip steeply in the Simplon Pass section (Streckeisen and Wenk, 1974). The complete picture of regional metamorphism extends across major structural discontinuities into the adjoining parts of the Helvetic domain to the north, where lower grades down to prehnite-pumpellyite facies are fully represented. The total regional facies series, prograde from north to south, is

$$\text{Zeolite} \rightarrow \text{prehnite-pumpellyite} \rightarrow \text{greenschist} \rightarrow \text{amphibolite}$$

The metamorphic paragenesis over almost the whole of the Lepontine province is that of the amphibolite facies, nearly all in what we have designated the high-

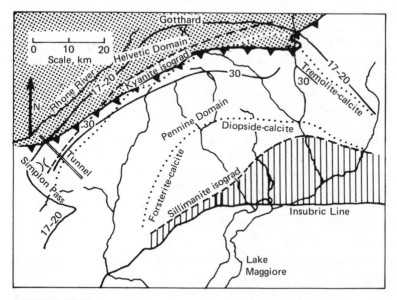

FIGURE 10-10
Metamorphic zones in part of Lepontine region, Swiss Alps (after E. Jäger, E. Niggli, and E. Wenk). Isograds for metapelites, dashed. Niggli's (1960) sillimanite zone ruled vertically. Wenk and Keller's (1969) isograds for An_{17-20} and An_{30} in amphibolites, full lines correspondingly numbered. Trommsdorff's isograds for first appearance of (1) tremolite, and (2) diopside or forsterite in metadolomites, dotted. Adjacent part of Helvetic domain lightly stippled.

pressure range.* This overlaps slightly from the Pennine into the southern fringe of the Helvetic domain along the southern border of the Grotthard massif. The Lepontine province has been so extensively investigated during the past two decades that it must surely rank as one of the most fully documented regions that illustrate progressive metamorphism in the amphibolite facies over a varied range of lithology (see summary and selected contributions cited by Frey et al., 1974, p. 258). The following account refers to the region west of the Bergell granitic pluton, where the metamorphic imprint is less complex than east of the pluton.

In *pelitic lithology* (Mesozoic metasediments) E. Niggli (1960, 1970) in particular has mapped successive regional zones of stilpnomelane, chloritoid (more locally, in the Gotthard region), kyanite, staurolite, and sillimanite (Fig. 10-10). His kyanite and almost coincident staurolite isograd mark the low-grade limit of the amphibolite facies. At this point, stilpnomelane has been eliminated, and chloritoid gives way to staurolite (via a zone a kilometer or two wide where the two minerals coexist). The typical metapelitic assemblage of the kyanite zone (about 30 km in width) is

Quartz-muscovite-biotite-kyanite-staurolite-almandine (± plagioclase

± paragonite)

At the sillimanite isograd fibrolite becomes widespread in metapelites but kyanite persists for some distance into the sillimanite zone. This is a region of abundant migmatites (that are not, however, confined entirely to the sillimanite zone). They are products of partial melting of Hercynian crystalline basement rock. But reworking culminating in partial fusion represents the climax of mid-Tertiary Alpine metamorphism (cf. Wenk, 1970), which is also responsible for the mineral assemblages developed in the obviously metamorphic components of the migmatites. The general metapelitic assemblage of the sillimanite zone is

Quartz-muscovite-biotite-sillimanite ± K-feldspar ± almandine

Siliceous *dolomitic bands* are widely distributed in the Triassic metasediments of the Lepontine region. In them, Trommsdorff (1966) traced a sequence of decarbonation reactions parallel to that discussed in Chap. 4 (Fig. 4-10), and established two corresponding isograds (dotted in Fig. 10-10) that conform to the regional geometric pattern of those mapped in metapelites.

1. Tremolite-dolomite-calcite: This reflects elimination of talc from carbonate assemblages, just inside the staurolite isograd. Less common, more siliceous rocks consist of tremolite-calcite-quartz (cf. Fig. 4-10*b*).

*On the regional map of Frey and co-authors (1974, Pl. 2), these rocks are marked "intermediate pressure amphibolite facies" to distinguish them from "high-pressure" products (blueschists and eclogites) of the Eoalpine episode to the southwest.

2. Diopside and forsterite, virtually simultaneously. Dolomite-tremolite is now unstable. Stable assemblages (cf. Fig. 4-10c and 4.10d) are

  Diopside-tremolite-calcite
  Diopside-calcite
  Forsterite (-chondrodite)-calcite

The width of the tremolite-carbonate zone between the two isograds is about 20 km, still within the kyanite-staurolite zone of metapelites.

  Wenk and Keller (1969) in an exhaustive study of Lepontine amphibolites record the familiar abrupt jump in anorthite content of plagioclase, from $An_{<5}$ to An_{17-20}, with a corresponding isograd close to that of kyanite in metapelites (Fig. 10-10). Near the isograd, albite and oligoclase coexist in some specimens (Wenk and Keller, 1969, p. 173). Thereafter there is a general increase in anorthite content with rising grade conforming to the geometric pattern of isograds drawn for other lithologies. The isograd for An_{30} is sharply defined, those drawn for higher values less so. But labradorite, $An_{>50}$, is virtually confined to amphibolites of the sillimanite zone. The commonest assemblages of the 20-km-wide oligoclase zone (between the An_{17-20} and An_{30} isograds) are

Hornblende-oligoclase-biotite ($\pm$garnet)
Hornblende-oligoclase-biotite-epidote
Hornblende-oligoclase ($\pm$garnet)

all with either sphene or rutile. Epidote decreases, and sphene becomes more widespread than rutile as the grade advances. In the sillimanite zone epidote has been eliminated, diopside is common, and garnet more so than at lower grades. The typical assemblage is now

  Hornblende-labradorite-diopside ($\pm$almandine)

with sphene the common titaniferous accessory.

  In calcite marbles plagioclase, which is a common constituent, also becomes increasingly calcic with advancing grade (Wenk, 1962). An isograd for An_{18} virtually coincides with that shown for amphibolites; but beyond this the anorthite content of plagioclase increases more rapidly but less regularly than in accompanying amphibolites. In marbles of the sillimanite zone, values of An_{80} to $An_{>90}$ are typical.

  Bodies of magnesian ultramafic rocks are present throughout the Lepontine region, though their distribution is too erratic to permit mapping of continuous isograds in this lithology. Nevertheless Trommsdorff and Evans (1974) have pieced together a prograde sequence of magnesian assemblages that on the whole is consistent with experimental and thermodynamic prediction. In general, magnesium silicates are highly sensitive to compositional variation in coexisting fluids, especially as to $X_{H_2O}^{fl}$ versus $X_{CO_2}^{fl}$. Reflecting this influence, ultramafic bodies of the Lepontine, as elsewhere, fall into two distinct types based on premetamorphic mineralogy: serpentinites consisting largely of serpentine minerals and with little or no carbonate; and "ophicarbonates" in which an abundant carbonate phase (typically calcite) is associated with chrysotile or other serpentines. Since the gas phase, especially in the opening stages of metamorphism, tends to be buffered by the initial mineral assemblage, these two lithologic types generate partially distinct series of metamorphic assemblages. So they will now be treated separately.

Progressive metamorphism of serpentinites in the Lepontine region has been studied especially by Trommsdorff and Evans (1974), whose conclusions are the main basis of what follows. Characteristic of greenschist assemblages of this lithology in the biotite zone of the Alps is the stable pair diopside-antigorite. This persists on into the lowest grade of the amphibolite facies, so that in the outer border, a few kilometers wide, of the kyanite zone typical metaserpentinite assemblages (Fig. 10-11a) are

1. Antigorite-forsterite-diopside
2. Antigorite-forsterite-tremolite
3. Antigorite-talc-tremolite

Just beyond the tremolite-calcite isograd of metadolomites antigorite-diopside breaks down and the metaserpentinite assemblages, continuing across most of the tremolite-calcite zone (Fig. 10-11b), are

4. Antigorite-tremolite-forsterite
5. Antigorite-tremolite-talc (less common)

Approaching the diopside-calcite isograd antigorite becomes eliminated in favor of either forsterite-talc or forsterite-anthophyllite (the latter apparently an inversion product of the strictly metamorphic polymorph magnesio-cummingtonite). In the Lepontine region anthophyllite is more persistently developed at this stage than talc. The corresponding regional assemblage

6. Anthophyllite-forsterite (-tremolite)

would be favored over talc-forsterite by relatively low $X_{H_2O}^{gas}$ (implying significant CO_2 in the gas) and by relatively high $Fe^{2+}/(Fe^{2+} + Mg)$ in the system (Trommsdorff and Evans, 1974, p. 344). At the diopside-calcite isograd, enstatite begins to become prominent in metaserpentinite. Thenceforth, up to highest grades in the sillimanite zone, although anthophyllite or even talc is found with forsterite, the dominant assemblage is

7. Enstatite-forsterite (-tremolite)

The paragenesis at this stage is shown in Fig. 10-11c. At maximum grade in the sillimanite zone green spinel may be a minor additional phase in assemblage 7— the product of dehydration of aluminous chlorite. There are also a few records of the ultimate dehydration product of serpentinite

8. Forsterite-enstatite-diopside

Turning now to *ophicarbonates*, assemblages in the outermost part (a few kilometers wide) of the kyanite zone are the same as in the greenschist facies beyond. Antigorite (the main silicate phase) coexists with any of the three car-

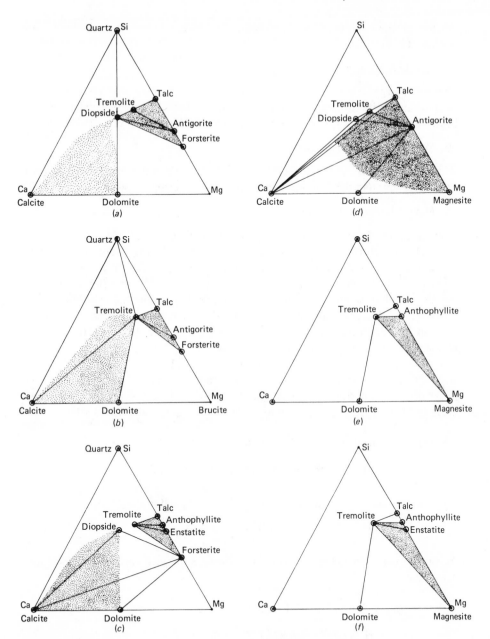

FIGURE 10-11

Amphibolite facies. Lepontine Alps. Typical phase assemblages in magnesian metamorphic rocks: (*a*)–(*c*) Metadolomites (light stipple) and metaserpentinites (dense stipple); (*d*)–(*e*) Ophi-carbonates (dense stipple) (data from V. M. Trommsdorff and B. W. Evans, 1974). Sense of increasing grade: (*a*) and (*d*), outer kyanite zone → (*b*) and (*e*), tremolite-calcite zone → (*c*) and (*f*), diopside-calcite and sillimanite zones.

bonates calcite, dolomite, and magnesite; but the commonest rocks by far are ophicalcites with

9. Calcite-antigorite-tremolite

The full paragenesis is illustrated in Fig. 10-11d. Close to the tremolite-calcite isograd, antigorite-carbonate pairs are eliminated. The ultimate product to emerge in the Lepontine region is the assemblage (Trommsdorff and Evans, 1974, Fig. 8):

10. Magnesite-anthophyllite-tremolite[*]

and this continues to the highest grades of the sillimanite zone (Fig. 10-11e). Equally common in the diopside-calcite and sillimanite zones however is

11. Magnesite-enstatite-tremolite

Chemographic relations at maximum grade are shown in Fig. 10-11f.

The full story of ophicarbonate metamorphism in the Lepontine is still by no means clear. But the brief account just presented serves to illustrate the influence of at least one pair of related chemical variables, $X_{H_2O}^{gas}$ versus $X_{CO_2}^{gas}$. Assuming the simplest situation in which gas composition is continuously buffered at the level stoichiometrically appropriate to the reaction in progress, we can distinguish between three, to some extent, overlapping cases (cf. Fig. 10-11). First, in metadolomites $X_{CO_2}^{gas}$ will be high relative to $X_{H_2O}^{gas}$, both during generation and subsequent elimination of tremolite (Fig. 10-11d–f) according to Eqs. 4-7 and 4-10. Second, transformations in ophicarbonates may be buffered by a wide range of gas composition. For example, breakdown of calcite-antigorite (Trommsdorff and Evans, 1974, p. 338) can be accomplished along alternative paths:

(1) 9 calcite + 4 antigorite + 5CO$_2$ → tremolite + 7 dolomite

$+ 7H_2O (X_{CO_2}^{gas} = 0.42; X_{H_2O}^{gas} = 0.58)$

(2) 2 calcite + 11 antigorite → tremolite + 14 forsterite + 2CO$_2$

$+ 21H_2O (X_{CO_2}^{gas} = 0.09; X_{H_2O}^{gas} = 0.91)$

Again, the common low-grade pair talc-magnesite (as in soapstone) can be eliminated thus:

(3) Talc + 5 magnesite → 4 forsterite + 5CO$_2$

$+ H_2O (X_{CO_2}^{gas} = 0.83; X_{H_2O}^{gas} = 0.17)$

Third, in the dehydration of serpentinite, the only active gas component is H_2O. But CO_2 may have a significant influence as an inert diluent, lowering f_{H_2O}. This would not only lower equilibrium temperature at constant pressure, but could

---

[*]Alternative assemblages such as tremolite-dolomite-forsterite have been recorded at this grade elsewhere in the Alps (Trommsdorff and Evans, 1974, p. 338).

affect the very nature of the dehydration equilibrium. We saw that at one stage alternative dehydration products are talc-forsterite and anthophyllite-forsterite. The two can be related by a univariant equilibrium

9 talc + 4 forsterite $\rightleftharpoons$ 5 anthophyllite + $4H_2O$

Clearly, under given *P–T* conditions, lowering f_{H_2O} by CO_2 in the gas phase would favor reaction from left to right; and it is to this condition that Trommsdorff and Evans (1974, p. 344) attribute persistence of the anthophyllite-forsterite pair in the Lepontine.

The general paragenesis depicted for the three lithologies in Fig. 10-11 represents all possible variations (under amphibolite-facies conditions) within an overall "system" of five components (CaO, MgO, SiO_2, H_2O, and CO_2). Each of the subtriangles in every diagram represents a four-phase assemblage (three solids plus a gas). By the phase rule, then, these equilibria are trivariant, the independent variables being P, T, $X_{H_2O}^{gas}$ (or $X_{CO_2}^{gas}$). In the light of previous discussion, it is readily seen how, given a wide range of possible gas composition, a single chemical system (represented by a point in any diagram) can be expressed by different phase assemblages at constant P and T; for $X_{H_2O}^{gas}$ must be defined in order completely to describe the system in mineralogical terms.

Influence of Pressure in Regional Amphibolite Facies Series

General Proposition

Up to this point the amphibolite facies has been treated as it develops by prograde regional metamorphism within respective general regimes of lower and of higher pressure. While not excluding some latitude in pressure along the metamorphic gradient, such treatment does imply that temperature is the main physical variable responsible for variations in the amphibolite facies parageneses along the prograde path. Clearly, however, when very extensive provinces of regional metamorphism are considered in toto, the changing metamorphic pattern on a very large scale may largely reflect regional pressure gradients, at different points along which prograde sequences in smaller subprovinces express local gradients in temperature. A single instance should suffice to illustrate this large-scale situation.

Amphibolite Facies Parageneses, Grenville Province, Ontario

The Precambrian Grenville tectonic province of the eastern Canadian Shield extends 450 km westward from the St. Lawrence along a 2000-km belt stretching from the Great Lakes to the northeast coast of Labrador (Fig. 10-12*a*). Its western margin is a major tectonic-chronologic discontinuity, the "Grenville Front." Like many another sector of an ancient craton, this is a region of repeated cycles of tectonism, plutonism, and metamorphism (e.g., Wynne-Edwards, 1969). There are radio-retentive memories of events at 2500, 1750, 1400, and finally 950×10^6 years (the Grenville orogeny itself). But it was in this last metamorphic cycle that the present imprint of regional metamorphism was imposed.

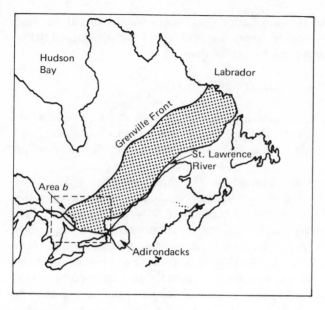

(a)

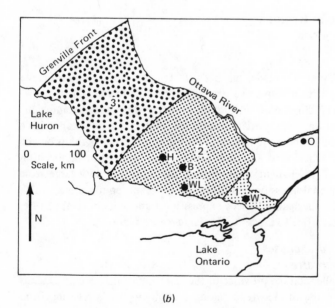

(b)

FIGURE 10-12
(a) Map showing location of Grenville tectonic province (stippled), Canadian shield. (b) Distribution of zones of increasing pressure $1 \rightarrow 3$ in southern strip of Grenville province (after W. Chesworth, 1971). (B, Bancroft; H, Harcourt; O, Ottawa; W, Westport; WL, Whetstone Lake.)

For the most part the general paragenesis, at least over the southern half of the province, conforms to the amphibolite facies. In synthesizing several recent studies in different parts of this region Chesworth (1971) has drawn a fairly well-sustained large-scale picture of a pressure gradient rising (albeit discontinuously) from southeast to northwest over a southerly strip 450 X 200 km immediately north of Lakes Ontario and Huron (Fig. 10-12). He has delineated in broad terms three zones in the following sequence of increasing pressure.

At the southeastern extremity, in the vicinity of Westport, a zone of minimum pressure (and incidentally of highest grade) displays the amphibolite-granulite transition as described by Wynne-Edwards and Hay (1963). In pelitic rocks, sillimanite, cordierite, and garnet are widespread, as is the pair K-feldspar-sillimanite; but andalusite occurs here and there. Staurolite and kyanite are unknown, and garnet is not a constituent of silica-saturated amphibolites. (This paragenesis will be elaborated in a later section.)

In the central zone, embracing Harcourt, Bancroft, and other well-documented areas, common mineral assemblages are reminiscent of some that are characteristic of the amphibolite facies in the Buchan zones of Scotland. All three Al_2SiO_5 polymorphs, along with both micas, garnet, staurolite, and cordierite appear in pelitic assemblages—even chloritoid locally at the lower grades. Again the pair hornblende-garnet is generally incompatible.

In the western zone, considered to represent maximum pressure, kyanite, sillimanite, almandine, staurolite, and muscovite are all common in metapelites. Andalusite and cordierite are notable absentees. Typical of quartz-bearing amphibolites is the pair hornblende-almandine. For details of paragenesis and petrochemistry the reader is referred to D. M. Carmichael (1970)[*] and Kwak (1968).

The total regional paragenetic sequence (called a "transcursive facies series" by Chesworth) is perhaps a facies series in the broadest sense, but one in which pressure rather than temperature is the control of observable broad variations in pattern. The zonal boundaries, by definition, are not isograds, though they mark linear discontinuities in facies pattern. Perhaps, as suggested by Chesworth, they are tectonically determined, possibly even with chronologic as well as structural implications. But here we are entering the realm of speculation.

AMPHIBOLITE–GRANULITE TRANSITION

General Nature of the Transition

The granulite facies as defined by Eskola (1939, pp. 360–363) is based on ideal assemblages of phases that may form by dehydration of micas and amphiboles at the culmination of metamorphism in Precambrian cratons. The principal anhydrous end products are various combinations of feldspars, sillimanite (or kyanite), almandine-rich garnets, cordierite, and clino- and ortho-pyroxenes. Eskola's *ACF* diagram (reproduced here as Fig. 10-15b) represents an ideal combination of phase

[*]The Whetstone Lake area described by Carmichael is a local anomaly. It lies in the central zone; but the paragenesis is that of the western zone.

assemblages, seldom achieved in nature. The breakdown of muscovite-quartz to K-feldspar plus sillimanite, though by no means a simple reaction (cf. Evans and Guidotti, 1966), is simpler than most other dehydration reactions leading to the granulite facies. And it is already in progress or complete within the amphibolite facies itself. When biotite joins in reaction it leads by a process of continuous transformation to assemblages with cordierite or almandine as well as sillimanite and K-feldspar. Another line of continuous reactions eliminates hornblende in favor of the pair diopside-hypersthene.[*] Clearly the complete amphibolite → granulite facies transition must cover a considerable range of temperature at any given pressure, and it will be affected too by compositional variables, especially $X_{H_2O}^{gas}$ and f_{O_2}.

Somewhere along the natural gradient of phase transformations, a line must be drawn arbitrarily dividing the amphibolite facies, in the strictest sense, from the granulite facies. This writer has here accepted the division as it has been drawn by a lifelong student of this pattern of metamorphism, A. F. Buddington (e.g., 1963, pp. 1163–1168). The diagnostic mineral assemblage of the full granulite facies by this definition is plagioclase-clinopyroxene-hypersthene-hornblende (with almandine as well at slightly higher grade).

The metamorphic problem that faces the petrologist is threefold. First it is necessary to define in mineralogical terms the paragenesis in substantial zones that in the field border on amphibolite-facies zones in the upgrade sense, or occupy an intermediate position between amphibolite- and granulite-facies zones. In the second place one must learn whether the transitional facies is a member of a prograde or a retrograde sequence; and in this connection microscopic and mezoscopic relations between assemblages in small domains may yield essential information. And finally, since the problem almost exclusively concerns ancient metamorphic events, there is the question of chronological as well as spatial transitions, i.e., of possible polymetamorphism. All three facets of the general problem recur again and again in the Precambrian "basement complexes" of continental shields. Here we concern ourselves mainly with descriptive aspects, noting at the time the possibilities of prograde versus retrograde transitional sequences in specific provinces. Postponed until the final chapter are compelling questions as to possible relations between almost ubiquitous granitic bodies and anorthosite massifs and metamorphism leading to the granulite facies.

Proposals have been put forward from time to time to set up mineralogically distinct subfacies of the granulite facies depending on the presence or complete absence of hornblende, the alternative occurrence of cordierite versus garnet, or of sillimanite versus kyanite. For arguments pro and con the reader is referred, with special reference to the Adirondacks, to DeWaard (1965a, 1965b) and Buddington (1966). Here, with the inevitably unique aspects of every local facies series in mind, such schemes are rejected. Instead it is proposed to illustrate the general as well as the particular details of transition by referring to two specific Proterozoic provinces: the northern borderland of the Adirondacks of northern New York State,

---

[*]Note that in derivatives of banded iron formation amphibole (Fe-rich cummingtonite) gives place to hedenbergite-ferrohypersthene at high grade still within the amphibolite facies.

and the Broken Hill mining region (Willyama complex) of south-central Australia. Brief references will be made also to retrograde transitions in other provinces.

Northwest Adirondacks, New York

In the northern part of New York State, the Adirondack massif and the adjacent Grenville lowlands to the west (Fig. 10-13) are a southeastern extension of the Grenville tectonic province. The lowland area is a metasedimentary (Precambrian) terrane in which marble, semipelitic gneiss, and amphibolites are copiously injected and permeated with granitic rocks, some of which form discrete phacoliths 10–30 km long. The massif itself is made up largely of igneous plutons: granite, syenite, anorthosite, and gabbro, with subordinate, but still extensive, enclosed and intervening masses of sedimentary and possibly volcanic rocks. All components of the massif—plutonic, volcanic, as well as sedimentary—have been affected profoundly by late Proterozoic high-grade regional metamorphism. Fully documented accounts of the metamorphic phenomena, with emphasis on facies relationships and mineral chemistry, include publications by Buddington (1963), Buddington et al. (1963), Engel and Engel (1960, 1962a, 1962b), and DeWaard (1964, 1965a). The classic older account is that of Buddington (1939).

The nature of the amphibolite-granulite transition is illustrated in unusual detail in the works of Engel and Engel (cited earlier) relating to progressive metamorphism across the Grenville lowlands to the border of the Adirondack massif. They summarize the evidence of prograde metamorphism along a 60-km section (from Emeryville to Colton[*]) inclined obliquely to the margin of the massif, as follows (Engel and Engel, 1962a, p. 39):

> The principal geologic features indicating a progressive increase in the grade of metamorphism in the direction of the massif are: (1) systematic and characteristic changes in the metamorphic assemblages of minerals in the paragneiss, amphibolite and associated marble; (2) an increase in the amount of "igneous-looking" granite and in the ratio of igneous to metasomatic granite; (3) an appreciable increase in grain size of minerals; (4) increasing dehydration, reduction, and basification of the paragneiss and amphibolite and progressive decarbonation of the marble; (5) a decrease in the thickness of paragneiss and marble; (6) a zonation in the distribution of mineral deposits formed during specific stages of the regional metamorphism; and (7) systematic changes in solid solutions, ratios of $^{18}O/^{16}O$ in oxides and silicates, and in other temperature-dependent mineral properties.

The same writers estimate the depth of overburden at the time of metamorphism as at least 10 km and possibly as great as 20 km. Individual bodies of gneiss and marble were thick enough (2–3 km) to justify a metamorphic model in which P_{CO_2} in marble and P_{H_2O} in paragneiss may be assumed to have approximated the load pressure (3–5 kb).

---

[*]Emeryville, 14 km west of Edwards, is 20 km distant from the nearest margin of the massif. Colton is just within it.

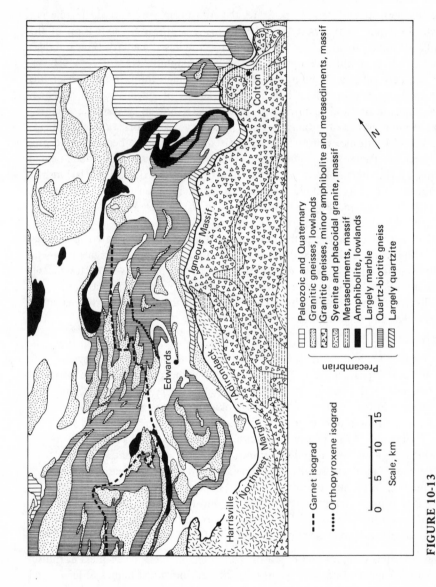

FIGURE 10-13

Map of portion of northern New York State, northwest of the Adirondacks (after A. E. J. Engel and C. E. Engel).

Progressive changes in mineral paragenesis from (*a*) the amphibolite facies near Emeryville and Edwards to (*b*) the granulite facies at Colton (Fig. 10-13) are as follows:

In amphibolites (Engel and Engel, 1962a, p. 43); figures in parentheses are mean modal percentages

(a) Hornblende (68)-andesine (19)-quartz (10)-ilmenite (2)-diopside (0.5)-sphene (0.5)

(b) Hornblende (22)-labradorite (39)-diopside (21)-hypersthene (14)-ilmenite (3.5)

In metasedimentary semipelitic gneiss (Engel and Engel, 1960, p. 1; Buddington, 1963, p. 1163)

(a) Quartz-biotite-oligoclase (minor muscovite, microcline, magnetite)
(b) Quartz-oligoclase (calcic)-almandine (minor K-feldspar)

In marble (Engel and Engel, 1960, p. 53)

(a) and (b) 1. Calcite-quartz
 2. Calcite-plagioclase (andesine to anorthite)-phlogopite
 3. Calcite-quartz-diopside (with residual undestroyed dolomite). The amount of diopside increases at the expense of dolomite with progressive metamorphism.

On the basis of mineralogical changes it is possible to draw three isograds. These, in order of increasing grade, are marked by

1. Disappearance of sphene in amphibolites
2. Appearance of abundant diopside in amphibolites; elimination of muscovite by the reaction

Quartz + biotite + muscovite + magnetite → almandine + K-feldspar

3. Appearance of hypersthene giving the granulite assemblage plagioclase-hornblende-diopside-hypersthene

At this third isograd, the mineral paragenesis may be classed within the granulite facies.

In the northwest Adirondacks and the adjoining Grenville lowland strip to the north, Buddington has mapped five zones of progressive metamorphism A to E. The area studied by Engel and Engel falls in zones A to C. Sphene is eliminated from amphibolites (isograd 1) within zone A; and the second isograd of Engel and Engel marks the boundary between zones A and B. Incoming hypersthene at isograd 3 defines the outer boundary of zone C and ushers in the granulite facies which continues through zones C to E (cf. p. 398).

For zones B and C, Buddington and Lindsley (1964, p. 337) have estimated possible limits of metamorphic temperature, based on compositions of coexisting iron-titanium oxide phases, as 550–625°C.

Amphibolite-Granulite Transition, Broken Hill District, South-Central Australia

The Broken Hill lead-mining region of New South Wales lies in an area of about 10,000 km² of high-grade mid-Proterozoic metamorphic rocks—an inlier enclosed by comparatively unmetamorphosed late Proterozoic and Paleozoic sediments. This is an area of repeated metamorphism. Binns (1964, 1965) has described in detail the mineral paragenesis (especially that of basic assemblages) imprinted by the first episode of metamorphism now dated radiometrically at about 1700×10^6 years. The effects of this early episode, the *Willyama metamorphism*, can be deciphered, scarcely affected by later events, over an area of about 1500 km² (shown in Fig. 10-14).

The dominant rocks are amphibolites of basaltic composition and quartzo-feldspathic "granitic" gneisses, which Binns interprets as metasediments. In any case, the "granitic" gneisses share the mineralogical and structural imprint of the Willyama metamorphism. Pelitic rocks are few, and calcareous rocks rare. Three metamorphic zones have been established (Fig. 10-14).

Zone A: The paragenesis is that of the amphibolite facies. Some characteristic assemblages are as follows:

1. Basic: hornblende-plagioclase (-labradorite-bytownite)-quartz-ilmenite. Some amphibolites contain combinations of clinozoisite, almandine, and biotite.
2. Pelitic: Sillimanite-muscovite-biotite-quartz-ilmenite. Minor almandine and plagioclase may also be present.

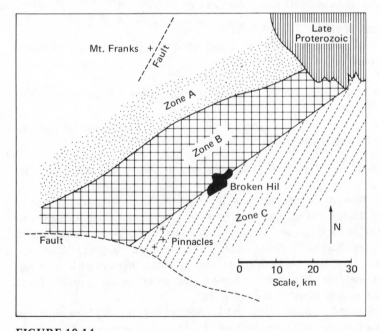

FIGURE 10-14
Isograds in mid-Proterozoic Willyama complex, Broken Hill district, western New South Wales, Australia (after R. A. Binns, 1964).

3. Quartzo-feldspathic ("granite"): quartz-plagioclase-K-feldspar-biotite.
4. Minor calcsilicate combinations of plagioclase, diopside, tremolite, hornblende, epidote minerals, wollastonite, vesuvianite.

Zone B: The paragenesis represents the maximum grade still in the amphibolite facies.

1. Amphibolites are mostly similar to those of zone A, but the hornblende is now brown or greenish brown instead of blue-green as in zone A amphibolites. There also are amphibolites that carry diopside or cummingtonite as additional phases.
2. Muscovite has been eliminated from pelitic rocks, which now are represented by sillimanite-biotite-almandine-K-feldspar-quartz (-cordierite-plagioclase)
3. Almandine becomes abundant in the quartzo-feldspathic assemblages.

Zone C: The paragenesis is now that of the granulite facies, and it continues as such for 25 km, in a direction normal to the trend of the isograds, up to the edge of the area investigated by Binns. A generalized *ACF* diagram to illustrate the paragenesis is given as Fig. 10-15*a*. Similar assemblages are found elsewhere in many granulite terranes and are the basis of one of DeWaard's (1966) principal subfacies.

1. The typical basic assemblage is hornblende-pyroxenes-plagioclase (with only minor quartz).

In these rocks the pyroxene may be diopside, hypersthene, or both. Hornblende has diminished in quantity and quartz has decreased even to the point of elimination. Some assemblages even lack hornblende completely.

2. The pelitic gneisses consist of sillimanite-almandine-cordierite-biotite-orthoclase-quartz.

Biotite has diminished in quantity as compared with pelitic assemblages in zone B.
Binns (1965) has traced the chemistry of the transition from the paragenesis of zone A to that of zone C. In hornblende the titanium content rises markedly at the brown-hornblende isograd. At the same time there is change in the mechanism by which the charge balance is maintained to accommodate substitution of Al for Si in the Z site of the structure. Binns (1965, p. 324) describes this in terms of changing proportions in the hypothetical end members of the hornblende series: tschermakitic hornblende, $Ca_2(Mg_4Al)(AlSi_7O_{22})(OH)_2$, is gradually eliminated; and there is a complementary increase in the edenite component $(NaCa_2)$-$Mg_5(AlSi_7O_{22})(OH)_2$. Where the orthopyroxene isograd marks the beginning of zone C, there is now a complete breakdown, expressed in its simplest form by

$$Ca_2(Mg_4Al)(AlSi_7O_{22})(OH)_2 \rightarrow CaAl_2Si_2O_8 + CaMgSi_2O_6$$

tschermakitic hornblende   anorthite   diopside

$$+ 3MgSiO_3 + H_2O$$

enstatite

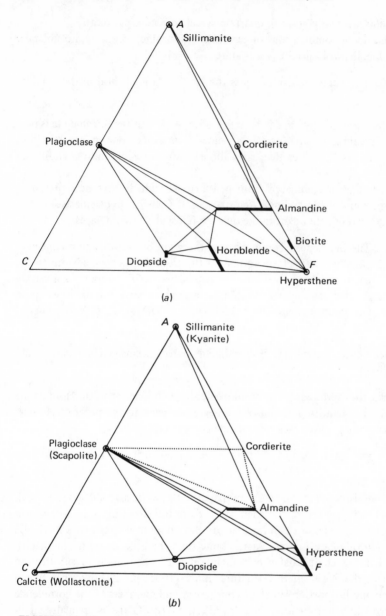

(a)

(b)

FIGURE 10-15
Granulite facies. *ACF* diagrams for rocks with excess SiO_2 and K_2O; quartz and K-feldspar are possible additional phases. (*a*) Broken Hill, Australia (from data of R. A. Binns, 1964, 1965); (*b*) generalized diagram for anhydrous phases (after P. Eskola, slightly modified).

Almandine, throughout the whole terrane, maintains a high $Fe^{2+}/(Fe^{2+} + Mg)$ ratio, but there seems to be a significant increase in the pyrope content with rising grade. In basic assemblages of all grades the grossularite content of garnets is consistently high. A typical composition is $Al_{63} Sp_8 Py_8 Gr_{19} An_2$ (zone C). Pelitic garnets are essentially almandines with virtually no grossularite component.

The compositions of coexisting magnetite-ilmenite pairs in zone C, evaluated against experimental data (Buddington and Lindsley, 1964), are compatible with crystallization at temperatures between 600–670°C under oxidizing conditions comparable with those controlled by a fayalite-magnetite-quartz buffer. These values overlap the temperature range inferred on the same basis for the beginning of the granulite facies in the Adirondacks (Buddington and Lindsley, 1964, p. 337)–550–625°C–but both estimates depend on the same geothermometer and the same calibration scale.

GRANULITE FACIES

General Mineralogical Characteristics

Figure 10-15*b* is an idealized scheme of chemographic relations between common anhydrous phases in the granulite facies. Each of the corresponding assemblages listed below is typical of the facies and is widely developed in many granulite provinces. But assemblages in individual areas tend to be complicated by additional presence of hornblende and/or biotite whose quantity and incidence decrease with increasing grade. With this proviso the following assemblages typify the granulite facies at its ultimate stage of dehydration.

A. Pelitic:
    1. Quartz-perthite-garnet-plagioclase-sillimanite (much more rarely, kyanite)
    2. Quartz-perthite-garnet-cordierite-sillimanite
B. Quartzo-feldspathic ("charnockitic"):
    3. Quartz-perthite-hypersthene-garnet-plagioclase
C. Metabasaltic (noritic, "basic charnockite," pyroxene-granulite):
    4. Plagioclase-hypersthene-diopside-garnet
    5. Plagioclase-hypersthene-diopside (-quartz)
D. Calcareous:
    6. Calcite-diopside-scapolite-sphene (-quartz)
    7. Calcite-diopside-plagioclase-quartz
    8. Calcite-forsterite-diopside
    9. Calcite-dolomite-forsterite
    10. Calcite-diopside-wollastonite-sphene
    11. Calcite-scapolite-wollastonite

Individual minerals have their own characteristics peculiar to or at least highly typical of the facies. Hypersthene carries significant $Al_2 O_3$ in some regions; and regardless of the $Fe^{2+}/(Fe^{2+} + Mg)$ ratio tends to be strongly pleochroic. Garnets are almandines commonly carrying 20–25 percent pyrope, 15–20 percent grossular-ite (e.g., Scharbert and Kurat, 1974, p. 115). K-feldspar is markedly perthitic and in hand specimens tends to be strongly colored in blues and greens; plagioclases likewise are antiperthitic, the products of exsolution from initially homogeneous phases with as much as 7 percent Or (Zen, 1959). Cordierite is widespread in certain provinces where it is accepted as an index of low pressure. Scapolite may accompany, or substitute for, plagioclase. Rutile and ilmenite are the characteristic titanium phases—never sphene. Olivine, corundum, and green spinel may be essential phases of silica-deficient rocks, and spinel may even appear in quartz-bearing assemblages. While sillimanite is the usual $Al_2 SiO_5$ polymorph, some granulites contain kyanite. A rare but seemingly characteristic phase in silica-deficient assemblages, rich in both Mg and Al, is sapphirine (Ramberg, 1948; Segnit, 1957; Muthuswami and Gnanasekaran, 1962; Herd et al., 1969).

Adirondack Massif, New York State

The granulite facies as defined by Buddington (1963) extends through the three zones (C, D, E) of maximum metamorphic grade in the rocks of the northwest Adirondack massif, where they cover an area of more than 10,000 km^2. Parageneses in (1) quartz-oligoclase-biotite gneiss, (2) metasyenite, (3) metadiorite, and (4) metagabbro are as follows (cf. also DeWaard, 1965a).

Zone C:

1. Quartz-biotite-oligoclase-almandine-magnetite
2. Microcline-oligoclase-quartz-hornblende
4. Labradorite-hornblende-clinopyroxene-hypersthene-ilmenite

Zone D:

2a. Oligoclase-microcline-hornblende-quartz
 b. K-feldspar-oligoclase-quartz-clinopyroxene-hypersthene-hornblende
3. Andesine-clinopyroxene-hornblende-quartz, with or without almandine and/or hypersthene
4. Labradorite-clinopyroxene-hypersthene-almandine-biotite (-hornblende)

Zone E:

2a. Microcline-oligoclase-quartz-hornblende (-minor biotite)
 b. Microcline-oligoclase-quartz-hornblende-hypersthene-clinopyroxene-almandine
4a. Plagioclase (An_{30} to An_{50})-orthopyroxene-clinopyroxene-almandine, with or without hornblende (up to 33 percent) or minor biotite
 b. Plagioclase (An_{30} to An_{55})-orthopyroxene-clinopyroxene-olivine-hornblende-almandine (±biotite)

Metamorphic temperature limits deduced from compositions of iron-oxide pairs are zone D, 600–640°C; zone E, 635–665°C. A case for temperatures possibly 150° higher has been argued by DeWaard (1967). But this appraisal rests on experimental data whose reliability is seriously open to question—e.g., the quartz-muscovite curve that figures prominently in the argument is located 100° higher than the curve adopted in this book (Fig. 4-3; cf. DeWaard's Fig. 2).

Central Highlands, Sri Lanka (Ceylon)

The greater part (30,000 km^2) of the island of Sri Lanka—a southeastern offshoot of peninsular India—is occupied by Precambrian crystalline rocks (Fig. 10-16). As described by Cooray (1961, 1962) and later elaborated by Hapuarachchi (1967, 1968, 1975) a central granulite facies belt (Highland series) is flanked on either side by belts of migmatite and granite gneiss bearing a younger metamorphic overprint of the amphibolite facies (Vijayan series of Cooray). Regional metamorphism of the Highland belt has been dated as earlier than 2100 × 10^6 years (A. R. Crawford, 1969). The imprint in the flanking belts is much younger (~1200 × 10^6 years).

Cooray (1961) demonstrated field transition between his two major units through a zone 10–15 km wide oblique to the strike of the Highland series in the Rangala area (Fig. 10-16). Here the "charnockitic" (hypersthene-granite-gneiss) members of the latter become "increasingly modified into streaky biotic gneisses"; and remnants of resistant quartzite and marble beds (as well as remaining relics of

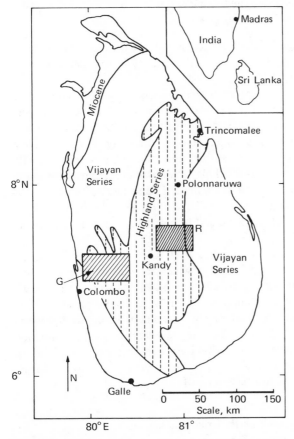

FIGURE 10-16
Distribution of Highland and Vijayan Series in Sri Lanka (after P. G. Cooray). Areas referred to in text: R, Rangala area (P. G. Cooray); G, Gampaha area (D. J. A. C. Hapuarachchi).

charnockite) persist in a terrane of migmatite and granitic biotite gneiss with the mineral characteristics of the amphibolite facies.

The principal assemblages of the granulite facies as recorded by Cooray (1961) with particular reference to the Rangala area are as follows:

A. Pelitic:
1. Quartz-orthoclase-plagioclase (An_{30} to An_{40})-almandine-biotite (-ilmenite, -magnetite)
2. Almandine-sillimanite-orthoclase-quartz (rocks termed khondalites)
3. Quartz-orthoclase-plagioclase-biotite-sillimanite-graphite
B. Calcareous:
4. Calcite-dolomite-forsterite (-diopside-phlogopite-graphite)
5. Diopside-scapolite (minor calcite)
C. Charnockitic[*]:
6. Quartz-orthoclase-plagioclase-biotite-hornblende-almandine
7. Plagioclase-hypersthene-almandine-hornblende
8. Plagioclase-hypersthene-diopside-hornblende

A notable feature is the absence of cordierite. Note also the universal presence of garnet in charnockitic rocks, in contrast with its rarity in the charnockites of Madras (see p. 401).

In his later summary of the regional geology, Cooray (1962) emphasized two features characteristic of the Highlands belt as a whole. First, the rocks are for the most part undoubtedly sedimentary. Massive beds can be traced for many kilometers; a thick marble belt, for example, runs continuously along the eastern boundary of the Highland series for 60 km or more. Second, charnockites, with all the characteristics of such rocks as developed elsewhere in Sri Lanka and southern India, are everywhere interbedded with the Highland metasediments. Interbanding of charnockite and metasediment can be seen on all scales from less than 1 to 100 m. Individual bands of quartzite and of charnockite can be traced continuously for 50–70 km.

West of the Highlands belt as described by Cooray is an extensive southwestern coastal belt (at least 130 $\times$ 30 km), in which the regional granulite paragenesis is different from that just described. Hornblende and biotite are much more prominent in the basic and quartzo-feldspathic assemblages, and pelitic rocks contain cordierite rather than garnet. The paragenesis here, which appears to be the product of a later Proterozoic imprint preceding the final amphibolite-facies event, has been described in detail by Hapuarachchi (e.g., 1972, 1975). It is exemplified in the eastern part of the Gampaha area (Fig. 10-16) and in the coastal area around Galle at the southwestern tip of the island:

A. Pelitic:
1. Cordierite-hypersthene-biotite-perthite-plagioclase-quartz
2. Cordierite-sillimanite-biotite-perthite-quartz (-magnetite)

---

[*]The name applied to all rocks whose compositions range more or less from granitic to gabbroic, and which contain hypersthene and/or almandine.

B. Quartzo-feldspathic (charnockitic):
   3. Hypersthene-diopside-hornblende-biotite-perthite-plagioclase-quartz
C. Amphibolites:
   4. Hypersthene-hornblende-plagioclase (-diopside)
   5. Hypersthene-diopside-garnet-hornblende-plagioclase
D. Calcareous:
   6. Diopside-scapolite-wollastonite (-sphene)

Thus paragenesis could mark a low-pressure transition from the granulite facies as developed earlier in the Highlands toward the hydrous assemblages of the amphibolite facies in the bordering areas of predominant granitic migmatite-gneisses.

Charnockite Series of Madras

The term *charnockite* is generally applied in India to rocks whose chemical compositions fall within the range of plutonic rocks (acid, basic, and ultramafic), whose textures recall those of corresponding plutonic rocks, but in which the characteristic mafic phase is hypersthene (with or without some combination of clinopyroxene, hornblende, or almandine). Their mineral assemblages correspond closely with those of the granulite facies. There has been a good deal of controversy about the origin of charnockites: igneous versus metamorphic. Doubtless both primary igneous and clearly metamorphic assemblages have been classed by various writers in India, Australia, and elsewhere as charnockitic. From a comprehensive study of charnockites of all types in Madras, southern India, Howie (1955, p. 762) concluded

> There can be little doubt that the rocks of the Madras charnockite series were originally igneous. . . . The chemistry of the Madras series affords strong confirmation of the view that these rocks were originally a series of calc-alkali plutonic rocks.

He was unable, however, to find decisive criteria on which to distinguish products of granulite-facies metamorphism from primary igneous rocks crystallizing in a similar deep-seated environment.

The essential charnockite assemblages as developed in Madras are:

1. Acid division: microcline (perthitic-plagioclase (An_{33})-quartz-hypersthene
2. Intermediate division: plagioclase (An_{33})-microcline-quartz-hypersthene-(diopside); rare hornblende
3. Basic division: labradorite-hypersthene-diopside-hornblende (-magnetite-ilmenite)
4. Ultrabasic division: hypersthene-diopside-hornblende (-magnetite-ilmenite-pyrite)

Noteworthy in contrast with Sri Lanka is absence of garnet from many (but not all) assemblages.

Special Mineralogical Traits

Prograde Trend within the Granulite Facies
The granulite facies is marked everywhere by common mineralogical features: prevalence of almandine in quartzo-feldspathic assemblages; the plagioclase-

hypersthene-diopside assemblage, generally with almandine and/or hornblende in basic rocks; simple calcareous assemblages in which diopside or quartz may be associated with calcite, while diopside and forsterite may occur with dolomite; absence of calc-aluminum silicates other than anorthite.

Zonal sequences show that decrease in hornblende and biotite in the paragenesis as a whole, and complementary increase in pyroxenes and garnet (or cordierite) is to be correlated with increasing metamorphic grade—rise or decrease in f_{H_2O}, in temperature, and perhaps change in pressure as well. The separate significance of two minerals, cordierite and kyanite, which, while typical of certain granulite provinces, are absent from others (kyanite in fact from most) deserves more comment.

Significance of Cordierite

Over very large granulite areas [Broken Hill in Australia, Finnish Lappland (Eskola, 1952), and southwestern Sri Lanka] cordierite is a characteristic phase, not just as an alternative to garnet but coexisting with it in textural equilibrium. Wynne-Edwards and Hay (1963) have studied mutual chemical relations of coexisting cordierite and garnet in the vicinity of Westport, Ontario, near the southern edge of the Grenville tectonic province (Fig. 10-12b). They interpret the local facies as an amphibolite-granulite transition. It was imprinted during the Grenville orogeny ($\sim$950 $\times$ 10^6 years). Cordierite and garnet occur in pelitic assemblages rich in both MgO and Al_2O_3, and all containing quartz and K-feldspar:

1. Almandine-sillimanite-cordierite-biotite-plagioclase
2. Almandine-sillimanite-biotite-plagioclase
3. Cordierite-sillimanite-biotite

The phase relations and range of composition of garnets are shown on the $A'F'M'$ projection in Fig. 10-17a. From a comparison of the compositions of associated garnet and cordierite in the several Ontario assemblages with each other, and with garnet-cordierite assemblages of other metamorphic facies, Wynne-Edwards and Hay conclude

1. Cordierite in pelitic assemblages of regional metamorphism is restricted to rocks low in CaO.
2. The incidence of cordierite in any paragenesis is favored by a high ratio MgO/FeO in the total rock composition.
3. The field of stability of cordierite on a rock-composition diagram expressed in terms of CaO, MgO, and FeO (Fig. 10-17b) diminishes, and that of almandine increases, with increasing pressure.

From these conclusions now supported by a good deal of experimental evidence (cf. Fig. 4-5) it may be inferred that pressure is a main factor controlling the incidence of cordierite in the granulite parageneses. In the transitional facies at Westport, Ontario, it can occur without garnet, but only in rocks so low in CaO that plagioclase is absent. In the southwestern sector of Sri Lanka cordierite is a principal member of several nongarnetiferous pelitic granulite assemblages reported by Hapuarachchi (1971, p. 436). In the Broken Hill region of Australia, cordierite

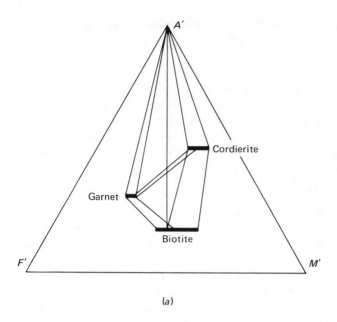

(a)

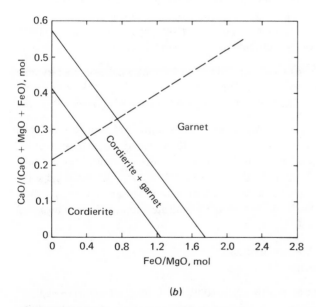

(b)

FIGURE 10-17

Amphibolite-granulite transition facies, Westport, Ontario: chemical relations between coexisting cordierite and garnet (after H. R. Wynne-Edwards and P. W. Hay, 1963). (a) $A'F'M'$ diagram for pelitic assemblages containing quartz, K-feldspar, and biotite. (b) Rock-composition fields (below dashed line) for assemblages with cordierite, cordierite-garnet, or garnet in pelitic rocks with quartz and K-feldspar.

is restricted to granulite assemblages also containing garnet. In the ancient granulites of central Sri Lanka, the stability field of cordierite seems to have been exceeded.

A recent reassessment of the relative roles of cordierite and garnet in pelitic assemblages of the granulite and related transitional facies (Dallmeyer, 1972) confirms the general conclusion of Wynne-Edwards and Hay. But it also brings out the "sensitivity of cordierite formation to minor variations in bulk composition—reflected in frequent interlayering of cordierite-bearing and cordierite-free assemblages within individual outcrops" (Dallmeyer, 1972, p. 52). The incidence of cordierite would seem to be only a general, certainly not a precise, index of relatively low metamorphic pressure.

Significance of Kyanite: The Moldanubian Province, Austria

Granulites of the Moldanubian province of lower Austria, a part of the Bohemian massif of classic literature, have been the subject of a series of studies by H. G. Scharbert and co-workers (e.g., Scharbert, 1971; Scharbert and Kurat, 1974; Scharbert et al., 1976; and earlier papers cited therein). This is an area of particular interest for three reasons: it is the type site of the "Saxon granulites" of classic European literature; it is one of the few regions where granulite metamorphism was imprinted in Phanerozoic times—during the Caledonian orogeny (Arnold and Scharbert, 1973); and of special interest regarding the topic now under discussion, the regionally prevalent Al_2SiO_5 polymorph is kyanite; sillimanite, where present, appears to have formed at the expense of earlier kyanite. The dominant primary lithologic components of the complex are

1. Quartzo-feldspathic (*Weiss-steinen*): quartz-perthite-plagioclase-garnet-kyanite (-orthopyroxene ±clinopyroxene ±prismatine)
2. Metabasaltic (*Trappgranulite*): hypersthene-diopside-garnet-plagioclase

In a later stage of the polymetamorphic cycle sillimanite and biotite developed in assemblage 1. With reference to the curves for the muscovite-quartz breakdown (to K-feldspar and Al_2SiO_5) and the kyanite-sillimanite inversion curve (independent of the disputed location of the triple point), the kyanite assemblage (1) indicates a regime of high pressure as well as temperature—estimated by Scharbert (1971, p. 265) as about 8–10 kb, 600–700°C, indicated in this book (Figs. 4-3 and 11-9) as >6-7 kb at ~750°C.

Influence of Granulite Metamorphism on Trace-Element Patterns

To students of magma genesis and thermal evolution of the crust the trace-element pattern—especially the contents of radioactive and radiogenic elements holds a peculiarly high significance. It is generally thought—and our survey of regional metamorphic paragenesis supports this—that rocks of the granulite facies constitute at least one important element in the deeper levels of continental crust. For this reason considerable attention has been devoted to their regional trace-element patterns (e.g., Lambert and Heier, 1967, 1968; Moorbath et al., 1969; Heier and Thoresen, 1971; Scharbert et al., 1976; Gray, 1977).

There is a general consensus that in most granulite terranes (including the Caledonian Saxon granulites of the Moldanubian province) extreme dehydration inherent in the metamorphic process has caused regional depletion of Th, U, and Rb—perhaps to some extent also K—below average crustal levels. As a corollary it follows that the capacity of granulites to generate heat has thereby been reduced; and the contents of radiogenic isotopes of Pb, Sr, and perhaps A in ancient granulites are correspondingly low.

Not all granulites, however, exhibit this pattern of depletion. Gray (1977) finds that Proterozoic granulites of the Musgrave ranges of central Australia have been depleted only in uranium. Concentrations of the other elements just mentioned fall within limits generally regarded as "normal."

Retrograde Transition, Granulite → Amphibolite Facies

Statement of the Problem

Imprints of both the granulite and the amphibolite facies cover very large areas in Precambrian cratons. Because of the long span of available time, anhydrous granulite terranes are especially vulnerable to later episodes of deformation and hydration whereby there may arise new assemblages of the amphibolite facies. Here the field and mineralogical transition between the two is retrograde. Some time ago Buddington (1963, p. 1180) raised a pertinent and provocative question in this context: could the "prograde" amphibolite-granulite transition in the Adirondacks be in fact a retrograde transition in the reverse sense? The prograde relation is still generally accepted for this as it is for some other provinces such as the Willyama complex of Australia. But as Drury (1974, p. 238) has aptly pointed out with special reference to the "Scourian-Laxfordian" problem in Scotland, metamorphic transitions between most contiguous granulite and amphibolite provinces are in essence retrograde and moreover of polymetamorphic origin. The problem is worth pursuing a little further with reference of specific cases, with these questions in mind: by what criteria can the prograde be distinguished from the retrograde sense of transition? What intermediate facies, if any, marks the retrograde transition?

Lewisian, Northwest Scotland

At the close of Chap. 2, something was said about overprinting of an Archaean $(2900-2600 \times 10^6$ years) granulite by an early Proterozoic $(2200 \times 10^6$ years) amphibolite episode in the Lewisian of northwestern Scotland, the most easterly remnant of the North Atlantic Archaean craton (Bridgewater, Watson, and Windley, 1973). Field and microscopic evidence clearly established the retrograde sense of transition; and radiometric dating has clinched the matter. In this region the granulite and the amphibolite facies are separate mineralogical entities (e.g., Sutton and Watson, 1951; Drury, 1974; Evans and Lambert, 1974). There are two distinct parageneses, each characterizing domains ranging from that of a small hand specimen to areas measured in tens of square kilometers or more:

A. Granulite facies (Badcallian episode, $2900-2600 \times 10^6$ years)
   1. Pyroxene granulites, e.g., plagioclase-diopside-hypersthene-garnet±brown hornblende or quartz. Both pyroxenes are aluminous ($Al_2O_3 \sim 5$ percent in hypersthene); garnet is a pyropic almandine (Evans and Lambert, 1974)

    2. Quartzo-feldspathic ("tonalitic") granulites, quartz-plagioclase ($An_{\sim 35}$) diopside-hypersthene (-magnetite-ilmenite)

B. Amphibolite facies (Invernian episode, 2200×10^6 years)

    3. Plagioclase-hornblende-epidote-biotite (-sphene) ±diopside

    4. Quartz-plagioclase-microcline-biotite

    Other assemblages occur in both facies. Conversion of the granulite to the amphibolite facies is apparent on every scale. Microscopically, hornblende is seen to replace hypersthene and then (with quartz) clinopyroxene; in the final stages the newer assemblage recrystallizes completely in crystalloblastic aggregates with no remaining textural sign of its granulite-facies parentage. On a larger scale domains of relict granulite mineralogy on every scale are cut by or enclosed within amphibolite domains. In the Scourian-Laxfordian area large domains of amphibolite are juxtaposed sharply against essentially granulitic domains. But in the extreme south of the Lewisian (cf. Drury, 1974) extensive areas of amphibolite mineralogy still enclose smaller relics of the parental granulite. What is particularly significant is that in domains of transition whether on the scale of a thin section or that of an outcrop assemblages of both facies, however intermixed, retain their mineralogical identity: there is no sign of a transitional assemblage in textural equilibrium.

Archaean of Western Greenland

The largest segment of the North Atlantic Archaean craton (Bridgewater et al., 1973) covers an area of over $150,000$ km^2 in southern Greenland south of latitude 66°N (Fig. 7-8). The western coastal strip (in places 100 km wide) projecting from beneath the inland ice has been the focus of recent intensive field and laboratory investigations by the Geological Survey of Greenland and British collaborators (including members of the Oxford Isotopic Geology Laboratory headed by S. Moorbath). The active history of the continuously exposed basement rocks covers the full span of Archaean history, from the earliest recorded terrestrial event ($\sim 3800 \times 10^6$ years) to stabilization at ~ 2600-2500×10^6 years. Some idea of its significance in crustal evolution and its bearing on problems of polymetamorphism can be gained from a few selected contributions: Oxford Isotopic Geology Laboratory and V. R. McGregor (1971); Windley (1972; 1977, pp. 1–18); Bridgewater, McGregor, and Windley, 1973; Bridgewater, Watson, and Windley (1973); Chadwick and Coe (1976). Structurally and radiometrically identified events concerning the present topic of polymetamorphic facies transition are as follows:

1. A gneissic granodioritic basement (Amitsoq gneiss) yielding dates as early as 3800×10^6 years (the oldest radiometrically verified terrestrial date) underwent amphibolite facies metamorphism culminating at $\sim 3600 \times 10^6$ years.

2. Intrusion of a basic dike swarm (Ameralik dikes) that, where present, allows positive field identification of the host rocks as Amitsoq gneiss.

3. Deposition of supracrustal sediments and volcanics (not much before 3000×10^6 years).

4. Emplacement of massive sheets of anorthosite.

5. Development of granodiorite plutons and migmatite-gneisses (Nûk gneiss, dated at ~2850 × 10^6 years).
6. Sweeping regional high-grade metamorphism in the granulite facies in some areas, at high grades of amphibolite facies in others (dated at 2850 × 10^6 years by a lead isochron).
7. Static retrograde metamorphism to the amphibolite facies (dated by K-Ar and Rb-Sr data at ~2500 × 10^6 years: a "cooling" date).

Thereafter this segment of the North Atlantic craton remained stable but for faulting and intrusion of several swarms of dikes.

The imprint of each of the three main metamorphic episodes survives virtually unchanged over individual large domains. Extensive tracts of amphibolites yielding the youngest radiometric date (2500 × 10^6 years) are thought to have undergone both preceding metamorphic events. Likewise, most of the granulite areas appear to have been derived from basement gneisses, previously affected by the 3600 million years metamorphism. In much abbreviated form, a generalized chronological sequence of selected widespread mineral assemblages—drawn from extensive data of Windley (1972)—is as follows (each being representative of specific domains):

A. Amitsoq gneiss (3900–3700 × 10^6 years), amphibolite facies:
   1. Garnet-hornblende-plagioclase-K-feldspar
   2. Garnet-hornblende-biotite-plagioclase-quartz
B. Assemblages of granulite facies (2850 × 10^6 years):
   3. Gneiss (probably lithologically equivalent to Amitsoq gneiss): orthopyroxene-clinopyroxene-biotite-plagioclase (±K-feldspar or hornblende)
   4. Metapelites (supracrustals of episode 3): sillimanite-garnet-biotite-quartz-plagioclase-cordierite
   5. Amphibolite: garnet-hornblende-pyroxene (diopside or hypersthene)-plagioclase (-quartz)
C. Gneisses and amphibolites of the amphibolite facies (2600–2500 × 10^6 years):
   6. Garnet-clinopyroxene-hornblende-plagioclase-quartz
   7. Garnet-clinopyroxene-hornblende-plagioclase-biotite (some with brown hornblende relics of the preceding granulite stage)
   8. Hornblende-clinopyroxene-plagioclase-biotite-epidote

Combined field and petrographic evidence shows that over large areas amphibolite-facies assemblages C above were formed by retrograde metamorphism of lithologic equivalents (assemblages B) in the granulite facies (cf. Windley, 1972, pp. 20–22). But there is no intermediate equilibrium paragenesis that could represent a truly transitional facies between granulite and amphibolite.

One of the most significant facts to emerge from all this work—though with no special bearing on the current topic—is that the earliest terrestrial rocks (Amitsoq gneisses) are metamorphosed granodiorites (essentially plutonic in origin). They have no resemblance whatever to almost contemporary (slightly older) lunar rocks, but they are in all respects analogous to other elements of the Greenland crust (Nûk gneiss) that were being generated a billion years later on the same general site (Oxford Isotopic Geology Laboratory and McGregor, 1971).

Anorthosites and the Granulite Facies

The Problem of Mutual Association

Massive anorthosite plutons are widespread within and in fact are virtually confined to Precambrian continental cratons. The well-known Adirondack type, consisting largely of andesine and locally carrying segregations of ilmenite, has an even narrower age span—about 1700–1100 $\times$ 10⁶ years. Both types, but especially the latter, are very commonly associated at least in a broad regional sense with tracts of metamorphic rocks in the granulite facies. What connection, if any, exists between the two sets of phenomena, the one plutonic, the other metamorphic? The question will be answered in terms of specific instances.

Nain Complex, Labrador

The world's most spectacular development of anorthosite plutons is in the eastern part of the Canadian Shield in the Grenville and Nain tectonic provinces of Quebec and Labrador (cf. Fig. 10-12a). Most are of the Adirondack type, emplaced in later Proterozoic times, but well prior to the Grenville orogeny (~950 $\times$ 10⁶ years). Granulite facies metamorphism is prevalent in large tracts of both tectonic provinces.

   The Nain plutonic complex of Labrador as described by Berg (1977), is a composite of plutons, many of them anorthosite, emplaced around 1500–1300 $\times$ 10⁶ years in a terrane previously affected by regional metamorphism (greenschist to amphibolite facies) that had culminated 300 million years previously (Hudsonian orogeny). Around individual plutons are aureoles 3–4 km wide, consisting of a great variety of high-grade anhydrous assemblages in aluminous and ferriginous metasediments: garnet-fayalite-hypersthene-spinel, garnet-sillimanite-cordierite-(quartz or spinel), and others. Controlling conditions include low values of f_{O_2} and of $p_{H_2O}^{gas}$, buffered by graphite—with CO probably the dominant gaseous species. Whether the facies be designated granulite or pyroxene-hornfels it is the direct product of intrusion of anorthosite at pressures estimated at between 4–7 kb.

Southwestern Quebec

Wynne-Edwards (1969) has presented a comprehensive picture of the interplay of successive tectonic overprintings, plutonism, and regional metamorphism (covering some 1300 million years of Proterozoic time) in a segment 20,000 km² in area of the Grenville province in southern Quebec (cf. Fig. 7-7). His map includes a very extensive anorthosite complex (Morin anorthosite) with the usual associated comagmatic plutons of pyroxene granites and syenites that are a familiar feature of the comparable Adirondack massif 200 km to the south. The date of intrusion is given as 1400 million years ago—long prior to that of regional metamorphism in the Grenville orogeny (950 $\times$ 10⁶ years). It was this latter event that is responsible for the present regional facies pattern, which is shared alike by the gneissic basement, its cover of Grenville sediments, and the anorthosite and associated plutons that invaded them. What concerns us here is this pattern of regional metamorphism, and particularly a delayed influence of the long-previous anorthosite intrusive event that it still retains.

   In the northern portion of Wynne-Edwards' map, remote from anorthosites, the northward prograde sequence displayed in the remetamorphosed basement is

1. Amphibolite facies: quartz-microcline-oligoclase-hornblende (green)-biotite
2. Transitional rocks with brown hornblende and green perthite
3. Granulite facies: quartz-perthite (green)-hornblende (brown)-hypersthene-diopside (-garnet).

Here two isograds, 10–20 km apart, have been mapped accordingly.

Toward the southern border the grade of metamorphism increases *southward* toward the locus of anorthosite intrusion; but here the amphibolite-granulite transition zone is telescoped to a width of a few hundred meters, and has been mapped as a single isograd. The high-grade mineral paragenesis duplicates that of the northern granulite zone and includes cofacial assemblages in basement rocks, metasediments, and the whole range of plutonics (anorthosites among them). Texturally these rocks differ strikingly from granulites of the northern zone: they are partially recrystallized mylonites that evidently responded to the Grenville deformation by brittle fracture. It would seem that within a broad contact zone tens of kilometers wide enclosing the anorthosite and related plutons all rocks were baked and thoroughly dehydrated during the 1400-million-year (Elsonian) plutonic event. In the subsequent Grenville orogeny these rocks responded to regional metamorphic conditions with the additional influence of internally buffered low $p_{H_2O}^{gas}$ (and low f_{O_2}), which is the main factor controlling the granulite facies in this southern sector.

The Overall Relation

The above, perhaps, are special cases; but it could be argued that the Nain aureoles represent the first stage of a more general cycle exemplified in the surroundings of the Morin anorthosite complex. In many cases, the Adirondack massif among them, intrusion of anorthosites long predates the granulite imprint displayed in associated granulites; but the intrusive event may have paved the way (as Wynne-Edwards has described) for the pattern of final regional metamorphism.

Nevertheless in general the relation between the two sets of phenomena, though not quite fortuitous, seems much more tenuous. Anorthosite plutonism and granulite metamorphism are both manifestations, in some instances certainly independent (as in Greenland), of a type of physical regime that has developed over and over again in now exposed segments of the ancient continental crust. Their relation may be analogous to one commonly encountered much later in time in a completely different environment of high pressure and low temperature—emplacement of serpentinites and blueschist metamorphism.

ECLOGITE FACIES

Definition and Scope of Treatment

According to generally accepted usage, the eclogite facies is defined by the diagnostic assemblage omphacite-garnet (pyropic almandine)-rutile, with or without either kyanite or quartz. This typifies eclogites in the strictest sense of definition; and the overall rock composition is essentially basaltic (without necessarily implying igneous parentage).

Other garnet-pyroxene rocks have also been described, and continue to be described, as "eclogite" in a broader sense. Such are diopside-almandine rocks that appear in the granulite and even in the amphibolite facies. Banno (1970) has included these in a valuable discussion of chemical variation in "eclogites" in relation to metamorphic facies and mode of occurrence. But even if such rocks in which the pyroxene lacks jadeite continue to be called eclogites, they do not belong to the eclogite facies as here defined and can be excluded from further discussion.

The unique character of the definitive pair omphacite-garnet gives the eclogite facies a unity that can scarcely be challenged. Yet the wide range of geologic environments in which eclogites are commonly found in itself implies that the *P-T* range encompassed by the facies is exceptionally broad. This conclusion was independently strengthened by results of a chemical survey of eclogites (in the strict sense) by Coleman and co-authors (1965) that brought out two significant generalizations: compositions of garnets vary between rather wide limits; and this variation and certain other features of mineral chemistry correlate well with marked differences in field occurrence. These authors therefore proposed to "discontinue the concept of an eclogite facies"—a proposition that this writer does not accept.

Rather it must be recognized that the eclogite *mineral facies*—to revert to Eskola's original terminology—covers rocks (some perhaps strictly igneous) that have recrystallized over an unusually wide range of depth, temperature, and pressure, extending far below the crust. Diamond-bearing eclogites and some associated rock fragments of kimberlite pipes must have ascended rapidly in their present form from depths well down into the upper mantle (cf. Carmichael et al., 1974, pp. 642–645). However important mantle petrology may be to geophysicists and to students of magma genesis, this topic remains outside the scope of a book that deals with metamorphism of crustal rocks. Accordingly the emphasis in this section is on eclogites and possible cofacial associates that are known to have formed, or may perhaps have formed, by metamorphism of crustal rocks.

Eclogites in Relation of Geologic Environment

Eskola (1920; 1939, p. 366) recognized a tendency, borne out on the whole by later work, for eclogites to occur in several distinct geologic environments.

1. Fragments in kimberlite breccias.
2. Streaks and lenses in bodies of peridotite, itself commonly garnetiferous.
3. Lenses enclosed in migmatitic gneiss in the amphibolite facies.
4. Blocks and small domains in a regional environment of blueschist metamorphism.

It is questionable perhaps whether classes 2 and 3 are sharply separable. Both are based on a region in western Norway where a granitic gneiss in the amphibolite facies encloses numerous dark-colored masses that in some areas are eclogite, in others composite blocks of interstreaked peridotite and eclogite.

Coleman and co-authors (1965) conducted a preliminary chemical-mineralogical survey of eclogites of each of Eskola's four classes and found significant correlation between garnet chemistry and mode of occurrence:

Group A (Eskola's classes 1 and 2): garnet $Pyr_{>55}$
Group B (Eskola's class 3): garnet Pyr_{30-55}
Group C (Eskola's class 4): garnet $Pyr_{<30}$

They also found a consistent tendency for the jadeite content of omphacite to be lower in Group A than in Group C. And later Banno (1970) established a correlation with partitioning of Fe and Mg between garnet and pyroxene. A distribution coefficient

$$K_D = \frac{X_{Fe}^{ga} \cdot X_{Mg}^{pyrox}}{X_{Mg}^{ga} \cdot X_{Fe}^{pyrox}}$$

ranges from values around 4 in "kimberlitic" eclogites to 25-30 in eclogites from blueschist provinces.

Beyond reasonable doubt fragments of eclogite and of garnet peridotite (lherzolite) that occur in kimberlite breccia pipes must have been transported directly from sources deep in the upper mantle. But, while a similar origin has been attributed to eclogites of class 2, and perhaps those of class 3, such an origin is no longer universally accepted for rocks of the type locality in Norway (cf. Brynhi, 1966, pp. 31, 54; Brynhi et al., 1970; Mysen and Heier, 1972). Their mineral chemistry should be examined separately from that of kimberlitic eclogites. Eclogites and cofacial rocks from the blueschist zone of the Pennine Alps have been shown beyond doubt to have originated by metamorphism of common crustal rocks. By inference a similar origin is now accepted for eclogites of blueschist belts in general.

Eclogites and Cofacial Rocks in Kimberlitic Breccias

The nature and origin of kimberlite pipes, and location of their sources deep in the upper mantle have been discussed elsewhere (Carmichael et al., 1974, pp. 522-527, 642, 657-658). We have already noted some distinctive chemical features of eclogites that habitually occur as xenoliths in these diatremes: high pyrope content (>55 percent) of garnet, variable but significant jadeite content (Jd_{10-30}) of omphacite, values ~4 for the distribution coefficient

$$K_D = \frac{X_{Fe}^{ga} \cdot X_{Mg}^{pyrox}}{X_{Mg}^{ga} \cdot X_{Fe}^{pyrox}}$$

There are very rare but authentic records of diamond (an index of extreme pressure) occurring as an integral constituent of eclogite in this environment.

Probably cofacial in a kimberlite pipe from Yakutia, Siberia, are fragments of a garnet-omphacite-kyanite rock, "grospydite," with calcic garnet of unique composition, $Gr_{63}Pyr_{18}Al_{17}Andr_2$. Bobrievitch and co-authors (1960), who recorded this assemblage, combined it with those of normal kimberlitic eclogites and associated garnet peridotites to construct an *ACF* diagram illustrating chemographic relations between associated phases in the eclogite facies (Fig. 10-18). Its validity depends on the plausible but unproved assumption that the different rock types on which it is based are cofacial; clearly it cannot be applied to assemblages of Groups B and C, which indeed must represent distinct general subfacies.

Eclogites in Regional Amphibolite Facies Environment

In the later Proterozoic crystalline basement of the Caledonian field belt of western Norway, there are areas in which eclogitic lenses of all sizes are enclosed in a regional migmatitic granite-granodiorite gneiss. Mineral assemblages of the gneiss and intercalated semipelitic schists everywhere are in the amphibolite facies. This is the region of Eskola's (1921) classic study, since elaborated in greater detail by Brynhi (1966) and other workers (e.g., Brynhi et al., 1969, 1970).

In some areas eclogite is interbanded and interstreaked on scales down to a centimeter or so with various kinds of peridotite—mainly dunite and garnet lherzolite. Whatever their ultimate source these ultramafics now possess a recrystallized tectonic fabric. Eclogites of this group are the type of Eskola's class 2, above.

Elsewhere eclogite fragments have a simple lithology and lack immediate peridotitic associates. Very commonly the smaller fragments are thickly rimmed

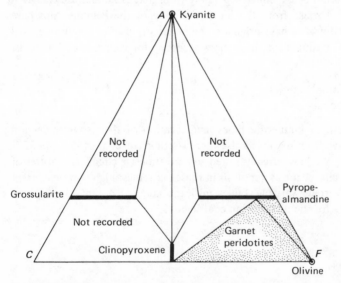

FIGURE 10-18

Eclogite facies. *ACF* diagram (somewhat problematical) based on eclogite, grosspydite, and garnet peridotite in kimberlite pipes of Siberia (after A. P. Bobrievitch, G. A. Smirnov, and V. S. Sobolev).

with dark hornblendic borders, the product of marginal retrograde metamorphism to the amphibolite or even to the greenschist facies.

The prevalent assemblage in both types, apart from the retrograde products is omphacite-garnet-rutile (-quartz-kyanite). Composition of the principal phases (Brynhi et al., 1969; Mysen and Heier, 1972) are: garnet, $Al_{40-50}Pyr_{30-40}Gr_{20}$, and omphacite, $Jd_{\sim 45}$. The Banno distribution coefficient, Fe/Mg in garnet/omphacite as reported for a large eclogite body (Hareidland eclogite) by Mysen and Heier is 7. These data fit those of Coleman and co-authors (1965) for eclogites of their Group B.

Ernst (1977) has given some chemical data for eclogite locally developed in a sheet of garnet lherzolite tectonically emplaced among nappes of the Lepontine Alps. Surrounding rocks are in the high-grade portion of the amphibolite facies. The eclogite itself consists of omphacite-garnet-rutile ±kyanite. Chemical-mineralogical data are: garnet, $Al_{39}Pyr_{37}Gros_{23}Sp_1$; omphacite, Di_{49}-$Jd_{43}Hd_8$; Banno distribution coefficient ~ 6. Again, the chemistry is consistent with Group B. Garnet of associated lherzolite is much more magnesian—Al_{19}-$Pyr_{67}Gr_9Uv_4Sp_1$.

Eclogite Facies in Young Mobile Belts

Franciscan Terrane, California

Widespread occurrence of "tectonic blocks" of eclogite and of coarsely crystalline glaucophane schist in the late Mesozoic Franciscan terrane of California (Borg, 1956; Coleman et al., 1965; W. A. Crawford, 1965) has already been covered in the previous chapter in connection with the blueschist facies. This association exemplifies a tendency for eclogites and blueschists to be loosely associated in young belts of blueschist metamorphism wherever those occur. Mineralogically and texturally the eclogites of California (and adjoining parts of Oregon) conform to a consistent type (Group C of Coleman and co-authors, 1965). Garnets are almandines with pyrope somewhat lower, grossularite rather higher than in garnet of mantle-derived eclogites: $Al_{60}Pyr_{10}Gr_{27}Sp_3$ is typical. Omphacites are relatively high in jadeite ($Jd_{\sim 40}$) and overlap those of metabasalts in the blueschist facies. The Banno distribution of coefficient (from data of Coleman et al., 1965) is 21 (Banno, 1970, p. 420).

Most eclogite blocks in the Franciscan show obvious signs of disequilibrium in the blueschist environment to which they were transported and in which they must have remained for some time. All kinds of retrograde changes are in evidence: garnet replaced by chlorite, aragonite, or even lawsonite; omphacite in process of replacement by glaucophane and lawsonite; rims of sphene developing round rutile granules.

On the other hand there are associated blocks that in some ways seem to represent a prograde transition from the blueschist toward but never reaching the eclogite facies. Typical assemblages of this kind are

Glaucophane-epidote-pumpellyite-omphacite
Omphacite-garnet-epidote (-glaucophane ±rutile)

There is no unequivocal evidence to show that Californian eclogites are indeed metamorphosed crustal rather than mantle-derived rocks. The former alternative has long been preferred for several reasons: persistent association with blueschists of crustal origin, a strong suggestion of prograde transition between the two facies, marked chemical-mineralogical differences from eclogites of undoubted mantle origin in kimberlite breccias. The matter is clinched in this writer's opinion by strong analogies on every count between Californian eclogites and those of the European Alps where crustal origins have been certainly established.

Eclogites and Cofacial Metatonalites, Piemont and Sesia-Lanzo Zones, Western Alps

Along the inside (eastern) borders of the Pennine domain (Piemont zone) and immediately adjoining Sesia-Lanzo zone (Fig. 9-16) blueschists were abundantly developed from crustal basalts and sediments during the earliest (Eoalpine) phase of Alpine metamorphism. Liberally sprinkled through the eastern part of the blueschist zone are blocks and small domains of approximately contemporaneous eclogite. The eclogites, too, have formed by direct replacement of ophiolitic pillow basalts (Bearth, 1959, 1965; cf. also Bianchi and Dal Piaz, 1963). Eclogitic assemblages have been partially overprinted by the blueschist facies as blueschist finally outlasted eclogite metamorphism in the Eoalpine event (Bearth, 1973, p. 299). Both parageneses were overprinted toward the west by greenschist assemblages during the Lepontine (mid-Tertiary) episode.

Compositions of eclogite garnets (Bearth, 1973, p. 318) range from $Al_{57}Pyr_{21}Gr_{20}Sp_2$ to $Al_{60}Pyr_{13}Gr_{23}Sp_4$ —conforming to those of Coleman's Group C. Typical omphacites range around $Di_{29}Hd_5Jd_{41}Ac_{16}Ts_9$. All stages of subsequent retrograde changes to blueschist assemblages (with omphacite or chloromelanite) are shown.

Of particular interest is the Eoalpine paragenesis displayed by remnants of the Hercynian granitic basement preserved in the Sesia-Lanzo zone (e.g., Compagnoni and Maffeo, 1973). These remarkable rocks, some still retaining perthitic and other igneous textures, have been converted to assemblages such as quartz-jadeite-zoisite-phengite-garnet-K-feldspar. Jadeite and zoisite have completely replaced plagioclase; biotite has been replaced by phengite garnet. It is not exceeding the limits of caution to place these metagranites and metatonalites of the Sesia-Lanzo zone as cofacial with closely associated eclogites of Group C in the same area. Garnets of the latter (Callegari and Viterbo, 1966) conform to Coleman's Group C type: $Al_{52-55}Pyr_{10-17}Gr_{\sim 24}Andr_5Sp_{<2}$.

Concluding Remarks

Eclogites, garnet lherzolites, and some rare associated rock types represent unchanged material transported from deep within the mantle. They are broadly cofacial and constitute a general subfacies whose chemical-mineralogical character has been designated Group A by Coleman and co-authors. Strongly contrasted with these are truly metamorphic eclogites derived from crustal rocks and now exposed in young blueschist belts. This is another subfacies (Coleman's

Group C)—very possibly a continuation of the blueschist facies series into realms of higher pressure. Other eclogite parageneses found in Proterozoic and later regions of amphibolite facies cannot be so clearly pinpointed. They have mineralogical affinities with Group A rather than Group B; and the personal preference of this writer is for tectonic transport from mantle sources. But there is a prevailing alternative opinion that these eclogites too may be truly metamorphic derivatives of deeply depressed crustal rocks.

11

Pressure-Temperature Regime of Regional Metamorphism and Related Phenomena

PREAMBLE: BROAD GENERALIZATIONS AND BASIC ASSUMPTIONS

Generalizations from Field Observations

From the descriptive survey now concluded, some significant generalizations— none without exception—emerge for synthesis and further inquiry.

1. The great areal extent of regional metamorphic terranes in linear belts of tectonic activity, such as the currently active circum-Pacific zone, the Cretaceous-Tertiary Alpine systems of Europe, the early-middle Paleozoic Appalachian and Caledonian systems, and the great "greenstone" belts of the Archaean, as well as in broad basins of deposition and depression, characteristic especially of earlier Precambrian times.
2. The episodic nature of tectonism and accompanying metamorphism within each protracted orogenic cycle of 10^8 years or more.
3. The existence of mineral facies of regional metamorphism; the simplicity both of individual mineral assemblages (on the scale of a rock specimen or smaller), and of regional paragenesis of varying lithology within mapped metamorphic zones.
4. Regional progression in mineral character (facies) as expressed by gradational

facies series, within which mapped isograds mark successive steps in a prograde sequence of mineral transformations (steps of increasing entropy in the corresponding sequence of metamorphic reactions).

5. The recurrence of generally similar but never identical facies series, which thus conform loosely but not precisely to recognizable patterns (e.g., Miyashiro's five broad pressure-related types).
6. Correlations of at least some such types with time and geographic-tectonic situation—the notable example being young blueschist series of the Pacific margin and other postulated plate sutures. (Is there some general perceptible trend of secular variation in pattern of regional metamorphism?)
7. Progressive textural change (increasing development of schistosity and microfolding, progressive coarsening of grain) that correlates broadly with increasing grade and reflects progressive change in rheologic response to stress under increasing temperature.
8. Appearance, in high-grade zones, of bands and streaks of quartzo-feldspathic material of "granitic" composition appropriate to a partial melt phase. These may be concentrated to the point of dominance over large areas variously termed migmatite complexes, centers of anataxis, or symmetamorphic granitic plutons (e.g., "Older" Dalradian granites). Are these the culminating products of metamorphism? Do they rather represent the vehicle by which heat was transferred from the deep crust and concentrated in the high-grade zones? Or would the granitic component of the migmatite be metasomatic—the product of "granitizing" fluids of extraneous and unknown origin?
9. Commonly but not invariably a posttectonic postmetamorphic upsurge of granitic magma embodied in cross-cutting plutons ("Newer Granites" of the Dalradian, and the Sierra Nevada batholith come to mind).
10. In sharp contrast is the negative role of basaltic magmas—the most voluminous of terrestrial magmas—in most cycles of regional metamorphism.
11. Perceptible but still imperfectly defined correlations between metamorphic pattern and tectonic situation, relationships that must certainly be pursued, constantly revised, and exploited as tectonic theory continues to evolve.

Related Inferences and Assumptions

Parallel with development of such descriptive geologic aspects we have set up what seem at present to be well founded assumptions, inferences, and propositions in order to interpret the geologic data quantitatively against the accepted background of experience and theory in chemistry and physics.

First, a common metamorphic mineral assemblage can be treated, in first approximation, as a heterogeneous system in equilibrium under a limited range of metamorphic pressure P and temperature T.

Second, a metamorphic facies is an association of phase assemblages, each of different chemical composition, having a common stability range of P and T.

Third, metamorphic pressures and temperatures are maintained long enough, at least many thousands of years, for bivariant equilibria to become established in each mineral assemblage without significant overstepping of curves of univariant equilibria. Nonhydrostatic pressure, especially at relatively low temperatures, tends to initiate cataclasis and flow, to raise free energies of strained crystals, and thus to accelerate chemical reactions leading to equilibrium.

Fourth, the preservation of high-temperature, high-pressure assemblages during postmetamorphic unloading is attributed largely to impermeability of the relatively anhydrous high-grade rocks to water. Another factor is the thermodynamically predictable, greater overstepping of the equilibrium boundary requisite to activate retrograde as contrasted with prograde reaction. Another contributing factor could concern relative rates of entry of the system into the regime of metamorphism and of subsequent exit during (possibly rapid) decompression and unloading.

Fifth, any mapped sequence of isograds in a facies series records a unique *T-P* gradient $\Delta T/\Delta P$ that we shall call the *metamorphic gradient*. It is related to but not identical with a depth gradient of temperature relative to depth below the surface ("metamorphic surface") at the time of the metamorphic event. Numerical evaluation of metamorphic gradients offers the greatest potential (seldom realized as yet) for developing a picture of the corresponding regional *P-T* retime.

Sixth, metamorphic temperatures and pressures—gas-compositional variables too—can be estimated by calibrating selected mineral assemblages against two closely interdependent, but for the most part independently assessed, sets of experimentally derived data: thermodynamic properties of participating phases, and results of experimental reversal of equilibria. The most rigorous approach is thermodynamic; for the course of any reaction is prescribed precisely by thermal and volume-related properties of all participants. Experimental reversal is a device designed to bypass thermodynamic appraisal where the basic data (as commonly as is the case) are subject to uncertainty, and so to provide tentative, indirectly derived values for pertinent thermodynamic properties (S, V, ΔH_f). (To geologists unfamiliar with thermodynamic reasoning, the direct experimental approach may appear to be the more tangible and satisfactory. But this is an illusion. Sooner or later all experimental "reversals" must stand up to thermodynamic scrutiny.)

Seventh, the quantitative evaluation of metamorphic gradients by whatever approach, however reliable the available data, requires simplifying assumptions as to the physical state of the metamorphic system, variously invoked to meet each particular case. Here are some of the possibilities that may be variously invoked:

1. Values of pressure on the fluid and the solid phases are the same and are equated with the thermodynamic variable P, that is, $P_f = P_s = P$.
2. In hydration-dehydration equilibria, $X_{H_2O}^{gas} = 1$; $p_{H_2O} = P_f = P$.
3. For equilibria involving CO_2 and H_2O, $X_{H_2O}^{gas}$ and $X_{CO_2}^{gas}$ are internally buffered stoichiometrically by the equilibrium reaction.
4. In systems under nonhydrostatic pressure, an increment equal to maximum shear stress (loosely called "tectonic overpressure") is added to the hydrostatic pressure (P of thermodynamics). (This factor is likely to be significant only at high values of P and low T, conducive to high values of "strength.")

Accuracy of calibration clearly reflects the validity of the assumptions that have been invoked. Inescapably the geologist will be faced with a choice of alternative estimates of metamorphic pressure and temperature, each endowed with the insidious aura of certainty conveyed by a set of numbers. Sometimes, however, the range of choice is narrow.

Objectives and Current Status of Continuing Inquiry

The aim of this concluding chapter is to take stock of progress toward solution of a series of interrelated problems concerning different aspects of the pressure-temperature regime that controls regional metamorphism in the crust. Topics will be pursued—to varying depths—in this order:

1. Correlation of the individual facies with restricted fields of pressure and temperature
2. Pressure-temperature limits of specific facies series with emphasis on
   a. Mineralogical identity, *P-T* calibration, and field topology of isograds and isograd surfaces
   b. *P-T* parameters of a metamorphic regime in relation to space, and related geometric gradients in *P* and *T*; thermal domes and depressions
   c. Tentative numerical evaluation of metamorphic gradients: selected cases
3. Regional metamorphism and granite plutonism
   a. Chronologic relations against the background of regional tectonism
   b. Field relations of isograd patterns to granitic plutons
   c. Metamorphism and migmatites
4. The quest for secular pattern in regional metamorphism.

MUTUAL RELATIONS OF FACIES IN THE *P-T* FIELD

Acting on the proposition that the paragenesis of each metamorphic facies reflects some finite *P-T* field within the total metamorphic range (perhaps 200–800°C and 1–15 kb), Eskola (1939, pp. 344–345), in his final comprehensive statement, presented a highly diagrammatic picture of possible mutual relations among all then-recognized facies within a framework of temperature and pressure. The only quantitative datum then available was the Goldschmidt curve for calcite-wollastonite-quartz equilibrium. Relative pressures were gauged from prevailing ideas regarding depth—much influenced by the doctrine of Grubenmann. Relative temperatures were estimated, with greater justification, on the basis of grade observed in mapped facies series. In Eskola's own words[*]:

> In the appended table [below] an attempt is made to present an overall view of facies. The table at the same time should serve as a *P-T* diagram in which positions of the facies names define a sequential series of pressure and temperature conditions of the individual facies. This sequence is certain with respect to the temperature ordinate, but most uncertain as to pressure; especially questionable is the true place of the granulite facies.

---

[*]Translated from the original text in German.

Schematic Arrangement of Metamorphic Facies in Relation to Pressure and Temperature as Pictured by P. Eskola (1939, p. 345). Coordinates Transformed

↑ Pressure increasing			Glaucophane-schist	Eclogite Granulite
		Epidote-amphibolite	Amphibolite	Pyroxene-hornfels
	Greenschist			
	Zeolite crystallization			Sanidinite

Temperature increasing →

It was a tenuous picture but valuable in three respects: it took stock of the outcome of three decades' progress on the significance of metamorphic paragenesis; it showed that depth was not the sole control of mineralogical variety in isochemical metamorphic rocks; it provided the springboard for future research along the many divergent lines that are exemplified in modern literature.

Subsequent progress along many of these lines, allowing for inevitable back-

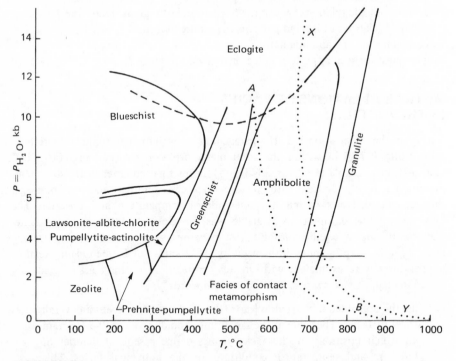

FIGURE 11-1

Tentative scheme of facies of regional metamorphism (all boundaries gradational) in relation to pressure and temperature ($P_{H_2O} \approx P$, except in low-temperature range of eclogite facies). Dashed boundaries indicate limits of eclogite facies under conditions of low water pressure ($P_{H_2O} \ll P$). Dotted curves show beginning of melting in the simplified granite system (quartz-orthoclase-albite) AB, and in basalt XY, in both cases in presence of excess water.

ward steps and unprofitable deviations, has now reached a point where Eskola's scheme can be revised with some confidence in a much more realistic form. Such a revision is illustrated in Fig. 11-1. This is based on (1) much improved knowledge of facies and isograd mineralogy; (2) the collective new comprehensive quantitative data of phase equilibria; (3) mutual juxtapositions of facies in mapped sequences; (4) the transitional nature of interfacies boundaries. It is emphasized that Fig. 11-1 reflects neither individual prejudices regarding the geometry of structure in specific metamorphic situations, nor preferred speculative doctrine as to the nature of tectonic mechanisms. Location of the low-*P*-low-*T* area somewhere within which must lie the two pumpellyite facies is dubious since relevant quantitative equilibrium data relating to prehnite and pumpellyite are still inadequate. All that is known is the prograde order

Zeolite → prehnite-pumpellyite → pumpellyite-actinolite → greenschist

in many mapped facies series.

EVALUATION OF METAMORPHIC PRESSURE–TEMPERATURE REGIMES FROM GEOLOGIC DATA

Statement of the Problem

The objective is to reconstruct the metamorphic pressure-temperature regime within the crustal domain beneath an area of mapped isograds. The regime can be described in terms of four parameters: respective topologies of isobaric and isothermal surfaces and the gradients in pressure $\Delta P \text{ km}^{-1}$ and in temperatures $\Delta T \text{ km}^{-1}$ respectively normal to these (P. H. Thompson, 1976). In the first instance none of these is known.

Geologic data are isograds and, where it is possible to measure them, isogradic surfaces. Though these record the imprint of a metamorphic event they are measured with respect to the *present* erosion surface, S_p. To transform data to metamorphic spatial coordinates the investigator must first determine (or in most cases perforce stipulate) the geometric relation between the present erosion surface, S_p and that at the time of metamorphism, S_m (Figs. 11-2 and 11-3). Even then to reconstruct the *P-T* regime from the isograd data is a difficult task that as yet has seldom been undertaken with any degree of success. But it is not insuperable; and once its nature is realized, it imposes rather strict constraints on speculation as to the physical significance of mapped metamorphic gradients.

Identity and Physical Significance of an Isograd

There are a very few simple isograds whose identity and physical significance are beyond much doubt. One is marked by the transition kyanite → sillimanite; another by elimination of laumontite and incoming of lawsonite.

Much more commonly an index mineral appears or is eliminated by a reaction involving perhaps half-a-dozen phases, some or all of them variable in composition.

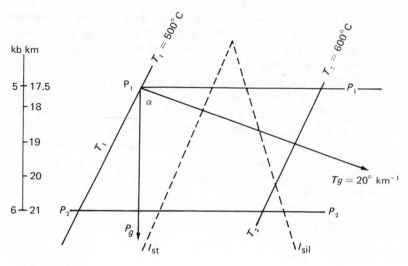

FIGURE 11-2
Geometric model of uniform *P-T* regime of metamorphism (cf. P. H. Thompson, 1976, Fig. 6a): P_1 and P_2 are isobars; T_1 and T_2 are isotherms; P_g and T_g are directions of pressure and temperature gradients.

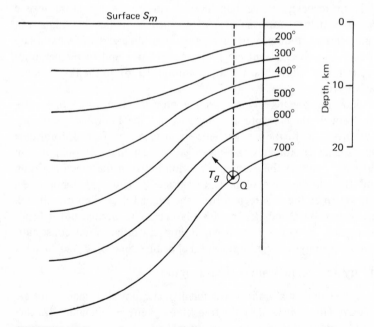

FIGURE 11-3
Geometric model showing isotherms in relation to the surface S_m at the time of metamorphism in a nonuniform *P-T* regime with thermal dome at right (cf. P. H. Thompson, 1976, Fig. 8c).

Here the first problem is to identify the reaction precisely by a mass-balanced equation connecting chemically equivalent phases on either side of the isograd. This involves chemical analysis of all participating phases. The equation that emerges applies strictly to the mapped isograd and cannot be transferred, without due caution, to similar isograds elsewhere.

In parts of New Zealand a biotite isograd has been mapped at the points where biotite first appears at the expense of the mineral combination muscovite-stilpnomelane-actinolite (cf. Fig. 9-19). Brown (1971, p. 296, no. 1) used chemical analyses of the participating phases to compute[*] a corresponding mass-balanced equation:

0.81 muscovite + 0.69 stilpnomelane + 0.28 actinolite + 0.14 sphene

$\rightleftharpoons$ 1 biotite + 0.23 chlorite + 5.21 quartz + 0.24 albite + 0.31 epidote

+ 1.47H_2O

Because of the large number of phases (ten in all) coexisting on the isograd, the variance in spite of the large number of components (ten in Brown's computation) must be low—in this case $\omega = (10 + 2 - 10) = 2$. So at any given temperature and pressure (or more appropriately f_{O_2} value) compositions of coexisting phases remain constant while reaction proceeds until one (usually stilpnomelane) is eliminated. This is an example of what J. B. Thompson (1957, p. 856) termed a *discontinuous* facies change resulting in a sharply defined isograd—here marked by entry of biotite and exit of the trio muscovite-stilpnomelane-actinolite.[†] Clearly Brown's biotite isograd could be calibrated in terms of $P(= P_{H_2O})$ and T if experimentally established distribution coefficients (for Fe/Mg in coexisting biotite, stilpnomelane, and chlorite) over an appropriate range of temperatures were available. At present this is not the case.

Other detailed studies point to a similar general conclusion (e.g., Evans and Guidotti, 1966; D. M. Carmichael, 1969; Guidotti, 1970; Cruikshank and Ghent, 1978). With modern facilities individual isograds can be formulated in precise terms; and due attention to the identity of minor phases (iron oxides, sulfides, carbonates, and graphite) makes it possible to set reasonable limits to significant variables such as $f_{H_2O}, f_{O_2}, f_{CO_2}, f_{CH_4}$, and so on (using experimentally calibrated buffers for comparison). But precise P-T calibration of all but the simplest isograd reactions, though promising, still remains elusive.

Current procedure is to concentrate on simple phase assemblages in zonal parageneses, comparing them with corresponding experimentally and thermodynamically established bivariant equilibria, preferably with mutually overlapping fields of stability. Free use has also been made of "accepted" geothermometers. With these, inherent difficulties stem from two partially independent sources:

---

[*]For method of computation see Brown (1971, pp. 294–295).

[†]Thompson (1957), while emphasizing the advantages of isograds marked by sharp discontinuities in facies, expressed some skepticism about the feasibility of their practical use "if observed at all."

discrepancies between alternative scales of calibration of the thermometer itself (as in oxygen-isotope geothermometry); uncertainty as to time of equilibration of the mineral pair with respect to the metamorphic event. Diffusion kinetics enter into this latter problem.

In spite of the complexity of the problem and the various uncertainties involved considerable progress has been made in evaluating some of the commoner isograd reactions. First appearance of K-feldspar plus an Al_2SiO_5 polymorph in metapelites is one of the more satisfactorily calibrated familiar isograds. Account was taken of such information in developing Fig. 11-1.

General Geometry of a Metamorphic Pressure–Temperature Regime

The geometry of a homogeneous pressure-temperature regime has been lucidly explained by P. H. Thompson (1976) as illustrated in Fig. 11-2.

P_1 and P_2 are isobaric surfaces parallel to the metamorphic surface S_m as earlier defined. T_1 and T_2 are isothermal surfaces inclined to P at any angle α. The pressure gradient (kb km^{-1}) is measured along P_g normal to P_1; its value where P surfaces are parallel to S_m is approximately 0.3 kb km^{-1} and the sign positive downward. The temperature gradient (degr km^{-1}) is measured along T_g normal to T_1. The magnitude of the temperature gradient can vary widely, not only from province to province but commonly from one domain to another within a single province. Except in unusual local situations its sign like that of the pressure gradient is positive downward.

The *mean geothermal gradient* ΔT km^{-1}, in the sense of general geologic usage expresses the average vertical gradient in temperature from some point in the crust to the surface. In the simplest possible case—where isobaric and isothermal surfaces are both parallel to the surface S_m, as in ideal burial metamorphism—the mean geothermal and the thermal gradients coincide geometrically. Both are vertical. But deep down within the domain the magnitude of the thermal gradient commonly falls off in depth. Here the mean geothermal gradient will have the greater magnitude of the two.

More commonly, where metamorphism is an aspect of orogeny, lateral variations can be expected in both the mean geothermal gradient and the topology of isothermal surfaces. With reference to a "stable" area over which the geothermal gradient is constant there will be thermal "domes" where the gradient increases and "depressions" where it decreases in the lateral sense. The right-hand side of Fig. 11-3 represents a thermal dome with respect to the regime represented on the left. Within the "dome" the mean geothermal gradient is 35° km^{-1}; it falls off on the left of the figure to half that value. On the flank of the dome at point Q, which seems to represent a rather common situation: the geothermal gradient, 30° km^{-1}, notably exceeds the thermal gradient, 17° km^{-1}.

Without turning to specific geologic situations the topology of any simply specified isogradic surface can be defined with reference to the P–T regime by making use of known P and T values for the corresponding isograd reaction. In Fig. 11-2, this has been done for two reactions using data shown in Figs. 4-2 and 4-4:

Kyanite $\rightleftharpoons$ sillimanite (I_{sil})

Incoming of staurolite (I_{st})

Thompson's geometric analysis has brought out some interesting generalizations. The geometry of the isograd pattern depends strongly on the temperature gradient and on the magnitude of the angle α. Only under special combinations of these will isograds be either isothermal or isobaric. One such potentially useful situation concerns dehydration reactions at pressures of a few kilobars and temperatures in the 400–700°C range. These mostly have a positive slope of about 8–10° kb^{-1}, so that, in a regime of moderate to high thermal gradient (say, $>15°$ km^{-1}), the isograd surface is approximately isothermal (cf. I_{st} in Fig. 11-3). For low thermal gradients, however, the same isograd surfaces diverge significantly from isothermals. Whether metamorphic grade appears to increase or to decrease with depth (pressure) depends entirely on the slope of the selected isograd surface (itself strongly influenced by the magnitude of α). Grade increases downward across the staurolite isograd I_g, upward across that for sillimanite, I_{sil}. There is nothing abnormal about the latter situation.

Geothermal Gradients

The term "geothermal gradient" is used by geophysicists in a more precise way to describe completely the vertical variation of temperature with depth, dT/dD in degr km^{-1} from the present erosion surface downward. Such a gradient also describes the regime of upward heat flow. Steady-state gradients in the crust could vary from rectilinear to curved (Fig. 11-4) according to whether the heat source

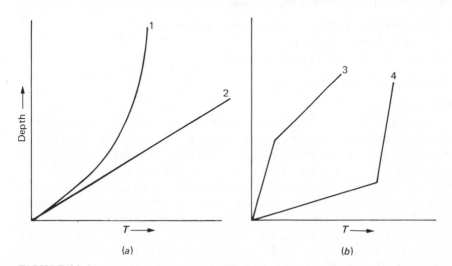

(a)   (b)

FIGURE 11-4
Some possible hypothetical geothermal gradients (after S. W. Richardson, 1970). (a) Steady-state gradients: (1) Subjacent heat source; (2) heat source distributed along gradient. (b) Temporary gradients: (3) caused by rapid sinking; (4) caused by vertical uplift of subjacent hot body.

is subcrustal or (more realistically) distributed within the crust. In tectonically active regions, however, a steady thermal state is scarcely to be expected: cold material can sink from above and hot masses be displaced upward, at rates sufficient to cause abrupt deflections of the dT/dD gradient in either sense. Moreover exothermic hydration reactions in masses of volcanic rocks and reverse endothermic dehydration reactions in sediments could affect the gradient where rates of reaction exceed those of conduction. Since conduction in rocks is a very slow process, such deflections from a steady state could persist for the duration of a metamorphic event.

Elucidation of the Geologic Record of a Metamorphic Event: Alternative Approaches

Possible relations between the mineralogical record (on the erosion surface S_p) of metamorphic pressure-temperature conditions and various types of geothermal gradients have been discussed by Richardson (1970). He starts with the familiar proposition (cf. Bowen, 1940; J. B. Thompson, 1955) to the effect that the fossil P-T distribution over the present erosion surface may be determined by referring mapped isograds to corresponding calibrated univariant curves on a petrogenic grid. This is the immediate objective of a regional study, with a view to transposing the findings into a metamorphic P-T regime as envisaged in P. H. Thompson's geometric model.

Different approaches have been tried with varying success at different levels of refinement. All yield information regarding mean geothermal gradients of metamorphism and so lead into the general problem of the regional metamorphic regime. They will be reviewed briefly under these headings.

1. Metamorphic P-T gradients on the present erosion surface.
2. P-T limits in small surface domains.
3. Concept of bathozones and bathograds.

Metamorphic Field Gradients

Definition
The most ambitious (and so far least successful) approach is to evaluate what will be called a metamorphic field gradient. This is a rectangular plot of geologically estimated P and T values for a succession of points on a traverse across the present erosion surface. Its slope (rectilinear, curved, even sinuate) expresses dT/dP, degr kb^{-1}. A straight line from any point on the gradient extrapolated to surface P-T represents the mean geothermal gradient at the corresponding point on the map.

Less precise than types of gradient already considered, the metamorphic gradient—which only by coincidence is identical with any of the others—is more tangible. It is recorded upon a finite crustal surface and can be evaluated in terms of geologic data—admittedly eked out perforce in many instances by "reasonable" geologic assumptions.

Relevant Data
The basic data concern the identity and field distribution of mapped isograds. Since these express reactions that (where experimentally calibrated) represent

equilibria whose variance is one or more, additional data are needed to fix simultaneously both temperature and pressure at the outcrop. Obviously of great potential here are standard geothermometers and geobarometers—most of them unfortunately still prone to uncertainty as to the scale of calibration.

Geothermometers are currently available for most of the metamorphic temperature range. But in the field of geobarometry there is a higher degree of uncertainty. To remedy this situation it is customary to fall back on depth estimates based on "reasonable" estimates of depths below the former erosion surface S_m. Alternative assumptions such as the following (all based to some degree on field evidence) can be made.

First, the metamorphic imprint outlasted or postdated regional deformation; the present erosion surface is isobaric with reference to the metamorphic regime; P was determined by depth (estimated or assumed) in the tectonic pile.

Second, the metamorphic regime was directly related to measurable stratigraphic depth in a subsequently tilted pile. The erosion surface is not isobaric.

Possibilities for constructing widely differing gradients from the same set of data are obvious; and equally prone to the influence of individual preferences are resulting models of the metamorphic regime. The problem has been developed in P. H. Thompson's (1976) discussion of the metamorphic regime in the Lepontine Alps.

Selected equilibria for evaluating isograds and boundaries between subfacies and facies, as shown in Figs. 11-5 and 11-6, are taken from Chap. 4 (where their individual merits have also been reviewed). The problem is somewhat different in the low-grade area from that in the area of medium to high grade; for in the former field, the critical curves have a steeper dT/dP gradient ($\sim$50° kb^{-1}) than the dehydration curves in the latter field ($\sim$10° kb^{-1} in the medium pressure range).

Critical curves and reference lines in the low-grade field are as follows (similarly lettered in Fig. 11-5).

A. Jadeite + quartz $\rightleftharpoons$ albite (Fig. 4-13)
B. Aragonite $\rightleftharpoons$ calcite (Fig. 4-13). Terminated at $S = 300°C$, the upper temperature for survival of aragonite during postmetamorphic cooling.
C. Laumontite $\rightleftharpoons$ lawsonite + 2 quartz + 2H$_2$O (Fig. 4-13)
D. Laumontite $\rightleftharpoons$ wairakite + 2H$_2$O (Fig. 4-13)
E. 4 lawsonite + 2 quartz $\rightleftharpoons$ 2 zoisite + pyrophyllite + H$_2$O (Nitsch, 1971)
F. Analcite + quartz $\rightleftharpoons$ albite + H$_2$O (Fig. 4-13)
G. Antigorite + brucite $\rightleftharpoons$ 2 forsterite + 3H$_2$O (Fig. 4-11, 1)

Also shown are experimentally determined minimal pressure limits for possible stable existence of two phases both widely distributed in the blueschist facies.

H. Impure jadeite (Jd$_{82}$Ac$_{14}$Di$_4$) plus quartz (Newton and Smith, 1967). (This coincides with the computed curve for Jd$_{50}$Di$_{50}$ from Fig. 4-13.) On thermodynamic grounds, the P–T limits of omphacite in absence of quartz should lie far to the right of and below H.
J. Glaucophane (ordered type; Papike and Clark, 1968).

Curves A–G, except perhaps at the high temperature ends of C and D (where they probably overlap the stability fields of prehnite and pumpellyite) are believed

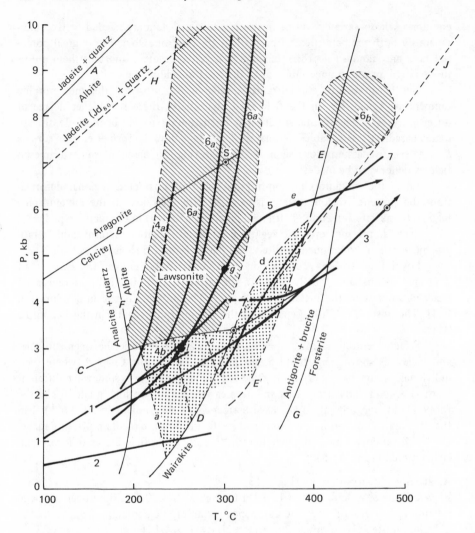

FIGURE 11-5

Estimated field gradients for selected low-pressure facies series (see text): (1) Taringatura Hills, New Zealand; (2) Puerto Rico; (3) Haast Schists, Otago, New Zealand northern and eastern borderland; (4) Caples and Haast Schists, New Zealand, northwestern borderland; (5) Blueschist belt, New Caledonia (to epidote isograd); (6a) sectors of Franciscan blueschist belt, California; (6b) Tectonic blueschist blocks, Franciscan, California; (7) Pumpellyite-actinolite and glaucophane greenschists, Sanbagawa belt, Japan. For significance of calibrated equilibrium curves, $A, B \ldots, a, b \ldots$, see text.

to represent stable equilibria. The general stipulated condition for all is $P_{H_2O} = P$, which must be closely approximated in many natural assemblages lacking carbonates.

Segments of low-grade interfacies boundaries (which, in fact, are bands, not sharp lines) can be identified with segments of some of the equilibrium curves of Fig. 11-5 as follows:

Upper *P–T* limit of *zeolite* facies, F–C–D$'$
Lower *P* limit of *lawsonite-albite-chlorite* facies, C
Lower *P* limit of *blueschist* facies, an undefined band above B and to the left of J
Lower *T* limit of the *greenschist* facies, E and its low-temperature extension (E$'$;
    hypothetical) against the tentatively postulated stability field of pumpellyite

In the absence of adequate data, one can only speculate on the respective stability fields of prehnite and pumpellyite, in relation to each other and to the adjacent fields of laumontite, wairakite, and lawsonite. Several experienced workers in the field have proposed topologies consistent with observed field relations (e.g., Coombs, 1960, pp. 346–348; 1971; Liou, 1971b, p. 407; E. H. Brown, 1977, p. 130). But these are all tentative and there are mutual discrepancies among them.

Gradient Curvature: Inherent Uncertainties

It must now be apparent that previous attempts to draw field gradients for specific facies series (e.g., Turner, 1968, p. 359) are subject to a good deal of uncertainty, especially with respect to degree and sense of curvature. These have important implications as to thermal doming or depression; for the rectilinear projection of any point on the curve to zero gives the mean geothermal gradient at the corresponding point on the map. There is little or nothing to justify the curvature (convex upward) of tentative gradients previously proposed (Turner, 1968, p. 359, curves 1*c*, 1*d*, and 1*e*) for some blueschist series. This implies thermal doming toward the higher grades—the very reverse of what is now considered likely almost to the point of certainty. These and most other curves previously proposed, including those tentatively put forward by Miyashiro (1961) in a more general context, should be modified or abandoned in their present form. They have served their initial purpose of demonstrating that all field gradients do not necessarily project back to surface *P* and *T*, and that many, perhaps most, will not be rectilinear along their full extent.

Against this somewhat pessimistic background we shall examine a few specific well-documented cases that illustrate the complexity of the problem and the kind of outcome that can be expected from this line of approach just described.

Two Gradients of Burial Metamorphism

In Fig. 11-5, curves 1 and 2 respectively represent possible gradients of burial metamorphism in a Triassic sedimentary pile in southern New Zealand (Taringatura Hills, Fig. 9-1) and in a Cretaceous volcanic-sedimentary sequence in Puerto Rico (cf. p. 302). There is no difficulty here as to relative pressure. The only reference points for temperature on the other hand are at the surface S_m (*P* and *T* approaching zero) and at the analcite curve F. The main interest of the two gradients is that they illustrate the sort of geothermal gradient to be expected in the upper levels of the Phanerozoic crust above domains undergoing metamorphism deeper down (>10 or 15 km).

Greenschist-Facies Gradients, Haast Schist
Terrane, New Zealand

For 150 km along its northern border against the neighboring Torlesse Group (Fig. 9-3), the Haast Schist block of southern New Zealand displays a consistent inward (NE → SW) prograde facies sequence

Zeolite → prehnite-pumpellyite → pumpellyite-actinolite → greenschist

A corresponding generalized metamorphic gradient, terminated in the chlorite zone where biotite is just beginning to appear in metavolcanics, is shown in Fig. 11-5 as curve 3. Pressures at maximum grade have been variously estimated as 5.5-6.5 kb from the crossite content of blue actinolites in equilibrium with quartz, albite, epidote, and magnetite (Brown, 1977) and from sphalerite-pyrite-pyrrhotite equilibria in a metamorphosed sulfide lode (Henley, 1975). This also indicates temperatures $\approx 480 \pm 40°C$ (w, curve 3) consistent with appearance of biotite in metavolcanics. Projected to zero these data define a mean geothermal gradient of 20-27° km^{-1} in this part of the province (east of Lake Wakatipu). This is slightly but perhaps significantly less than the burial gradient at Taringatura Hills which might, for want of better data, be considered typical of the zeolite → prehnite-pumpellyite transition elsewhere in the New Zealand geosyncline. Curve 3 as drawn would represent a nearly uniform regional mean geothermal gradient within a *P–T* regime controlled essentially by depth. Slight upward concavity suggests minor thermal depression toward the south and west; but a rectilinear course could equally well have been drawn. Curve 3 implies regional postmetamorphic differential uplift of the interior of the Haast Schist terrane with respect to the borderlands. The observed pressure gradient, some 3-4 kb along a westward 100 km traverse from the Haast-Torlesse boundary to the vicinity of Lake Wakatipu, requires regional tilting of 5-8°. Prior to extensive pre-Tertiary peneplanation there was in fact profound postmetamorphic disturbance along the borderlands. Bishop's (1974) detailed study of the Torlesse-Haast metamorphic transition near Dansey's Pass (A, Fig. 9-3) beautifully demonstrates local steeply dipping attitudes of isograd and isotect surfaces in this section of the northeastern border. By contrast a regionally uniform metamorphic grade (chlorite zone) that prevails over the extensive central outcrop of the Haast terrane is evidence that isograds are only gently inclined to the present erosion surface over most of the schist region. This geometric situation in turn is consistent with a model of almost uniform regional geothermal gradient.

Metamorphic (and geothermal) gradients inward from the southwestern margins of the Haast Schist block must be decidedly lower than that of curve 3. Here the inward facies transition includes lawsonite-albite-chlorite assemblages between the prehnite-pumpellyite and facies of higher grade (cf. Fig. 9-11). More than one gradient is reflected in different sectors of the southwest borderland. In some (e.g., curve 4*a*) presence of aragonite indicates gradients no greater than about 10°km^{-1}. Curve 4*b*, on the other hand, represents a possible metamorphic gradient eastward across the area mapped by Kawachi in the Caples terrane northwest of Lake Wakatipu. The dashed continuation represents a major dislocation and narrow zone of mélange at the junction with the Haast Schist terrane to the east. It probably expresses discontinuity in time as well as in place; for the lawsonite assemblages of the western borderland yield radiometric ages significantly older than those recorded on most of the Haast block.

P–T *Relations among Facies of Low*
Temperatures and Pressure: Unsolved Problems

However one draws gradients such as 3 and 4 leading from minimum grades into the field of the greenschist facies, prehnite- and pumpellyite-bearing assemblages overlap stability fields of wairakite (and to a lesser degree that of lawsonite) as shown in Fig. 11-5. There are even rare records in other regions (cf. Fig. 9-6) of prehnite regionally trespassing into the aragonite field! There is no reason to assume wide prevalence of disequilibrium in the natural phase assemblage. The regularity of pattern in their geologic sequence suggests the very opposite. Underlying seeming anomalies and marked divergence of opinion among those who have studied the problem (e.g., Coombs, 1971; Liou, 1971; and authors cited therein) are uncertainties stemming from three possible sources; lack of reliable data on equilibria involving prehnite, pumpellyite, and lawsonite; the influence of buffered fluid composition—notably X_{H_2O} versus X_{CO_2}; and even perhaps (in the low-temperature region that favors brittle response to stress) divergence of P_{fl} from lithostatic pressure P_l.

Not only are experimental or computed data lacking for such key equilibria as that involving elimination of prehnite in pumpellyite assemblages, but the nature of the reaction itself—which certainly involves chlorite—has not been satisfactorily identified (cf. Bishop, 1972, p. 3188). The general model presented by Liou (1971, pp. 397–403) is based on a Schreinemakers treatment of systems in which kaolin plays a vital role. Yet there is no evidence—at least in some of the better-documented cases (Bishop, 1971, p. 3188)—that kaolin is present in either assemblage on the prehnite-disappearance isograd. We are forced to fall back on field evidence provided by natural isograd sequences—the very material that we hope ultimately to evaluate in more precise numerical terms of P and T. Some implications of field evidence are these:

1. Between the zeolite and the greenschist facies there are successive intermediate facies in a general prograde sequence prehnite-pumpellyite → pumpellyite-actinolite (cf. Coombs, 1971, p. 324, Fig. 2).
2. At pressures greater than 1–2 kb, the laumontite ⇌ wairakite equilibrium appears to be metastable with respect to equilibria involving prehnite and pumpellyite.
3. Lawsonite-chlorite-quartz appears to be unstable with respect to pumpellyite along the high-temperature border of the lawsonite field (cf. also Coombs, 1971, p. 324; Liou, 1971, p. 407).
4. At pressures below the lawsonite-laumontite-wairakite triple point (which must itself represent a metastable univariant equilibrium) laumontite must be metastable with respect to prehnite and (in the presence of chlorite) pumpellyite.

On the basis of such observations I have ventured to draw highly tentative curves (dotted in Fig. 11-5) to show possible relative positions of "isograd reactions" generally consistent with the field data[*]:

---

[*]None is even partially calibrated with respect to experimental data. Slopes are equally uncertain, since the reactions themselves have not been precisely formulated.

a Prehnite in
b Pumpellyite in
c Prehnite out (cf. Bishop, 1972, p. 3988)
d Lawsonite out
E' Pumpellyite out (cf. Bishop, 1972, p. 3190)

The field of the two pumpellyite facies is shown stippled.

Presence of carbonates in common low-grade assemblages implies that fluid composition (especially X_{CO_2} versus X_{H_2O}) could vary significantly from one geologic situation to another. Anomalies are to be expected; indeed it is surprising to find that parageneses close to the zeolite facies show such regularity. Only aragonite is independent of variations in fluid composition at constant lithostatic pressure. So occasional trespass of the "low-pressure" phase prehnite into the high-pressure stability field of aragonite can readily be explained in terms of relatively low X_{H_2O} in the fluid phase.

Metamorphic Gradients in Blueschist Facies Series: Preliminary Generalizations

From the unique low-temperature–high-pressure regime of blueschist facies series certain generalizations are applicable peculiarly to this end of the spectrum of regional metamorphic gradients.

First, the high-pressure–low-temperature combination itself is proved beyond doubt by key minerals of the paragenesis: presence of lawsonite, jadeite (Jd_{80})-quartz, omphacite, and by inference glaucophane their habitual associate; survival of aragonite during the postmetamorphic cooling cycle. At the low-grade end of most series zeolites and prehnite, indices of low pressure, demonstrate the unusually large pressure span of the field gradient—a half dozen kilobars at least. It follows that sections of the present surface outcrop must have been differentially tilted or otherwise displaced with respect to the erosion surface S_m at the time of metamorphism. In rare cases, for example, in parts of the blueschist belt of New Caledonia, pressure can be shown to increase with stratigraphic depth in a simply tilted section, and the depth increment can be taken as a measure of ΔP. But this situation, a special and extreme case of burial metamorphism, is rare.

Second, oxygen-isotope fractionation data are available for several blueschist facies series and have been critically evaluated by Taylor and Coleman (1968) and Black (1974). Temperature ranges estimated on this basis can be accepted with some confidence; but, because of current disagreement as to scales of calibration absolute values of temperature must be viewed with greater caution. Values based on the scale advocated by Epstein and Taylor (1967) at least do not violate constraints imposed by other lines of reasoning, and so, in accordance with the preferences of writers just cited, have been tentatively accepted here. Temperatures evaluated on other scales would be even lower.

Third, it is hard to escape the implications of quartz-jadeite and aragonite-bearing rocks that blueschist and metamorphism commonly leads into a field of very high pressure and temperatures not much above 300°C. Oxygen-isotope temperatures (whatever the scale of calibration) are strikingly consistent with this temperature limitation.

Fourth, in spite of great uncertainty as to their precise location, the inferred fields of pumpellyite, actinolite, and prehnite-pumpellyite (Fig. 11-5) must be taken into account at the low-grade ends of blueschist gradients. In a number of cases, for example, the prehnite-pumpellyite field is bypassed; this situation, if confirmed, implies very low values for dT/dP at temperatures near 300°C and hence for mean geothermal gradients as well.

Blueschist Gradient, Northern New Caledonia

The most carefully documented blueschist gradient that has yet been proposed refers to a northward traverse 35 km long across the blueschist belt of northern New Caledonia, from the upper levels of the southwestern mélange zone near Koumac to the northeastern coast near Balade (Fig. 9-12). The prograde zonal sequence northeastward from the lawsonite isograd (lower limit of mélange) has already been described (pp. 230–231). Nearer to Koumac, it is preceded, within the mélange zone itself, by zeolite and prehnite-pumpellyite assemblages of still lower grade. The gradient shown as curve 5 in Fig. 11-5 was plotted directly from data of Diessel and co-authors (1979), supported by the structural studies of Briggs and others (1977). Temperatures were based on oxygen-isotope data (Black, 1974) using the scale of Epstein and Taylor (1967).[*] Pressures were estimated by detailed mapping across the belt from the southwestern edge of the mélange zone to the epidote isograd. In this section the broad structure is simple—a pile of upper Cretaceous sediments and volcanics, locally fossiliferous, dipping consistently to the southwest and overlain by a thick stack of similarly dipping slices in the mélange zones. Isograds trend parallel to the regional strike, so it has been assumed that isograd surfaces, once horizontal, have been tilted with the bedding subsequently to metamorphism. On this assumption, metamorphic pressures were estimated as proportional to stratigraphic-tectonic depth, with allowance for a local break in the lawsonite zone where part of the section has been faulted out. The corresponding sinuous gradient (curve 5, Fig. 11-5) conforms to constraints imposed by relevant equilibrium curves: it lies entirely below the field of aragonite, and entry points of lawsonite, *l* and of epidote (exit lawsonite), *e* fall close to the experimentally established curves. The total picture is internally consistent; but it is emphasized that its basis is essentially geologic, with calibrated equilibria playing a confirmatory role.

Franciscan Blueschist Belt, California

Because of its great extent and generally disturbed structure, the Franciscan terrane of California (Fig. 9-13) cannot be expected to yield as coherent a picture of metamorphic P–T conditions as that developed for New Caledonia. No single gradient could realistically express conditions for the whole region; and even where regional maps are available local gradients are likely to be highly discontinuous because of postmetamorphic dislocations, some of them obvious in the field and marked by sharp breaks in facies. The family of curves *6a* has been devel-

---

[*]Preferred by Black as more realistic than values 100° lower on the scale of Clayton and co-authors (1972)—a provisional conclusion that is accepted here. The total range of temperatures (>300°) can scarcely be challenged.

oped rather diagrammatically to bring out the variety as well as the unity of the regional pattern.

Perhaps least interrupted (though probably disrupted by sharp breaks in facies), gradients in Northern California and in the Cazadero and Diablo sections further south might be located in the shaded area 6a (permitting extensive survival of aragonite and presence of quartz and jadeite, and consistent with a single oxygen-isotope temperature, 290°C, recorded by Taylor and Coleman, 1968, p. 1746). Area 6b is suggested as a possible field for epidote- and garnet-bearing blueschists of tectonic blocks.

High-Pressure Gradient, Sanbagawa Belt, Japan

Curve 7 represents a general gradient (if such can be drawn) for the facies series zeolite → pumpellyite-actinolite → blueschist → greenschist transition → amphibolite, as described from different sections of the Sanbagawa belt (Fig. 9-14 and accompanying text). It is drawn to bypass the respective fields of prehnite-pumpellyite, aragonite, and lawsonite, but to enter the field where ordered glaucophane could exist stably.[*] The maximum pressure, 7 kb, corresponds to E. H. Brown's (1977) estimate based on crossite content of alkali amphiboles coexisting with iron oxides, albite, chlorite, and epidote. The facies series is remarkable among blueschist sequences for entry of biotite where maximum grade is reached in the amphibolite facies (beyond the limits of Fig. 11-5).

Metamorphic Gradients, High-Grade Facies Series

Isograd Evaluation

Some univariant curves used to evaluate isograds and mineral assemblages in the amphibolite and granulite facies are shown as quantitative background for Fig. 11-6 (taken from Chap. 4):

(A) Chlorotoid $\rightleftharpoons$ staurolite

for the pure ferrous system (Richardson, 1968), to represent the lower stability limit (first point of entry) of staurolite in metapelites.

(B) Kyanite $\rightleftharpoons$ sillimanite

(C) Muscovite + quartz $\rightleftharpoons$ K-feldspar + Al_2SiO_5

A curve of potential value, still largely unexploited is

(D) 5 antigorite $\rightleftharpoons$ 12 forsterite + 2 talc + $18H_2O$

Also useful where there is evidence of anatexis in place (some migmatite complexes) are various curves representing the lower temperature limits of fusion in

---

[*]Its high-T limit, J in Fig. 11-5, is not precise.

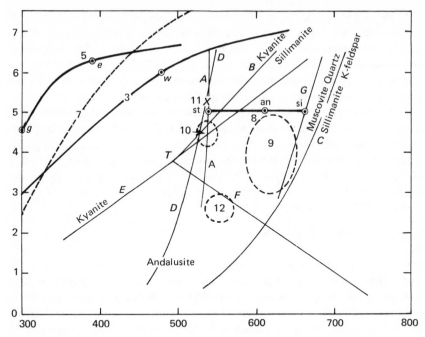

FIGURE 11-6
Estimated field gradients (3, 5, 7, 8) and *P-T* limits (9, 10, 11, 12) for selected amphibolite
facies series (see text): (3) Haast Schist, northwestern sector adjoining Alpine Fault, New
Zealand; blueschist belt, New Caledonia (epidote and hornblende zones); (7) Sanbagawa belt,
Japan (high-grade zones); (8) Lepontine Alps, Switzerland; (9) Sillimanite zones, Maine;
(10) Staurolite-kyanite zone, British Columbia; (11) Almandine zone, northeastern Dalradian
(Barrovian sector), Scotland; (12) Andalusite-staurolite zone, northeastern Dalradian (Buchan
sector), Scotland. Calibrated equilibrium curves lettered as in text; *G*, sillimanite isograd,
Lepontine Alps, as estimated by Hoschek (1968).

systems closed or open to water. Univariant curves for reactions involving carbonates cannot be plotted unequivocally in Fig. 11-6, where one of the coordinates
stipulates $P_{H_2O} = P$, but they help to build more comprehensive models where
fluid-compositional variables play a significant role.

On the whole, temperature is easier to evaluate than pressure, especially above
about 4 kb where typical dehydration curves (such as A and C) have low dT/dP
gradients—8–12° kb^{-1}. An obvious single point of reference is the Al_2SiO_5 triple
point. This has been moved about so much and so often by experimental geochemists, that with added uncertainty regarding possible metastability of individual polymorphs, it has come to be viewed with some skepticism by many geologists. Yet of
its qualitative value there can be little doubt. Now that the triple point has been
removed from the 8-kb level[*] and settled (more permanently, we hope) around 4
kb, andalusite can be used with some confidence as an indicator of low pressure
(<4 kb). It remains in fact the most satisfactory such index available to date.

---

[*]Wide differences among alternate gradients proposed for the same facies series (e.g.,
the Barrovian and the Buchan series of Scotland) may reflect nothing more than individual
preferences for Al_2SiO_5 triple points ranging from 3–8 kb.

A useful indirect approach to setting limits to pressure values is possible where the high-grade series to be evaluated is regionally continuous with a low-grade series with mineral indices of high pressure. Thus, in parts of the Sanbagawa belt of Japan and in the Haast Schist terrane of New Zealand (see below) respective points of entry of the amphibolite facies (curves 7 and 3, Figs. 11-5 and 11-6) must be located at pressures close to 7 and 6 kb respectively.

While standard geothermometers continue to be employed, geobarometry, because of lack of agreement as to scales of calibration, is far from satisfactory. Of the high-grade cordierite-garnet pair, all that can be said is that the two phases can coexist between about 2 and 5 kb, the less magnesian cordierites—$Fe^{2+}/(Fe^{2+} + Mg) > 0.3$—being confined to the lower levels of pressure. Coexisting pyroxenes in the granulite facies have some potential as indicators of both pressure (Wood and Banno, 1973) and temperature (Hewins, 1975).

Amphibolite Facies, Southern Alps, New Zealand

A northeasterly prolongation of the Haast Schist terrane follows the line of the southern Alps, where differential uplift in the late Tertiary amounts to at least 3 km (high points in the existing topography) and probably a good deal more. Westerly increase in metamorphic grade, from the greenschist into the amphibolite facies (cf. Fig. 1-16), reaches a climax close to the Alpine Fault (Cooper, 1972; Wallace, 1974). Among the dominant quartz-andesine-almandine-biotite-muscovite schists (metagraywackes), there are rare but significant pelitic assemblages with staurolite or kyanite. Amphibolites are high-grade types with almandine, rarely clinopyroxene. Massive bodies of coarse pegmatite indicate local onset of anatexis (Wallace, 1974, p. 257). Presence of staurolite and an oxygen-isotope temperature of 539–550°C indicate temperatures of at least 550°C (Wallace, 1975). Taking into account also the fact of local incipient melting at a structurally deeper level, Wallace suggests even higher maximum temperatures.

Curve 3, Fig. 11-6 has been drawn for a high-grade limit tentatively placed at 650°C, 7 kb. The corresponding mean geothermal gradient at this point would be ~27° km^{-1}—which agrees with values suggested for the greenschist facies series in the vicinity of Lake Wakatipu 70 km to the south. Clearly there is no compelling reason to postulate any marked westward increase in the thermal gradient of the regional *P-T* regime such as was formerly proposed (Turner, 1968, p. 383). Steepening of isogradic surfaces toward the west could reflect known postmetamorphic differential uplift along the Alpine Fault rather than thermal doming during metamorphism.

There is nothing in the culminating mineral paragenesis that even hints at affinities with the eclogite facies, such as have been noted for highest grades in the hornblende zone of the New Caledonian blueschist belt at estimated temperatures up to 560°C and pressures exceeding 7 kb (curve 5, Figs. 11-5 and 11-6).

Amphibolite Facies, Lepontine Alps

The most sophisticated attempts yet made to develop models of a complete *P-T* regime of regional metamorphism have been focused on the Lepontine province of the central Alps (cf. Fig. 10-10 and accompanying text). The surviving metamorphic imprint belongs entirely to the mid-Tertiary Lepontine phase of Alpine metamorphism ($\sim$35–40 $\times$ 10^6 years). Basic data relevant to the problem are these:

1. Metamorphism postdated the period of Alpine nappe building, and crystallization outlasted penetrative deformation responsible for present foliated structure. Pressure across the present erosion surface thus was controlled by the superincumbent stratigraphic-tectonic load. Unfortunately, estimates of maximum thickness of the overlying pile vary between wide limits, allowing choice of pressure anywhere between about 4 and 10 kb (cf. Niggli, 1970; E. Wenk, 1970, pp. 35–36; Frey et al., 1974, p. 276).

2. Regarding the attitude of isobaric surfaces in relation to the erosion surface S_p, two models have been proposed:

a. E. Niggli (1970) advocates postmetamorphic tectonic doming of the high-grade southeastern sector to account for the partially concentric regional pattern of isograds (Fig. 10-10).
b. E. Wenk (1970) on the other hand postulates metamorphic isobaric surfaces essentially parallel to the present erosion surface. In this model the isograd pattern must indicate thermal doming (increase of the thermal gradient) toward the southeast.

3. Everywhere in the Lepontine province isogradic surfaces dip steeply. Along the 20 km NW–SE profile afforded by the Simplon Tunnel (Fig. 11-7), the dip is between 60 and 75° (both ±15°) to the northwest (Streckeisen and Wenk, 1974), with metamorphic grade increasing southeastward. In the Val Mesolcina, some 70 km to the east, isogradic surfaces are nearly vertical (P. H. Thompson, 1976).

4. Two crucial isograds studied by Thompson express reactions approximating

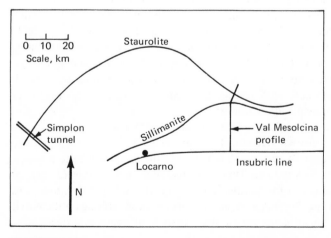

FIGURE 11-7
Simplified map of Lepontine province, central Alps, showing configuration of staurolite and sillimanite isograds (after Jäger et al., 1967) and relative locations of Simplon Tunnel and Val Mesolcina profiles as discussed in text (see also Fig. 10-10).

Chlorite + muscovite ⇌ staurolite + biotite + quartz + H_2O

(staurolite isograd)

Staurolite + muscovite + quartz ⇌ biotite + sillimanite + H_2O

(sillimanite isograd)

Hoschek (1967) evaluated this latter reaction experimentally, and his equilibrium curve is reproduced as G in Fig. 11-6. Where Thompson mapped them in the Val Mesolcina, the isograds are about 9 km apart; in the Simplon area, they are separated by 35 km.

5. Whether or not there has been some postmetamorphic tectonic doming, the regional steep dip of isogradic surfaces over so large an area compels a model of thermal doming toward the southeast. Isothermal and isobaric surfaces must intersect at high angles (cf. Fig. 11-2) with the thermal gradient correspondingly increasingly southeastward.

On the above basis Thompson (1976) has developed an attractive model of the P–T regime of metamorphism in the Val Mesolcina area: isogradic surfaces marking entry of staurolite and sillimanite have a high positive dP/dT slope on a P–T diagram such as Fig. 11-6, so they must be essentially isothermal in the metamorphic regime. The present erosion surface is assumed to have been isobaric at the time of metamorphism (as in Wenk's regional model); α values must be correspondingly high, at least 50–70°.

A clue as to metamorphic pressures is provided by Al_2SiO_5 polymorphs. Kyanite is present on either side of both isograds in Val Mesolcina. But on and beyond the sillimanite isograd it is accompanied by newly formed sillimanite (fibrolite). P–T conditions must have been close to the kyanite-sillimanite equilibrium. Locally, beyond a mappable isograd between and inclined to the other two, andalusite appears in quartz segregations, where it partially replaces coexisting kyanite. Pressures cannot have been more than a kilobar or so above the Al_2SiO_5 triple point T. Conforming to the above restrictions, and within possible limits prescribed by Thompson (1976, p. 288) is curve 8 in Fig. 11-6. Sillimanite crystallizing beyond the sillimanite isograd *si* would be truly stable; andalusite crystallizing at *an* would be stable with respect to kyanite but metastable relative to sillimanite (Ostwald's principle in operation).

The mean geothermal gradient ranges from 30° km^{-1} at *st* to 38° km^{-1} at *si*. In the Val Mesolcina the thermal gradient of the regime is ~11° km^{-1}; but where the two critical isograds diverge to become 35 km apart in the Simplon area to the west it would be only about 3° km^{-1}. So Thompson reasoned that southward thermal doming which is so marked in the southeastern sector of the Lepontine zone, was significantly weaker in the Simplon area; and postmetamorphic tilting on the Niggli model may have had some influence on the steep attitude of isogradic surfaces.

Miscellaneous Local Evaluations

In the past decade a number of local evaluations have been proposed for small domains or single isograds within the broad field of high-grade metamorphism.

These help to fill in the general picture of the total *P–T* regime of regional meta-morphism, and provide information regarding the range of magnitude of mean geothermal gradients recorded by different facies in various tectonic situations and perhaps in relation to time as well. Most such evaluations rest on combined calibrated phase equilibria, geothermometry, and geobarometry; so they illus-trate the potential and present limitations of the quantitative approach to natural equilibria.

Two American examples, obviously analogous in some respects to the high-grade Lepontine pattern, are listed without critical comment below.

Discontinuous isograd between the first and second sillimanite zones, Appa-lachian mid-Paleozoic metamorphic belt, Maine (Guidotti, 1970). The isograd reaction (cf. Hoschek, 1967) is essentially the same as at the sillimanite isograd in the Lepontine Alps.

Staurolite + Na-rich muscovite + quartz $\rightleftharpoons$ sillimanite + biotite

+ K-rich muscovite + albite + H_2O (±almandine)

Staurolite-kyanite zone, Esplanade Range, British Columbia (Ghent, 1975), is a local culmination (thermal dome) in a zonal sequence marked by biotite-chlorotoid → garnet → staurolite-kyanite in Proterozoic metapelites.

The garnet zone, close to the garnet isograd, base of the Dalradian (overlying the Moinian) southwest Highlands, Scotland (Richardson and Powell, 1976). This point is based on calcite-dolomite geothermometry checked against carbonate equilibria with tremolite, chlorite, oligoclase, and clinozoisite "without recourse to the bloody field of the Al_2SiO_5 phase diagram"!

General agreement between these independent evaluations and P. H. Thompson's model for a closely similar lithologic-mineralogical metamorphic pattern in the Lepontine Alps is at least reassuring as to the methods of evalua-tion in current use.

Granulite Regimes: Miscellaneous Calibrated Points

Because uniformity of facies is characteristic of most Precambrian granulite ter-ranes, facies series that have been mapped there typically include only high-grade amphibolite and transitional facies in addition to the granulite facies proper. Isograds are few and widely spaced. It would be idle therefore to attempt to recon-struct field gradients comparable to those that embrace facies of lower grade elsewhere.

Recent literature includes many instances of *P–T* calibrations proposed for individual well-documented granulite parageneses. All are based on various types of preferred geothermometers and geobarometers. And since there are marked internal inconsistencies among *P* and *T* values obtained by different methods and by different workers in the same areas, it is not surprising to find a wide spread among numerical estimates of pressure and temperature for the granulite regime in general. There is a general consensus of the broadest kind on these the following points.

1. The total range of pressure encompassed by the facies is wide—possibly 3–8 or 9 kb. Widespread prevalence of cordierite, especially varieties relatively rich in iron is an accepted index of low pressure. But how low? A glance at Holdaway and Lee's diagram (Fig. 4-5) for equilibrium between cordierite and garnet suggests values probably below 3–4 kb at temperatures around 700–750°C. Occurrence of diopside-forsterite in associated massive marbles is supporting evidence of low pressure. At the other extreme, kyanite (instead of the much commoner sillimanite) in quartz-perthite granulites suggests pressures perhaps above 7 kb (cf. Fig. 4-3).

2. Temperatures exceed those of complete breakdown of quartz-muscovite (cf. Fig. 4-3) and continue well into the field of fusion of quartzo-feldspathic rocks even in a regime of water deficiency. To place the temperature range as between 700–900°C seems reasonable. Various favored geothermometers on the whole support this overall estimate, though conflicts arise when attempts are made to pinpoint the metamorphic temperature to ±50°.

Below are listed, without critical comment, a few of the many recent estimates that have been proposed (the reader must turn to the original sources to form his or her own opinion regarding their validity).

1. Adirondacks, New York:
   a. 525–625°C (Buddington and Lindsley, 1964, p. 337): based on Fe-Ti oxide equilibria
   b. 700–760°C, $P \sim 10$ kb, $P_{H_2O} \sim 1.7$ kb (DeWaard, 1967): based on alkali-feldspar solvus, pyroxene equilibria, quartz-muscovite breakdown and minimal melting curves
2. Willyama complex, New South Wales, Australia (cordierite granulites):
   a. 600–670°C (Binns, 1965): based on Fe-Ti oxide equilibria
   b. 700–800°C (Binns, 1966): based on the experimental breakdown of hornblende
   c. 800–830°C (Hewins, 1975, p. 206): based on two-pyroxene geothermometer
3. Madras, India (charnockites):
   a. 800–870°C (Wood and Banno, 1973, p. 122): based on two-pyroxene geothermometer
   b. 849–860°C (Hewins, 1975, p. 207): same basis
   c. 850°C (Saxena, 1979, p. 234): based on garnet-clinopyroxene geothermometer
4. Hercynian kyanite granulites, Moldanubian province, Austria: 760°C, 11 kb, low P_{H_2O} (Scharbert and Kurat, 1974): based on kyanite ⇌ sillimanite curve, breakdown of muscovite-quartz, and partial melting of quartz-feldspar
5. Archaean Scourie granulites, Lewisian, northwestern Scotland: 1050–1250°C, 15 ± 3 kb (O'Hara and Yarwood, 1978): based on ilmenite-magnetite, orthopyroxene-clinopyroxene, and hypersthene-plagioclase-magnetite intergrowths, all believed to have exsolved from homogeneous phases during postmetamorphic cooling

Finally there are two much-cited aspects of granulite metamorphism that are still open to vigorous debate. The first concerns the relation between granulites and granitic magmas that are mutually associated in many Precambrian migmatite complexes. Some writers (e.g., Fyfe, 1973, and elsewhere) see partial fusion as the essential process by which granulites (the refractory residues) attain their condition of extreme dehydration (see pp. 466-467). But there are others, who following the classic reasoning of Barrow and of Barrell, look at granitic magma as the vehicle by which the necessary heat to bring about granulite metamorphism, was transported from subjacent hotter zones of the deep crust or the mantle (e.g., G. Brown in discussion of O'Hara and Yarwood, 1978, p. 456). Again many students of charnockite-granulite provinces in India see the granitic (charnockitic) component of migmatites as a direct product of crystallization of granitic magma in a granulite *P-T* regime; the magma thus invoked could be either (a) injected into the basic host (pyroxene granulite) or (b) formed more or less in place by deep-seated anatexis (for a summary of past and current ideas see Bhattacharyya, 1977, pp. 215-216).*

The second point of debate concerns the nature of geothermal gradients in Precambrian granulite metamorphism. It has been claimed, and with some justification, that the *P-T* regime of cordierite granulites (perhaps 3-4 kb, 700-800°C), implies an unusually high mean geothermal gradient for large sectors of the Precambrian crust—50-80° km^{-1}. But this view also has many critics among workers in Precambrian metamorphic geology. In a recent symposium, for example, gradients no higher than 20-30° km^{-1} were advocated for many, perhaps most Precambrian granulite terranes (cf. O'Hara and Yarwood, 1978; Watson, 1978).

Admittedly, then, a wide latitude of choice is open today with regard to pressure-temperature regimes in the Precambrian crust. Appearances of precision conveyed by numbers computed along sophisticated lines of modern geothermometry could be illusory. Powell's (1978) recent critical discussion of pyroxene and other geothermometers in this very context sounds a salutary note of caution.

Crustal Regime of the Eclogite Facies

Eclogites stand apart from other metamorphic rocks. No certain field transition has yet been demonstrated between the eclogite and any other facies. So one may ask whether the stability field of the eclogite facies is or has ever been encompassed by pressure-temperature regimes that develop in sectors of the deep crust. And if so what are the likely limits of pressure and temperature conducive to stable crystallization of eclogite assemblages in rocks of basaltic composition? Information bearing on such questions has been gleaned from these sources: the field environment of eclogites of proved crustal origin, mutual association of eclogitic with other mineral assemblages on the scale of a hand specimen or an outcrop, and experimental data on phase equilibria in basaltic systems at high pressure and temperature. These lines of evidence will be considered in turn.

In blueschist belts eclogites of a distinctive type ("Group C") are found

---

*This paper is a lucid review of the extensive work of Indian geologists on charnockites and related granulites in southern India, a region of repeated metamorphism with episodes dated at 3100-2500, 2300-2100, 1350, and 500 million years ago. The Madras charnockites date from the first episode, 2600 million years ago.

repeatedly as tectonic blocks along with other blocks of amphibolite and high-grade blueschist. It may fairly be inferred that in some sectors of the deeper crust the stability fields of all three facies may be mutually adjacent. In other words there is a strong probability that one part of the eclogite field extends to temperatures as low as 400–550°C at pressures perhaps no greater than 12–15 kb.

Although large-scale field transitions have yet to be demonstrated, there are hints of prograde blueschist → eclogite and amphibolite → eclogite sequences on the scale of a hand specimen, and in the mineralogy of certain rocks in which characteristic eclogitic phases such as omphacite, rutile, and garnet appear to be in textural equilibrium with other phases (hornblende, albite) that are alien to eclogites proper. Here too is a strong suggestion that the respective fields of blueschist, amphibolite, and eclogite facies impinge on one another.

Also on a small scale (microscopic to that of an outcrop) some eclogites have been shown to have formed directly from common crustal rocks—gabbros and basalts. And very rarely—as in the Sesia-Lanzo zone of the Alps—cofacial rocks containing quartz and almost pure jadeite have formed by metamorphism of crustal granodiorites. All such transitions have this in common—the parent materials and the eclogitic products alike are essentially anhydrous.

Finally evidence of retrograde reactions common in eclogites of Group C indicates that whatever may have been the path by which the parental rocks were brought into the eclogite field, the return journey was via the respective stability fields of the blueschist or the greenschist facies.

Most experimental work on phase equilibria in eclogitic and related systems has been directed toward problems of the petrology and geochemistry of the upper mantle. Some of the conclusions that have been reached by Green and Ringwood (1967) and others have been summarized elsewhere (I. S. E. Carmichael et al., 1974, pp. 628-630). The gist of them is that in anhydrous systems eclogite is stable with respect to pyroxene granulite at pressures above and temperatures below a curve with a rather flat positive slope (XY in Fig. 11-8) that passes through the two points 6 kb–500°C and 20 kb–1000°C. At moderate to high metamorphic temperatures (500° to perhaps 800°C) neither assemblage of course is stable in the typical aqueous metamorphic environment. Their place is taken there by amphibolite assemblages with hornblende and plagioclase or at temperatures higher than those of curve CD (Fig. 11-8) by a partially melted equivalent. In the absence of direct experimental data Fry and Fyfe (1969) have calculated a curve JZ for the amphibolite (eclogite + water) transition—which itself is metastable in the field of partial melting (i.e., from J to K).

None of the data are claimed to be precise. But they clearly demonstrate two points essential to our present problem. First that in a water-deficient environment eclogite is stable at high pressures (>10 kb) at rather low metamorphic temperatures (below 600°C). Second, in the presence of excess water eclogite is unstable over the whole range of pressure and temperature likely to be encountered even in the deep crust. Such facts were taken into account in depicting a diagrammatic field of the eclogite facies in Fig. 11-1. How then may a water-deficient environment develop in the deeper crust at pressures and temperatures not far from or even overlapping those of the blueschist and the amphibolite facies?

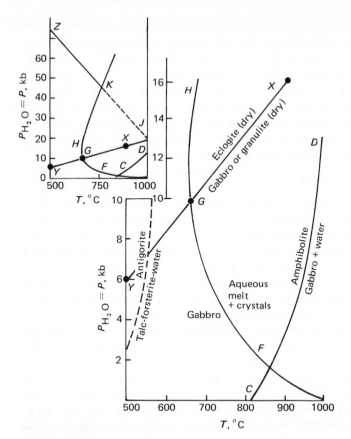

FIGURE 11-8

Phase relationship bearing on stability field of eclogite assemblages. XY, gabbro–eclogite transition (after D. H. Green and A. E. Ringwood, 1967). FH, curve of incipient melting of gabbro with excess water (after H. S. Yoder and C. E. Tilley, 1962, and I. B. Lambert and P. J. Wyllie, 1968; taken from N. Fry and W. S. Fyfe, 1969). CD, amphibolite–gabbro transition (after C. E. Tilley and H. S. Yoder, 1962).

One answer comes from a study of the rocks themselves: relatively anhydrous rocks such as basalt or granite in some cases appear to have been transported downward too rapidly to have become hydrated on the way. They may thus reach an environment deep enough for metamorphism into eclogitic assemblages, provided there is no significant access to water at the site of metamorphism (in the presence of water they would have yielded blueschist or amphibolitic assemblages). Other possible situations conducive to development of eclogite have been tentatively suggested by Fry and Fyfe (1969, pp. 4, 5). Even partially hydrated basaltic materials, possibly amphibolite itself, could become dehydrated to eclogitic phase assemblages if they were surrounded by or closely adjacent to a domain in which a buffering reaction kept f_{H_2O} continuously at a low level. One such water buffer could be

Olivine + pyroxene + water $\rightleftharpoons$ serpentine

Serpentine minerals have a high vapor pressure (i.e., affinity for water) compared with amphiboles. The serpentinizing reaction could be effective, of course, only within the stability field of antigorite—at 10 kb perhaps $<500°C$ (cf. Fig. 4-11). Development of omphacite in serpentinite might be explained this way.

To sum up, there seems little doubt that eclogites of crustal origin (Group C), can develop at pressures above about 10 kb in the low–medium range of metamorphic temperature ($<600°C$). An essential condition is low f_{H_2O}, whether engendered by the anhydrous condition of the parent system or by buffering reactions of hydration in the surrounding environment.

Bathograds and Bathozones

Over forty years ago D. S. Korzhinskii (1937) proposed a scheme to relate metamorphic parageneses to depth in terms of mineral assemblages developed at high temperatures in carbonate rocks (with $P_{CO_2} = P$). Each of his proposed "depth facies" covered the whole range of metamorphic temperature within some limited range of pressure (depth). Thus his larnite-merwinite and gehlenite-monticellite facies represent metamorphism at very shallow depth. His Aldan facies, named after the granulite terranes of the Aldan massif, defines a deep zone in which high pressure prohibits development of wollastonite but permits formation of forsterite and diopside in dolomitic limestones. Korzhinskii's system of depth facies was never adopted in western countries (cf. Turner, 1948, pp. 60, 101). Much later a hint of something akin to Korzhinskii's basic idea appears in J. B. Thompson and Norton's summary of Appalachian metamorphism (Zen et al., 1968, pp. 319–327). Across the metamorphic province in New England, they drew a sweeping albeit somewhat generalized boundary, cutting mapped isograds at all angles, to delimit two areas respectively marked by sporadic presence and complete absence of andalusite in pelitic schists. The boundary so drawn, in a region where metamorphic temperatures varied widely, has isobaric implications; for it separates pressure regions respectively below and above the invariant Al_2SiO_5 triple point.

D. M. Carmichael (1978) has now enlarged and elaborated this concept to cover possible pressure relations among selected commonly observed mineral combinations in metapelites of the amphibolite facies. The individual phases are 10 in number: quartz, K-feldspar, sodic plagioclase, muscovite, biotite, staurolite, garnet, kyanite, sillimanite, and andalusite. The whole comprehensive "system" has seven components (SiO_2, Al_2O_3, K_2O, Na_2O, FeO, MgO, and H_2O) exclusive of CaO and minor "impurities" whose influence on the phase assemblages seems to be insignificant. Individual critical equilibria are simpler, the extreme case being kyanite $\rightleftharpoons$ sillimanite (one component, two phases, univariant). Recognized univariant equilibria intersect in invariant points; and five of these, including the Al_2SiO_5 triple point, are considered by Carmichael to be significant for present purposes. Collectively they cover a pressure range of 2–7 kb, within which each invariant point could be a potentially precise index of pressures. All have been calibrated, with varying precision, by means of combined experimental and thermodynamic data.

Each invariant point separates two critical assemblages (having no phase in

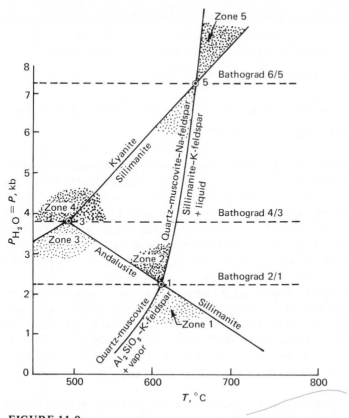

FIGURE 11-9
Bathograds passing through invariant points 1, 3, and 5 in the more comprehensive model (five invariant points) of D. M. Carmichael (1978, Fig. 2).

common) stable respectively above and below the corresponding pressure. Three such points are shown in Fig. 11-9 (with fields of critical phase assemblages stippled). Above point 1 sillimanite-muscovite takes the place of the low-pressure assemblage andalusite-muscovite. Point 3 separates the respective pressure fields of (kyanite ⇌ sillimanite) and andalusite, as mapped in the field by J. B. Thompson and Norton. Point 5 is the basis for allocating kyanite granulites (with kyanite-K-feldspar-quartz) to the realm of high pressure above ~7 kb (cf. Turner, 1968, p. 359; Scharbert and Kurat, 1974, pp. 126–127).

Carmichael's invariant equilibria are as follows (pressure increasing from left to right and in numerical order):

(1) K-feldspar + andalusite + vapor ⇌ quartz + muscovite + sillimanite

$$P_{H_2O} = P = 2.2 \text{ kbars}$$

(2) Biotite + garnet + andalusite + vapor ⇌ quartz + muscovite + staurolite

+ sillimanite $P_{H_2O} = P = 3.5$ kbars

(3) Andalusite $\rightleftharpoons$ kyanite + sillimanite $P = 3.8$ kb

(4) Quartz + muscovite + staurolite + sillimanite $\rightleftharpoons$ biotite + garnet

    + kyanite + vapor $P_{H_2O} = P = 5.5$ kb*

(5) Quartz + Na-feldspar + muscovite + sillimanite $\rightleftharpoons$ K-feldspar + kyanite

    + granitic liquid $P_{H_2O} = P = 7.1$ kb

Each reaction involves ($n + 2$) phases in an n-component system within the comprehensive "system" of 7 components. Strictly the invariant condition requires that compositions of all participating phases be constant, and identical moreover with those used in experimental calibration. To the extent that this may not be true, application of Carmichael's model to specific provinces is subject to corresponding uncertainty. Note that as more precise experimental data become available other possible invariant points involving other phases (e.g., cordierite) could be introduced into Carmichael's scheme.

If an invariant point is to be located within half a kilobar—which is necessary in Carmichael's treatment—the relevant univariant curves must intersect at a fairly high angle. Once again we must rely heavily on the kyanite $\rightleftharpoons$ sillimanite curve, for this (with a well-established slope $dT/dP \approx 50°$ kb^{-1}) is strongly oblique to hydration-dehydration curves, which, above about 4 kb, have a much steeper slope ($dT/dP \approx 8$–$15°$ kb^{-1}). Much less reliable is the slope of the andalusite $\rightleftharpoons$ sillimanite inversion curve.

A generally applicable sequence of *bathozones*, numbered in order of increasing pressure, has been founded on observed critical assemblages respectively permitted (listed below) and precluded within limits of pressure prescribed by each of the five invariant points. Other assemblages that may be present in no way affect the bathozonal scheme, which thus utilizes a minimum quantity of mineralogical data.

1. Below point 1: K-feldspar-andalusite
2. Between points 1 and 2: quartz-muscovite-sillimanite; biotite-garnet-andalusite
3. Between points 2 and 3: quartz-muscovite-staurolite-sillimanite; andalusite
4. Between points 3 and 4: kyanite $\rightleftharpoons$ sillimanite; quartz-muscovite-staurolite-sillimanite
5. Between points 4 and 5: biotite-garnet-kyanite; quartz-Na-feldspar-muscovite-sillimanite
6. Above point 5: K-feldspar-kyanite (plus granitic material)

To map bathozones on a regional scale (the objective of Carmichael's approach) the distribution of all the above critical assemblages is plotted from available records. Lines separating the zones so delineated have been termed *bathograds*. Each is designated by a pair of numerals representing the two zones that it separates. Thus bathograd 4/3, the common boundary between zones 4 and 3, is the low-pressure limit of kyanite $\rightleftharpoons$ sillimanite as mapped in New England by Thompson and Norton (slightly modified in Fig. 11-10*a*).

---

*Value as revised by D. M. Carmichael (personal communication to H. C. Helgeson).

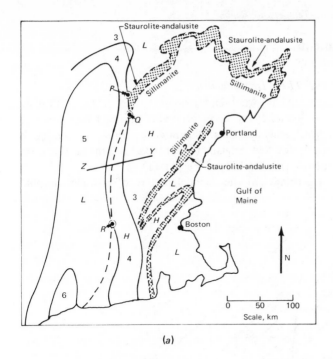

(a)

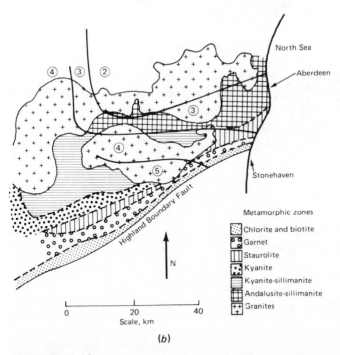

(b)

FIGURE 11-10

Pelitic bathozones (after D. M. Carmichael, 1978), numbered as in text, in relation to pelitic isograds (dashed). (a) New England: staurolite zone stippled; L and H, respectively, denote areas of lower and of higher grade with respect to isograds for staurolite-andalusite and inversion of andalusite to sillimanite; (b) Barrovian sector, northeast Dalradian, Scotland; metamorphic zones, isograds, and outlines of granite plutons after G. A. Chinner, 1966 (slightly modified by M. P. Atherton, 1977); bathograds, full lines; isograds, dashed.

Bathograds, *P-T* Gradients, and Metamorphic Regimes

Geometric Relations and Their Implications

The geometric relations between bathograds and isograds in the same region provide interesting material (not yet exploited) to be incorporated into regional models of *P-T* regimes. Here are several generalizations, illustrated by two of Carmichael's bathozonal maps—respectively for New England (Fig. 11-10*a*) and the northeastern sector of the Scottish Dalradian (Fig. 11-10*b*, cf. Fig. 11-11).

1. A bathozonal map brings out the regional pattern of postmetamorphic

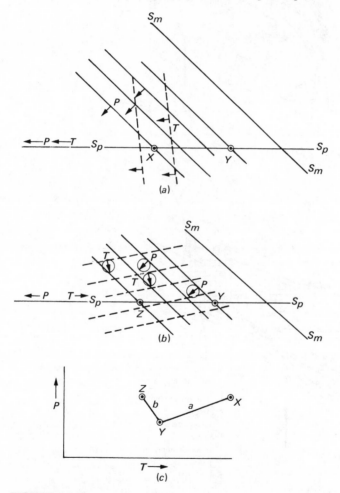

FIGURE 11-11

Vertical sections normal to mean trend of acutely intersecting or parallel isograds and bathograds to illustrate two of several possible alternatives relating field gradients of *P* and *T* on present erosion surface S_p to geometry of metamorphic thermal doming and postmetamorphic tilting (doming) of the erosion surface S_m at the time of metamorphism. (*a*) Postmetamorphic tilting (upward toward left) coincides with thermal doming (in the same sense). (*b*) Thermal doming (toward right) is in the opposite sense to structural tilting (upward toward left). (*c*) Slopes of *P-T* field gradients *YX*, *YZ* corresponding, respectively, to (*a*) and (*b*).

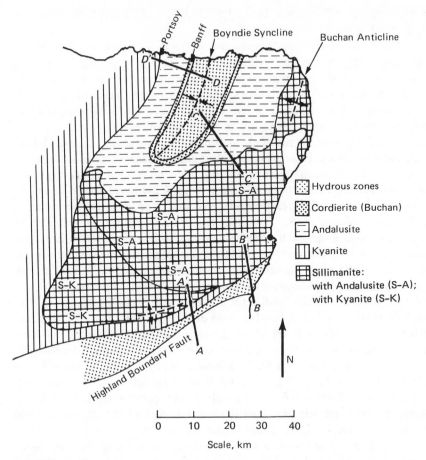

FIGURE 11-12

Isograd and zonal pattern in the northeastern Dalradian (slightly simplified after B. Harte, 1975) showing sites of Harte's field gradients lettered *AA′, BB′, CC′, DD′* as in Fig. 11-13. Main structures dashed: BS, Boyndie Syncline; BA, Buchan Anticline; HBF, Highland Boundary Fault. Like most maps of zoning in the northeast Dalradian that have appeared in the past decade, the essential pattern is that of Chinner's earlier map (Chinner, 1966, p. 163) which itself incorporates the classic work of Barrow, Tilley, and Read.

folding and differential uplift; it shows the present configuration of successive depth levels at the time of metamorphism. In other words it separates out the effects of postmetamorphic from various episodes of pre- and synmetamorphic deformation. Thus in Fig. 11-10*a* the elongate lobe comprising zones 4 to 6 in the western sector reveals a postmetamorphic anticlinal structure plunging NNE— in complete accord with the structural picture of that part of the Appalachians developed by conventional mapping (Rodgers, 1970, p. 114; cf. D. M. Carmichael, 1978, p. 784). The bathograd trend along the western margin of the Buchan zones in the northeastern Dalradian of Scotland (D. M. Carmichael, 1978, Fig. 7) conforms to a broad postmetamorphic synclinal structure (plunging gently southwest), the Boyndie syncline (cf. Fig. 11-12), that figures prominently in literature on metamorphism and structure in the Highlands (e.g., Chinner, 1966; Atherton, 1977, p. 337, Fig. 5).

2. Regionally parallel bathograds and medium- to high-grade dehydration isograds (essentially isothermals) with grade and pressure increasing in the same sense are consistent with a simple regime of metamorphism controlled by depth. This could be the situation in the lawsonite zone of New Caledonia, where out-crops of stratigraphic horizons and successive levels of depth are equivalent to bathograds. Other geometric relations, however, are possible, e.g., postmetamorphic uptilting coinciding with the site of metamorphic thermal doming (cf. Fig. 11-11a).

3. More generally bathograds and dehydration isograds (near-isothermals) intersect obliquely, indicating postmetamorphic flexure, or thermal doming in the sense of increasing grade, or both. Except perhaps in extreme geologic situations, temperature and pressure increase simultaneously with depth below any point on the synmetamorphic surface S_m. Yet grade and pressure need not increase sympa-thetically in traverses across the present erosion surface S_p, even where these are drawn normal to the trend of acutely intersecting isograds and bathograds. Thus, in Fig. 11-10a, grade increases and pressure falls from Z to Y. Such a situa-tion can arise where postmetamorphic downtilting coincides on the map with a site of metamorphic thermal doming (in the sense of increasing grade). It is illus-trated diagrammatically in Fig. 11-11b. Again in Barrow's zones of the northeastern Dalradian, Carmichael's bathograds and the classic isograds intersect at an acute angle, grade increasing and pressure decreasing in a general northward sense (Fig. 11-10b). This is consistent with W. Q. Kennedy's (1948, p. 231) "thermal anti-cline" toward the north, combined with uptilting, as advocated by some geologists, along the Highland Boundary Fault. It should be noted, however, that opinion on the geometry of thermal-structural relations in this part of the Highlands is still divided (cf. Atherton, 1977, Fig. 5, and related discussion).

4. Any point of intersection of a bathograd and a near-isothermal isograd gives the local value of the mean geothermal gradient at that point. The 4/3 bathograd that limits the andalusite field in New England obliquely intersects the staurolite and then the first sillimanite isograd some 20 km to the south, at P and at Q in the state of Vermont (Fig. 11-10a). From the points of intersection of Carmichael's 4/3 datum (3.8 kb) upon the respective curves for entry of staurolite and sillimanite (curves A and G, Fig. 11-6), computed mean geothermal gradients are 40 degr km^{-1} at P and 48 degr km^{-1} at Q. Similarly, an intersection of the 5/4 bathograd (5.5 kb) with the sillimanite isograd in Massachusetts (at R) gives a computed mean geothermal gradient of 30° km^{-1}. These are shown as dashed segments P, Q, and R in Fig. 11-14. Available oxygen-isotope temperatures for Vermont staurolite zone schists (545–595°C; Garlick and Epstein, 1967), com-bined with pressures on the 4/3 bathograd yield similar values—42 ± 2° km^{-1}. And again the value computed from oxygen-isotope temperatures in the sillimanite zone near the 5/4 bathograd in Dutchess County, New York, near lower left corner of Fig. 11-10a would be significantly lower no greater than 32° km^{-1}. The second intersection (equivalent to the triple point) defines a gradient $dT/dP = 550/(3.8 \times 3.5) = 41°$ km^{-1}; at the staurolite intersection, the gradient is somewhat lower: $dT/dP = 490/(3.8 \times 3.5) = 37°$ km^{-1}.

5. D. M. Carmichael (1978, Fig. 2) compares some of the standard types of facies series proposed by Miyashiro (1961) and elaborated by Hietanen (1967) in terms of corresponding mean geothermal gradients at some common temperature (say, 650°C or 750°C) representing the maximum grade. (It is emphasized again that these are not metamorphic field gradients as registered on the erosion surface.) Some of his evaluations are as follows:

At 650°C: Abukuma type (Japan type of Hietanen) $dT/dP > 80°$ km^{-1}; Buchan type, $dT/dP < 80°$ km^{-1}, $>55°$ km^{-1}; Barrovian type, $dT/dP < 40°$ km^{-1}, $>25°$ km^{-1}

At 750°C: Saxon type (e.g., Moldanubian kyanite granulites) $dT/dP < 30°$

Barrovian and Buchan Gradients Reevaluated

Since Read (1952) first distinguished between a Barrovian and a Buchan pattern of metamorphism in the Scottish Dalradian, these have figured as standards for comparison in later and more elaborate schemes to represent facies series and supposedly global types of metamorphic regime by some form of *P-T* gradient (e.g., Miyashiro, 1961; Hietanen, 1967; Turner, 1968, p. 359). It is appropriate, then, to conclude our discussion by returning to the original scene to see what progress has been made in sharpening the picture of the Barrovian and Buchan regimes. What is their definitive character in terms of pressure and temperature? What is the basis of quantitative evaluation underlying each of the numerous gradients that have been proposed? How are the two contemporaneous patterns related to each other? [For the type localities in the northeastern Dalradian—(see Fig. 11-12)—are only 50 km apart.]

Some of the gradients that have been proposed in the past two decades are reproduced in Fig. 11-13. The various curves are all tentative generalized gradients drawn to reflect the individual authors' views of facies in relation to pressure and temperature (cf. Fig. 11-1), some with a superficial background of first-hand experience in the Dalradian field. Some curves, notably 3 and 4, might represent ideal uniform geothermal gradients; the others are generalized field gradients, those of the present author at least (1, 6, 8) drawn without much heed to possible implications of curvature regarding thermal "doming" or "depression." They pointed the way toward a line of inquiry; but in them we are not likely to find clear answers to the questions just posed.

Turning now to gradients that have been put forward during the last dozen years by writers with considerable experience in the Dalradian field (cf. Atherton, 1977, pp. 358-363): all are presented as field gradients; but most of them are rectilinear and project back to surface *P* and *T*, thereby implying a uniform geothermal gradient within the limited sectors of the Dalradian that they depict. All are quantified to some degree by points calibrated for *P* and *T* with reference to "accepted" curves for appropriate phase equilibria—entry of staurolite, the kyanite ⇌ sillimanite inversion, the Al_2SiO_5 triple point, the initial breakdown of quartz-muscovite to sillimanite plus K-feldspar. Mutual discrepancies hinge mainly on personal preference (and temporarily prevailing fashion) for alternative calibrations of these equilibria.

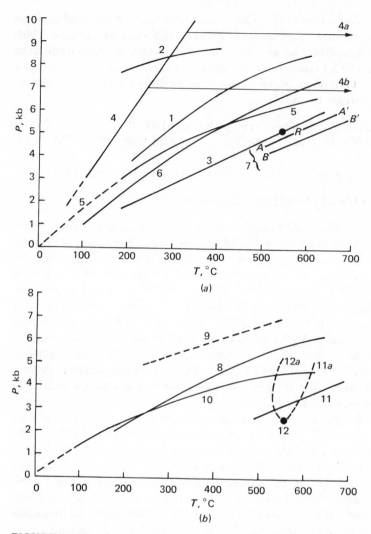

FIGURE 11-13

Various *P-T* gradients proposed for (*a*) the Barrovian, (*b*) the Buchan facies series, northeastern Dalradian, Scotland; letters *AA'*, *BB'* correspond to section lines in Fig. 11-12: 1 and 8 (Fyfe et al., 1958, Figs. 107 and 108); 2 and 9 (Miyashiro, 1961, Fig. 4); 3 (MacNamara, 1965); 4 (Chinner, 1966); 5 and 10 (Hietanen, 1967, Fig. 1); 6 (Turner, 1968, p. 359, 363); 7, 11, and 11a (Harte, 1975, Fig. 2b; (see also Atherton, 1977, Fig. 6); 12 and 12a (Turner, this book); *R* (evaluated by Richardson and Powell, 1976).

The most influential essay, perhaps, has been that of Chinner (1966). He postulated a chronologic break between the main metamorphic imprint and a somewhat later thermal overprinting responsible for widespread crystallization of sillimanite. (This concept has subsequently been sustained for the Buchan region; but its applicability to Barrow's sillimanite zone is still debated.) Curve 4 in Fig. 11-13 shows Chinner's model diagrammatically: the full line is a uniform geothermal gradient representing the regime during the first (main) episode; horizontal lines join it to a series of points (arrow heads) representing the sillimanite overprint. There are other interesting aspects of Chinner's model; e.g., he shows obliquely intersecting hypothetical isothermals and isobars in the Barrovian region (1966, Fig. 8), and a hypothetical field gradient (1966, Fig. 5*b*, *abc*; see also pp. 183 and 184 for discussion) with a steep negative slope across the kyanite and sillimanite zones. Chinner's quantitative evaluation unfortunately is marred by location of the Al_2SiO_5 triple point at the impossibly high pressure then fashionable (~8 kb at ~300°C), and of the quartz-muscovite breakdown about 100° above today's generally accepted values.

Harte (1975) drew a series of field gradients for limited profiles, 10–15 km long, (*AA'*, *BB'*, and so on, in Fig. 11-12) across the isograd trends in the Barrovian and Buchan regions. They are carefully calibrated against a "petrogenic grid," in which, however, the Al_2SiO_5 triple point is placed $1\frac{1}{2}$ kb higher and the quartz-muscovite breakdown (following A. B. Thompson's, 1974, computed curve) at somewhat higher temperature than values used in this book.

Curves 7, Barrovian (cf. Fig. 1-12): $A \rightarrow A'$ northward, a little east of Barrow's map; $B \rightarrow B'$ northward from Stonehaven, east coast

Curves 11 and 11*a*, Buchan: 11, *CC'*, southeastward with grade increasing, Read's type area; 11*a*, *DD'*, westward, with increasing grade, south of Portsoy, Moray Firth, from Buchan zones into Barrovian (kyanite zone)

To fit the equilibrium values here adopted, the typical Buchan paragenesis andalusite-staurolite-quartz-muscovite has here been relocated at point 12; and from this a tentative field gradient across the Buchan-Barrovian transition near Portsoy (alternative to Harte's 11*a*) has been projected as 12*a*.

A single point in the Barrovian region, calibrated by Richardson and Powell (1976) stands out as what seems to be the most precisely established datum of the *P–T* regime. It is located at 5 kb, 535°C (point *R*, Fig. 11-13*a*), and represents a level low down in the Dalradian inside the almandine isograd. Richardson and Powell see the Barrovian regime in this area as controlled by a uniform steady-state linear geothermal gradient, 30° km^{-1}, which thus would also represent the field gradient in this vicinity.

To return now to our original question: what, according to current opinion of those most familiar with the scene, are the definitive characteristics of the respective *P–T* regimes of Barrovian and Buchan metamorphism? Field gradients, although representing an essential preliminary step, will not provide a full or unequivocal answer; for their configurations depend upon local variations within the regional regime along the chosen profiles. The answer must lie in the range of mean geothermal gradients that collectively covers all the local data (i.e., the field gradients). Fig. 11-14 presents such a picture conforming to the better-documented data of Fig. 11-13. Each facies series could be within the corresponding spectrum there presented: between 28° km^{-1} and 33° km^{-1} for the Barrovian, between 45° km^{-1} and 60° km^{-1} for the Buchan series. There is considerable latitude in each. So, while Fig. 11-14 appears to differentiate rather sharply between the two patterns, it must be emphasized that this conclusion applies to two particular

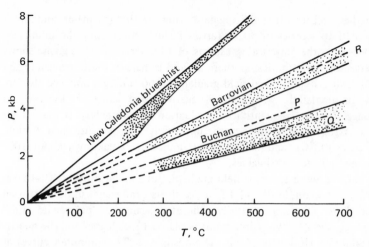

FIGURE 11-14
Probable limits of geothermal gradients for Barrovian and Buchan facies series, Dalradian, Scotland (based on selected data from Fig. 11-13). Densely stippled area indicates my preference for Buchan regime; dashed lines are local gradients at P, Q, and R in Fig. 11-10a (New England). Tentatively proposed regime for blueschist metamorphism, New Caledonia, shown for comparison.

facies series in particular locations. They represent regimes of Paleozoic metamorphism during the Grampian orogeny as it is recorded in the Scottish Dalradian. Clearly to transfer the same names to other regimes or types of regime elsewhere is unwarranted, or at least hazardous procedure. Note for example three estimated partial gradients for traverses across the staurolite and sillimanite isograds in New England (P, Q, and R, Fig. 11-10a); for these have been classified by some as "Barrovian" in character.

Progress as Seen in Retrospect

It is the fundamental significance of metamorphic gradients rather than success so far achieved in their evaluation that justifies so lengthy a treatment of the subject. What has been accomplished so far is to grasp the complexity and variety of a central problem once perceived in such simple terms by Becke and Grubermann (pp. 49–53); to demonstrate the nature of potentially fruitful lines of future investigation; to show what sort of data are needed; and to present tentative numerical solutions to subsidiary questions (especially regarding pressure-temperature gradients of various kinds) in selected cases (specific facies series). Perhaps we have indeed outgrown the simple proposition of Becke and Grubermann, but they pointed the way for subsequent development of ideas on the role of depth in regional metamorphism. This debt is implicit in the statement that closes D. M. Carmichael's (1978, p. 793) recent essay:

Ideally the mapping of bathograds should provide a means of "filtering out" the effects of temperature and of bulk composition on metamorphic grade, so that the effect of pressure can be clearly perceived. . . . Tentatively it may be anticipated that bathozones and bathograds may come to serve the same purpose that Grubenmann's (1910) "depth-zone" classification of metamorphic grade[*] was mistakenly thought to serve.

REGIONAL METAMORPHISM IN RELATION TO OROGENY, PLUTONISM, AND TIME

Statement of a Complex Problem

At the conclusion of an earlier discussion it was stated (Turner and Verhoogen, 1960, p. 669) that

> large-scale crustal deformation (alpine folding), batholithic intrusion, and regional metamorphism are geographically associated, broadly synchronous, but partially independent manifestations of thermal (and mechanical?) disturbances in the mantle, not in the crust.

Viewed in the light of this statement, the *P-T* gradients inferred from any individual facies series, or the *P-T* regime deduced from the zonal distribution of facies in a metamorphic terrane, give some indication regarding the magnitude of a correlated thermal disturbance in the deep crust and the underlying mantle. To relate the thermal aspect of metamorphism to geographically associated orogeny and plutonism (intrusion of granite batholiths, development of migmatite complexes), it is necessary to explore the possible relations of all three, not only in space, but also in time.

Two decades ago, we closed a discussion of metamorphic facies (Fyfe, Turner, and Verhoogen, 1968, pp. 237-239) by setting up some hypothetical gradients of regional metamorphism with the purpose of raising some essential questions still requiring an answer.

> In regional metamorphism the temperature distribution and the pressure-temperature relationship are determined partly by depth, partly by the rate of supply of heat [from the focus of thermal disturbance in the depths], and partly by the rate and nature of the metamorphic reactions themselves. . . . It is conceivable that the temperature at a given depth might fluctuate in time. . . . Transition from one facies to the next might be effected at constant pressure. The gradients shown for regional metamorphism of the Buchan and Barrovian types are drawn arbitrarily in Figure 108 [curves 8 and 1, Fig. 11-13].
>
> In spite of their highly speculative nature Figures 107 and 108 [and the same may be said of Figs. 11-1, 11-5 and 11-6 in this book] illustrate the kind of relations that must exist between facies. If they

---

[*]Grubenmann's book, as the title shows, was concerned with *rocks* (mineral assemblages), not with metamorphic *grades* that the rocks imply. It was rocks that he set out to codify in terms of known chemical compositions and assumed depth of crystallization.

emphasize the imperfection of present knowledge they also serve to show where additional field, petrographic and experimental data are most needed. Relations in the right-hand portion of the diagrams, where fields of several facies impinge on the field of granitic magmas, raise questions such as these: What are the general relations of granulites to granites? ... What is the significance of the cordierite and hornblende granulites? Is the broad transition field between granulites and pyroxene hornfelses (at pressures between 4 and 7 kilobars in Figure 107) commonly attained in nature? Along the low temperature border ... the tentative disposition of facies boundaries raises yet other questions: Is low-grade regional metamorphism commonly the result of deep burial alone? Should not progressive regional metamorphism in some cases lead to metamorphic zones characterized by glaucophane schists, greenschists and amphibolites in order of increasing grade?

To some of these questions, especially those relating to low-grade metamorphism, tentative answers (by no means always in agreement) have been offered. Low-grade metamorphism in limited regions certainly can be attributed to simultaneous rise in temperature and pressure along "normal" geothermal gradients during progressive burial. A similar situation has been the dominant influence in regions where mean geothermal gradients at various points on the present surface coincide and surface gradients dT/dP are essentially rectilinear. Elsewhere at the high-grade end of the field gradient temperatures are too low (blueschist facies) or too high (granulite facies) to conform to what are generally accepted normal gradients in the modern crust. There is no longer any question that in the low-grade field widespread regional metamorphism can occur without accompanying penetrative strain sufficient to induce schistosity.

In the region of high temperature and pressure the picture is more obscure. Some of the old questions remain unanswered. But on the whole the mutual relations of metamorphic crystallization, large-scale deformation, and emplacement of large bodies of granitic rock have become clarified. This we owe especially to two relatively new lines of approach, both involving detailed field work amplified by use of newer techniques in the laboratory. One is radiometric dating of critical stages in crystallization of metamorphic minerals and of granitic rocks. The other is study of metamorphic textures with a view to relating episodes of crystallization to episodes of deformation (folding) as revealed by statistical analysis of tectonite fabrics.

Time Relations between Metamorphic Crystallization, Deformation, and Granite Plutonism

Criteria of Deformational History

The strain history of a deformed rock mass is recorded in successive generations of *s*-surfaces (bedding, foliation, etc.) and the geometry of their fold patterns. It is usually possible to recognize in any large domain, or even in a single outcrop, several episodes of folding. These are conventionally designated F_1, F_2, and so on.

Within any large domain, there are usually smaller domains that are homogeneous with respect to geometry and style of small-scale folds. In such a domain it is possible to determine the geometry, especially the mean attitude of fold axes, B, of folds of the same generation (say, F_2) as developed in preexisting s-surfaces. Thus bedding S is found to be folded about an axis B_{S_1}; and a foliation S_2 is synchronously folded about an axis B_{S_2}, whose attitude usually is inclined to that of B_{S_1}. If at the same time, a new cleavage S_3 has developed parallel to the axial planes of folds in S_2, the axis of these folds may be designated more precisely as $B_{S_2}^{S_3}$. The strain history of any domain whose fabric is homogeneous may be worked out by statistical treatment of many measured attitudes of linear and planar elements: lineations, fold axes, segments of s-surfaces, optical directions and cleavage or twin planes in crystals, and so on. This is the method of fabric analysis (*Gefügekunde*), first developed by Sander (1930, 1948, 1950). It has been described in English, with some modifications, additions, and illustrative examples, in books by Turner and Weiss (1963) and J. G. Ramsay (1967). The nomenclature employed here is that of Turner and Weiss.

The history of deformation in most metamorphic regions that have been studied in this way (among them the Alps, the Highlands of Scotland, and the Otago and Alpine schist zones of New Zealand) typically commences with large-scale recumbent folding of bedding and of whole stratigraphic units, culminating in overthrusting and nappe development. This is followed by one or more episodes of folding on a smaller scale, each affecting any of the s-surfaces—notably, foliations and segregation laminae—that may have formed during previous episodes. The latest manifestation is likely to be strain-slip cleavage or a generation of small-scale kinks in plane-foliated rocks. Correlated microscopic phenomena are lamellar twinning in calcite and dolomite, kinking of mica crystals, and appearance of swarms of "deformation lamellae" in quartz.

Crystallization in Relation to Episodes of Deformation

From the first, as he developed his philosophy and method of fabric analyses, Sander (e.g., 1950, pp. 295–306) related the crystallization of the constituent minerals of deformed rocks to periods of deformation recorded in recognizable s-surfaces and folds. With reference to a particular episode of deformation, he classed crystallization as pre-, syn- (para-), or posttectonic. The principal criteria employed are textural. Clearly, a crystal of mica that has been bent into partial alignment with a strain-slip cleavage S_3 is pretectonic with respect to that particular structure. Conversely, an albite porphyroblast that crosses and encloses microfolds in S_2 is posttectonic in relation to S_2. By far the most general situation is one in which tabular and prismatic crystals tend to be aligned in the various s-surfaces and lineations but themselves lack any evidence of strain. And in such rocks, unstrained and more or less equant grains of quartz, calcite, or feldspar show no obvious relation to any s-surface. Here there are two possibilities: the grain fabric may have developed simultaneously with, or subsequently to, the last major episode of deformation.

In the various attempts that have been made during the past two decades to correlate changing P-T conditions with the successive episodes of folding, perhaps too much weight has been assigned to textural details as the principal criterion of a period of crystallization. Although important in relation to history of textural development, the mutual relations between grain boundaries are less significant with respect to our present problem. Considering the whole assemblage of phases seen in a microsection as a system in equilibrium, we must ask, "At what point in the tectonic history of the rock was that assemblage as a whole 'frozen in' as we now see it?" It is to this point in time that we may assign the P-T regime inferred from mineralogical criteria. The porphyroblasts of kyanite and staurolite; the large "cross biotites" cutting the principal foliation S; the crystals of quartz, micas, and feldspars aligned in S; and the grains of similar and other minerals enclosed in the porphyroblast, are considered as a unit. This unit reflects the P-T conditions appropriate to the whole assemblage. The texture shows that these have outlasted the episode of deformation responsible for S; but judging from the rapidity of experimental annealing and grain growth, the interval of time so expressed may be insignificant.

Throughout this book we have paid little attention to disequilibrium in meta-morphic phase assemblages. Departures from equilibrium obvious enough to be recognized beneath the microscope nevertheless are common. And the partial development of a new assemblage (evidence of a P-T change in time) can usually be related to some stage in the strain history of the rock. Particularly instructive are recognizably retrogressive changes on the microscopic scale. Local chloritiza-tion of biotite and garnet on cleavage surfaces place the development of these in a regime of waning temperature, postdating the metamorphic event expressed by the main assemblage. Such changes, accompanied by a decrease in grain size and development of new platelets of chlorite and muscovite, may ultimately produce a rock of phyllitic aspect—a phyllonite (E. B. Knopf, 1931)—whose fabric is dominated by the latest s-surface and whose essential mineralogy is that of a low-grade facies. But relict, partially destroyed grains of staurolite and garnet may still survive as evidence of a preceding episode of higher temperature. Then there are regions such as the western Alps (Bearth, 1962) and eastern India (A. B. Roy, 1966) where retrogressive changes are most obvious on the macroscopic scale.

Most valuable on a large scale is the relation, or lack of it, between isograd patterns and structural trends of major stratigraphic units. It has been found repeatedly, especially where high topographic relief facilitates observation on a large scale, that the pattern of isograds and isogradic surfaces is simpler than that of the large-scale structures. The two generally appear to be totally independent; and the P-T regime expressed by the zones of progressive metamorphism must have been imprinted late in the tectonic history; later, at any rate, than the initial period of large-scale folding and nappe development.

While the mineralogical imprint of metamorphism very commonly appears to have outlasted the main phases of deformation with which it is spatially asso-ciated, this is not invariably the case. In an area of 150 km^2 in the Precambrian of India mapped by Naha (1962), biotite, garnet, and staurolite isograds faithfully follow the trend of major first-generation folds in twice-folded metasediments. Much more commonly, the structural and associated posttectonic isogradic pattern developed during an orogenic cycle have both been disturbed, sometimes much later, by unrelated simple regional flexures and dislocations. This we have seen in the Appalachians, the eastern Dalradian, and the western border of the Haast Schist block adjoining the Alpine Fault in New Zealand. Such late postmetamorphic disturbance can be perfectly mirrored in the configuration of bathograds (cf. Fig. 11-10).

Relations in the Northeastern Dalradian, Scotland

Nowhere has the complexity of possible chronologic relationships and repeated interplay between episodic deformation, bursts of plutonic activity, and regional metamorphism been more clearly demonstrated than in Barrow's classic ground—the northeastern sector of the Scottish Dalradian (cf. Atherton, 1977). Here broad chronologic relationships—as in many other provinces—were established on classic lines mainly by field mapping. In the Dalradian, the Newer Granite plutons have long been recognized on structural grounds as posttectonic. Their cross-cutting contacts have no relation to even the late-generation fold patterns in the country rock. They are also late with respect to crystallization; for they have generated their own aureoles, superimposed upon the local mineral paragenesis of regional metamorphism. Moreover, their distribution is not obviously related to the broad pattern of Barrow's zones. The Older Granite complexes, on the other hand, include gneissic rocks that have been affected at least by the later episodes of deformation. Contacts with metamorphic rocks tend to be gradational and structurally conformable. Local contact aureoles have seldom been recognized. Finally there is a tendency for the Older Granite complexes to be located in zones of high-grade regional metamorphism, even though the isograds do not, as in much of New England, wrap conformably round the exposed granite contacts.

In most orogenic belts granitic magmas play virtually the solo role in plutonism coeval with regional metamorphism; but rarely, as in the northeastern Dalradian a local part must be assigned as well to intrusion of basaltic magma.

The comprehensive picture of metamorphism, deformation, and plutonism in the Grampian orogeny has been clarified and elaborated by extensive radiometric dating (K/A and Rb/Sr). The total time span is perhaps 150 million years, covering late Cambrian to early Devonian times. The full sequence of events (Bell, 1968; Dewey and Parkhurst, 1970; Atherton, 1977, pp. 355–356, 351, 363–366), which we recently summarized with emphasis on granite plutonism (I. S. E. Carmichael et al., 1974, pp. 583–589) briefly is as follows:

1. Emplacement of premetamorphic granitic plutons—one type of the classic Older Granites; late Cambrian (550×10^6 years).
2. Three episodes of folding (F_1–F_3) in quick succession. These comprise the "climactic" episode of the Grampian orogeny and fall within a span of 30 million years (510–480×10^6 years). The regional mineralogical imprint dates mainly from a static period following the F_2 episode; but it was modified later by overprinting of sillimanite growth and development of migmatite complexes (Older Granites) after the F_3 folding. Still later followed localized retrograde changes. Contrary to earlier views, Buchan metamorphism in the north is now

thought to be coeval with Barrovian to the south in the eastern Dalradian (cf. Atherton, 1977, p. 336). Most of the foliated Older Granite plutons and migmatite complexes belong to or somewhat postdate the climactic episode of metamorphism. They fall within Ordovician age limits (500–440 × 10^6 years). The extensive gabbro sheet (or sheets) of the Huntley-Portsoy district, inland from the north coast, has been shown to be older than was once supposed, and provided the heat source responsible for sillimanite overprinting in this region (Ashworth, 1975).

3. The main regional upsurge of granitic magma represented by Newer Granite plutons came much later: it has been dated in Scotland as Silurian to early Devonian (420–400 × 10^6 years). By this time, postmetamorphic elevation and erosion were already far advanced.

Genetic Relations between Regional Metamorphism and Granitic Plutonism

The Central Question

Massive development or intrusion of granitic magma is a common accompaniment, both in place and broadly in time, of regional metamorphism. In such cases can there be some direct causative relation between the two phenomena? Or are they independent manifestations of thermal perturbation deeper in or below the crust? Bearing upon these questions, and not all pointing in the same directions, are other facts perhaps not as striking as the common closely knit granitic-metamorphic syndrome, but equally well established:

1. There is commonly a great lag in time between regional metamorphism and regional upsurge of granitic magma late in the orogenic cycle (Dalradian of Scotland; Sierra Nevada of California).

2. It is not surprising that granitic magma plays no part in regional metamorphism displayed by low-grade facies series. But there are also extensive amphibolite-facies provinces (e.g., the Pennine domain of the Alps, the western border of the Haast Schist block in New Zealand) where broadly coeval granitic plutons are insignificant or completely lacking.

3. With very rare exceptions basaltic magma, although the most voluminous of all on the global scale, has no place in the picture of regional metamorphism.

Such general situations reflect the response of rocks (commonly stepped up by synchronous or immediately preceding strain) to a variety of pressure-temperature regimes controlled by heat flow across the mantle-crust interface. The wide spectrum of grade expressed by isograd patterns is controlled by depth and proximity to thermal domes and depressions, whatever their origin. To postulate control by concealed bodies of granite magma is warranted only when there is independent supporting evidence (e.g., presence of negative gravity anomalies).

The central question seems already to have been partially answered. Granite plutonism and regional metamorphism can be closely interrelated processes of the deep crust (by contrast with generation of basaltic magmas whose origins must be sought deeper down in the upper mantle itself). The mutual relation must be to some degree indirect; for either phenomenon may occur on a regional scale without the other. In those rare cases where basaltic magma has influenced the regional metamorphic imprint, it seems to have arrived as if accidentally from a more remote though probably related sphere of thermal disturbance.

The question of possible causative relationships between granite plutonism and regional metamorphism where the two are associated, goes back to the days of Lyell, and still sparks controversy. As a prelude to further consideration we must first review the field and chronological relationships in those numerous provinces where the two phenomena are most obviously intertwined.

Isograd Patterns Related to Granitic Plutons

The southeast Dalradian terrane is one of many in which there appears to be some relation between the pattern of isograds and the field distribution of more or less contemporary granite-migmatite complexes (Older Granites). The same relation has been demonstrated in the central Pyrenees (Zwart, 1963); and in Vermont, New Hampshire, and other New England states; in southern Finland (Orijärvi); and in the Ryoke belt of Japan. In every case, the granite complexes are located in areas of maximum metamorphic grade—a fact repeatedly emphasized by Read (e.g., 1957) in his classic series of essays on granites, granitization, and metamorphism. In certain areas (e.g., New Hampshire and the Pyrenees), the high-grade sillimanite zones concentrically border individual structural domes in most of which intrusive granitic bodies are concentrated. Two interpretations have been placed on these patterns of regional metamorphism.

First, it is possible that intrusive granite plutons are the immediate source of heat for metamorphism, just as in a contact aureole. This was Barrow's original view regarding Dalradian metamorphism, as implied by the title of his classic paper of 1893: "On an intrusion of muscovite-biotite gneiss in the southeast Highlands of Scotland, and its accompanying metamorphism." In another early classic, Barrell (1921, p. 266) stated that in the New England region of the eastern United States, "regional metamorphism is intimately related to batholithic intrusion," and that metamorphic recrystallization is "largely and directly related to batholithic heat and emanations." The same interpretation has been reiterated more recently (e.g., Billings, 1937, pp. 557, 558; White and Billings, 1951, p. 693) for metamorphism related to granite-injected structural domes in New Hampshire.

This simple explanation fails to account for what is probably the most significant feature of regional metamorphism. This is the enormous total quantity of heat necessary to drive to completion the whole series of endothermic dehydration and decarbonation reactions involved in progressive metamorphism of an initially cool sedimentary mass (cf. Turner and Verhoogen, 1960, p. 666). To this writer, therefore, a second alternative (though far short of a complete explanation) is preferable. It has been hinted or directly invoked by individual workers in the specific regions mentioned above (e.g., Lyons, 1955, pp. 105, 139; Zwart, 1963, pp. 152-154). According to this second model, the granites and migmatites are the culminating "products" of high-grade metamorphism. It is immaterial, with regard to the present problem, whether metamorphism culminates in partial fusion, or whether the granitic bodies are formed by metasomatism (granitization) without participation of a silicate-melt phase—a magma. The intrusive character of the granitic bodies is compatible with either mode of origin, if one accepts (as this writer does not), the idea that a mica schist, in becoming converted to granitic gneiss, can thereby be rendered mobile without partial fusion. All high-grade facies series have *P-T* gradients that impinge on or enter the field of incipient fusion of granitic rocks. The most likely origin of the central granitic gneiss massifs seems to be by partial or complete fusion at ultrametamorphic temperatures.

Under the stimulus of Read's earlier discourses on granitization in relation to metamorphism, it was fashionable twenty years ago to appeal to alkali metasomatism at high temperature as the essential factor in the genesis of migmatite complexes. Today the fashion is to invoke differential fusion of pelitic and semipelitic metasediments, with segregation of the melt phase, the final product being a laminated or veined migmatite (cf. Turner and Verhoogen, 1960, pp. 383, 387-388, 669-672). This is of course by no means a new theory. It is as old as the concept of metamorphism itself and is inherent in Charles Lyell's model of plutonism.

What is still debated today is the role of metasomatism in the fusion process. Some of the most detailed geochemical studies on a regional scale support a model in which an essential role is assigned to large-scale diffusion and concentration of alkalis and other elements [e.g., Engel and Engel, 1963 (northern Adirondacks); P. E. Brown, 1967 (northern Scotland)]. Other regional investigations, notably those of Mehnert and his colleagues (1957, 1961, 1963), have led to the opposite conclusion that regional transformation of metasedimentary schist and gneiss into granite migmatite does not necessarily involve any significant change in the whole rock mass, viewed on a large scale. Scale indeed may prove to be the crux of the problem. On a very small scale, that of an albite porphyroblast, metamorphism involves profound metasomatism. On the scale of a hand specimen, the same metamorphism may be isochemical. The system represented by a migmatite complex and its environment may comprise a few thousand cubic kilometers of rock. To evaluate possible changes in total composition of a system on so large a scale, and the possible degree of ionic exchange with whatever may lie beneath, presents a formidable task in sampling. Few, however, would now deny that the "granitic" fraction of migmatites was once largely or completely liquid, though some prefer to term them "mobilized granite" or "mobilizate." This conclusion receives strong support from the cummulative data of experiments on rock fusion at high water pressures. In particular, Winkler and his co-workers showed that, given a sufficient supply of water from an external source, metagraywackes heated above 700°C at $P_{H_2O} = 2$ kb yield a substantial fraction of granite-granodiorite melt (Winkler and von Platten, 1960; Winkler, 1974, pp. 289-301).

But where is the ultimate heat source, and what is its nature? Is it possible to locate the immediate source in a thermal "high" or "focus"? Still completely unknown is the ultimate source of heat (presumably in the mantle beneath) and the vehicle (perhaps water) of its upward transport to thermal highs as now identified at the surface.

The Scottish Dalradian: An Illustration
of Changing Ideas on Heat Sources

Fashion of thinking regarding thermal aspects of relations between regional metamorphism and granite plutonism has changed and fluctuated since Barrow first mapped his regional zones in Scotland—nowhere more than with respect to the Dalradian terrane itself (cf. Atherton, 1977, pp. 363-366). Barrow (1898, 1912) saw the limited segment of the zonal sequence in the Perthshire Highlands as part of a vast thermal aureole imprinted by the gneissic Older Granite plutons of the sillimanite zone. When E. B. Bailey (1923) and Tilley (1925a) began to map metamorphic zones in the Highlands they rejected this simple idea in favor of depth control. Tilley (Elles and Tilley, 1930) who with the aid of Gertrude Elles extended Barrow's zones along the full length of the southern Highlands, favored a thermal regime controlled essentially by stratigraphic depth—what today might be termed "regional pretectonic burial metamorphism." Bailey, with his experience of Alpine structure in mind, demonstrated the close relation that exists in the Dalradian between metamorphic crystallization and penetrative deformation.[*] He invoked the influence of tectonically controlled depth.

> The metamorphic zones of the South-West Highlands are superimposed upon one another in order of increasing crystallization from above downwards. The surfaces separating the various zones are often gently, though distinctly inclined with reference to the surfaces separating the various tectonic nappes (Bailey, 1923, p. 322).

So for more than half a century progressive metamorphism in the Dalradian has been attributed, with minor variations, to a regional thermal regime controlled by geothermal gradients and culminating, in the deep hot zones, in local anatexis that gave rise to the Older Granite migmatite complexes. W. Q. Kennedy (1948) introduced an important modification by appealing to local intensification of heat flow above a locus of upward convection in the mantle. He envisaged a large-scale thermal dome in the northeast—and this became and has remained a widely accepted element in models of Dalradian metamorphism.

H. H. Read (1952 and earlier publications), like Harker (1932), recognized the distinctive mineralogy (with low-pressure implications) of what came to be called the Buchan type of metamorphism in the northeast (cf. Fig. 1-11*b*). He saw in this the thermal influence of a locus of migmatitization. Out of this emerged the now generally accepted idea of a later thermal overprinting that gave rise to extensive crystallization of sillimanite in the northeast and perhaps as well in Barrow's sillimanite zone to the south. Chinner (1966, p. 172), in developing this concept outlined his view of the situation thus:

> One might therefore interpret the general distribution of metamorphic rocks in north-eastern Scotland as resulting from a two-stage process: the development of kyanite and andalusite zones by general pressure-temperature distribution corresponding to a geothermal gradient . . . , followed by local temperature rise bringing what are now the areas characterized by sillimanite and gneiss into the fields of sillimanite stability, partial melting, muscovite-quartz reaction, or all three.

---

[*]He figured (1923, p. 329) S-shaped and spiral trains of inclusions in albite and garnet porphyroblasts as evidence of what today is termed "syntectonic crystallization."

Chinner's model in no way assumes a causative role for the Older Granite migmatite complexes.

Finally there is now a growing recognition of the thermal influence of the great basic sheet ("Newer Gabbro") of the Huntley-Portsoy area inland from the Moray Firth coast of the Buchan region. The date of its intrusion has now been placed as closely following the climax of Dalradian metamorphism (Dewey and Pankhurst, 1970). Ashworth (1975) has shown that sillimanite overprinting (development of both a sillimanite and a sillimanite-orthoclase zone) in the Buchan region was the direct result of intrusion of the gabbro sheet into rocks still at quasimetamorphic temperatures.

How does opinion stand today? Control of the thermal regime by a steady-state heat flux through the deep crust is strongly favored. This model has received recent support from a detailed thermal-mineralogical study close to the garnet isograd at a point just above the underlying Moinian on the northern edge of the Southwest Dalradian (Richardson and Powell, 1976). A careful estimate, based on calcite-dolomite compositions and univariant equilibria involving carbonates and various silicates, places temperature at $535°C$ and pressure at 5.3 kb (Fig. 11-6, point 11). A corresponding mean steady-state geothermal gradient would be $\sim 28°$ km^{-1}. Richardson and Powell show that 500 million years ago the contents of ^{232}Th, ^{238}U, and ^{40}K in the Dalradian would have been sufficient, with a modest contribution from the underlying Moinian, to maintain just such a gradient.[*]

Widely, but not universally accepted, adjuncts to the depth-control model are these:

1. The granite-migmatite complexes (Older Granites) represent the local culmination, not the prime cause, of metamorphic heat flux.
2. The mean geothermal gradient was not everywhere the same. It was significantly higher in the Buchan than in the Barrovian zones (to part of which the estimate of $28°$ km^{-1} applies). And the gradient rises and then falls across Kennedy's thermal dome in the northeast.
3. Late influx of basaltic magma (Insch gabbro sheet) in the northeast was responsible for the sillimanite overprinting in that region.

To the present writer the thermal model outlined above, while admittedly still tentative, seems unusually satisfactory. This, however, is the judgment of an outsider having but superficial personal acquaintance with Highland geology. It is not wholly acceptable to some who have been working for years in the field, and who still feel that local upward movement of anatectic magmas has had a significant influence on details of the zonal pattern (e.g., Atherton, 1977, p. 366).

Anatexis and Regional Metamorphism

In the upper temperature range of high-grade regional metamorphism—650–750°C, 4–7 kb—many common rocks (pelitic, semipelitic, volcanogenic sediments) are already within the field of partial melting—provided there is an adequate supply of

---

[*]Richardson and Powell offer some timely comments regarding implications and constraints of their model with respect to tectonic models of Grampian orogeny, now in rather general vogue, that invoke a major zone of subduction in Ordovician times.

water. Most of the experimentally established melting curves that are customarily used as illustrations are based on water-saturated systems for which $P_{H_2O} = P$. Most familiar is the so-called minimum granite-melting curve of Bowen and Tuttle (1958) which represents an extreme case of incipient melting in the $KAlSi_3O_8$-$NaAlSi_3O_8$-SiO_2 system in the presence of excess water. This curve cuts deeply into the *P-T* regime of high-grade metamorphism (Fig. 11-1). But it would be a mistake to take Bowen and Tuttle's curve as a general datum for assessing anatexis in metamorphism. Most natural melts so produced are a good deal more complex than the simple, low-temperature quartz-orthoclase-albite eutectic. And more important still, the experimentally derived curve applies to water-saturated melts, which at depths of 10–25 km would contain no less than 7–14 percent water by weight—which in terms of molar concentration could make water the most abundant species in the melt. This situation has great significance in many aspects of igneous petrology (cf. I. S. E. Carmichael et al., 1974, pp. 322–328, 594, and works cited therein). But in the present context it is enough to stress four points that bear on the problem of anatexis metamorphism.

First, in natural closed systems (in which influx of water from outside is precluded) the temperature of incipient melting is considerably higher than that on the minimum melting curve of "granite."

Second, in such systems the water content of the melt is buffered by the hydrous silicates that are the sole source of supply. Thus at a depth of 25 km muscovite-quartz-feldspar would begin to melt about 730°C (cf. Fig. 4-3) as compared with 630°C on the water-saturated "granite" curve; the content of water, buffered by muscovite, would be less than half that of the corresponding water-saturated melt under similar conditions.

Third, the anatectic product will be a granitic to granodioritic melt (depending on the composition of the parent rock) in equilibrium with an assemblage of solid (metamorphic) phases.

Fourth, not all quartzo-feldspathic streaks and veinlets in schists and amphibolites are of anatectic origin. There can be no question, for example, that quartz-albite veins in metagraywackes of the greenschist facies, even where they are cross-cutting and simulate ptygmatic folds, are products of metamorphic differentiation—that little-understood process of diffusion and solution that is responsible for so much of the foliated structure of schistose rocks (cf. Turner, 1941). In the Paleozoic amphibolite facies sector of the Fiordland metamorphic terrane at the southwest corner of South Island, New Zealand (Fig. 9-3), an extensive migmatite complex* has developed by anatexis, virtually in place, around the upper reaches of Lake Manapouii. The parent materials are amphibolites and quartz-biotite-hornblende-plagioclase-epidote schists (metagraywackes?). Far from the migmatite area these rocks are locally and sparsely veined by narrow quartz-plagioclase segregations whose plagioclase is identical in composition with that of the enclosing rock. I regard these as products of metamorphic differentiation, not anatexis. Their composition is in no way "granitic."

---

*Originally described forty years ago by the present writer as an intrusive trondhjemitic pluton.

Migmatites in Relation to Metamorphic Facies

Viewing anatexis from the igneous standpoint we have described the products, migmatites, as heterogeneous rocks consisting of two contrasted lithologic components that are intimately mixed (interlayered, streaked) on the scale of an outcrop: "one light colored and granitic [in the broad sense of the term] ... the other dark and metamorphic (for example, biotite schist, amphibolite)" (I. S. E. Carmichael et al., 1974, p. 572). For growth of ideas regarding the significance of migmatites and genetic relations between their contrasted components, the reader is referred to our earlier summary (1974, pp. 572–575). Today there seems to be a fair consensus regarding the physical processes concerned (e.g., see Mehnert, 1968): partial fusion (anatexis) to yield the granitic fraction; relative displacement (flow) of melt with respect to solid, and on a larger scale of the composite partially fused mass with respect to overlying solid metamorphic rocks; and diffusion of ions, especially K^+ and Na^+, through the medium of a postulated aqueous pore fluid (possible only when crystallization of the original melt fraction has proceeded far enough to bring its water content to the saturation level).

Attention of metamorphic petrologists tends to be focused on the residual solid lithologic component of migmatites. Two broad classes of migmatite can be recognized on this basis: those in which the metamorphic mineral assemblage is respectively in the amphibolite or in the granulite facies.

Most familiar, perhaps because they are more widely distributed, are amphibolite-facies migmatites. The metamorphic component is usually rich in biotite, hornblende, or both; and this condition, together with relatively low temperatures inferred from the facies itself, strongly suggests melting in a water-saturated system. A logical further inference is buffering of the water content by continuous influx of water from some external (deep crustal?) source.

In recent years attention has been increasingly focused on the second class of migmatite—that in which the refractory solid assemblage is in the granulite facies. This type is widely developed in large sectors of Precambrian cratons. In quarry walls in southern Sri Lanka (cf. Fig. 10-16), one can see large streaks and lenses of quartzo-feldspathic granulite ("charnockite")—conspicuous because of the greasy bluish luster of their perthitic feldspars—swimming in engulfing masses of biotite-hornblende "granite" gneiss. This latter would seem to represent the product of anatexis of rocks whose relics are now (and almost certainly were previously) in the granulite facies (an alternative model is late retrograde metamorphism of preexisting granulite). Granulite migmatites are regionally developed in the Proterozoic (2000×10^6 years) basement of western Brazil bordering the Atlantic coast. They are beautifully displayed in and around Rio de Janeiro where they have been studied in detail by Leonardos and Fyfe, who reached these conclusions (1974, p. 211).

> a) The Atlantic belt is characterized by migmatite terrain. On all scales from microscopic to regional, nonintrusive charnockitic rocks are mixed with granitic or granodioritic components. The assemblages and form suggest partial melting: the granitic material being the mobile phase while charnockitic portions form the residue.

b) Hypersthene tonalites and similar apparently intrusive rocks (sometimes also termed charnockites) are present in some areas. Where clearly intrusive, they may represent the extreme product of progressive melting.

c) Hyper-aluminous quartzites and gneisses with garnet, cordierite, sillimanite and spinel are frequent in the migmatite terrain. These rocks often lack any evidence of the presence of a molten component. In immediately underlying gneisses granite mobilizates are present. Thus partial melts appear to form first in less refractory members.

d) Attitudes of foliation change from rather flat to steep across Rio bay from Leblon to Niteroi. Charnockitic rocks increase towards Niteroi. It appears that we may have a complete, continuous section from a melting and collection region to a rising pluton; a classic Taylor instability (Ramberg, 1967; Fyfe, 1973).

Granulites are generally regarded as ultimate products of regional metamorphism of common crustal rocks via the amphibolite facies. Extreme dehydration is involved in the final prograde step. How can this have been achieved? Obviously bearing on this question is another and more recently discovered chemical property of many granulites. Over large areas they have been significantly depleted in certain large-ion lithophile elements: K, Rb, Pb, Cs, Th, U, Y, and heavier rare-earth elements (Heier, 1960, 1964, 1973; Lambert and Heier, 1967, 1968; Tarney et al., 1972).[*] This, however, is not a universal pattern of granulite chemistry: completely anhydrous granulite assemblages of the Musgrave Ranges, central Australia (metamorphosed at 1200×10^6 years) have a geochemical pattern in all ways consistent with their igneous (plutonic) parentage except for strong depletion in uranium (Gray, 1977).

Four models of dehydration and minor element depletion, each probably applicable in specific instances are in current vogue.

1. Expulsion of water during a metamorphic amphibolite-granulite facies transition induced by rising temperature: the simple model of prograde metamorphism with $P_{H_2O} \approx P$.
2. Regional metamorphism of rocks previously dehydrated in aureoles surrounding anorthosite massifs of an earlier plutonic cycle—as in parts of the Grenville province, Quebec (Wynne-Edwards, 1969).
3. Prograde dehydration of amphibolite-facies rocks, but without significant increase in temperature, under a steady influx of CO_2, supplied from some external source, with f_{H_2O} thereby externally buffered at low levels. This mechanism seems to have been effective in the Proterozoic amphibolite-granulite province of southern Norway, where Touret (1971) found that fluid inclusions in granulites (but not in rocks of the neighboring amphibolite zone) are unexpectedly rich in CO_2.
4. Partial anatexis of high-grade metamorphic rocks in an environment closed to

---

[*]A fact of great significance to geochemists with reference to problems of isotope geochemistry and the geothermal regimes (e.g., Collerson and Fryer, 1978).

access of externally supplied water. The melt phase, from the first strongly undersaturated in water, acts as a sink into which are withdrawn all the water and many of the trace elements listed above (e.g., Lambert and Heier, 1967, 1968; Fyfe, 1973).

Evolution of trace-element patterns peculiar to granulites, and hence probably to much of the lower crust, has implications far beyond our immediate objective. It is sufficient here to reiterate that in granulite-migmatite complexes the granitic (formerly magmatic) component represents partial fusion at the culmination of metamorphism—one of the processes of "reworking" of deep crustal rocks that can significantly lower their heat-producing capacity. Partial melting could and in many cases probably does play the dominant role in the dehydration process leading to the granulite chemistry of the unfused residue. Not all granulites, however, have formed thus. And possibly the only peculiar geochemical characteristics common to all rocks of the granulite facies are a high degree of dehydration, strong depletion in uranium, and a significantly low K/Rb ratio (cf. Gray, 1977, p. 88).

METAMORPHIC FACIES IN RELATION TO GEOLOGIC TIME

As the older history of the earth unfolds in the light of radio-chronology, the uniformiterian principle has come to be regarded less as a "law" than as a useful brake on unwarranted speculation. More and more, in all branches of geology secular or episodic variation has been revealed in fundamental processes—the genesis of magmas and of ores, sedimentation, and of course the evolution of terrestrial life (e.g., Sutton and Windley, 1974). So now, as we conclude our survey of the facies metamorphic rocks it is appropriate, and certainly intriguing, to ask such questions as these: What aspects of mineralogical pattern in regional metamorphism have been repeated without discernable change from the earliest times to the present? And in complementary counterpart are there any elements in facies patterns that appear to be unique to particular eras, more especially to later as opposed to earlier times, or vice versa? Finally, is there any evidence of secular, i.e., gradual evolution in metamorphic pattern, or are such changes as can be perceived of a more or less random episodic nature? All these questions have been asked, and answers given with varying degrees of conviction by writers concerned with the broader problems of plate tectonics and terrestrial evolution—Windley (1973), 1977), Fyfe (1976), Windley and Smith (1976), and a score of others that they cite.

Here our frame of reference is more limited; and our concern is simply to list what seem to be significant facts—pointers along the way for future inquiry—that have so far emerged from the mineral facies of metamorphic rocks seen in chronologic perspective:

First, most familiar facies of regional metamorphism seem to belong equally to all ages. Just as the essential elements in Phanerozoic magmatism—intrusion of granodioritic plutons, outpouring and sheet-injection of basaltic magma—were equally prominent in the earliest times, so likewise it appears to be with metamorphic facies series dominated by the amphibolite, the greenschist, and lower-grade facies of burial metamorphism. Tectonic environments were different, but the mineralogical products of metamorphism were much the same. So far no significant change in facies has been reported at the Archaean-Proterozoic boundary. A legitimate inference is that in some segments of the Precambrian crust geothermal gradients were never greatly different from those considered "normal" today ($<40°$ km^{-1}).

Second, a notable departure from uniformity was the repeated regional development of low-pressure granulite facies series throughout the whole of the Archaean and the Proterozoic as contrasted with later times. Their typical representatives are cordierite-sillimanite assemblages in the pelitic-semipelitic composition range. Rocks of the granulite facies are very rare in the Phanerozoic; and those that have been recorded are mostly high-pressure types with kyanite and no cordierite. But there are also Precambrian granulites that bear the hallmark of high pressure.

Third, the blueschist facies is almost exclusively Phanerozoic, and most blueschist series date back no more than 250 million years. The same may be said of eclogites of "Group C," those that are certainly or probably derivatives of crustal rocks. Precambrian eclogites are much more limited in their occurrence. The best-known (those of southern Norway) are later Proterozoic, and they and closely associated garnet peridotites appear to be intruders into the crust, tectonically emplaced fragments of upper-mantle rock.

There are some who would see in items 2 and 3 evidence of secular lowering of geothermal gradients from early Archaean times onward. To me the argument taken alone, is unconvincing, even though the change in facies pattern would fit such a model if it were based on independent evidence. That is a matter for discussion in a much broader context. There are questions, however, to which purely petrologic evidence can be expected to yield some sort of answer; and general propositions that can be sustained or struck down largely on the evidence of metamorphic rocks. To conclude the review of metamorphic facies, here are some of them.

Has the virtual absence of the granulite facies from the scene of Phanerozoic metamorphism other than short-term chronological significance? Alternatively were there intermittent comparably long periods of granulite famine somewhere in the vast span of Precambrian time? How well will the proposition of high Precambrian geothermal gradients—plausible though it undoubtedly is—stand up to the test of future detailed quantitative estimates based on mineralogy and geochemistry of metamorphic rocks? What is the underlying significance of the sudden entry of blueschist and (probably) associated eclogite metamorphism in the last installment of terrestrial history? Is it born of slow secular cooling of the crust; or (more likely to this author) is it the product of an entirely new pattern of tectonism unique to our own times? Will a careful search of the Archaean record reveal unique facies variants, still undiscovered, to match those aspects of ancient tectonism that seem to be so peculiarly Archaean?

Much of future inquiry in the metamorphic field is likely to be focused on these and other problems with a chronological and tectonic bias. Today we stand on a threshold, with blueschists, eclogites, and granulites offering encouraging signs of possibilities ahead. Remaining as a major objective, which can never be completely, perhaps even satisfactorily accomplished, is a fuller understanding of variation in facies pattern, secular or episodic, throughout geologic time. Paradoxically the future of metamorphic research would seem to lie in the older Precambrian.

Bibliography

Adams, H. G., L. H. Cohen, and J. L. Rosenfeld: Solid-inclusion piezothermometry, *Am. Mineral.*, vol. 60, pp. 574–598, 1975.

Agrell, S. O., M. G. Brown, and D. McKee: Deerite, howieite and zussmanite, from the Franciscan of the Laytonville district, California, *Am. Mineralogist*, vol. 50, pp. 278–279, 1965.

Agrell, S. O., and J. M. Langley: The dolerite plug at Tievebulliagh near Cushendall, Co. Antrim, *Proc. Roy. Irish Acad. Sec. B*, vol. 59, no. 7, pp. 93–127, 1958.

Aguirre, L., B. Levi, and R. Offler: Unconformities as mineralogical breaks in the burial metamorphism of the Andes, *Contrib. Mineral. Petrol.*, vol. 66, pp. 361–366, 1978.

Akaad, M. K.: The northern aureole of the Ardara pluton of County Donegal, *Geol. Mag.*, vol. 93, pp. 377–398, 1956.

Albee, A. L.: A petrogenic grid for the Fe-Mg silicates of pelitic schists, *Am. J. Sci.*, vol. 263, pp. 512–536, 1965a.

Albee, A. L.: Phase equilibria in three assemblages of kyanite-zone pelitic schists, Lincoln Mountain Quadrangle, central Vermont, *J. Petrol.*, vol. 6, pp. 246–301, 1965b.

Almond, D. C.: Metamorphism of Tertiary lavas in Strathaird, Skye, *Trans. Roy. Soc. Edinburgh*, vol. 65, no. 16, pp. 413–434, 1964.

Althaus, E.: Der Stabilitätsbereich des Pyrophyllits unter dem Einfluss von Säuren. I, *Contrib. Mineral. Petrol.*, vol. 13, pp. 31–50, 1966.

Althaus, E.: Experimental evidence that the reaction of kyanite to form sillimanite is at least bivariant, *Am. J. Sci.*, vol. 267, pp. 273–277, 1969.

Althaus, E., E. Karotke, K. H. Nitsch, and H. G. F. Winkler: An experimental reexamination of the upper stability limit of muscovite plus quartz, *Neues Jahrb. Mineral. Monat.*, vol. 7, pp. 325–336, 1970.

Amstutz, G. E. (ed.): "Spilites and Spilitic Rocks," Springer-Verlag, New York, 1974.

Anderson, A. T.: The dimensions of oxygen isotopic equilibrium attainment in prograde metamorphism, *J. Geol.*, vol. 75, pp. 323–332, 1967.

Aramaki, S.: Sillimanite and cordierite from volcanic xenoliths, *Am. Mineralogist*, vol. 46, pp. 1154–1165, 1961.

Argand, E.: Les nappes de recouvrement des Aspes pennines et leurs prolonguements structuraux, *Matériaux Carte géol. Suise*, n.s., 31, 1911.

Arnold, A., and H. Scharbert: Rb-Sr-altersbestimmungen an Granuliten der südlichen Böhmischen Masse in Österreich, *Schweiz. Mineral. Petrogr. Mitteil.*, vol. 53, pp. 61–78, 1973.

Aronson, J. L.: Reconnaissance rubidium-strontrum geochronology of New Zealand plutonic and metamorphic rocks. *New Zealand J. Geol. Geophys.*, vol. 8, pp. 401–423, 1965.

Ashworth, J. R.: The sillimanite zone of the Huntley Portsoy area in the northeast Dalradian, Scotland, *Geol. Mag.*, vol. 112, pp. 113–136, 1975.

Atherton, M. P.: The garnet isograd in pelitic rocks and its relation to metamorphic facies, *Am. Mineralogist*, vol. 49, pp. 1331–1348, 1964.

Atherton, M. P.: The variation in garnet, biotite, and chlorite composition in medium grade pelitic rocks from the Dalradian, Scotland, *Contrib. Mineral. Petrol.*, vol. 68, pp. 347–371, 1968.

Atherton, M. P.: The metamorphism of the Dalradian rocks of Scotland, *Scott. J. Geol.*, vol. 13, pp. 331–370, 1977.

Atherton, M. P., M. H. Naggar, and W. S. Pitcher: Kyanite in some thermal aureoles, *Am. J. Sci.*, vol. 275, pp. 432–443, 1975.

Bailey, E. B.: The metamorphism of the southwest Highlands, *Geol. Mag.*, vol. 60, pp. 317–331, 1923.

Bailey, E. H., W. P. Irwin, and D. L. Jones: Franciscan and related rocks and their significance in the geology of western California. *California Div. Mines Bull. 183*, 1964.

Bailey, E. H., and D. L. Jones: On-land Mesozoic oceanic crust in the California Coast Ranges, *U.S. Geol. Surv. Prof. Paper* 700-C, pp. 70–81, 1970.

Banno, S.: Glaucophane schists and associated rocks in the Omi district, Japan, *Jap. J. Geol. Geog.*, vol. 29, pp. 29–44, 1958.

Banno, S.: Notes on rock-forming minerals (10), glaucophanes and garnets from the Kôtu district, Shikoku, *Geol. Soc. Japan J.*, vol. 65, pp. 658–663, 1959.

Banno, S.: Petrologic studies on Sanbagawa crystalline schists in the Bassi-Ino district, Central Shikoku, Japan, *Univ. Tokyo, J. Fac. Sci.*, vol. 15, pp. 203–319, 1964a.

Banno, S.: Alumina content of orthopyroxene as a geologic barometer, *Jap. J. Geol. Geog.*, vol. 35, pp. 115–121, 1964b.

Banno, S.: Classification of eclogites in terms of physical conditions of their origin, *Phys. Earth Planet. Interiors*, vol. 3, pp. 405–421, 1970.

Barrell, J.: Geology of the Marysville mining district, Montana, *U.S. Geol. Surv. Prof. Paper* 57, 1907.

Barrell, J.: Relations of subjacent igneous invasion to regional metamorphism, *Am. J. Sci.*, vol. 1, pp. 1–19, 174–186, 245–267, 1921.

Barrow, G.: On an intrusion of muscovite-biotite gneiss in the south-east Highlands of Scotland and its accompanying metamorphism, *Geol. Soc. London Quart. J.*, vol. 49, pp. 330–358, 1893.

Barrow, G.: On the geology of the lower Dee-side and the southern Highland border, *Geologists Assoc. Proc.*, vol. 23, pp. 268–284, 1912.

Barth, T. F. W.: Structural and petrologic studies in Dutchess County, New York, Pt. II, *Bull. Geol. Soc. Am.*, vol. 37, pp. 775–850, 1936.

Bateman, P., et al.: The Sierra Nevada batholith, *U.S. Geol. Surv. Prof. Paper* 414-D, 1963.

Beach, A.: Amphibolitization of Scourian granulites, *Scott. J. Geol.*, vol. 10, pp. 35–43, 1974.

Bearth, P.: Geologie und Petrographie des Monte Rosa, *Beitr. Geol. Karte Schweiz*, vol. 96, 1952.

Bearth, P.: Über Eclogite, Glaucophanschiefer, und metamorphen Pillowlaven, *Schweiz. Mineral. Petrog. Mitteil.*, vol. 39, pp. 267–286, 1959.

Bearth, P.: Versuch einer Gliederung alpinmetamorpher Serien der Westalpen, *Schweiz. Mineral. Petrog. Mitteil.*, vol. 42, pp. 127–137, 1962.

Bearth, P.: Zur Entstehung alpinotyper Eclogite, *Schweiz. Mineral. Petrog. Mitteil.*, vol. 45, pp. 179–188, 1965.

Bearth, P.: Zur mineralfaziellen Stellung der Glaucophangesteine der Westalpen, *Schweiz. Mineral. Petrog. Mitteil.*, vol. 46, pp. 13–24, 1966.

Bearth, P.: Zur Eklogithildung in den Westalper, *Fortsch. Mineral.*, vol. 47, pp. 27–33, 1970.

Bearth, P.: Gesteins und Mineralparagesen aus den Ophiolithen von Zermatt, *Schweiz. Mineral. Petrogr. Mitteil.*, vol. 53, pp. 299–334, 1973.

Becke, F.: Über Mineralbestand und Struktur der kristallinischen Schiefer, *Akad. Wiss. Vienna Denkschr., Math.-Natv. Kl.*, vol. 75, pp. 1–53, 1913 (first published, 1903).

Becke, F.: Ueber Diaphthorite, *Mineral. Petrog. Mitteil.*, vol. 28, pp. 369–375, 1909.

Becke, F.: Zur Faciesklassifikation der metamorphen Gesteine, *Mineral. Petrog. Mitteil.*, vol. 35, pp. 215–230, 1921.

Bell, K.: Age relations and provenance of the Dalradian Series of Scotland, *Bull. Geol. Soc. Am.*, vol. 79, pp. 1167–1194, 1968.

Benson, W. N.: The tectonic conditions accompanying the intrusion of basic and ultrabasic igneous rocks, *Nat. Acad. Sci. (U.S.A.)*, vol. 19, *Mem.* 1, 1926.

Berg, J. H.: Dry granulite mineral assemblages in the contact aureoles of the Nain Complex, Labrador, *Contrib. Mineral. Petrol.*, vol. 64, pp. 33–52, 1977.

Best, M. G.: Petrology and structural analysis of metamorphic rocks in the southwestern Sierra Nevada foothills, California, *Univ. Calif. Berkeley Publ. Geol. Sci.*, vol. 42, no. 3, pp. 111–158, 1963.

Best, M. G., and L. E. Weiss: Mineralogical relations in some pelitic hornfelses from the southern Sierra Nevada, California, *Am. Mineralogist*, vol. 49, pp. 1240–1266, 1964.

Bhattacharyya, C.: Present status of the charnockite problem with special reference to the progress of research on charnockites and orthopyroxene granulites of India, *Indian J. Earth Sci.*, S. Roy vol., pp. 195–223, 1977.

Bianchi, A., and G. Dal Piaz: Gli inclusi "micascisti eclogitici" della zona Sesia, *Giorn. Geol. Ann. Museo. Geol. Bologna*, ser. 2a, vol. 31, pp. 39–76, 1963.

Bickle, M. J., and R. Powell: Calcite-dolomite geothermometry for iron-bearing carbonates, *Contrib. Mineral. Petrol.*, vol. 59, pp. 281–292, 1977.

Billings, M. P.: Regional metamorphism in the Littleton-Moosilauke area, New Hampshire, *Bull. Geol. Soc. Am.*, vol. 48, pp. 463–566, 1937.

Binns, R. A.: Zones of progressive regional metamorphism in the Willyama complex, Broken Hill district, New South Wales, *Geol. Soc. Australia J.*, vol. 11, pp. 283–330, 1964.

Binns, R. A.: The mineralogy of metamorphosed basic rocks from the Willyama complex, Broken Hill district, New South Wales, *Mineral. Mag.*, vol. 35, pp. 306–326, 561–587, 1965.

Birch, F.: Compressibility; elastic constants, *Geol. Soc. Am. Mem.* 97, pp. 97–175, 1966.

Birch, F., and P. Lecomte: Temperature-pressure plane for albite composition, *Am. J. Sci.*, vol. 258, pp. 209–217, 1961.

Bishop, D. G.: Progressive metamorphism from prehnite-pumpellyite to greenschist facies in the Dansey Pass area, Otago, New Zealand, *Bull. Geol. Soc. Am.*, vol. 83, pp. 3177–3198, 1972.

Bishop, D. G.: Stratigraphic, structural, and metamorphic relationship in the Dansey Pass area, Otago, New Zealand, *New Zealand J. Geol. Geophys.*, vol. 17, pp. 301–335, 1974.

Black, P. M.: Paragonite and phengitic muscovite from New Caledonian blueschists, *Geol. Soc. Am. Ann. Meeting, Atlantic City Abstr.*, vol. 14, 1969.

Black, P. M.: Hornfelses from Paritu, Coromandel County, *J. Roy. Soc. New Zealand*, vol. 2, pp. 211–228, 1972.

Black, P. M.: Mineralogy of New Caledonian metamorphic rocks, I. Garnets from the Ouégoa district, *Contrib. Mineral. Petrol.*, vol. 38, pp. 221–235, 1973a.

Black, P. M.: Mineralogy of New Caledonian metamorphic rocks, II. Amphiboles from the Ouégoa district, *Contrib. Mineral. Petrol.*, vol. 39, pp. 55–64, 1973b.

Black, P. M.: Mineralogy of New Caledonian metamorphic rocks, III. Pyroxenes and major element partitioning between coexisting pyroxenes, amphiboles, and garnets from the Ouégoa district, *Contrib. Mineral. Petrol.*, vol. 45, pp. 281–288, 1974a.

Black, P. M.: Oxygen isotope studies of metamorphic rocks from Ouégoa district, New Caledonia, *Contrib. Mineral. Petrol.*, vol. 47, pp. 197–206, 1974b.

Black, P. M.: Regional high-pressure metamorphism in New Caledonia: phase equilibria in the Ouégoa district, *Tectonophys.*, vol. 43, pp. 89–107, 1977.

Black, P. M., and R. N. Brothers: Blueschist ophiolites in the mélange zone of northern New Caledonia, *Contrib. Mineral. Petrol.*, vol. 65, pp. 69–78, 1977.

Blackburn, W. H.: The spatial extent of chemical equilibrium in some high-grade metamorphic rocks from the Grenville of southeastern Ontario, *Contrib. Mineral. Petrol.*, vol. 19, pp. 72–92, 1968.

Blake, M. C., R. N. Brothers, and M. A. Lanphere: Radiometric ages of blueschists from New Caledonia, "Internat. Sympos., Geodynamics in South-west Pacific, Nouméa, New Caledonia, 1976," pp. 279–282, Editions Technip, Paris, 1977.

Blake, M. C., W. P. Irwin, and R. G. Coleman: Upside-down metamorphic zonations, blueschist facies, along a regional thrust in California and Oregon, *U.S. Geol. Surv. Prof. Paper* 575-C, pp. 1–9, 1967.

Bloxam, T. W.: Jadeite-bearing metagraywackes in California, *Am. Mineralogist*, vol. 41, pp. 488–496, 1956.

Bobrievitch, A. P., G. I. Smirnov, and V. S. Sobolev: On the mineralogy of xenoliths of grossularite-pyroxene-disthene rock in kimberlite of Yakutia, *Geol. i Geofiz., Akad. Nauk SSSR, Sibirsk. Otd.*, no. 3, pp. 17–24, 1960.

Boettcher, A. L., and P. J. Wyllie: Revision of the calcite-aragonite transition, *Nature*, vol. 213, pp. 792–793, 1967.

Boles, J. R., and D. S. Coombs: Mineral reactions in zeolitic Triassic tuff, Hokonui Hills, New Zealand, *Bull. Geol. Soc. Am.*, vol. 86, pp. 163–173, 1975.

Borg, I. Y.: Glaucophane-schists and eclogites near Healdsburg, California, *Bull. Geol. Soc. Am.*, vol. 67, pp. 1563–1584, 1956.

Borg, I. Y.: Optical properties and cell parameters in the glaucophane-riebeckite series, *Contrib. Mineral. Petrol.*, vol. 15, pp. 67–92, 1967.

Bottinga, Y., and M. Javoy: Comments on oxygen isotope geothermometry, *Earth Planet. Sci. Letters*, vol. 20, pp. 250–265, 1973.

Boucot, A. J., and J. B. Thompson: Metamorphosed Silurian brachiopods from New Hampshire, *Bull. Geol. Soc. Am.*, vol. 74, pp. 1313–1334, 1963.

Bowen, N. L.: "The Evolution of the Igneous Rocks," Princeton University Press, Princeton, N. J., 1928.

Bowen, N. L.: Progressive metamorphism of siliceous limestone and dolomite, *J. Geol.*, vol. 48, pp. 225–274, 1940.

Bowen, N. L., and J. F. Schairer: The system $MgO-FeO-SiO_2$, *Am. J. Sci.*, vol. 29, pp. 151–217, 1935.

Bowen, N. L., and O. F. Tuttle: The system $MgO-SiO_2-H_2O$, *Bull. Geol. Soc. Am.*, vol. 60, pp. 439–460, 1949.

Bowen, N. L., and O. F. Tuttle: Origin of granite in the light of experimental studies in the system $NaAlSi_3O_8-KAlSi_3O_8-SiO_2-H_2O$, *Geol. Soc. Am. Mem.*, 74, 1958.

Boyd, F. R.: Hydrothermal investigations of amphiboles, in P. H. Abelson (ed.), "Researches in Geochemistry, 1," pp. 377–396, Wiley, New York, 1959.

Brauns, R.: "Die kristallinen Schiefer des Laacher See-Gebietes und ihre Umwandlung zur Sanidinit," Stuttgart, 1911.

Bridgewater, D., and K. D. Collerson: The major petrological and geochemical characters of the 3,600 m.y. Uivak gneisses from Labrador, *Contrib. Mineral. Petrol.*, vol. 54, pp. 43–59, 1976.

Bridgewater, D., and K. D. Collerson: On the origin of early Archaean gneisses: A reply [to Glikson, 1977], *Contrib. Mineral. Petrol.*, vol. 62, pp. 179-191, 1977.

Bridgewater, D., and W. S. Fyfe: The pre-3 b.y. crust: fact-fiction-fantasy, *Geoscience Canada*, vol. 1, pp. 7-11, 1974.

Bridgewater, D., V. R. McGregor, and B. F. Windley: Stages in the development of the early Precambrian crust of Greenland, *Geol. Soc. S. Africa Spec. Publ.* 3, pp. 475-477, 1973.

Bridgewater, D., J. Watson, and B. F. Windley: The Archaean craton of the North Atlantic region, *Phil. Trans. Roy. Soc. London*, A, vol. 273, pp. 493-512, 1973.

Briggs, R. M., H. W. Kobe, and P. M. Black: High-pressure metamorphism of stratiform sulphide deposits from the Diahot region, New Caledonia, *Mineral. Deposita (Berl.)*, vol. 12, pp. 263-279, 1977.

Brothers, R. N.: Glaucophane schists from the North Berkeley Hills, California, *Am. J. Sci.*, vol. 252, pp. 614-626, 1954.

Brothers, R. N.: The structure and petrography of graywackes near Auckland, New Zealand, *Trans. Roy. Soc. New Zealand*, vol. 83, pp. 465-482, 1956.

Brothers, R. N.: Lawsonite-albite schists from northernmost New Caledonia, *Contrib. Mineral. Petrol.*, vol. 25, pp. 185-202, 1970.

Brothers, R. N.: High-pressure schists in northern New Caledonia, *Contrib. Mineral. Petrol.*, vol. 4b, pp. 109-127, 1974.

Brouwer, H. A., and C. G. Egeler: The glaucophane facies metamorphism in the schistes lustrés nappe of Corsica, *Koninkl. Ned. Akad. Wetenschap. Verslag Gewone Vergader. Afdel. Nat.*, vol. 48, pp. 1-71, 1952.

Brown, E. H.: The greenschist facies in part of eastern Otago, New Zealand, *Contrib. Mineral. Petrol.*, vol. 14, pp. 259-292, 1967.

Brown, E. H.: Phase relations of biotite and stilpnomelane in the greenschist facies, *Contrib. Mineral. Petrol.*, vol. 31, pp. 275-299, 1971.

Brown, E. H.: Comparison of the mineralogy and phase relations of blueschists from the North Cascades, Washington, and greenschists from Otago, New Zealand, *Bull. Geol. Soc. Am.*, vol. 85, pp. 333-344, 1974.

Brown, E. H.: A petrogenic grid for reactions producing biotite and other Al-Fe-Mg silicates in the greenschist facies, *J. Petrol.*, vol. 16, pp. 258-271, 1975.

Brown, E. H.: The crossite content of Ca-amphibole as a guide to pressure of metamorphism, *J. Petrol.*, vol. 18, pp. 53-72, 1977a.

Brown, E. H.: Phase equilibria among pumpellyite, lawsonite, epidote, and associated minerals in low grade metamorphic rocks, *Contrib. Mineral. Petrol.*, vol. 64, pp. 123-136, 1977b.

Brown, E. H.: Phase relations of Na-pyroxene in blueschists and eclogites of the Franciscan Formation, California, U.S.A., in V. A. Zharikov, V. I. Fonarev, and S. P. Korikowskii (eds.), "Problems of Physico-chemical Petrology," *D. S. Korzhinskii vol. Inst. Exp. Mineral* and *Inst. Geol. Ore Deposits, U.S.S.R.*, 1978.

Brown, G. C., and W. S. Fyfe: Kyanite andalusite equilibrium, *Contrib. Mineral. Petrol.*, vol. 33, pp. 227-231, 1971.

Brown, P. E.: Major element composition of the Loch Coire migmatite complex, Sutherland Scotland, *Contrib. Mineral. Petrol.*, vol. 14, pp. 1-26, 1967.

Brown, W. H., W. S. Fyfe, and F. J. Turner: Aragonite in California glaucophane schists, and the kinetics of the aragonite-calcite transition, *J. Petrol.*, vol. 3, pp. 566-582, 1962.

Bryan, W. H., and O. A. Jones: Contributions to the geology of Brisbane. No. 2 The structural history of the Brisbane schists, *Proc. Roy. Soc. Queensland*, vol. 65, pp. 25-50, 1954.

Brynhi, I.: Reconnaissance studies of gneisses, ultrabasites, eclogites and anorthosites in outer Nordfjord, western Norway, *Norges Geol. Undersök.*, no. 241, 1966.

Brynhi, I., H. J. Bollingberg, and P. R. Graff: Eclogites in quartzofeldspathic gneisses in Nordfjord, west Norway, *Norsk Geol. Tidsskr.*, vol. 49, pp. 133-225, 1969.

Brynhi, I., D. H. Green, H. Heier, and W. S. Fyfe: On the occurrence of eclogite in western Norway, *Contrib. Mineral. Petrol.*, vol. 26, pp. 12-19, 1970.

Bucher, W. H.: Fossils in metamorphic rocks; a review, *Bull. Geol. Soc. Am.*, vol. 64, pp. 275–300, 1953.

Buddington, A. F.: Adirondack igneous rocks and their metamorphism, *Geol. Soc. Am. Mem. no. 7*, 1939.

Buddington, A. F.: Isograds and the role of H_2O in metamorphic facies of orthogneisses of the northwest Adirondack area, New York, *Bull. Geol. Soc. Am.*, vol. 74, pp. 1155–1182, 1963.

Buddington, A. F.: The occurrence of garnet in the granulite-facies terrane of the Adirondack Highlands, *J. Petrol.*, vol. 7, pp. 331–335, 1966.

Buddington, A. F., J. Fahey, and A. Vlisidis: Degree of oxidation of Adirondack iron oxide and iron-titanium oxide minerals in relation to petrogeny, *J. Petrol.*, vol. 4, pp. 138–169, 1963.

Buddington, A. F., and D. H. Lindsley: Iron-titanium oxide minerals and synthetic equivalents, *J. Petrol.*, vol. 5, pp. 310–357, 1964.

Burnham, C. W.: Contact metamorphism of magnesian limestones at Crestmore, California, *Bull. Geol. Soc. Am.*, vol. 70, pp. 879–920, 1959.

Burnham, C. W., J. R. Holloway, and N. F. Davis: Thermodynamic properties of water to $1000°C$ and 10,000 bars, *Geol. Soc. Am. Spec. Paper*, 132, 1969.

Callegari, E., and C. Viterbo: I graniti delle eclogiti compressa nella "formazione dei micascisti eclogitici" della zona Sesia-Lanzo, *Rend. Soc. Mineral. Italiana*, Anno 22, pp. 3–25, 1966.

Cann, J. R.: Spilites from the Carlsberg Ridge, Indian Ocean, *J. Petrol.*, vol. 10, pp. 1–19, 1969.

Carmichael, D. M.: On the mechanism of prograde metamorphic reactions in quartz-bearing pelitic rocks, *Contrib. Mineral. Petrol.*, vol. 20, pp. 244–267, 1969.

Carmichael, D. M.: Intersecting isograds in the Whetstone Lake area, Ontario, *J. Petrol.*, vol. 11, pp. 147–181, 1970.

Carmichael, D. M.: Metamorphic bathozones and bathograds: A measure of the depth of post-metamorphic uplift and erosion on a regional scale, *Am. J. Sci.*, vol. 278, pp. 769–797, 1978.

Carmichael, I. S. E., F. J. Turner, and J. Verhoogen: "Igneous Petrology," McGraw-Hill, New York, 1974.

Carr, R. M., and W. S. Fyfe: Synthesis fields of some aluminium silicates, *Geochim. Cosmochim. Acta*, vol. 21, pp. 99–109, 1960.

Carter, N. L.: Steady state flow of rocks, *Rev. Geophys. und Space Phys.*, vol. 14, pp. 301–360, 1976.

Chadwick, B., and K. Coe: New evidence relating to Archaean events in southern Greenland, in B. F. Windley (ed.), "The Early History of the Earth," pp. 203–313, Wiley Interscience, New York, 1976.

Chakraborty, K. R., and S. K. Sen: Regional metamorphism of pelitic rocks around Kandra, Singhbkum, Bihar, *Contrib. Mineral Petrol.*, vol. 16, pp. 210–232, 1967.

Chatterjee, N. D.: On the widespread occurrence of oxidized chlorites in the Pennine zone of the western Italian Alps, *Contrib. Mineral. Petrol.*, vol. 12, pp. 325–353, 1966.

Chatterjee, N. D., and W. Johannes: Thermal stability and standard thermodynamic properties of $2M_1$-muscovite, $KAl_2[AlSi_5O_{10}(OH)_2]$, *Contrib. Mineral. Petrol.*, vol. 48, pp. 89–114, 1974.

Chernosky, J. V.: The stability of chrysotile, $Mg_3Si_2O_5(OH)_4$ and the free energy of formation of talc $Mg_3Si_4O_{10}(OH)_2$ (abstract): *Geol. Soc. Am. Abstr. with Programs*, vol. 5, p. 575, 1973.

Chernosky, J. V.: The stability of anthophyllite—a reevaluation based on new experimental data, *Am. Mineralogist*, vol. 61, pp. 1145–1155, 1976.

Chesterman, C. W.: Contact metamorphism of the Twin Lakes region, Fresno County, California, *Calif. J. Mines Geol.*, vol. 38, pp. 243–281, 1942.

Chesterman, C. W.: Intrusive ultrabasic rocks at Leach Lake Mountain, California, *Rept. Intern. Geol. Congr. 21st Session, Norden, 1960*, vol. 18, pp. 208–215, 1960.

Chesworth, W.: Metamorphic facies series in the Grenville province of Ontario, *Tectonophys.*, vol. 14, pp. 71-78, 1972.

Chinner, G. A.: Pelitic gneisses with varying ferrous/ferric ratios from Glen Clova, Angus, Scotland, *J. Petrol.*, vol. 1, pp. 178-217, 1960.

Chinner, G. A.: The distribution of pressure and temperature during Dalradian metamorphism, *Geol. Soc. London Quart. J.*, vol. 122, pp. 159-186, 1966.

Christie, O. H. J.: Feldspar structure and the equilibrium between plagioclase and epidote, *Am. J. Sci.*, vol. 260, pp. 149-153, 1962.

Clark, S. P. J.: A redetermination of equilibrium relations between kyanite and sillimanite, *Am. J. Sci.*, vol. 259, pp. 641-650, 1961.

Clark, S. P. J.: Thermal conductivity [of rocks and minerals], *Geol. Soc. Am. Mem.* 97, pp. 459-482, 1966.

Clark, S. P. J., E. C. Robertson, and F. Birch: Experimental determination of kyanite-sillimanite equilibrium relations at high temperatures and pressures, *Am. J. Sci.*, vol. 255, pp. 628-640, 1957.

Clayton, R. N., J. R. Goldsmith, K. J. Karel, T. K. Mayeda, and R. C. Newton: Limits on the pressure effect of isotopic fractionation, *Geochim. Cosmochim. Acta*, vol. 39, pp. 1197-1201, 1975.

Clayton, R. N., J. R. O'Neil, and T. K. Mayeda: Oxygen isotope exchange between quartz and water, *J. Geophys. Res.*, vol. 77, no. 17, pp. 3057-3067, 1972.

Coleman, R. G.: Jadeite deposits of the Clear Creek area, New Idria district, San Benito County, California, *J. Petrol.*, vol. 2, pp. 209-247, 1961.

Coleman, R. G., and D. E. Lee: Glaucophane-bearing metamorphic types of the Cazadero area, California, *J. Petrol.*, vol. 4, pp. 260-301, 1963.

Coleman, R. G., D. E. Lee, L. B. Beatty, and W. W. Brannock: Eclogites and eclogites: Their differences and similarities, *Bull. Geol. Soc. Am.*, vol. 76, pp. 483-508, 1965.

Collerson, K. D., and B. J. Fryer: The role of fluids in the formation and subsequent development of early continental crust, *Contrib. Mineral. Petrol.*, vol. 67, pp. 151-168, 1978.

Compagnoni, R., and B. Maffeo: Jadeite-bearing metagranites and related rocks in the Monte Mucrone area (Sesia-Lanzo zone, western Italian Alps), *Schweiz. Mineral, Petrogr. Mitteil.*, vol. 53, pp. 355-378, 1973.

Compton, R. R.: Significance of amphibole paragenesis in the Bidwell Bar region, California, *Am. Mineralogist*, vol. 43, pp. 890-907, 1958.

Compton, R. R.: Contact metamorphism in Santa Rosa Range, Nevada, *Bull. Geol. Soc. America*, vol. 71, pp. 1383-1416, 1960.

Coombs, D. S.: The nature and alteration of some Triassic sediments from Southland, New Zealand, *Trans. Roy. Soc. New Zealand*, vol. 82, pt. 1, pp. 65-109, 1954.

Coombs, D. S.: Lower grade mineral facies in New Zealand, *Rept. Intern. Geol. Congr. 21st Session, Norden, 1960*, vol. 13, pp. 339-351, 1960.

Coombs, D. S.: Some recent work on the lower grades of metamorphism, *Australian J. Sci.*, vol. 24, pp. 203-215, 1961.

Coombs, D. S.: Present status of the zeolite facies, *Advances in Chem. Ser. No. 101*—"Molecular Sieve Zeolites, 1," pp. 317-327, 1971.

Coombs, D. S.: On the mineral facies of spilitic rocks and their genesis, in G. C. Amstutz (ed.), "Spilites and Spilitic Rocks," pp. 373-386, Springer, New York, 1974.

Coombs, D. S., A. J. Ellis, W. S. Fyfe, and A. M. Taylor: The zeolite facies with comments on the interpretation of hydrothermal syntheses, *Geochim. Cosmochim. Acta*, vol. 17, pp. 53-107, 1959.

Coombs, D. S., C. A. Landis, R. J. Norris, J. M. Sinton, D. J. Borns, and D. Craw: The Dun Mountain ophiolite belt, New Zealand, its tectonic setting, constitution, and origin, *Am. J. Sci.*, vol. 276, pp. 561-603, 1976a.

Coombs, D. S., Y. Nakamura, and M. Vuagnat: Pumpellyite-actinolite facies schists of the Taveyanne Formation near Loèche, Valais, Switzerland, *J. Petrol.*, vol. 17, pp. 440-471, 1976b.

Cooper, A. F.: Piedmont schist from the Haast River, New Zealand, *Mineral. Mag.*, vol. 38, pp. 64–71, 1971.

Cooper, A. F.: Progressive metamorphism of metabasic rocks from Haast Schist group of southern New Zealand, *J. Petrol.*, vol. 13, pp. 457–492, 1972.

Cooray, P. G.: Geology of the country around Rangala, *Dept. Mineral., Geol. Surv. Ceylon, Mem. No. 2*, 1961.

Cooray, P. G.: Charnockites and their associated gneisses in the Pre-Cambrian of Ceylon, *Geol. Soc. London Quart. J.*, vol. 118, pp. 239–273, 1962.

Craigh, G. Y.: "The Geology of Scotland," Oliver and Boyd, Edinburgh, 1965.

Crawford, A. R.: India, Ceylon and Pakistan: New age data and comparison with Australia. *Nature*, vol. 223, pp. 380–384, 1969.

Crawford, M. L.: Composition of plagioclase and associated minerals in some schists from Vermont, U.S.A. and South Westland, New Zealand, *Contrib. Mineral. Petrol.*, vol. 13, pp. 269–294, 1966.

Crawford, W. A.: Studies in Franciscan metamorphism near Jenner, California, doctoral thesis, University of California, Berkeley, 1965.

Crawford, W. A., and W. S. Fyfe: Calcite-aragonite equilibrium, *Science*, vol. 144, pp. 1569–1570, 1964.

Crawford, W. A., and W. S. Fyfe: Lawsonite equilibria, *Am. J. Sci.*, vol. 263, pp. 262–270, 1965.

Cruickshank, R. D., and E. D. Ghent: Chloritoid-bearing pelitic rocks of the Horsethief Creek group, southeastern British Columbia, *Contrib. Mineral. Petrol.*, vol. 65, pp. 333–339, 1978.

Dallmeyer, R. D.: Compositional controls on cordierite-bearing assemblages in high-grade regional metamorphism, *24th Internat. Geol. Congr.* 1972, sect. 2, pp. 52–63, 1972.

Danielsson, A.: Calcite-wollastonite equilibrium, *Geochim. Cosmochim. Acta*, vol. 1, pp. 55–69, 1950.

Davidson, L. R.: Variation in ferrous iron-magnesium coefficients of metamorphic pyroxenes from Quairading, Western Australia, *Contrib. Mineral. Petrogr.*, vol. 19, pp. 239–259, 1968.

Davis, B. T. C., and F. R. Boyd: The join $Mg_2Si_2O_6$-$CaMgSi_2O_6$ at 30 kilobars pressure and its application to pyroxenes from kimberlites, *J. Geophys. Research*, vol. 71, pp. 3567–3576, 1966.

Day, H. W.: The high-temperature stability of muscovite plus quartz, *Am. Mineralogist*, vol. 58, pp. 255–262, 1973.

De Béthune, S.: Formation of metamorphic biotite by decarbonation, *Lithos*, vol. 9, pp. 309–318, 1976.

Deer, W. A., R. A. Howie, and J. Zussman: "Rock-forming Minerals," vol. 1, Wiley, New York, 1962.

Denmead, A. K.: A survey of the Brisbane schists, *Proc. Roy. Soc. Queensland*, vol. 39, pp. 71–106, 1928.

De Roever, W. P.: Igneous and metamorphic rocks in eastern Central Celebes, in H. A. Brouwer (ed.), "Geological Explorations in the Island of Celebes," pp. 65–173, North-Holland Publishing Co., Amsterdam, 1947.

De Roever, W. P.: Preliminary notes on glaucophane-bearing and other rocks from southeast Celebes, *Koninkl. Ned. Akad. Wetenschap., Proc., Ser. B*, vol. 53, no. 9, pp. 1–12, 1950.

De Roever, W. P.: Genesis of jadeite in low-grade metamorphism, *Am. J. Sci.*, vol. 253, pp. 283–289, 1955.

De Roever, W. P.: Some differences between post-Paleozoic and older regional metamorphism, *Geol. Mijnbow*, vol. 18, pp. 123–127, 1956.

De Roever, W. P.: Sind die Alpinotypen Peridotitmassen veilleicht tectonisch verfrachtete Bruchstücke der Peridotitschale ?, *Geol Rundschau*, vol. 46, pp. 137–146, 1957.

De Roever, E. W. F., F. F. Beunk, and C. Kleft: Blue amphibole-albite-chlorite assemblages from Fuscaldo (S. Italy) and the role of glaucophane in metamorphism, *Contrib. Mineral. Petrol.*, vol. 58, pp. 221–234, 1976.

De Waard, D.: Anorthite content of plagioclase in basic and pelitic crystalline schists as related to metamorphic zoning in the Usu massif, Timor, *Am. J. Sci.*, vol. 257, pp. 553–562, 1959.

De Waard, D.: Mineral assemblages and metamorphic subfacies in the granulite-facies terrane of Little Moose Mountain syncline, South-central Adirondack Highlands, *Koninkl. Ned. Akad. Wetenschap. Proc., Ser. B*, vol. 67, pp. 344–362, 1964.

De Waard, D.: The occurrence of garnet in the granulite-facies terrane of Adirondack Highlands, *J. Petrol.*, vol. 6, pp. 165–191, 1965a.

De Waard, D.: A proposed subdivision of the granulite facies, *Am. J. Sci.*, vol. 263, pp. 455–461, 1965b.

De Waard, D.: The biotite-cordierite-almandite subfacies of the hornblende-granulite facies, *Can. Mineralogist*, vol. 8, pt. 4, pp. 481–492, 1966.

De Waard, D.: Absolute *P-T* conditions of granulite-facies metamorphism in the Adirondacks, *Koninkl. Ned. Akad. Wetenschap. Amsterdam Proc.*, sec. 13, vol. 70, pp. 400–410, 1967.

De Waard, D., and M. Walton: Precambrian geology of the Adirondack highlands, a reinterpretation, *Geol. Rundschau*, vol. 56, pp. 596–662, 1967.

Dewey, J. F., and J. M. Pankhurst: The evolution of the Scottish Caledonides in relation to their isotopic age pattern, *Roy. Soc. Edinburgh Trans.*, vol. 68, pp. 361–389, 1970.

Diessel, C. F. K., R. N. Brothers, and P. M. Black: Coalification and graphitization in high-pressure schists in New Caledonia, *Contrib. Mineral. Petrol.*, vol. 68, pp. 63–78, 1979.

Drury, S. A.: Chemical changes during retrogressive metamorphism of Lewisian granulite facies rocks from Coll and Tiree, *Scott. J. Geol.*, vol. 10, pp. 237–256, 1974.

Dungan, M. A.: Metastability in serpentine-olivine equilibria, *Am. Mineralogist*, vol. 62, pp. 1018–1029, 1977.

Durrell, C.: Metamorphism in the southern Sierra Nevada northeast of Visalia, California, *Univ. Calif. Publ., Bull. Dept. Geol. Sci.*, vol. 25, no. 1, pp. 1–118, 1940.

Eberl, D., and J. Hower: Kinetics of illite formation, *Bull. Geol. Soc. Am.*, vol. 87, pp. 1326–1330, 1976.

Edwards, A. B.: Differentiation of the dolerites of Tasmania, *J. Geol.*, vol. 50, pp. 451–480, 1942.

Elles, G. L., and Tilley, C. E.: Metamorphism in relation to structure in the Scottish Highlands, *Trans. Roy. Soc. Edinburgh*, vol. 56, pt. 3, pp. 621–646, 1930.

Engel, A. E. J., and C. E. Engel: Progressive metamorphism and granitization of the major paragneiss, northwest Adirondack mountains, New York, Part 1, *Bull. Geol. Soc. Am.*, vol. 69, pp. 1369–1414, 1958.

Engel, A. E. J., and C. E. Engel: Progressive metamorphism and granitization of the major paragneiss, northwest Adirondack mountains, Part 2, New York, *Bull. Geol. Soc. Am.*, vol. 71, pp. 1–58, 1960.

Engel, A. E. J., and C. E. Engel: Progressive metamorphism of amphibolite, northwest Adirondack mountains, New York, *Bull. Geol. Soc. Am.*, A. F. Buddington vol., pp. 37–82, 1962a.

Engel, A. E. J., and C. E. Engel: Hornblendes formed during progressive metamorphism of amphibolites, northwest Adirondack mountains, New York, *Bull. Geol. Soc. Am.*, vol. 73, pp. 1499–1514, 1962b.

Engel, A. E. J., and C. E. Engel: Metasomatic origin of large parts of the Adirondack phacoliths, *Bull. Geol. Soc. Am.*, vol. 74, pp. 349–354, 1963.

Epstein, S., and H. P. Taylor: Variation in $O^{18/16}$ in minerals and rocks, in P. H. Abelson (ed.), "Researches in Geochemistry," vol. 2, pp. 29–62, Wiley, New York, 1967.

Ernst, W. G.: Mineral parageneses in Franciscan metamorphic rocks, Panoche Pass, California, *Bull. Geol. Soc. Am.*, vol. 76, pp. 879–914, 1965.

Ernst, W. G.: Tectonic contact between the Franciscan mélange and the Great Valley crustal sequence, *J. Geophys. Research*, vol. 75, pp. 826–901, 1970.

Ernst, W. G.: Metamorphic zonations on presumably subducted lithospheric plates from Japan, California, and the Alps, *Contrib. Mineral. Petrol.*, vol. 34, pp. 43–59, 1971a.

Ernst, W. G.: Petrologic reconnaissance of Franciscan metagraywackes from the Diablo Range, central California Coast Ranges, *J. Petrol.*, vol. 12, pp. 413–437, 1971b.

Ernst, W. G.: Mineralogic study of eclogitic rocks from the Alpe Arami, Lepontine Alps, southern Switzerland, *J. Petrol.*, vol. 18, pp. 371–398, 1977.

Ernst, W. G.: Occurrence and mineralogical evolution of blueschist belts with time, *Am. J. Sci.*, vol. 272, pp. 657–668, 1972.

Ernst, W. G.: Interpretative synthesis of metamorphism in the Alps, *Bull. Geol. Soc. Am.*, vol. 84, pp. 2053–2078, 1973a.

Ernst, W. G.: Blueschist metamorphism and *P-T* regimes in active subduction zones, *Tectonophys.*, vol. 17, pp. 255–272, 1973b.

Ernst, W. G. (ed.): "Metamorphism and Plate Tectonic Regimes," Dowden, Hutchinson, & Ross, Stroudsburg, Pa., 1975a.

Ernst, W. G. (ed.): "Subduction Zone Metamorphism," Dowden, Hutchinson, & Ross, Stroudsburg, Pa., 1975b.

Ernst, W. G., and Y. Seki: Petrologic comparison of the Franciscan and Sanbagawa terranes, *Tectonophys.*, vol. 6, pp. 463–478, 1967.

Ernst, W. G., H. Onuki, and M. C. Gilbert: Comparative study of low-grade metamorphism in the California Coast Ranges and the outer metamorphic belt of Japan, *Geol. Soc. Am. Mem. 124*, 1970.

Eskola, P.: On the petrology of the Orijärvi region of southwestern Finland, *Bull. Comm. Géol. Finlande*, no. 40, 1914.

Eskola, P.: On the relation between the chemical and mineralogical composition in the metamorphic rocks of the Orijärvi region, *Bull. Comm. Géol. Finlande*, no. 44 (English summary pp. 109–145), 1915.

Eskola, P.: On the eclogites of Norway, *Vidensk. Skr. Kristania (Oslo), I, Mat.-Naturv. Kl.*, no. 8, 1921.

Eskola, P.: On contact phenomena between gneiss and limestone in western Massachusetts, *J. Geol.*, vol. 30, pp. 265–294, 1922.

Eskola, P.: Die metamorphen Gesteine, "Die Entstehung der Gesteine" (T. F. W. Barth, C. W. Correns, P. Eskola), pp. 263–407, Springer, Berlin, 1939.

Eskola, P.: Orijärvi reinterpreted, *Compt. Rend. Soc. Géol. Finlande*, vol. 23, pp. 93–102, 1950.

Eskola, P.: On the granulites of Lappland, *Am. J. Sci.*, Bowen vol., pp. 133–171, 1952.

Essene, E. J., and W. S. Fyfe: Omphacite in Californian metamorphic rocks, *Contrib. Mineral. Petrol.*, vol. 15, pp. 1–23, 1967.

Essene, E. J., W. S. Fyfe, and F. J. Turner: Petrogenesis of Franciscan glaucophane schists and associated metamorphic rocks, California, *Beitr. Mineral. Petrog.*, vol. 11, pp. 695–704, 1965.

Eugster, H. P.: The beginnings of experimental petrology, *Science*, vol. 173, pp. 481–489, 1971.

Evans, B. W.: Coexisting albite and oligoclase in some schists from New Zealand, *Am. Mineralogist*, vol. 49, pp. 173–179, 1964.

Evans, B. W.: Application of a reaction-rate method to the breakdown equilibria of muscovite and muscovite plus quartz, *Am. J. Sci.*, vol. 263, pp. 647–667, 1965.

Evans, B. W., and C. V. Guidotti: The sillimanite-potash feldspar isograd in western Maine, U.S.A., *Contrib. Mineral. Petrol.*, vol. 12, pp. 25–62, 1966.

Evans, B. W., H. Oterdoom, and V. Trommsdorff: Stability of chrysotile and antigorite in the serpentine multisystem, *Schweiz. Mineral. Petrogr. Mitteil.*, vol. 56, pp. 79–93, 1976.

Evans, B. W., and V. Trommsdorff: Regional metamorphism of ultramafic rocks in the central Alps, *Schweiz. Mineral. Petrogr. Mitteil.*, vol. 50, pp. 481–492, 1970.

Evans, B. W., V. Trommsdorff, and W. Richter: Petrology of an eclogite-metarodingite suite at Cima di Gagnone, Ticino, Switzerland, *Am. Mineralogist*, vol. 64, pp. 15–31, 1979.

Evans, C. R., and R. St. J. Lambert: The Lewisian of Lochinver, Sutherland, *J. Geol. Soc. London*, vol. 130, pp. 125–150, 1974.

Fawcett, J. J., and H. S. Yoder: Phase relations of chlorites in the system $MgO-Al_2O_3-SiO_2-H_2O$, *Am. Mineralogist*, vol. 51, pp. 353–380, 1966.

Ferry, J. M.: P, T, f_{CO_2}, and f_{H_2O} during metamorphism of calcareous sediments in the Waterville-Vassalboro area, south-central Maine, *Contrib. Mineral. Petrol.*, vol. 57, pp. 119–143, 1976.

Floran, R. J., and J. J. Papike: Mineralogy and petrology of the Gunflint Formation, Minnesota-Ontario; correlation of compositional and assemblage variations at low to moderate grade, *J. Petrol.*, vol. 19, pp. 215–288, 1978.

Foland, K., and K. W. Muessig: A Paleozoic age for some charnockitic-anorthositic rocks, *Geology*, vol. 6, pp. 143–146, 1978.

Francis, G. H.: Further petrological studies in Glen Urquhart, Inverness-shire, *Bull. Brit. Museum Nat. Hist.*, vol. 1, pp. 165–199, 1964.

French, B. M.: Some geologic implications of equilibrium between graphite and a C-H-O gas at high temperatures and pressures, *Rev. Geophys.*, vol. 4, pp. 293–253, 1966.

Frey, M.: The step from diagenesis to metamorphism in pelitic rocks during Alpine orogenesis, *Sedimentol.*, vol. 15, pp. 261–279, 1970.

Frey, M.: Progressive low grade metamorphism of a black shale formation, central Swiss Alps, *J. Petrol.*, vol. 19, pp. 95–135, 1978.

Frey, M., and E. Niggli: Illit-Kristallinität, Mineralfazien and Inkohlungsgrad, *Schweiz. Mineral. Petrogr. Mitteil.*, vol. 58, pp. 229–334, 1971.

Frey, M., J. C. Hunziker, W. Frank, J. Bocquet, G. V. Dal Piaz, E. Jäger, and E. Niggli: Alpine metamorphism of Alps: A review, *Schweiz. Mineral. Petrogr. Mitteil.*, vol. 54, pp. 247–290, 1974.

Frey, M., E. Niggli, P. Rogwiller, and C. Schimdler: Progressive niedriggradige metamorphose glaukonitführender Horizonte in den helvetischen Alpen der Ostschweiz, *Contrib. Mineral. Petrol.*, vol. 39, pp. 185–218, 1973.

Frost, B. R.: Contact metamorphism of serpentinite, chloritic blackwall, and rodingite at Paddy-go-easy Pass, Central Cascades, Washington, *J. Petrol.*, vol. 16, pp. 272–313, 1975.

Fry, N., and W. S. Fyfe: Eclogites and water pressure, *Contrib. Mineral. Petrol.*, vol. 24, pp. 1–6, 1969.

Fyfe, W. S.: Hydrothermal synthesis and determination of equilibrium between minerals in the subsolidus region, *J. Geol.*, vol. 68, pp. 553–566, 1960.

Fyfe, W. S.: On the relative stability of talc, anthophyllite, and enstatite, *Am. J. Sci.*, vol. 260, pp. 460–466, 1962.

Fyfe, W. S.: Metamorphism in mobile belts: The glaucophane schist problem, *Leicester Lit. and Phil. Soc. Trans.*, vol. 61, pp. 36–54, 1967a.

Fyfe, W. S.: Stability of Al_2SiO_5 polymorphs, *Chem. Geology*, vol. 2, pp. 67–76, 1967b.

Fyfe, W. S.: The granulite facies, partial melting and the Archaean crust, *Phil. Trans. Roy. Soc. London*, A, vol. 273, pp. 457–461, 1973.

Fyfe, W. S.: Heat flow and magmatic activity in the Proterozoic, *Phil. Trans. Roy. Soc. London*, A, vol. 280, pp. 655–660, 1976.

Fyfe, W. S., and F. J. Turner: Reappraisal of the metamorphic facies concept, *Contrib. Mineral. Petrol.*, vol. 12, pp. 354–364, 1966.

Fyfe, W. S., F. J. Turner, and J. Verhoogen: Metamorphic reactions and metamorphic facies, *Geol. Soc. Am. Mem.*, 73, 1958.

Fyfe, W. S., and R. Zardini: Metaconglomerates in the Franciscan formation near Pacheco Pass, California, *Am. J. Sci.*, vol. 265, pp. 819–830, 1967.

Ganguly, J.: Activity-composition relations of jadeite in omphacitic pyroxene: Theoretical deductions, *Earth Planet. Sci. Letters*, vol. 19, pp. 145–153, 1973.

Ganguly, J.: Staurolite stability and related parageneses, *J. Petrol.*, vol. 13, pp. 335–365, 1972.

Garlick, G. D., and S. Epstein: Oxygen-isotope ratios in coexisting minerals of regionally metamorphosed rocks, *Geochim. Cosmochim. Acta*, vol. 31, pp. 181–214, 1967.

Gass, L. G., and J. D. Smewing: Intrusion, extrusion and metamorphism at constructive margins: Evidence from the Troodos massif, Cyprus, *Nature*, vol. 242, pp. 26–29, 1973.

Ghent, E. D.: Glaucophane-schist facies metamorphism in the Black Butte area, northern Coast Ranges, California, *Am. J. Sci.*, vol. 263, pp. 385–400, 1965.

Ghent, E. D.: Temperature, pressure, and mixed volatile equilibria attending metamorphism of staurolite-kyanite-bearing assemblages, Esplanade Range, British Columbia, *Bull. Geol. Soc. Am.*, vol. 86, pp. 1654–1660, 1975.

Ghent, E. D.: Plagioclase-garnet-Al$_2$SiO$_5$-quartz: A potential geobarometer-geothermometer, *Am. Mineralogist*, vol. 61, pp. 710–714, 1976.

Ghent, E. D., J. W. Jones, and J. Nicholls: A note on the significance of the assemblage calcite-quartz-plagioclase-paragonite-graphite, *Contrib. Mineral. Petrol.*, vol. 28, pp. 112–116, 1970.

Gilluly, J.: Keratophyres of eastern Oregon and the spilite problem, *Am. J. Sci.*, vol. 29, pp. 225–252, 336–352, 1935.

Glikson, A. Y.: On the origin of early Archaean gneisses, *Contrib. Mineral. Petrol.*, vol. 62, pp. 171–178, 1977.

Glikson, A. Y., and I. B. Lambert: Vertical zonation and petrogenesis of the early Precambrian crust in Western Australia, *Tectonophys.*, vol. 30, pp. 55–89, 1976.

Goldschmidt, V. M.: Die Kontaktmetamorphose im Kristianiagebiet, *Kristiania Vidensk. Skr., I, Math-Naturv. Kl. 11*, 1911a.

Goldschmidt, V. M.: Die Gesetze der Mineralassociation vom Standpunkt der Phasenregel, *Zeits. Anorgan. Chem.*, vol. 71, pp. 313–322, 1911b.

Goldschmidt, V. M.: Die Gesetze der Gesteinsmetamorphose mit Beispielen aus der Geologie des südlichen Norwegens, *Vidensk. Skr., I, Math-Naturv. Kl.*, no. 22, 1912.

Goldschmidt, V. M.: Geologisch-petrographische Studien im Hochgebirge des südlichen Norwegens: III, Die Kalksilikatgneise und Kalksilikatglimmerschiefer im Trondhjem-Gebiete, *Vidensk. Skr., Math-Naturv. Kl.*, no. 10, Oslo, 1915.

Goldschmidt, V. M.: V, Die Injektionmetamorphose im Stavanger-Gebiete, *Vidensk. Skr., Math-Naturv. Kl.*, no. 10, Oslo, 1921.

Goldsmith, J. R., D. L. Graf, and G. I. Joensuu: The occurrence of magnesian calcites in nature, *Geochim. Cosmochim. Acta*, vol. 7, pp. 212–230, 1955.

Goldsmith, J. R., and R. C. Newton: *P-T* relations in the system CaCO$_3$-MgCO$_3$ at high temperatures and pressures, *Am. J. Sci.*, vol. 267A, pp. 160–190, 1969.

Gordon, T. M., and H. J. Greenwood: The reaction: dolomite + quartz + water = talc + calcite + carbon dioxide, *Am. J. Sci.*, vol. 268, pp. 225–242, 1970.

Graf, D. L., and J. R. Goldsmith: Dolomite-magnesian calcite relations at elevated temperatures and CO$_2$ pressures, *Geochim. Cosmochim. Acta*, vol. 7, pp. 109–128, 1955.

Gray, C. M.: The geochemistry of central Australian granulites in relation to the chemical and isotopic effects of granulite facies metamorphism, *Contrib. Mineral. Petrol.*, vol. 65, pp. 79–89, 1977.

Green, D. H.: The petrogenesis of the high-temperature peridotite intrusion in the Lizard area of Cornwall, *J. Petrol.*, vol. 5, pp. 134–188, 1964.

Green, D. H., and A. E. Ringwood: An experimental investigation of the gabbro to eclogite transformation and its petrological applications, *Geochim. Cosmochim. Acta*, vol. 31, pp. 767–833, 1967.

Greenly, E.: The geology of Anglesey, vol. 1, *Mem. Geol. Surv. Gt. Brit.*, 1919.

Greenwood, H. J.: Metamorphic systems involving two volatile components, *Carnegie Inst. Wash. Yearbook No. 61*, pp. 82–85, 1962.

Greenwood, H. J.: The synthesis and stability of anthophyllite, *J. Petrol.*, vol. 4, pp. 317–351, 1963.

Greenwood, H. J.: Mineral equilibria in the system MgO-SiO$_2$-H$_2$O-CO$_2$, in P. H. Abelson (ed.), "Researches in Geochemistry II," pp. 542–547, Wiley, New York, 1967.

Greenwood, H. J.: Thermodynamically valid projections of extensive phase relationships, *Am. Mineralogist*, vol. 60, pp. 1–8, 1975.

Griggs, D. T., and J. Handin (eds.): Rock deformation, *Geol. Soc. Am. Mem. 79*, 1960.

Grindley, G. W.: Structure of the alpine schists of South Westland, Southern Alps, New Zealand, *New Zealand J. Geol. and Geophys.*, vol. 6, pp. 872–930, 1963.

Grubb, P. L. C.: Silicates and their paragenesis in the Brockman iron formation of Wittenoom Gorge, Western Australia, *Econ. Geol.*, vol. 66, pp. 281-292, 1971.

Grubenmann, U.: "Die Kristallinen Schiefer," Borntraeger, Berlin, 1904.

Grubenmann, U., and P. Niggli: "Die Gesteinsmetamorphose," Borntraeger, Berlin, 1924.

Guidotti, C. V.: The mineralogy and petrology of the transition from the lower to the upper sillimanite zone in the Oquossoc area, Maine, *J. Petrol.*, vol. 11, pp. 277-336, 1970.

Haas, H., and M. J. Holdaway: Equilibria in the system Al_2O_3-SiO_2-H_2O involving the stability limits of pyrophyllite, *Am. J. Sci.*, vol. 273, pp. 449-464, 1973.

Hall, A. L.: The Bushveld complex as a metamorphic province, *Geol. Soc. South Africa Trans.*, vol. 18, pp. xxii-xxxvii, 1916.

Hall, A. L.: The Bushveld igneous complex of central Transvaal, *Geol. Surv. South Africa, Mem.*, no. 28, 1932.

Hall, W. E., and E. M. MacKevett: Geology and ore deposits of the Darwin Quadrangle, Inyo County, California, *U.S. Geol. Surv. Prof. Papers*, no. 368, 1962.

Hapuarachchi, D. J. A. C.: Hornblende-granulite subfacies mineral assemblages from areas in Ceylon, *Geol. Mag.*, vol. 104, pp. 29-34, 1967.

Hapuarachchi, D. J. A. C.: Cordierite and wollastonite-bearing rocks of south-western Ceylon, *Geol. Mag.*, vol. 105, pp. 317-324, 1968.

Hapuarachchi, D. J. A. C.: Evolution of the granulites and subdivision of the granulite facies in Ceylon, *Geol. Mag.*, vol. 109, pp. 435-443, 1972.

Hapuarachchi, D. J. A. C.: The granulite facies in Sri Lanka (Ceylon), *Geol. Surv. Dept., Sri Lanka, Prof. Paper no 4*, 1975.

Harker, A.: The Tertiary igneous rocks of Skye, *Mem. Geol. Surv. United Kingdom*, 1904.

Harker, A.: Anniversary address of the president, *Geol. Soc. London Quart. J.*, pp. li-lxxx, 1919.

Harker, A.: "Metamorphism," Methuen, London, 1932.

Harker, A., and J. E. Marr: The Shap granite and the associated igneous and metamorphic rocks, *Geol. Soc. London Quart. J.*, vol. 47, pp. 266-328, 1891.

Harker, R. I., and O. F. Tuttle: Studies in the system CaO-MgO-CO_2, Part 1, *Am. J. Sci.*, vol. 253, pp. 209-224, 1955.

Harker, R. I., and O. F. Tuttle: Experimental data on the P_{CO_2}-T curve for the reaction: Calcite + quartz $\rightleftharpoons$ wollastonite + carbon dioxide, *Am. J. Sci.*, vol. 254, pp. 239-256, 1956.

Härme, M., and V. Pertunen: Magnesia metasomatism at Hirvas, northern Finland, *Géol. Surv. Finland Bull.*, no. 250, 1971.

Harris, N. B. W.: The significance of garnet and cordierite from Sioux lookout region of the English River gneiss belt, northern Ontario, *Contrib. Mineral. Petrol.*, vol. 55, pp. 91-104, 1976.

Harte, B.: Determination of a pelite petrogenic grid for the eastern Scottish Dalradian, *Carnegie Inst. Wash. Yearbook No. 74*, pp. 438-446, 1975.

Hashimoto, M.: On the prehnite-pumpellyite-metagraywacke facies, *J. Geol. Soc. Japan*, vol. 72, pp. 253-265, 1966.

Hay, R. L.: Zeolites and zeolitic reactions in sedimentary rocks, *Geol. Soc. Am. Spec. Paper* no. 85, 1966.

Heald, M. T.: Structure and petrology of the Lovell Mountain quadrangle, New Hampshire, *Bull. Geol. Soc. Am.*, vol. 61, pp. 43-89, 1950.

Heard, H.: Effects of large changes in strain rate in the experimental deformation of Yule marble, *J. Geol.*, vol. 71, pp. 162-195, 1963.

Heier, K. S., and Thoresen, K.: Geochemistry of high-grade metamorphic rocks, Lofoten-Vestralen, north Norway, *Geochim. Cosmochim. Acta*, vol. 35, pp. 89-99, 1971.

Helgeson, H. C.: Solution chemistry and metamorphism, in P. H. Abelson (ed.), "Researches in Geochemistry, vol. 2," Wiley, New York, 1967.

Helgeson, H. C.: Thermodynamics of hydrous systems at elevated temperatures and pressures, *Am. J. Sci.*, vol. 267, pp. 729-804, 1969.

Helgeson, H. C., J. M. Delany, H. W. Nesbitt, and D. K. Bird: Summary and critique of the thermodynamic properties of rock-forming minerals, *Am. J. Sci.*, vol. 278A, 229 pp., 1978.

Hemley, J. J., J. W. Montoya, C. L. Christ, and P. B. Hostetler: Mineral equilibria in the MgO-SiO₂-H₂O system, *Am. J. Sci.*, vol. 277, pp. 322–351, 1977.

Hemley, J. J., J. W. Montoya, D. R. Shaw, and R. W. Luce: Mineral equilibria in the MgO-SiO₂-H₂O system, II, *Am. J. Sci.*, vol. 277, pp. 353–383, 1977.

Hemingway, B. S., and R. A. Robie: Enthalpies of formation of low albite (NaAlSi₃O₈) gibbsite [Al(OH)₃], and NaAlO₂, *U.S. Geol. Surv. Jour. Res.*, vol. 5, pp. 413–429, 1977.

Henley, R. W.: Metamorphism of the Moke Creek Lode, Otago, New Zealand, *New Zealand J. Geol. Geophys.*, vol. 18, pp. 229–237, 1975.

Herd, R. K., B. F. Windley, and M. Ghisler: The mode of occurrence and petrogenesis of the sapphirine-bearing rocks of West Greenland, *Grønlands Geol. Undersog.*, Rap. no. 24, 1969.

Hermes, O. D.: Paragenetic relationships in an amphibolitic tectonic block in the Franciscan terrain, Panoche Pass, California, *J. Petrol.*, vol. 14, pp. 1–32, 1973.

Herz, N.: Anorthosite belts, continental drift, and the anorthosite event, *Science*, vol. 164, pp. 944–947, 1969.

Hess, P. C..: The metamorphic paragenesis of cordierite in pelitic rocks, *Contrib. Mineral. Petrol.*, vol. 24, pp. 196–207, 1969.

Hewins, R. G.: Pyroxene geothermometry of some granulite facies rocks, *Contrib. Mineral. Petrol.*, vol. 50, pp. 205–209, 1975.

Hietanen, A.: On the facies series in various types of metamorphism, *J. Geol.*, vol. 75, pp. 187–214, 1967.

Hietanen, A.: Generation of potassium-poor magmas in the northern Sierra Nevada and the Svecofennian of Finland, *U.S. Geol. Surv. J. Res.*, vol. 3, pp. 631–645, 1975.

Holdaway, M. J.: Stability of andalusite and the aluminum silicate phase diagram, *Am. J. Sci.*, vol. 271, pp. 97–131, 1971.

Holdaway, M. J., and S. M. Lee: Fe-Mg cordierite stability in high-grade pelitic rocks based on experimental, theoretical, and natural observations, *Contrib. Mineral. Petrol.*, vol. 63, pp. 175–198, 1977.

Holland, J. G., and R. St. J. Lambert: The chemistry and origin of the Lewisian gneisses of the Scottish mainland, *Precambrian Res.*, vol. 2, pp. 166–188, 1975.

Hori, F.: On the role of water in heat transfer from a cooling magma, *Coll. Gen. Educ., Univ. Tokyo, Sci. Paper*, vol. 14, pp. 121–127, 1964.

Hoschek, G.: Untersuchungen Zum Stabilitätsbereich von Chloritoid und Staurolith, *Contrib. Mineral. Petrol.*, vol. 14, pp. 123–162, 1967.

Hoschek, G.: Zur Stabilitätsgrenze von Staurolith, *Naturwiss.*, vol. 8, p. 200, 1968.

Hoschek, G.: The stability of staurolite and chloritoid and their significance in metamorphism of pelitic rocks, *Contrib. Mineral. Petrol.*, vol. 22, pp. 208–232, 1969.

Howie, R. A.: The geochemistry of the charnockite series of Madras, India, *Trans. Roy. Soc. Edinburgh*, vol. 62, pt. 3, pp. 725–768, 1955.

Hsu, K. J.: Principles of mélanges and their bearing on the Franciscan-Knoxville problem, *Bull. Geol. Soc. Am.*, vol. 79, pp. 1063–1074, 1968.

Hsu, K. J.: The concept of the geosyncline yesterday and today, *Trans. Leicester Lit. Phil. Soc.*, vol. 66, pp. 26–48, 1972.

Hutton, C. O.: An occurrence of the mineral pumpellyite in the Lake Wakatipu region, western Otago, New Zealand, *Mineral. Mag.*, vol. 24, pp. 529–533, 1937.

Hutton, C. O.: Metamorphism in the Lake Wakatipu region, western Otago, *New Zealand Dept. Sci. Ind. Res. Geol. Mem. 5*, 1940.

Hutton, C. O., and F. J. Turner: Metamorphic zones in north-west Otago, *Trans. Roy. Soc. New Zealand*, vol. 65, pp. 405–406, 1936.

Iwasaki, M.: Metamorphic rocks of the Kôtu-Bizan area, eastern Sikoku, *Univ. Tokyo J. Fac. Sci.*, sec. 2, vol. 15, pp. 1–90, 1963.

Jaeger, J. C.: The temperature in the neighborhood of a cooling intrusive sheet, *Am. J. Sci.*, vol. 255, pp. 306–318, 1957.

Jaeger, J. C.: Temperatures outside a cooling intrusive sheet, *Am. J. Sci.*, vol. 257, pp. 44–54, 1959.

James, H. L.: Zones of regional metamorphism in the Pre-Cambrian of northern Michigan, *Bull. Geol. Soc. Am.*, vol. 66, pp. 1455–1488, 1955.

James, H. L., and R. N. Clayton: Oxygen isotope fractionation in metamorphosed iron formation of the Lake Superior region in iron-rich rocks, in "Petrologic Studies" (Buddington volume), *Geol. Soc. Am.*, New York, pp. 217–239, 1962.

Jamieson, J. C.: Phase equilibrium in the system calcite-aragonite, *J. Chem. Phys.*, vol. 21, pp. 1385–1390, 1953.

Jasmund, K., and G. Hentschel: Seltene Mineralparagenesen in den Kalksteineinschlüssen der Lava des Ettringer Bellerberges bei Mayen (Eifel), *Beitr. Mineral. Petrog.*, vol. 10, pp. 296–314, 1964.

Johannes, W.: Experimental investigation of the reaction forsterite + H_2O ⇌ serpentine + brucite, *Contrib. Mineral. Petrol.*, vol. 19, pp. 309–315, 1968.

Johannes, W.: An experimental investigation of the system $MgO-SiO_2-H_2O-CO_2$, *Am. J. Sci.*, vol. 267, pp. 1083–1104, 1969.

Johannes, W., P. M. Bell, H. K. Mao, A. L. Boettche, D. W. Chapman, J. F. Hays, R. C. Newton, and S. Seifert: An interlaboratory comparison of piston-cylinder calibration using the albite-breakdown reaction, *Contrib. Mineral. Petrol.*, vol. 32, pp. 24–38, 1971.

Johnson, M. R. W.: Some time relations of movement and metamorphism in the Scottish Highlands, *Geol. Mijnbouw*, vol. 42, pp. 121–142, 1963.

Johnston, J., and P. Niggli: The general principles underlying metamorphic processes, *J. Geol.*, vol. 21, pp. 481–516, 588–624, 1913.

Jolly, W. T.: Zeolite and prehnite-pumpellyite facies in south central Puerto Rico, *Contrib. Mineral. Petrol.*, vol. 27, pp. 204–224, 1970.

Jolly, W. T.: Regional metamorphism zonation as an aid in the study of Archaean terrains: Abitibi region, Ontario, *Can. Mineralogist*, vol. 12, pp. 499–508, 1974.

Jolly, W. T., and R. E. Smith: Degradation and metamorphic differentiation of the Keweenawan tholeiitic lavas of northern Michigan, U.S.A., *J. Petrol.*, vol. 13, pp. 273–309, 1972.

Joplin, G. A.: The exogenous contact-zone at Ben Bullen, New South Wales, *Geol. Mag.*, vol. 72, pp. 385–400, 1935.

Joplin, G. A.: "A Petrography of Australian Metamorphic Rocks," Angus and Robertson, Sydney, 1968.

Kamineni, D. C.: Chemical mineralogy of some cordierite-bearing rocks near Yellowknife, Northwest Territories, Canada, *Contrib. Mineral. Petrol.*, vol. 53, pp. 293–310, 1975.

Kanisawa, S.: Metamorphic rocks of the southwestern part of the Kitakami mountainland, Japan, *Tohoku Univ. Sci. Repts.*, Ser. 3, vol. 9, pp. 155–198, 1964.

Kawachi, Y.: Geology and petrochemistry of weakly metamorphosed rocks in the Upper Wakatipu district, southern New Zealand, *New Zealand J. Geol. Geophys.*, vol. 17, pp. 169–208, 1974.

Kawachi, Y.: Pumpellyite-actinolite and contiguous facies metamorphism in part of the upper Wakatipu district, South Island, New Zealand, *New Zealand J. Geol. Geophys.*, vol. 18, pp. 401–441, 1975.

Kelley, K. K.: High-temperature heat-content, heat-capacity and entropy data for the elements and inorganic compounds, *U.S. Bur. Mines Bull.*, 584, 1960.

Kelley, K. K.: Heats and free energies of formation of anhydrous silicates, *U.S. Bur. Mines Rep. Invest.*, 5901, 1962.

Kelley, K. K., and E. G. King: Entropies of the elements and inorganic compounds, *U.S. Bur. Mines Bull.*, 592, 1961.

Kennedy, G. C.: Pressure-volume-temperature relations in water at elevated temperatures and pressures, *Am. J. Sci.*, vol. 248, pp. 540–564, 1950.

Kennedy, G. C.: Pressure-volume-temperature relations in CO_2 at elevated temperatures and pressures, *Am. J. Sci.*, vol. 252, pp. 225–241, 1954.

Kennedy, W. Q.: On the significance of thermal structure in the Scottish Highlands, *Geol. Mag.*, vol. 85, pp. 229–234, 1948.

Kennedy, W. Q.: Zones of progressive regional metamorphism in the Moine schists of the western Highlands of Scotland, *Geol. Mag.*, vol. 86, pp. 43–56, 1949.

Kepezhinskas, K. B.: Pressure variability during medium-temperature metamorphism of metapelites, *Lithos*, vol. 6, pp. 145–158, 1973.

Kepezhinskas, K. B., and V. V. Khlestov: The petrogenic grid and subfacies for middletemperature metapelites, *J. Petrol.*, vol. 18, pp. 114–143, 1977.

Kern, R., and A. Weisbrod: "Thermodynamics for Geologists," Freeman, Cooper, San Francisco, 1967.

Kerrick, D. M.: Experiments on the upper stability limit of pyrophyllite at 1.8 kb and 3.9 kb water pressure, *Am. J. Sci.*, vol. 266, pp. 204–214, 1968.

Kerrick, D. M.: Contact metamorphism in some areas of the Sierra Nevada, California. *Bull. Geol. Soc. Am.*, vol. 81, pp. 2913–2938, 1970.

Kerrick, D. M.: Experimental determination of the muscovite + quartz stability with $P_{H_2O} <$ P_{total}, *Am. J. Sci.*, vol. 272, pp. 946–958, 1972.

Kerrick, D. M., K. E. Crawford, and A. F. Randazzo: Metamorphism of calcareous rocks in three roof pendants in the Sierra Nevada, California, *J. Petrol.*, vol. 14, pp. 303–325, 1973.

Kerrick, D. M., K. E. Crawford, and A. F. Randazzo: Review of metamorphic mixed volatile $(H_2O\text{-}CO_2)$ equilibria, *Am. Mineralogist*, vol. 59, pp. 729–762, 1974.

Kisch, H.: Zeolite facies and regional rank of bituminous coals, *Geol. Mag.*, vol. 103, pp. 414–422, 1966.

Kisch, H.: Coal-rank and burial-metamorphic mineral facies, in "Advances in Organic Geochemistry, 1968," pp. 407–425, Pergamon Press, Oxford, 1969.

Kisch, H.: Anthracite and meta-anthracite coal ranks associated with "anchimetamorphism" and "very-low-stage" metamorphism, *Koninkl. Ned. Akad. Wetenschap. Amsterdam Proc., Ser. B*, vol. 77, pp. 81–118, 1974.

Kitahara, S., S. Takenouchi, and G. C. Kennedy: Phase relations in the system $MgO\text{-}SiO_2\text{-}H_2O$ at high temperatures and pressures, *Am. J. Sci.*, vol. 264, pp. 223–233, 1966.

Knopf, A.: The Marysville granodiorite stock, Montana, *Am. J. Sci.*, vol. 35, pp. 834–844, 1950.

Knopf, E. B.: Retrogressive metamorphism and phyllonitization, *Am. J. Sci.*, vol. 21, pp. 1–27, 1931.

Knopf, E. B., and A. I. Jonas: Geology of the McCalls Ferry–Quarryville district, Pennsylvania, *U.S. Geol. Surv. Bull.*, 799, 1929.

Korzhinskii, D. S.: Mobility and inertness of components in metasomatosis, *Acad. Sci. U.S.S.R., Bull.*, ser. geol. no. 1, pp. 35–60, 1936.

Korzhinski, D. S.: Dependence of mineral stability on depth, *Soc. russe Mineral., Mem.*, ser. 2, vol. 66, no. 2, pp. 369–396, 1937.

Korzhinskii, D. S.: Open systems with perfectly mobile components and the phase rule, *Izv. Acad. Nauk. USSR*, ser. geol. no. 2, 1949.

Korzhinskii, D. S.: "Physicochemical Basis of the Analysis of the Paragenesis of Minerals" (English translation), Consultants' Bureau, New York, 1959.

Korzhinskii, D. S.: On thermodynamics of open systems and the phase rule, *Geochim. Cosmochim. Acta*, vol. 31, pp. 1177–1180, 1967.

Kracek, F. C., J. J. Neuvonen, and G. Burley: A thermodynamic study of the stability of jadeite, *Washington Acad. Sci. J.*, vol. 41, pp. 373–383, 1951.

Kretz, R.: Chemical study of garnet biotite and hornblende from gneisses of southwestern Quebec, with emphasis on distribution of elements in coexisting minerals, *J. Geol.*, vol. 67, pp. 371–402, 1959.

Kretz, R.: Some applications of thermodynamics to coexisting minerals, *J. Geol.*, vol. 69, pp. 361–387, 1961.

Kretz, R.: Distribution of magnesium and iron between orthopyroxene and clinopyroxene in natural mineral assemblages, *J. Geol.*, vol. 71, pp. 773–785, 1963.

Kretz, R.: Analysis of equilibrium in garnet-biotite-sillimanite gneisses from Quebec, *J. Petrol.*, vol. 5, pp. 1–20, 1964.

Kubler, B.: La cristallinité de l'illite et les zones tout à fait supérieures du métamorphisme, in "Etages Tectoniques," pp. 105–122, Neuchatel, à la Baconnière, 1967.

Kubler, B., J. Martini, and M. Vuagnat: Very low grade metamorphism in the western Alps, *Schweiz. Mineral. Petrogr. Mitteil.*, vol. 54, pp. 461–469, 1974.

Kuniyoshi, S., and J. G. Liou: Contact metamorphism of the Karmutsen volcanics, Vancouver Island, British Columbia, *J. Petrol.*, vol. 17, pp. 73–99, 1976.

Lambert, I. B., and K. S. Heier: The vertical distribution of uranium, thorium and potassium in the continental crust, *Geochim. Cosmochim. Acta*, vol. 31, pp. 377–390, 1967.

Lambert, I. B., and K. S. Heier: Geochemical investigation of deep-seated rocks in the Australian shield, *Lithos*, vol. 1, pp. 30–53, 1968.

Lambert, R. St. J.: The metamorphic facies concept, *Mineral. Mag.*, vol. 34, pp. 283–291, 1965.

Lambert, R. St. J., and W. S. McKerrow: The Grampian orogeny, *Scott. J. Geol.*, vol. 12, pp. 271–292, 1976.

Landis, C. A., and D. G. Bishop: Plate tectonics and regional stratigraphic-metamorphic relations in the southern part of the New Zealand Geosyncline, *Bull. Geol. Soc. Am.*, vol. 83, pp. 2267–2284, 1972.

Landis, C. A., and D. S. Coombs: Metamorphic belts and orogenesis in southern New Zealand, *Tectonophys.*, vol. 4, pp. 501–518, 1967.

Lee, D. E., R. G. Coleman, H. Bastron, and V. C. Smith: Garnet types from the Cazadero area, California, *J. Petrol.*, vol. 4, pp. 460–492, 1963.

Leith, C. K., and W. J. Meade: "Metamorphic Geology," Holt, Rinehart, and Winston, New York, 1915.

Leonardos, O. H., and W. S. Fyfe: Ultrametamorphism and melting of a continental margin: The Rio de Janeiro region, Brazil, *Contrib. Mineral. Petrol.*, vol. 46, pp. 201–214, 1974.

Levi, B.: Burial metamorphism of a Cretaceous volcanic sequence west from Santiago, Chile, *Contrib. Mineral. Petrol.*, vol. 24, pp. 30–49, 1969.

Lillie, A. R.: The structural geology of lawsonite and glaucophane schists of the Ouégoa district, New Caledonia, *New Zealand J. Geol. Geophys.*, vol. 13, pp. 72–116, 1970.

Lillie, A. R.: Structures in the lawsonite-glaucophane schists of New Caledonia, *Geol. Mag.*, vol. 112, pp. 225–236, 1975.

Lillie, A. R., and R. N. Brothers: The geology of New Caledonia, *New Zealand J. Geol. Geophys.*, vol. 13, pp. 145–183, 1970.

Lillie, A. R., and B. M. Gunn: Steeply plunging folds in the Sealy Range, southern Alps, *New Zealand J. Geol. Geophys.*, vol. 7, pp. 403–423, 1964.

Lindsley, D. H.: Equilibrium relations of coexisting pairs of Fe-Ti oxides, *Carnegie Inst. Wash. Yearbook No. 62*, pp. 60–66, 1963.

Liou, J. G.: Analcime equilibria, *Lithos*, vol. 4, pp. 389–462, 1971a.

Liou, J. G.: *P-T* stability fields of laumontite, wairakite, lawsonite and related minerals in the system $CaAl_2Si_2O_8-SiO_2-H_2O$, *J. Petrol.*, vol. 12, pp. 379–411, 1971b.

Loomis, A. A.: Contact metamorphic reactions and processes in the Mt. Tallac roof remnant, Sierra Nevada, California, *J. Petrol.*, vol. 7, pp. 221–245, 1966.

Lovering, T. S.: Heat conduction in dissimilar rocks and the use of thermal models, *Bull. Geol. Soc. Am.*, vol. 47, pp. 87–100, 1936.

Lovering, T. S.: Temperatures near and in intrusions, *Econ. Geol.*, 50th anniversary vol., pp. 249–281, 1955.

Lumbers, S. B.: Geology of the North Bay area, district of Nispissing and Parry Sound, *Ontario Dept. Mines Geol. Rept.*, 94, 1971.

Lyell, C.: "Principles of Geology," 7th edition, pp. 170–175, J. Murray, London, 1847.

Lyell, C.: "Manual of Elementary Geology," sixth ed., Appleton, New York, 1860.

Lyons, J. B.: Geology of the Hanover quadrangle, New Hampshire–Vermont, *Bull. Geol. Soc. Am.*, vol. 66, pp. 105–146, 1955.

MacDonald, G. J. F.: Gibbs free energy of water at elevated temperatures and pressures with applications to the brucite-periclase equilibrium, *J. Geol.*, vol. 63, pp. 244–252, 1955.

MacGregor, A. C.: Scottish pyroxene-granulite hornfelses and the Odenwald beerbachites, *Geol. Mag.*, vol. 68, pp. 506–521, 1931.

McGregor, V. R.: The early Precambrian gneisses of the Godthaab district, west Greenland, *Phil. Trans. Roy. Soc. London*, A, vol. 273, pp. 343–358, 1973.

McKee, B.: Widespread occurrence of jadeite, lawsonite, and glaucophane in central California, *Am. J. Sci.*, vol. 260, pp. 596–610, 1962.

McKerrow, W. S.: The chronology of Caledonian folding in the British Isles, *Nat. Acad. Sci. Proc.*, vol. 48, pp. 1905–1913, 1962.

Majundar, A. J., and R. Roy: Fugacities and free energies of CO_2 at high pressures and temperatures, *Geochim. Cosmochim. Acta*, vol. 10, pp. 311–315, 1956.

Mason, B. H.: Metamorphism in the southern Alps of New Zealand, *Am. Mus. Nat. Hist. Bull. 123*, pp. 211–248, 1962.

Mather, J. D.: The biotite isograd and the lower greenschist facies in the Dalradian rocks of Scotland, *J. Petrol.*, vol. 11, pp. 253–275, 1970.

Mathews, R. T.: The greenstones of the Petrie-Mt. Mee area, Queensland, *Univ. Queensland Papers, Dept. Geol.*, vol. 4, no. 6, pp. 1–37, 1954.

Maxwell, D. T., and J. Hower: High-grade diagenesis and low-grade metamorphism of illite in the Precambrian Belt Series, *Am. Mineral.*, vol. 52, pp. 843–857, 1967.

Means, W. D.: Mesoscopic structures and multiple deformation in the Otago schists, *New Zealand J. Geol. Geophys.*, vol. 6, 801–816, 1963.

Mehnert, K. R.: Neue Ergebnisse zur Geochemie der Metamorphose, *Geol. Rundschau*, vol. 51, pp. 384–394, 1961.

Mehnert, K. R.: Petrographie und Abfolge der Granitisation um Schwarzwald, IV, *Neues Jahrb. Mineral. Abhandl.*, vol. 99, pp. 161–199, 1963.

Mehnert, K. R.: "Migmatites and the Origin of Granitic Rocks," Elsevier, Amsterdam, 1968.

Mehnert, K. R., and A. Willgallis: Zum Alkalihaushalt der Granitisation im Schwarzwald, *Neues Jahrb. Mineral. Abhandl.*, vol. 91, pp. 104–130, 1957.

Melson, W. G.: Equilibria in calc-silicate hornfels, Lewis and Clark County, Montana, *Am. Mineralogist*, vol. 51, pp. 402–421, 1966.

Melson, W. G., and T. H. Van Andel: Metamorphism in the Mid-Atlantic Ridge, 22° N latitude, *Marine Geol.*, vol. 4, pp. 165–186, 1966.

Metz, P.: Experimentell Untersuchung der Metamorphose von Kieselig dolomitischen Sedimenten, II. Der Beldungs bedingungen des Diopsids, *Contrib. Mineral. Petrol.*, vol. 28, pp. 221–250, 1970.

Metz, P.: Experimental investigation of the metamorphism of siliceous dolomites, III, *Contrib. Mineral. Petrol.*, vol. 58, pp. 137–148, 1976.

Metz, P., and V. Trommsdorff: On phase equilibria in metamorphosed siliceous dolomites, *Contrib. Mineral. Petrol.*, vol. 18, pp. 305–309, 1968.

Meyer, C., and J. J. Hemley: Wall rock alteration, in H. L. Barnes (ed.), "Geochemistry of Hydrothermal Ore Deposits," pp. 167–235, Holt, Rinehart, and Winston, New York, 1967.

Miller, J. A., and P. E. Brown: Potassium-argon age studies in Scotland, *Geol. Mag.*, vol. 102, pp. 106–134, 1965.

Misch, P.: Stable association anorthite-wollastonite and other calc-silicate assemblages in amphibolite facies series of Nanga Parbat, northwest Himalayas, *Contrib. Mineral. Petrol.*, vol. 10, pp. 315–356, 1964.

Miyakawa, K.: A peculiar porphyroblastic albite schist from Nichinan-cho, Tottori Prefecture, southwest Japan, *Nagoya Univ. J. Earth Sci.*, vol. 12, pp. 1–16, 1964.

Miyashiro, A.: Calcium-poor garnet in relation to metamorphism, *Geochim. Cosmochim. Acta*, vol. 4, pp. 179–208, 1953.

Miyashiro, A.: Regional metamorphism of the Gosaisyo-Takanuki district in the central Abukuma plateau, *Tokyo University J. Fac. Sci.*, sec. 2, vol. 11, pp. 219–272, 1958.

Miyashiro, A.: Thermodynamics of reactions of rock-forming minerals with silica, *Jap. J. Geol. Geog.*, vol. 31, no. 1, pp. 71-84; no. 2, pp. 107-111, 1960.

Miyashiro, A.: Evolution of metamorphic belts, *J. Petrol.*, vol. 2, pp. 277-311, 1961.

Miyashiro, A.: Orogeny, regional metamorphism, and magmatism in the Japanese islands, *Geol. Foren Kobenhavn Medd. fra. Dansk*, vol. 17, pp. 390-446, 1967 (reprinted in Ernst, 1975, pp. 142-198).

Miyashiro, A.: Pressure and temperature conditions and tectonic significance of regional and ocean-floor metamorphism, *Tectonophys.*, vol. 13, pp. 141-159, 1972.

Miyashiro, A., and S. Banno: Nature of glaucophanitic metamorphism, *Am. J. Sci.*, vol. 256, pp. 97-110, 1958.

Miyashiro, A., and Y. Seki: Mineral assemblages and subfacies of the glaucophane-schist facies, *Jap. J. Geol. Geogr.*, vol. 29, pp. 199-208, 1958.

Miyashiro, A., and F. Shido: Progressive metamorphism in zeolite assemblages, *Lithos*, vol. 3, pp. 251-260, 1970.

Miyashiro, A., F. Shido, and M. Ewing: Metamorphism in the Mid-Atlantic Ridge near 24° and 30° N, *Phil. Trans. Roy. Soc. London*, A, vol. 268, pp. 589-603, 1971.

Moorbath, S., and R. G. Park: The Lewisian chronology of the southern portion of the Scottish mainland, *Scott. J. Geol.*, vol. 8, pp. 51-74, 1971.

Moorbath, S., H. Welke, and N. H. Gale: The significance of lead isotope studies in ancient high-grade metamorphic basement complexes as exemplified by the Lewisian rocks of northwest Scotland. *Earth Planet. Sci. Letters*, vol. 6, pp. 245-256, 1969.

Moore, J. G.: Petrology of deep-sea basalt near Hawaii, *Am. J. Sci.*, vol. 263, pp. 40-52, 1965.

Moore, J. G.: Water content of basalt erupted on the ocean floor, *Contrib. Mineral. Petrol.*, vol. 28, pp. 272-279, 1970.

Moores, E. M.: Petrology and structure of the Vourinos ophiolitic complex of northern Greece, *Geol. Soc. Am. Spec. Paper* 118, 1969.

Moores, E. M., and F. J. Vine: The Troodos massif, Cyprus, and other ophiolites as oceanic crust, *Phil. Trans. Roy. Soc. London*, A, vol. 268, pp. 443-466, 1971.

Morey, G. W.: The solubility of solids in gases, *Econ. Geol.*, vol. 52, pp. 225-251, 1957.

Mori, T.: Geothermometry of spinel lherzolites, *Contrib. Mineral. Petrol.*, vol. 59, pp. 261-279, 1977.

Mueller, R. F.: Compositional characteristics of equilibrium relations in mineral assemblages of metamorphosed iron formation, *Am. J. Sci.*, vol. 258, pp. 449-497, 1960.

Muffler, L. J., and D. E. White: Active metamorphism of upper Cenozoic sediments in the Salton Sea geothermal field and Salton Trough, southeastern California, *Bull. Geol. Soc. Am.*, vol. 80, pp. 157-182, 1969.

Muir, I. D., and C. E. Tilley: The compositions of coexisting pyroxenes in metamorphic assemblages, *Geol. Mag.*, vol. 95, pp. 403-408, 1958.

Muthuswami, T. N., and R. Gnanasekaran: The structure and phase-petrology of the metamorphic complex Devandanapatti, Madurai district, *Annamalai Univ. J.*, vol. 23, pp. 183-196, 1962.

Mysen, B. O., and K. S. Heier: Petrogenesis of eclogites in high grade metamorphic gneisses, exemplified by the Harlidland eclogite, western Norway, *Contrib. Mineral. Petrol.*, vol. 36, pp. 73-94, 1972.

Naggar, M. H., and M. P. Atherton: The composition and metamorphic history of some aluminum silicate-bearing rocks from the aureoles of the Donegal granites, *J. Petrol.*, vol. 11, pp. 549-589, 1970.

Naha, K.: Metamorphism in relation to stratigraphy, structure, and movements in part of East Singhbhum, eastern India, *Quart. J. Geol. Mining Metall. Soc. India*, vol. 37, pp. 41-88, 1965.

Newton, R. C.: Some calc-silicate equilibrium relations, *Am. J. Sci.*, vol. 264, pp. 204-222, 1966.

Newton, R. C., and J. V. Smith: Investigations concerning the breakdown of albite at depth in the earth, *J. Geol.*, vol. 75, pp. 268-286, 1967.

Niggli, E.: Stilpnomelan als gesteinsbildendes Mineral in den Schweizer Alpen, *Schweiz. Mineral. Petrog. Mitteil.*, vol. 36, pp. 511–514, 1956.

Niggli, E.: Mineral-zonen der Alpinen Metamorphose in den Schweizer Alpen, *Rept. Intern. Geol. Congr. 21st Session, Norden*, vol. 13, pp. 132–138, 1960.

Niggli, E.: Alpine Metamorphose und alpine Gebirgsbildung, *Fortschr. Mineral.*, vol. 47, pp. 16–26, 1970.

Niggli, P.: Die Chloritoidschiefer des nordöstlichen Gotthardmassives, *Beitr. Geol. Karte Schweiz.*, vol. 36, pp. 17–93, 1912.

Niggli, P.: "Rocks and Mineral Deposits" (trans. R. L. Parker), Freeman, San Francisco, 1954.

Nitsch, K. H.: Die Stäbilitat von Lawsonit, *Naturwiss.*, vol. 55, 1968.

Noble, J. A., and J. O. Harder: Stratigraphy and metamorphism in a part of the northern Black Hills and the Homestake mine, Lead, South Dakota, *Bull. Geol. Soc. Am.*, vol. 59, pp. 941–975, 1948.

O'Hara, M. J.: Melting of garnet peridotite at 30 kilobars, *Carnegie Inst. Wash. Yearbook No. 62*, pp. 71–76, 1963.

O'Hara, M. J.: Coexisting pyroxenes in four-phase lherzolites, in P. J. Wyllie (ed.), "Ultramafic and Related Rocks," pp. 395–403, Wiley, New York, 1967.

O'Hara, M. J., and G. Yawood: High pressure-temperature point on an Archaean geotherm, *Phil. Trans. Roy. Soc. London*, A, vol. 288, pp. 441–456, 1978.

O'Neil, J., and H. P. Taylor: Oxygen isotope equilibrium between muscovite and water, *J. Geophys. Res.*, vol. 74, pp. 6012–6022, 1969.

Osborne, G. D.: The metamorphosed limestones and associated contaminated igneous rocks of the Carlingford district, Co. Louth, *Geol. Mag.*, vol. 69, pp. 209–233, 1932.

Oxford Isotopic Geology Laboratory and V. M. McGregor: Isotopic dating of very early Precambrian amphibolite facies gneisses from the Godthaab district, west Greenland, *Earth Planet. Sci. Letters*, vol. 12, pp. 246–259, 1971.

Pabst, A.: The garnets of the glaucophane schists of California, *Am. Mineral.*, vol. 16, pp. 327–333, 1931.

Packham, G. H., and K. A. W. Crook: The principle of diagenetic facies and some of its implications, *J. Geol.*, vol. 68, pp. 392–407, 1960.

Page, B. M.: Geology of the Coast Ranges of California, in E. H. Bailey (ed.), "Geology of Northern California," *California Div. Mines Bull. 190*, pp. 255–276, 1966.

Page, B. M.: Ocean crust and mantle fragment in subduction complex near San Luis Obispo, California, *Bull. Geol. Soc. Am.*, vol. 83, pp. 957–972, 1972.

Park, R. G.: Observations on Lewisian chronology, *Scott. J. Geol.*, vol. 6, pp. 379–400, 1970.

Parker, R. B.: Petrology and structure of the pre-Tertiary rocks in western Alpine County, California, doctoral dissertation, University of California, Berkeley, 1953.

Parker, R. B.: Petrology and structure of pregranitic rocks in the Sierra Nevada, Alpine County, California, *Bull. Geol. Soc. Am.*, vol. 72, pp. 1789–1805, 1961.

Paterson, M. S.: Nohydrostatic thermodynamics and its applications, *Rev. Geophys. Space Phys.*, vol. 11, pp. 355–389, 1973.

Pippard, A. B.: "The Elements of Classical Thermodynamics," Cambridge University Press, Cambridge, 1966.

Pitcher, W. S., and G. W. Flinn (eds.): "Controls of Metamorphism," Wiley, New York, 1965.

Pitcher, W. S., and H. H. Read: The aureole of the main Donegal granite, *Geol. Soc. London Quart. J.*, vol. 116, pp. 1–36, 1960.

Pitcher, W. S., and H. H. Read: Contact metamorphism in relation to manner of emplacement of the granites of Donegal, Ireland, *J. Geol.*, vol. 71, pp. 261–296, 1963.

Pitcher, W. S., and R. S. Sinha: The petrochemistry of the Ardara aureole, *Geol. Soc. London Quart. J.*, vol. 113, pp. 393–408, 1958.

Platt, J. B., J. G. Liou, and B. M. Page: Franciscan blueschist-facies metaconglomerate, Diabolo Range, California, *Bull. Geol. Soc. Am.*, vol. 87, pp. 581–591, 1976.

Porteous, W. G.: Metamorphic index minerals in the eastern Dalradian, *Scott. J. Geol.*, vol. 9, pp. 9–43, 1973.

Poty, B. P., H. A. Stadler, and A. M. Weisbrod: Fluid inclusion studies in quartz from fissures of western and central Alps, *Schweiz. Mineral. Petrog. Mitteil.*, vol. 54, pp. 717–752, 1974.

Powell, R.: The thermodynamics of pyroxene geotherms, *Phil. Trans. Roy. Soc. London*, A, vol. 288, pp. 457–470, 1978.

Price, D.: Thermodynamic functions of carbon dioxide, *Ind. Eng. Chem.*, vol. 47, pp. 1649–1652, 1955.

Quinn, A. W., and H. D. Glass: Rank of coal and metamorphic grade of rocks of the Narragansett Basin of Rhode Island, *Econ. Geol.*, vol. 53, pp. 563–575, 1958.

Ramberg, H.: Chemical thermodynamics in mineral studies, "Physics and Chemistry of the Earth," pp. 226–252, Pergamon Press, New York, 1964.

Ramsay, C. R.: The origin of biotite in Archaean metasediments near Yellowknife, N.W.T., Canada, *Contrib. Mineral. Petrol.*, vol. 42, pp. 43–74, 1973.

Ramsay, C. R.: The cordierite isograd in Archaean meta-sediments near Yellowknife, N.W.T., Canada, *Contrib. Mineral. Petrol.*, vol. 47, pp. 27–40, 1974.

Ramsay, C. R., and D. C. Kamineni: Petrology and evolution of an Archaean metamorphic aureole in the Slave craton, Canada, *J. Petrol.*, vol. 18, pp. 460–486, 1977.

Ramsay, J.: "Folding and Fracturing of Rocks," McGraw-Hill, New York, 1967.

Ransome, F. L.: The geology of Angel Island, *Bull. Dept. Geol. Univ. California*, vol. 1, pp. 193–240, 1894.

Ransome, F. L.: On lawsonite, a new rock-forming mineral, *Bull. Dept. Geol. Univ. California*, vol. 1, pp. 301–312, 1895.

Read, H. H.: Metamorphism and migmatization in the Ythan Valley, Aberdeenshire, *Trans. Geol. Soc. Edinburgh*, vol. 15, pp. 265–279, 1952.

Read, H. H.: "The Granite Controversy," Interscience, New York, 1957.

Reed, J. J.: Regional metamorphism in southeast Nelson, *New Zealand Geol. Surv. Bull.*, no. 60, 1958.

Rice, J. M.: Contact metamorphism of impure dolomitic limestone in the Boulder aureole, Montana, *Contrib. Mineral. Petrol.*, vol. 59, pp. 237–259, 1977.

Richardson, S. W.: The relation between a petrogenic grid, facies series, and the geothermal gradient in metamorphism, *Fortschr. Mineral.*, vol. 47, pp. 65–76, 1970.

Richardson, S. W.: Staurolite stability in part of the system Fe-Al-Si-O-H, *J. Petrol.*, vol. 9, pp. 467–488, 1968.

Richardson, S. W., P. M. Bell, and M. C. Gilbert: Kyanite-sillimanite equilibrium between 700°C and 1500°C, *Am. J. Sci.*, vol. 266, pp. 513–541, 1968.

Richardson, S. W., P. M. Bell, and M. C. Gilbert: Experimental determination of the kyanite-andalusite and andalusite-sillimanite equilibria; the aluminum silicate triple point, *Am. J. Sci.*, vol. 267, pp. 259–272, 1969.

Richardson, S. W., and R. Powell: Thermal causes of the Dalradian metamorphism in the central Highlands of Scotland, *Scott. J. Geol.*, vol. 12, pp. 237–268, 1976.

Robie, R. A.: Thermodynamic properties of minerals, *Geol. Soc. Am. Mem.* 97, pp. 437–458, 1966.

Robie, R. A., B. S. Hemmingway, and J. R. Fisher: Thermodynamic properties of minerals and related substances at 298.15 K and 1 bar (10^5 Pascals) pressure and at higher temperatures, *U.S. Geol. Surv. Bull.*, 1452, 1978.

Robie, R. A., and D. R. Waldbaum: Thermodynamic properties of minerals and related substances, *U.S. Geol. Surv. Bull.*, 1259, 1968.

Rodgers, J.: "The Tectonics of the Appalachians," Interscience (Wiley), New York, 1970.

Roedder, E.: The composition of fluid inclusions, in M. Fleischer (ed.), Data of geochemistry, 6th ed., *U.S. Geol. Surv. Prof. Paper* 440 JJ, 1972.

Rose, R. L.: Metamorphic rocks of the May Lake area, Yosemite Park, and a metamorphic facies problem, *Bull. Geol. Soc. Am.*, vol. 69, p. 1703, 1958.

Rosenbusch, H.: Die Steiger Schiefer und ihre Kontaktzone an den Graniten von Barr–Andlau und Hohwald, *Abh. Geol. Spezialkarte Elsass-Lothringen*, vol. 1, pp. 79–393, 1877.

Rosenbusch, H., and A. Osann: "Elemente der Gesteinslehre," Nagele, Stuttgart, 1923.

Roy, A. B.: Interrelation of metamorphism and deformation in central Singhbhum, eastern India, *Geol. Mijnbouw*, vol. 45, pp. 365–374, 1966.

Rumble, D.: Gibbs phase rule and its application in geochemistry, *J. Washington Acad. Sci.*, vol. 64, pp. 199–208, 1974.

Rutland, R. W. R.: Discussion: The control of anorthite content of plagioclase in metamorphic crystallization, *Am. J. Sci.*, vol. 259, pp. 76–79, 1961 (with further discussion *ibid.*, vol. 260, pp. 153–157, 1962).

Ryzhenko, B. N., and V. P. Volkov: Fugacity coefficients of some gases in a broad range of temperature and pressure, *Geochem. Internat.*, vol. 8, pp. 899–913, 1971.

Sander, B.: Über Zusammenhänge zwischen Teilbewegung und Gefüge in Gesteinen, *Tschemaks Mineral. Petrogr. Mitteil.*, vol. 30, pp. 281–314, 1911.

Sander, B.: "Gefügekunde der Gesteine," Springer, Berlin, Vienna, 1930.

Sander, B.: "Einführung in die Gefügekunde der Geologischen Körper," Springer, Vienna. Part 1, 1948; Part II, 1950.

Sawatzki, G., and M. Vuagnat: Sur la présence du facies à zeolites dans les grès de Taveyanne du synclinal de Thônes (Haute-Savoie, France), *Soc. de Phys. et Hist. Nat. de Genève, Comptes Rend. des Seánces*, vol. 6, pp. 69–79, 1971.

Saxena, S. K.: Crystal-chemical aspects of distribution of elements among certain coexisting rock-forming silicates, *Neues Jahrb. Mineral. Abh.*, vol. 108, pp. 292–323, 1968.

Saxena, S. K.: "Thermodynamics of Rock-forming Crystalline Solutions," Springer, Heidelberg, 1973.

Saxena, S. K.: Garnet-clinopyroxene geothermometer, *Contrib. Mineral. Petrol.*, vol. 70, pp. 229–235, 1979.

Schaer, J. P., and F. Jeanrichard: Mouvements verticaux anciens et actuels dans les Alpes suisses, *Ecol. Geol. Helvet.*, vol. 67, pp. 101–119, 1974.

Schaer, J. P., G. M. Reiner, and G. A. Wagner: Actual and ancient uplift rate in the Gotthard region, Swiss Alps: A comparison between precise levelling and fission-track apatite age, *Tectonophys.*, vol. 29, pp. 293–300, 1975.

Scharbert, H. G.: Die Granulite des südlichen niederösterreichischen Moldanubikums, *Neues. Jahrb. Mineral. Abhandl.*, vol. 101, pp. 27–66, 1964.

Scharbert, H. G.: Cyanit und Sillimanit in Moldanubischen Granuliten, *Tschermaks Mineral. Petrogr. Mitteil.*, vol. 16, pp. 252–267, 1971.

Scharbert, H. G., J. Karkisch, and I. Steffan: Uranium, thorium and potassium in granulite facies rocks, Bohemian massif, Lower Austria, Austria, *Tschermaks Mineral. Petrogr. Mitteil.*, vol. 23, pp. 223–232, 1976.

Scharbert, H. G., and G. Kurat: Distribution of some elements between coexisting ferromagnesian minerals in Moldanubian granulite facies rocks, Lower Austria, Austria, *Tschermaks Mineral. Petrogr. Mitteil.*, vol. 21, pp. 110–134, 1974.

Schwarcz, H. P., R. N. Clayton, and T. Mayeda: Oxygen isotopic studies of calcareous and pelitic metamorphic rocks, New England, *Bull. Geol. Soc. Am.*, vol. 81, pp. 2299–2316, 1970.

Schwartz, G. M., and J. H. Todd: Comments on retrograde metamorphism, *J. Geol.*, vol. 49, pp. 177–189, 1941.

Searle, E. J.: Xenoliths and metamorphosed rocks associated with the Auckland basalts, *New Zealand J. Geol. Geophys.*, vol. 5, pp. 384–403, 1962.

Sederholm, J. J.: Studien über archäische Eruptivgesteine aus dem südwestlichen Finnland, *Tschernaks Mineral. Petrog. Mitteil.*, vol. 12, pp. 97–142, 1891.

Sederholm, J. J.: On the geology of Fennoscandia with special reference to the Precambrian, *Bull. Comm. Geol. Finlande*, no. 98, 1932.

Segnit, R. E.: Sapphirine-bearing rocks from MacRobertson Land, Antarctica, *Mineral. Mag.*, vol. 31, pp. 690–697, 1957.

Segnit, R. E., and G. C. Kennedy: Reactions and melting relations in the system muscovite-quartz at high pressures, *Am. J. Sci.*, vol. 259, pp. 280–287, 1961.

Seki, Y.: Petrological study of hornfelses in the central part of the Median Zone of Kitakami Mountainland, *Saitama Univ. Sci. Repts.*, ser. B, vol. 2, no. 3, pp. 307–361, 1957.

Seki, Y.: Glaucophanitic regional metamorphism in the Kanto Mountains, central Japan, *Jap. J. Geol. Geography, Trans.*, vol. 29, pp. 705–715, 1960a.

Seki, Y.: Jadeite in Sanbagawa crystalline schists of central Japan, *Am. J. Sci.*, vol. 258, pp. 705–715, 1960b.

Seki, Y.: Geology and metamorphism of Sanbagawa crystalline schists in the Tenryu district, central Japan, *Saitama University Sci. Repts.*, ser. B, vol. 3, pp. 75–92, 1961.

Seki, Y.: Prehnite in low-grade metamorphism, *Saitama Univ. Sci. Repts.*, ser. B, vol. 5, pp. 29–42, 1965.

Seki, Y.: Facies series in low-grade metamorphism, *J. Geol. Soc. Japan*, vol. 75, no. 5, pp. 255–266, 1969.

Seki, Y., W. G. Ernst, and H. Onuki: Phase proportions and physical properties of minerals and rocks from the Franciscan and Sanbagawa metamorphic terranes, a supplement to *Geol. Soc. Am. Mem. 124*, Japan Soc. Promotion Sci., Tokyo, 1969.

Seki, Y., Y. Oki, H. Onuki, and S. Odaka: Metamorphism and vein minerals of north Tanzawa Mountains, central Japan, *Jour. Japan. Assoc. Mineral. Petrol. Econ. Geol.*, vol. 66, no. 1, pp. 1–21, 1971.

Seki, Y., H. Onuki, K. Okumara, and J. Takashima: Zeolite distribution in the Katayama geothermal area, Onikobe, Japan, *Jap. J. Geol. Geogr.*, vol. 40, no. 2–4, pp. 63–79, 1969.

Seki, Y., and M. Yamasaki: Aluminian ferroanthophyllite from Kitakami Mountainland, northeastern Japan, *Am. Mineralogist*, vol. 42, pp. 506–520, 1957.

Sen, S.: Evolution of the metamorphic rocks of east Nanohum, India, *Proc. Natl. Inst. Sci. India*, A, vol. 25, pp. 118–138, 1959.

Shieh, Y. N., and H. P. Taylor: Oxygen and hydrogen isotope studies of contact metamorphism in the Santa Rosa range, Nevada, and other areas, *Contrib. Mineral. Petrol.*, vol. 20, pp. 306–356, 1969a.

Shieh, Y. N., and H. P. Taylor: Oxygen and carbon isotope studies of contact metamorphism of carbonate rocks, *J. Petrol.*, vol. 10, pp. 307–331, 1969b.

Simonen, A.: On the petrology of the Aulanko area in southeastern Finland. *Bull. Comm. Géol. Finlande*, no. 143, 1948.

Skinner, B. J.: Thermal expansion, in S. P. Clark (ed.), "Handbook of Physical Constants" (*Geol. Soc. Am. Mem.*, no. 97), pp. 75–96, 1966.

Skinner, B. J., S. P. Clark, and D. E. Appleman: Molar volumes and thermal expansions of andalusite, kyanite, and sillimanite, *Am. J. Sci.*, vol. 259, pp. 651–668, 1961.

Skippen, G. B.: Experimental data for reactions in siliceous marbles, *J. Geol.*, vol. 79, pp. 457–481, 1971.

Skippen, G. B.: An experimental model for low pressure metamorphism of siliceous dolomitic marble, *Am. J. Sci.*, vol. 274, pp. 487–509, 1974.

Slaughter, J., D. M. Kerrick, and V. J. Wall: Experimental and thermodynamic study of equilibria in the system $CaO-MgO-SiO_2-H_2O-CO_2$, *Am. J. Sci.*, vol. 275, pp. 143–162, 1975.

Smewing, J. D., and I. G. Gass: Metabasalts from the Troodos massif, Cyprus: Genetic implications deduced from petrography and trace-element geochemistry, *Contrib. Mineral. Petrol.*, vol. 51, pp. 49–64, 1975.

Smith, J. P.: The paragenesis of the minerals in the glaucophane-bearing rocks of California, *Am. Phil. Soc. Proc.*, vol. 45, pp. 183–242, 1907.

Smith, R. E.: Redistribution of major elements in the alteration of some basic lavas during burial metamorphism, *J. Petrol.*, vol. 9, pp. 191–219, 1968.

Smith, R. E.: Zones of progressive regional burial metamorphism in part of the Tasman geosyncline, eastern Australia, *J. Petrol.*, vol. 10, pp. 144–163, 1969.

Smulikowski, K.: Comments on eclogite facies in regional metamorphisms, *Rept. Intern. Geol. Congress 21st Session, Norden, 1960*, vol. 13, pp. 372–382, 1960.

Spooner, E. T. C., and W. S. Fyfe: Sub-sea-floor metamorphism, heat and mass transfer, *Contrib. Mineral. Petrol.*, vol. 42, pp. 287–304, 1973.

Steiner, A.: Hydrothermal rock alteration at Wairakei, New Zealand, *Econ. Geol.*, vol. 48, pp. 1–13, 1953.

Steinmann, G.: Die Ophiolithischen Zonen in den Mediterranen Kettengebirge, *Internat. Geol. Congr. Madrid, 1926, Compt. Rend.*, fass 2, pp. 637–667, 1927.

Streckeisen, A., and E. Wenk: On steep isogradic surfaces in the Simplon area, *Contrib. Mineral. Petrol.*, vol. 47, pp. 81–95, 1974.

Sugi, K.: On the metamorphic facies of the Misaka Series, *Jap. J. Geol. Geogr.*, vol. 9, no. 1–2, pp. 87–142, 1931.

Sugi, K.: A preliminary study on the metamorphic rocks of southern Abukuma Plateau, *Jap. J. Geol. Geogr.*, vol. 12, no. 3–4, pp. 115–151, 1935.

Suppe, J.: Interrelationships of high-pressure metamorphism, deformation, and sedimentation in Franciscan tectonics, U.S.A., *24th Internat. Geol. Congress*, sect. C, pp. 552–559, 1972.

Surdam, R. C.: Low-grade metamorphism of tuffaceous rocks in the Karmutsen Group, Vancouver Island, British Columbia, *Bull. Geol. Soc. Am.*, vol. 84, pp. 1911–1922, 1973.

Sutton, J.: Some structural problems in the Scottish Highlands, *Rept. Intern. Geol. Cong., 21st Session, Norden*, 1960, vol. 18, pp. 371–383, 1960.

Sutton, J., and J. Watson: The pre-Torridonian metamorphic history of the Loch Torridon and Scourie areas in the northwest Highlands, and its bearing on the classification of the Lewisian, *Geol. Soc. London Quart. J.*, vol. 106, pp. 241–308, 1951.

Sutton, J., and B. F. Windley: The Precambrian, *Sci. Progress, Oxford*, vol. 61, pp. 401–420, 1974.

Suwa, K.: Petrological and geological studies on the Ryoke metamorphic belt, *J. Earth Sci., Nagoya University*, vol. 9, pp. 274–303, 1961.

Suzuki, J.: Petrological study of the crystalline schist system of Shikoku, Japan. *Hokkaido Imp. Univ., J. Fac. Sci.*, ser. 4, vol. 1, pp. 27–111, 1930.

Taliaferro, N. L.: The Franciscan-Knoxville problem, *Bull. Am. Assoc. Petrol. Geologists*, vol. 27, pp. 109–219, 1943.

Tanner, P. W. G.: Progressive regional metamorphism of thin calcareous bands from the Moinian rocks of N.W. Scotland, *J. Petrol.*, vol. 17, pp. 100–134, 1976.

Tarney, J., A. C. Skinner, and J. W. Sheraton: A geochemical comparison of the major Archaean gneiss units from northwest Scotland and east Greenland, *24th Internat. Geol. Congr., Montreal*, sect. 1, pp. 162–174, 1972.

Taylor, H. P.: Oxygen isotope studies of hydrothermal deposits, in H. L. Barnes (ed.), "Geology of Hydrothermal Deposits," pp. 109–142, Holt, Rinehart, and Winston, New York, 1967.

Taylor, H. P., and R. G. Coleman: O^{18}/O^{16} ratios of coexisting minerals in glaucophane-bearing metamorphic rocks, *Bull. Geol. Soc. Am.*, vol. 79, pp. 1727–1756, 1968.

Taylor, H. P., and S. Epstein: Relationship between O^{18}/O^{16} ratios in coexisting minerals of igneous and metamorphic rocks, *Bull. Geol. Soc. Am.*, vol. 73, pp. 461–480, 675–694, 1962.

Thomas, H. H.: On certain xenolithic Tertiary minor intrusions in the island of Mull, *Geol. Soc. London Quart. J.*, vol. 78, pp. 229–259, 1922.

Thomas, H. H.: The geology of Ardnamurchan, northwest Mull, and Coll, *Geol. Surv. Scotland Mem.*, 1930.

Thompson, A. B.: A note on the kaolinite-pyrophyllite equilibrium, *Am. J. Sci.*, vol. 268, pp. 454–458, 1970a.

Thompson, A. B.: Laumontite equilibria and the zeolite facies, *Am. J. Sci.*, vol. 269, pp. 267–275, 1970b.

Thompson, A. B.: Analcite-albite equilibria at low temperatures, *Am. J. Sci.*, vol. 271, pp. 72–92, 1971.

Thompson, A. B.: Calculation of muscovite-paragonite-alkali-feldspar phase relations, *Contrib. Mineral. Petrol.*, vol. 46, pp. 173–194, 1974a.

Thompson, A. B.: Gibbs energy of aluminous minerals, *Contrib. Mineral. Petrol.*, vol. 48, pp. 123–136, 1974b.

Thompson, A. B.: Mineral reactions in pelitic rocks: Prediction and calculation of P-T-X (Fe-Mg) relations, *Am. J. Sci.*, vol. 276, pp. 401–454, 1976.

Thompson, J. B.: The graphical analysis of mineral assemblages in pelitic schists, *Am. Mineralogist*, vol. 42, pp. 842–858, 1957.

Thompson, J. B.: Local equilibrium in metasomatic processes, in P. H. Abelson (ed.), "Researches in Geochemistry," pp. 427–457, Wiley, New York, 1959.

Thompson, J. B.: Geochemical reaction in open systems, *Geochim. Cosmochim. Acta*, vol. 34, pp. 529–551, 1970.

Thompson, J. B., and S. A. Norton: Paleozoic regional metamorphism in New England and adjacent areas, pp. 319–327, in Zen et al., "Studies of Appalachian Geology," Interscience (Wiley), New York, 1968.

Thompson, P. H.: Mineral zones and isograds in "impure" calcareous rocks, an alternative means of evaluating metamorphic grade, *Contrib. Mineral. Petrol.*, vol. 42, pp. 63–80, 1970.

Thompson, P. H.: Isograd patterns and temperature distributions during regional metamorphism, *Contrib. Mineral. Petrol.*, vol. 57, pp. 277–295, 1976.

Tilley, C. E.: Contact metamorphism in the Comrie area of the Perthshire Highlands, *Geol. Soc. London Quart. J.*, vol. 80, pp. 22–71, 1924a.

Tilley, C. E.: The facies classification of metamorphic rocks, *Geol. Mag.*, vol. 61, pp. 167–171, 1924b.

Tilley, C. E.: Metamorphic zones in the southern Highlands of Scotland, *Geol. Soc. London Quart. J.*, vol. 81, pp. 100–112, 1925a.

Tilley, C. E.: Petrographic notes on some chloritoid rocks, *Geol. Mag.*, vol. 62, pp. 309–319, 1925b.

Tilley, C. E.: On some mineralogical transformations in crystalline schists, *Mineral. Mag.*, vol. 21, pp. 34–36, 1926.

Tilley, C. E.: On larnite and its associated minerals from the contact zone of Scawt Hill, Co. Antrim, *Mineral. Mag.*, vol. 22, pp. 77–86, 1929.

Tilley, C. E.: Tricalcium disilicate (rankinite), a new mineral from Scawt Hill, Co. Antrim, *Mineral. Mag.*, vol. 26, pp. 190–196, 1942.

Tilley, C. E.: Earlier stages in the metamorphism of siliceous dolomites, *Mineral. Mag.*, vol. 28, pp. 272–276, 1948.

Tilley, C. E.: The zoned contact skarns of the Broadford area, Skye, *Mineral. Mag.*, vol. 29, pp. 621–666, 1951a.

Tilley, C. E.: A note on the progressive metamorphism of siliceous limestones and dolomites, *Geol. Mag.*, vol. 88, pp. 175–178, 1951b.

Tilley, C. E., and H. S. Yoder: Origin of basaltic magmas, *J. Petrol.*, vol. 3, pp. 342–532, 1962.

Tobisch, O. T.: Observations on primary deformed sedimentary structures in some metamorphic rocks from Scotland, *Jour. Sediment. Petrol.*, vol. 35, pp. 415–419, 1965.

Tómasson, J., and H. Kristmannsdóttir: High temperature alteration minerals and thermal brines, Reykjanes, Iceland, *Contrib. Mineral. Petrol.*, vol. 36, pp. 123–134, 1972.

Touret, J.: Le facies granulite de Norvège méridoniale. II Les inclusions fluides, *Lithos*, vol. 4, pp. 423–436, 1971.

Tracy, R. J., P. Robinson, and A. B. Thompson: Garnet composition and zoning in the determination of temperature and pressure of metamorphism, central Massachusetts, *Am. Mineralogist*, vol. 61, pp. 762–775, 1976.

Trommsdorff, V.: Progressive metamorphose kieseliger Karbonatgesteine in den Zentralalpen zwischen Bernina und Simplon, *Schweiz. Mineral. Petrogr. Mitteil.*, vol. 66, pp. 431–460, 1966.

Trommsdorff, V.: Change in *T–X* during metamorphism of siliceous dolomitic rocks of the central Alps, *Schweiz. Mineral. Petrogr. Mitteil.*, vol. 52, pp. 1–4, 1972.

Trommsdorff, V., and B. W. Evans: Progressive metamorphism of antigorite schist in the Bergell tonalite aureole (Italy), *Am. J. Sci.*, vol. 272, pp. 423–437, 1972.

Trommsdorff, V., and B. W. Evans: Alpine metamorphism of peridotitic rocks, *Schweiz. Mineral. Petrogr. Mitteil.*, vol. 54, pp. 333–352, 1974.

Trümpy, R.: The timing of orogenic events in the Central Alps, in K. A. de Jong and R. Scholten (eds.), "Gravity and Tectonics," Van Bemmelen vol., Wiley, New York, pp. 229–251, 1973.

Tsuboi, S.: Petrographic notes (11); Pumpellyite from Asahine, *Jap. Jour. Geol. Geogr.*, vol. 13, p. 333, 1936.

Tuominen, H. V., and T. Mikkola: Metamorphic Mg-Fe enrichment in the Orijärvi region as related to folding, *Compt. Rend. Soc. Géol. Finlande*, vol. 23, pp. 67–92, 1950 (with further discussion, ibid., vol. 24, pp. 234–238, 1951).

Turner, F. J.: The metamorphic and intrusive rocks of southern Westland, *Trans. New Zealand Inst. (Roy. Soc. New Zealand)*, vol. 63, pp. 178–284, 1933.

Turner, F. J.: Schists from the Forbes Range and adjacent country, western Otago, *Trans. Roy. Soc. New Zealand*, vol. 64, pp. 161–174, 1934.

Turner, F. J.: Contribution to the interpretation of mineral facies in metamorphic rocks, *Am. J. Sci.*, vol. 29, pp. 409–421, 1935.

Turner, F. J.: Hornblende gneisses, marbles and associated rocks from Doubtful Sound, Fiordland, New Zealand, *Trans. Roy. Soc. New Zealand*, vol. 68, pp. 570–598, 1939.

Turner, F. J.: The development of pseudostratification by metamorphic differentiation in the schists of Otago, New Zealand, *Am. J. Sci.*, vol. 239, pp. 1–16, 1941.

Turner, F. J.: Mineralogical and structural evolution of the metamorphic rocks, *Geol. Soc. Am. Mem.*, no. 30, 1948.

Turner, F. J.: Thermodynamic appraisal of steps in progressive metamorphism of siliceous dolomitic limestone, *Neues Jahrb. Mineral. Monatsh.*, 1967, pp. 1–22, 1967.

Turner, F. J.: Uniqueness versus conformity to pattern in petrogenesis, *Am. Mineralogist*, vol. 55, pp. 339–348, 1970.

Turner, F. J., and J. Verhoogen: "Igneous and Metamorphic Petrology," McGraw-Hill, New York, 1960.

Turner, F. J., and L. E. Weiss: "Structural Analysis of Metamorphic Tectonites," McGraw-Hill, New York, 1963.

Ueda, Y., T. Nozawa, H. Onuki, and Y. Kawachi: K-Ar ages of some Sanbagawa rocks, *J. Japan. Assoc. Mineral. Petrol. Econ. Geol.*, vol. 72, pp. 311–365, 1977.

Ulbrich, H., and E. Merino: An examination of standard enthalpies of formation of selected minerals in the system SiO_2-Al_2O_3-Na_2O-K_2O-H_2O, *Am. J. Sci.*, vol. 274, pp. 510–542, 1974.

Vallance, T. G.: Spilites again: Some consequences of the degradation of basalts, *Linnean Soc. New South Wales Proc.*, vol. 85, pp. 8–52, 1969.

Vallance, T. G.: Spilitic degradation of a tholeiitic basalt, *J. Petrol.*, vol. 15, pp. 79–96, 1974.

Vance, J. A.: Metamorphic aragonite in the prehnite-pumpellyite facies, northwest Washington, *Am. J. Sci.*, vol. 266, pp. 299–315, 1968.

Van Hise, C. R.: A treatise on metamorphism, *U.S. Geol. Surv. Monogr.*, 47, 1904.

Verhoogen, J.: Les Pipes de kimberlite du Katanga, *Ann. Serv. Mines*, Bruxelles, vol. 9 (1938), pp. 3–46, 1940.

Verhoogen, J., F. J. Turner, C. Wahrhaftig, L. E. Weiss, and W. S. Fyfe: "The Earth," Holt, Rinehart, and Winston, New York, 1970.

Vogt, T.: Sulitelmafeltets geologi og petrografi, *Norges Geol. Undersk.*, no. 121 (with English summary, pp. 449–550, 558–560), 1927.

Vuagnat, M.: Remarques sur la trilogie serpentinites-gabbros-diabase dans la bassin de la Méditerranée occidentale, *Geol. Rundsch.*, vol. 53, pp. 336–358, 1963.

Wagner, G. A., G. M. Reiner, and E. Jäger: Cooling ages by apatite fission-track, mica Rb-Sr and K-Ar dating: the uplift and cooling history of the Central Alps, *Mem. Inst. Geol. Mineral. Univ. Padova*, 30, 1977.

Wallace, R. G.: Metamorphism of the Alpine Schist, Mataketake Range, south Westland, New Zealand, *J. Royal Soc. New Zealand*, vol. 4, pp. 253–266, 1974.

Wallace, R. G.: Staurolite from the Haast Schist in south Westland, *New Zealand J. Geol. Geophys.*, vol. 18, pp. 343–348, 1975.

Walter, L. S.: Experimental studies on Bowen's decarbonation series, *Am. J. Sci.*, vol. 261, pp. 488–500, 773–779, 1963.

Ward, R. F.: Petrology and metamorphism of the Wilmington complex, Delaware, Maryland and Pennsylvania, *Bull. Geol. Soc. Am.*, vol. 70, pp. 1425–1458, 1969.

Watanabe, T.: Geology and mineralization of the Surian district, Tyôsen (Korea), *J. Fac. Sci. Hokkaido Univ.*, ser. 4, vol. 6, pp. 205–303, 1943.

Watson, J. V.: Precambrian thermal regimes, *Phil. Trans. Roy. Soc. London*, A, vol. 288, pp. 431–440, 1978.

Weeks, W. F.: A thermochemical study of equilibrium relations during metamorphism of siliceous carbonate rocks, *J. Geol.*, vol. 64, pp. 245–270, 1956.

Weill, D.: Stability relations in the Al_2O_3-SiO_2 system calculated from solubilities in the Al_2O_3-SiO_2-Na_3AlF_6 system, *Geochim. Cosmochim. Acta*, vol. 30, pp. 223–227, 1966.

Weill, D., and W. S. Fyfe: A preliminary note on the relative stability of andalusite, kyanite, and sillimanite, *Am. Mineralogist*, vol. 46, pp. 1191–1195, 1961.

Weill, D., and W. S. Fyfe: A discussion of the Korzhinski and Thompson treatment of thermodynamic equilibrium in open systems, *Geochim. Cosmochim. Acta*, vol. 28, pp. 565–576, 1964.

Weiss, L. E.: "The Minor Structures of Deformed Rocks," Springer-Verlag, New York, 1972.

Wellman, H. W.: Talc-magnesite rock and quartz-magnesite rock, Cobb-Takaka district, New Zealand, *New Zealand J. Sci. Technology*, vol. 24, no. 3B, pp. 103B–127B, 1942.

Wenk, E.: Plagioklas als Indexmineral in den Zentralalpen, *Schweiz. Mineral. Petrogr. Mitteil.*, vol. 42, pp. 139–152, 1962.

Wenk, E.: Zur Regionalmetamorphose und ultrametamorphose im Lepontin, *Fortschr. Mineral.*, vol. 47, pp. 34–51, 1970.

Wenk, E., and F. Keller: Isograde in Amphibolitserien der Zentralalpen, *Schweiz. Mineral. Petrogr. Mitteil.*, vol. 49, pp. 157–198, 1969.

Wenk, H. R., E. Wenk, and J. H. Wallace: Metamorphic mineral assemblages in pelitic rocks of the Bergell Alps, *Schweiz. Mineral. Petrogr. Mitteil.*, vol. 54, pp. 507–554, 1974.

White, W. S., and M. P. Billings: Geology of the Woodsville Quadrangle, Vermont–New Hampshire, *Bull. Geol. Soc. Am.*, vol. 62, pp. 647–696, 1951.

Willemse, J.: The "floor" of the Bushveld igneous complex, *Geol. Soc. South Africa Trans.*, vol. 62, pp. xxi–lxxx, 1959.

Williams, G. H.: The greenstone schist areas of the Menominee and Marquette regions of Michigan, *U.S. Geol. Surv. Bull.*, no. 62, 1890.

Williams, H., F. J. Turner, and C. M. Gilbert: "Petrography," Freeman, San Francisco, 1954.

Williamson, D. H.: Petrology of chloritoid and staurolite rocks north of Stonehaven, Kincardineshire, *Geol. Mag.*, vol. 90, pp. 353–361, 1953.

Wilson, H. D.: Structure of lopoliths, *Bull. Geol. Soc. Am.*, vol. 67, pp. 289–300, 1956.

Wilson, H. H.: Late Cretaceous eugeosynclinal sedimentation, gravity tectonics and ophiolite emplacement in Oman Mountains, Southeast Arabia, *Am. Assoc. Pet. Geologists Bull.*, vol. 53, pp. 626–671, 1969.

Windley, B. F.: Anorthosites of southern West Greenland, *Am. Assoc. Petroleum Geol. Mem. 12*, pp. 899–915, 1969.

Windley, B. F.: Regional geology of early Precambrian high-grade metamorphic rocks in west Greenland, Part I, *Geol. Surv. Greenland Rept. 46*, 1972.

Windley, B. F.: Crustal developments in the Precambrian, *Phil. Trans. Roy. Soc. London*, A, vol. 273, pp. 321–341, 1973.

Windley, B. F.: "The Evolving Continents," Wiley, New York, 1977.

Windley, B. F., and J. V. Smith: Archaean high grade complexes and modern continental margins, *Nature*, vol. 260, pp. 671–675, 1976.

Winkler, H. G. F.: Abolition of metamorphic facies, introduction of the four divisions of metamorphic stage and of a classification based on isograds in common rocks, *Neues Jahrb. Mineral., Monats.*, Jahrg. 1970, pp. 189–248, 1970.

Winkler, H. G. F.: "Petrogenesis of Metamorphic Rocks," third ed., Springer-Verlag, New York, 1974.

Winkler, H. G. F., and H. von Platten: Experimentelle Gesteinsmetamorphose–V, *Geochim. Cosmochim. Acta*, vol. 24, pp. 250–259, 1960.

Wiseman, J. D. H.: The central and southwest Highland epidorites, *Geol. Soc. London Quart. J.*, vol. 90, pp. 354–417, 1934.

Wood, B. J.: Fe^{2+}-Mg^{2+} partition between coexisting cordierite and garnet–a discussion of the experimental data, *Contrib. Mineral. Petrol.*, vol. 40, pp. 253–258, 1973.

Wood, B. J., and S. Banno: Garnet-orthopyroxene and orthopyroxene-clinopyroxene relationships in simple and complex systems, *Contrib. Mineral. Petrol.*, vol. 42, pp. 109–124, 1973.

Wood, B. L.: The Otago Schist megaculmination: Its possible origins and tectonic significance in the Rangitata Orogeny of New Zealand, *Tectonophysics*, vol. 47, pp. 339–368, 1978.

Woodcock, N. H., and A. H. F. Robertson: Origins of some ophiolite-related metamorphic rocks of the "Tethyan" belt, *Geology*, vol. 5, pp. 373–376, 1977.

Wyckoff, D.: Metamorphic facies in the Wissahickon schist near Philadelphia, Pennsylvania, *Bull. Geol. Soc. Am.*, vol. 63, pp. 25–58, 1952.

Wyllie, P. J.: The petrogenic model, an extension of Bowen's petrogenic grid, *Geol. Mag.*, vol. 99, pp. 558–569, 1962.

Wyllie, P. J., and J. L. Hass: The system CaO-SiO_2-CO_2-H_2O. ii–the petrogenic model, *Geochim. Cosmochim. Acta*, vol. 30, pp. 525–543, 1966.

Wynne-Edwards, H. R.: Tectonic overprinting in the Grenville province, southwestern Quebec, *Geol. Assoc. Canada, Spec Paper*, 5, 1969.

Wynne-Edwards, H. R., and P. W. Hay: Coexisting cordierite and garnet in regionally metamorphosed rocks from the Westport area, Ontario, *Can. Mineralogist*, vol. 7, pp. 453–478, 1963.

Yoder, H. S.: The MgO-Al_2O_3-SiO_2-H_2O system and the related metamorphic facies, *Am. J. Sci.*, Bowen vol., pp. 569–627, 1952.

Yoder, H. S.: Role of water in metamorphism, *Geol. Soc. Am. Spec. Paper 62*, pp. 505–524, 1955.

Yoder, H. S.: Akermanite-CO_2, *Carnegie Inst. Wash. Yearbook No. 72*, pp. 450–453, 1973.

Yoder, H. S., and C. W. Chesterman: Jadeite of San Benito County, California, *California Div. Mines Spec. Rept.* 10-C, 1951.

Yoder, H. S., and H. P. Eugster: Synthetic and natural muscovites, *Geochim. Cosmochim. Acta*, vol. 8, pp. 225–280, 1955.

Yoder, H. S., and C. E. Tilley: Origin of basaltic magmas: An experimental study of natural and synthetic rock systems, *J. Petrol.*, vol. 3, pp. 342–532, 1962b.

Zen, E.: Metamorphism of lower Paleozoic rocks in the vicinity of the Taconic range in west-central Vermont, *Am. Mineralogist*, vol. 45, pp. 129–175, 1960.

Zen, E.: Construction of pressure-temperature diagrams for multicomponent systems after the method of Schreinemakers, *U.S. Geol. Surv. Bull.* 1225, 1966.

Zen, E.: The stability relations of the polymorphs of aluminum silicate: A survey and some comments, *Am. J. Sci.*, vol. 267, pp. 297–309, 1969.

Zen, E.: Gibbs free energy, enthalpy, and entropy of ten rock-forming minerals: Calculations, discrepancies, implications, *Am. Mineralogist*, vol. 57, pp. 524–553, 1972.

Zen, E.: Burial metamorphism, *Can. Mineralogist*, vol. 12, pp. 445–455, 1974a.

Zen, E.: Prehnite- and pumpellyite-bearing assemblages, west side of the Appalachian metamorphic belt, Pennsylvania to Newfoundland, *J. Petrol.*, vol. 15, pp. 197–242, 1974b.

Zen, E.: The phase-equilibrium calorimeter, the petrogenic grid, and a tyranny of numbers, *Am. Mineralogist*, vol. 62, pp. 189–204, 1977.

Zen, E., and J. V. Chernosky: Correlated free energy values of anthophyllite, brucite, clinochrysotile, enstatite, forsterite, quartz and talc, *Am. Mineralogist*, vol. 61, pp. 1156–1166, 1976.

Zen, E., W. S. White, J. B. Hadley, and J. B. Thompson: "Studies of Appalachian Geology," Interscience (Wiley), New York, 1968.

Zwart, H. J.: On the determination of polymetamorphic mineral associations and its application to the Bosost area (Central Pyrenees), *Geol. Rundschau*, vol. 52, pp. 38–65,
1962.

Zwart, H. J.: Some examples of the relations between deformation and metamorphism from
the central Pyrenees, *Geol. Mijnbouw*, vol. 42, pp. 143–154, 1963.

Zwart, H. J.: Geological map of the Paleozoic of the central Pyrenees, Sheet 6, *Leidse Geol.
Mededel.*, vol. 33, pp. 193–254, 1965.

Author Index

References with three or more authors have been treated in the Index as follows: Both text and bibliography page numbers are given for the first author; bibliography page numbers only are given for other authors.

Subject Index

Abyssites in ophiolites, 216
ACF diagram, 183–184
Actinolite, blue, in greenschists, 345–346, 350
   crossite content and pressure, 345–346
   immiscibility with hornblende, 364
Actinolite isograd, 37, 39
   in Vermont, 351
   (*See also* Tremolite isograd)
Activated complex, 79
Activation energy, 79
   computation of, 83
Activation entropy, 80
Activity of component, 71
Adirondacks (New York State):
   amphibolite facies in, 391–393
   amphibolite-granulite transition in, 44, 237
   anorthosite in, 239, 408
   granite plutonism and metamorphism, 43–44
   granulite facies in, 238, 393, 398, 441
   isograds in, 44
AFM, A'F'M' diagrams, 186–190

Akermanite, stability of, 163, 296
AKF diagram, 184–186
Albite:
   with oligoclase, 352, 360, 361, 363
   stability of, 175–178, 359
   with ankerite, 361
Albite-epidote-hornfels facies, 204–205, 244
   characteristic paragenesis, 204–205, 245–247, 295
   chemographic phase diagrams, 246, 247
   disequilibrium problem, 291
     status of andalusite, 245
     status of talc, 245
   illustrative examples: Coast Range batholith, Canada, 248
     Paritu, New Zealand, 247–248
     Sierra Nevada, California, 265
     Tôno aureole Japan, 258
   relation to greenschist facies, 205, 248
   temperature-pressure regime of, 247, 295–296
Almandine, as pressure index, 160, 375
   stability of, 158–160
Almandine isograd, 27–30, 35, 37, 344, 350